A member of
School Specialty
Science

CPO Science Earth Science

First Edition

Copyright © 2007, 2012 CPO Science, a member of School Specialty Science

978-1-58892-476-6

Part Number: 492-3460

Printing 5—September, 2015

Printed by RR Donnelley, Kendallville, IN

CPO Science

80 Northwest Boulevard

Nashua, New Hampshire 03063

(866)588-6951

http://www.cposcience.com

Printed and Bound in the United States of America

Credits

Writers

Mary Beth Abel Hughes - Author
B.S., Marine Biology, College of Charleston; M.S., Biological Sciences, University of Rhode Island.

Mary Beth has been a principal writer with CPO Science since 2000. She taught science and math at an innovative high school and at the college level. She has expertise in scientific research, inquiry-based teaching methods, and science curriculum development.

James Sammons - Author
B.S., Chemistry and Biology, University of Rhode Island.

Has taught middle school science for 30 years. Recognized by the Department of Energy Residence in Science and Technology program, the NAST, WGBH's Nova science program, and the National Association of Geoscience Teachers. Jim is a member of the Geological Society of America and the American Geophysical Union.

Scott Eddleman – Author
B.S., Biology, Southern Illinois University; M.Ed., Harvard University.

Taught for 13 years in urban and rural settings. Developed science-based school-to-career programs. Nationally recognized teacher trainer in inquiry-based and project-based instruction. Worked on National Science Foundation funded projects at TERC. Scott has been a principal writer and curriculum developer for CPO Science since 1999.

Pamela J. W. Gore, Ph.D.– Content review
B.S., University of Maryland, College Park; M.S., M.Phil., and Ph.D., The George Washington University.

Professor of Geology, Georgia Perimeter College.

Daniel P. Murray, Ph.D. - Content review
A.B., Dartmouth College; M.S., Brown University; Ph.D., Brown University.

Department of Geosciences, University of Rhode Island.

Patsy Eldridge - Writer
B.S., Biology, Grove City College; M.Ed., Tufts University.

Experienced high school Physical Science teacher and national hands-on science trainer and presenter. As an adjunct professor for Endicott College in Beverly, MA, and the College of Charleston, developed content-intensive Physical Science courses for pre- and in-service educators. Technical background in the medical device field. Patsy has developed curriculum and training materials with CPO Science since 2000.

Senior Editor

Lynda Pennell – Executive Vice President
B.A., English; M.Ed., Administration, Reading Disabilities, Northeastern University; CAGS Media, University of Massachusetts, Boston.

Nationally known for high school restructuring and integrating academic and career education. Served as director at an urban school for five years and has 17 years teaching/administrative experience in Boston public schools. Lynda has led development at CPO Science since 1999.

Editorial Consultants

Christine Golden
B.A., Psychology, Gordon College; M.B.A., Rivier College.

Project manager at *Imperial Communications* since 1999. With 22 years in publishing, now owner and managing editor of *Big Dog Publishing* services. Christine's work centers on editing K-12 textbook material.

Contributing Writers

Laine Ives
B.A., Gordon College; graduate coursework at Cornell University's Shoals Marine Laboratory and Wheelock College.

Taught high school English overseas and environmental education at a middle school in New England.

Melissa N. G. Vela
B.A. Earth and Environmental Science, Lehigh University; M.S., Agricultural and Biological Engineering, Cornell University; M.Ed., Curriculum and Instruction, Boston College.

Melissa has many years of teaching experience at the middle and high school levels in the subject areas of astronomy, meteorology, oceanography, geology, physical science, and algebra.

Kristen Dolcimascolo
B.A. Biology from the University of Delaware.

Has taught middle school science for over 6 years. She has also taught middle school math. Currently, she teaces 7th grade at Wayland Middle School in Massachusetts.

Jill Elenbaas
B.A., Biology and Environmental Studies, Bowdoin College.

Jill is an 8th grade science teacher at Wayland Middle School (Wayland, MA).

Art and Illustration

Jesse Van Valkenburgh - Design and Illustration
B.F.A., Illustration, Rochester Institute of Technology.

Has worked in prepress film production and design. Jesse has worked at PC Connection in Merrimack, N.H., as a graphic designer doing catalog and direct mailing design, logo design, and illustration.

Polly Crisman – Design and Illustration
B.F.A., University of New Hampshire.

Graphic artist with expertise in advertising and marketing design, freelance illustrating, and caricature art. Polly is the CPO Science primary book illustrator and manages all files.

Bruce Holloway – Cover Design and Illustration
Pratt Institute, N.Y.; Boston Museum School of Fine Arts.

Created all CPO Science book covers and many of the CPO specific designs. Expertise in product design, advertising, and three-dimensional exhibit design. Commissioned for the New Hampshire Duck Stamp for 1999 and 2003.

Connections

Catherine C. Reed
B.S., Secondary Education, Akron University; M.Ed., Administration and Curriculum, Baldwin-Wallace College.

Taught middle school science and has worked as a middle school specialist for 20 years. Catherine's work has included curriculum development and professional development in the area of inquiry learning.

Sharon O. Faulkner is an educational freelance writer who lives in Andover, Mass.

John K. Manos is an educational freelance writer who lives in Evanston, Ill.

Laura J. Tierney is a freelance writer living in Chelmsford, Mass.

Beverly Vissoe teaches sixth-grade reading at Readington Middle School, Readington, N.J.

Assessment

Mary Ann Erickson
B.S, Naval Architecture and Marine Engineering, Massachusetts Institute of Technology.

Has experience running a technical writing consulting business, and writing process control manuals for water treatment plants, software design documentation for simulation software, and operator manuals for mining equipment.

Kelly A. Story
B.S., Chemistry, Gordon College; M.S., Chemistry, University of Massachusetts, Lowell.

Taught chemistry and maintains a position as lab instructor at Gordon College, Wenham, Mass.

David H. Bliss
B.S., Science, Cornell University; M.Ed., Zoology.

Has taught for 39 years in the science field: biology, chemistry, earth science, and physics. David has been science department chairman of Mohawk Central School District in Mohawk, N.Y.

Equipment Design

Thomas Narro – Senior Vice President
B.S., Mechanical Engineering, Rensselaer Polytechnic Institute.

Accomplished design and manufacturing engineer; experienced consultant in corporate re-engineering and industrial-environmental acoustics.

Danielle Dzurik
Bachelor of Industrial Design, Auburn University.

At CPO Science, Danielle focusses on product development, new product design, and improving older designs.

Material Support

Kathryn Gavin – Quality Control and Purchasing Manager

Responsible for quality control and purchasing and works with product engineering on all new development. Kathryn has been assuring total quality of CPO Science equipment for ten years.

Technical Support

Tracy Morrow – Framemaker Specialist, Technical Editor and Trainer
B.A., English, Texas A&M University; M.A., English, Sam Houston State University.

Taught middle school in Klein, Texas, a suburban region outside Houston, for nine years; at Tomball College in Tomball, Texas, for five years; and worked as a technical writer in the oil and gas, airlines, and real estate industries. Tracy offers consulting services and technical training; her expertise is in the editing program Framemaker.

Reviewers

Pamella Ferris
Physics Teacher
Evans High School, Evans, GA

Brian E. Goodrow
Physical Science Teacher
Apple Valley Middle School, Apple Valley, CA

Sylvia Gutman
Science Teacher, Department Chairwoman
David A. Brown Middle School
Wildomar, CA Lake Elsinore Unified School
District

Tony Heinzman
Science Teacher
Apple Valley Middle School, Apple Valley, CA

Philip L. Hunter
Science Department Chairman
Johnson Middle School, Westminster, CA

Nancy Joplin
English-Language Arts Department Chairwoman
Ray Wiltsey Middle School, Ontario, CA

Brad Joplin
Science Teacher
Ray Wiltsey Middle School, Ontario, CA

Margaret J. Kilroy
Chemistry Teacher
Cartersville High School, Cartersville, GA

Dakhine Lee
Special Education Department Chair
Lewis Fraiser Middle School, Hinesville, GA

Jason C. Lee
Science Teacher
Long County High School, Ludowici, GA

Mark Matthews
Physics and Chemistry Teacher
Union Grove High School, McDonough, GA

Kelly McAllister
Science Teacher
Gage Middle School, Riverside, CA

Bianca N. McRae
Science Teacher, Department Chairwoman
Menifee Valley Middle School, Menifee, CA

Jodye Selco, Ph.D.
Professor, Center for Education and Equity in
Math, Science, and Technology
California State Polytechnic University, Pomona,
CA

Tia L. Shields
Life Science/Health and English Language
Learning Teacher
Nicolas Junior High School, Fullerton, CA

Sharon Strefling
Science Teacher
Camden County High School, Kingsland, GA

Robert M. Strong
6th Grade Language Arts Teacher
Union Grove Middle School, McDonough, GA

Special Thanks

Dr. Geerat Vermeij
Professor of Marine Ecology and Paleoecology,
University of California, Davis

Mary Doval Graziose
University of California, Davis

Michael Vela, Molly Nix, and **Kristen Johnson**
Concord-Carlisle High School, Massachusetts

Naomi Hicks and **Steve Hicks**

Michael S. Abbott
Commander, NOAA (Ret.), Port Captain, NOAA
Port Office, Woods Hole, MA

Dr. Adam Dziewonski
Frank B. Baird, Jr. Professor of Science, Department
of Earth and Planetary Science, Harvard University

Todd McLeish
University of Rhode Island News Bureau

Joan Buhrman
American Society of Civil Engineers

John M. Watson
USGS

David A. Abel
Freelance Photographer

Philip F Stetkiewicz, Jr.
Freelance Photographer

Ms. Laurie Clugh
Hillside Middle School, Ohio

Garrett Euler and **Katy Loften**

Apollo Diamond, Inc.

ShutterStock, Inc.

On each page of the student text, there are aids to help you find information, understand concepts, and answer questions. The following introduction includes sample pages with indicators that point out the page contents and reading aids.

Unit Pages and Chapter Pages

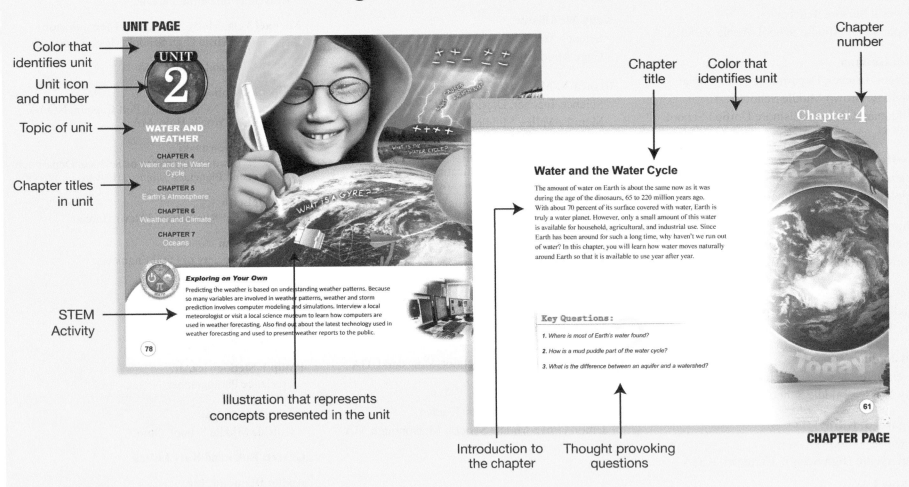

UNIT PAGE

Color that identifies unit

Unit icon and number

Topic of unit

Chapter titles in unit

STEM Activity

Illustration that represents concepts presented in the unit

Chapter number

Chapter title

Color that identifies unit

Introduction to the chapter

Thought provoking questions

CHAPTER PAGE

Student Text Pages

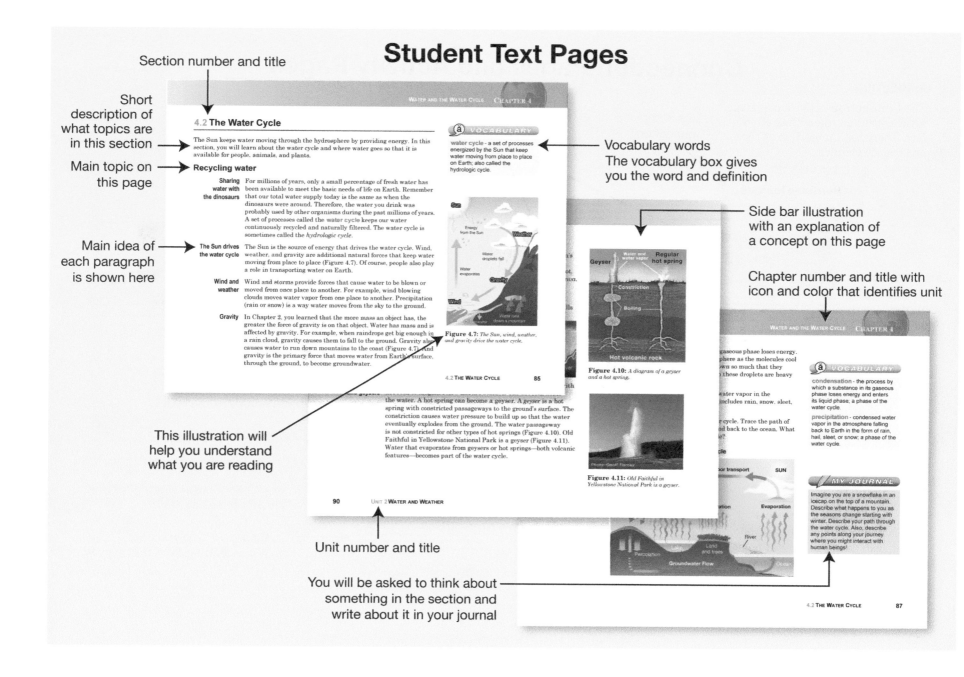

Section number and title

Short description of what topics are in this section

Main topic on this page

Main idea of each paragraph is shown here

This illustration will help you understand what you are reading

Vocabulary words
The vocabulary box gives you the word and definition

Side bar illustration with an explanation of a concept on this page

Chapter number and title with icon and color that identifies unit

Unit number and title

You will be asked to think about something in the section and write about it in your journal

Connection Pages and Activity Pages

CONNECTION

The **Connection** is like a magazine article about an interesting science fact. There is a Connection at the end of each chapter.

Title of the Connection

Photos and illustrations to support your understanding

Main idea heading

Unit color and Chapter number

Research ◆**CONNECTION**

Hurricane Hunters

If there's a hurricane to be hunted, it's usually done by one of the specially-equipped NOAA (National Oceanic and Atmospheric Administration) planes. Two of the world's most popular research planes are based in Tampa, Florida.

NOAA hurricane hunter WP-3D Orion and Gulfstream IV aircraft in flight.

They are both Lockheed WP-3D Orion planes and are commonly known as Kermit and Miss Piggy. In fact, the noses of both planes are painted with the pictures of these famous Muppet characters. These hurricane-hunting planes log between 300 and 400 hours of flight time each year. The primary purpose of their missions is to help forecast hurricanes. Information like the intensity and strength of a storm is gathered. A typical flight aboard Kermit or Miss Piggy can last to eight hours and cover over 2,000 nautical miles. One nautical mile is equal to 1,852 meters. It's not your typical vacation flight.

Flying a hurricane mission

You could think of Kermit and Miss Piggy as flying meteorological laboratories. The planes are equipped with state-of-the-art instrumentation. On a typical hurricane mission, the plane will be occupied by 18 highly-qualified individuals. Hurricane-hunting

crew members include pilots, flight engineers, navigators, scientists, and meteorologists. The pilots have a difficult job trying to keep the plane level. They fly through high winds and pounding rains filled with turbulence. Turbulence is any irregular atmospheric motion. In simpler terms, it's more of an up-and-down motion, or the feeling of bumpiness. The crew flies through a lot of turbulence before they reach the storm's eye wall and finally the eye (the center of the hurricane). The eye is often a calm and clear area. The eye wall surrounds the eye and has the highest wind speeds of the storm. As you can imagine, everything must be bolted down securely to withstand all the turbulence. Just about everything on the plane is tied down or Velcroed, even the pencils and pens!

Plane instrumentation

Detailed pictures and data of the weather systems in the upper atmosphere are collected during a mission. The NOAA

Dropsonde

These canisters contain several sensors used to measure air temperature, humidity, and atmospheric pressure at different places in the storm. They are dropped from the bottom of the plane through a chute. A parachute attached to the canister allows it to drop downward slowly. As it falls, data are collected and transmitted back to the plane. A GPS (global positioning system) receiver is used to monitor the location and wind speed of the storms. Scientists can drop as many as 50 dropsondes during a hurricane mission.

Hurricane facts

Hurricanes are tropical cyclones, which are warm, low-pressure storms that form in the tropics. They rotate counter-clockwise (to the left) in the Northern Hemisphere, and clockwise (to the right) in the Southern Hemisphere.

You can see the direction in the NOAA satellite image that tracked hurricane Katrina in 2005. When these storms reach a wind speed between 63 and 118 km/h (39 and 73 mph), they are known as a tropical storm and are given a name by the National Hurricane Center (NHC) in Miami, Florida. A tropical storm becomes a hurricane when the winds become 119 km/h (74 mph)

categorize the hurricanes. The scale goes from 1 through 5 and is based on wind speed.

Forecasting hurricanes

Isaac Ginis is a professor of oceanography at the Graduate School of Oceanography at the University of Rhode Island. He is considered to be one of the most accurate hurricane forecasters in the world.

According to Ginis, ocean water temperature is the key factor in forecasting hurricanes. Warm ocean water causes hurricane winds to intensify. However, the winds stir up the water so that deeper, cooler water rises to the ocean surface. The cooler water can reduce the intensity of the hurricane. This information helped Ginis develop an ocean model that shows ocean currents and temperature. It is used today by the NOAA to help predict hurricane intensity. Ginis's ocean model and an atmospheric model created by NOAA are considered some of the most accurate models in hurricane forecasting since 2001.

QUESTIONS

1. If a hurricane-hunting plane flew an 8-hour mission that covered 2,000 nautical miles, how many meters would the crew have traveled?
2. What conditions are needed to form a hurricane?
3. Explain the major difference between a hurricane in the Northern Hemisphere and the Southern Hemisphere.
4. Why is it important to accurately forecast hurricanes?

116 CHAPTER 5 EARTH'S ATMOSPHERE

UNIT 2 WATER AND WEATHER 117

ACTIVITY

An **Activity** is another hands-on project that you can do in school or at home. This activity will help you learn more about the information in the chapter.

CHAPTER *Activity*

Bernoulli's Principle

Our atmosphere and golf balls

In addition to providing us with air to breathe, the air in our atmosphere is useful for playing sports, travelling, and all sorts of things. Because of air and how it flows around objects, a baseball pitcher can throw a "sinker," an airplane can fly, and a golf ball can soar for long distances.

A short history of golf balls

In the 1840s, a golf ball was made from the heated and molded parts of a Malaysian tree—the gutta-percha gum tree. The balls were called *gutties*. Golf players at the time realized that old gutties with nicks (little dents or scratches) went further than new ones. So, golfers started to nick the gutties on purpose. In the early 1900s, balls were made of rubber and coated with a latex. Circular depressions called dimples were made in the balls. By 1930, a standard weight and size was established for golf balls and approximately 400 dimples were put on each ball.

Standard golf balls are made with approximately 400 dimples.

What is Bernoulli's principle?

Bernoulli's principle states that as air moves faster, its pressure decreases. If a golf ball were smooth, air would flow over it at the same speed at the top and bottom. Because of the dimples and the backspin caused by hitting the ball with the golf club, the air flowing over the top is moving faster than the air flowing under the ball. The faster air creates a low pressure so the ball experiences a "lift." Bernoulli's principle was developed by Daniel Bernoulli, a Swiss mathematician and scientist. Now, try to create Bernoulli's principle using three methods.

Materials

(A) Cheeseball snack food and bendable straw, (B) ping-pong ball and blow dryer, and (C) paper strip (3 inches × 9 inches)

What you will do

A: Put the bendable straw in your mouth with the short section bent at a 90° angle up into the air. Place the cheeseball on the end of the straw. Blow through the straw. Can you get the cheeseball to be suspended in the air above the straw? Keep trying. It can be done.

B: Use a blow dryer and ping pong ball for the same effect. Hold the blow dryer up vertically so that the ball can be supported by the air flow.

C: Hold the paper strip with your hand so that the 3-inch side is just below your lips and the length of the paper strip is hanging below your lips. Blow over the paper strip.

Applying your knowledge

a. Explain why the activities demonstrated Bernoulli's principle. You may diagram your answer if you want.

b. One of the diagrams below represents a baseball called a "sinker" thrown by a pitcher. The other represents a golf ball. High pressure (H) and low pressure (L) regions, and the direction of air currents around the balls are indicated. Identify which ball is the "sinker" and which ball is the golf ball. Explain your reasoning. *Hint*: Identify where the air is flowing faster over each ball.

118 CHAPTER 5 EARTH'S ATMOSPHERE

Questions to help you understand the article's main ideas

Questions to help you apply what you learned from this activity

Assessment Pages

By answering these questions, you will have a quick check on what you remembered from the section.

This gives you an interesting way to learn more about information in the section

This part of the review asks you to fill in sentences with vocabulary words

These questions are answered after reading the chapter.

CHAPTER 4 WATER AND THE WATER CYCLE

4.1 Section Review

1. Earth is often called a "water planet." Why?
2. How much of Earth's surface is covered by water? How much is covered by land?
3. The hydrosphere contains all the water on Earth. Name four locations where you find water.
4. How is Earth's atmosphere part of the hydrosphere?
5. In what phase of matter is most water found on Earth—gas, solid, or liquid?
6. The second most abundant form of water on Earth is ice. Where can most of this frozen water be found?
7. What would happen if all of the frozen water on Earth melted? How would this event affect people living in coastal areas?
8. Compare surface water and groundwater.
9. What is the water table?
10. In which place—desert or rainforest—would the water table be further underground? Explain your answer.
11. In which season might the water table be further underground—during a dry summer or during a rainy spring?
12. How does water shape Earth's surface?
13. Write a short paragraph describing a personal observation of how water shapes Earth's surface.
14. Write a short paragraph that explains why water is so important for human beings.
15. Like people, animals depend on water. Identify the water environment in which each animal in Figure 4.6 lives. You may need to do research to find the answers.

CHALLENGE

Water in the universe

As far as scientists know, Earth is the only place in our solar system that has liquid water.

Find out why! After performing your research, write a short paragraph that describes your findings.

A. Polar bear

B. Starfish

C. Rainbow trout

Photo "A" by Kathy Crane, NOAA.
Photo "C" by Eric Engbretson, US.
Photo "D" by William W. Hartley, U

Figure 4.6: *Quest*

84   UNIT 2 WATER AND WEATHER

Chapter 4 Assessment

Vocabulary

Select the correct term to complete the sentences.

hydrosphere	glacier	groundwater
surface water	water cycle	water table
reservoir	evaporation	transpiration
condensation	precipitation	surface runoff
aquifer	watershed	percolation
atmosphere	water vapor	

Section 4.1

1. All the water on Earth is included in the _____.
2. _____ is water that collects underground.
3. A(n) _____ forms when more ice accumulates than melts.
4. A(n) _____ is a protected lake that is used to store water.

17. _____ occurs when liquid water moves through a porous substance.

Concepts

Section 4.1

1. How is Earth's atmosphere a part of the hydrosphere?
2. The amount of water on Earth has remained about the same for millions of years. How is this possible?
3. If all the water on Earth could fit in a one gallon container, the amount of frozen water would be equal to about one-third of a cup. How does this amount of water compare to the amount of freshwater and ocean water on Earth.
4. True or False: The water table level stays the same year round? Explain your answer.

CHAPTER 4 WATER AND THE WATER CYCLE

b. Into what body of water does it flow?

12. Name one process of the water cycle that is involved in a volcanic eruption. Explain your answer.

13. What is the difference between a geyser and a hot spring?

Math and Writing Skills

Section 4.1

1. Match these water resources with their percentage of Earth's total water resources:

Freshwater	a. 0.001%
Soil moisture	b. 1.7%
Ocean (salt water)	c. 96.5%

2. Pick a freshwater lake that you know about and research it. Make a colorful brochure that highlights the benefits of this lake to people. Include photographs if you have or find them.

3. Select one of your favorite foods or products and find out how water is involved in making it. Make a poster to display your findings.

Section 4.2

4. In a short paragraph, explain how the Sun, wind, and gravity are involved in the water cycle.

5. Explain how water could go from precipitation, to surface runoff, to groundwater, to an aquifer, to the ocean.

6. Imagine you are a raindrop.
   a. Write a paragraph that explains what could happen to you after you fall to the ground in a desert environment.
   b. Now, write a paragraph that explains what could happen to you after you fall to the ground in an environment that is below 0°C. *Note:* Icy ground is not porous.

7. *Evapotranspiration* is evaporation from surface water plus transpiration from plants. This graph shows evapotranspiration over one year. Come up with a hypothesis to explain the data shown in the graph.

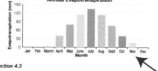

Annual Evapotranspiration

Section 4.3

Chapter Projects—Snow-making and the Water Cycle

During the winter, some people like to go skiing. However, the weather doesn't always cooperate and ski resorts have to make their own snow. In other words, the ski resorts participate in the water cycle by forcing liquid water to become snow (frozen snow).

- Making snow takes a lot of water. For example, it takes about 285,000 liters of water to create a 6-inch blanket of snow covering 61 meters × 61 meters. The system in a good-sized ski slope can convert 18,927 to 37,854 liters of water to snow every minute!
- Making snow also takes a lot of energy. Snow-making machines use fossil fuels and cause pollution.

Research and write a report on how snow-making affects the environment in snow resort towns. Find out how ski resorts work to minimize their impact on the environment.

If you go skiing in the winter, find out how the ski resort you visit makes snow. Find out if the ski resort takes steps to protect the environment!

96   UNIT 2 WATER AND WEATHER

...d ice, liquid water, and

...cipate in the water cycle.

...ation and evaporation.

... their leaves:

b. sugar enters the plant.
d. sunlight enters the ...plant.

...what is in groundwater, what

...d for the Southern Ocean?

...to find the St. Lawrence ...Lakes.

...ow?

...CYCLE   95

This tells you where to find the information

Some questions ask you to write out short answers or solve a problem

Graphs, diagrams, or charts will help you in answering questions

Table of Contents

UNIT 2 — WATER AND WEATHER

Table of Contents

UNIT 6

ASTRONOMY

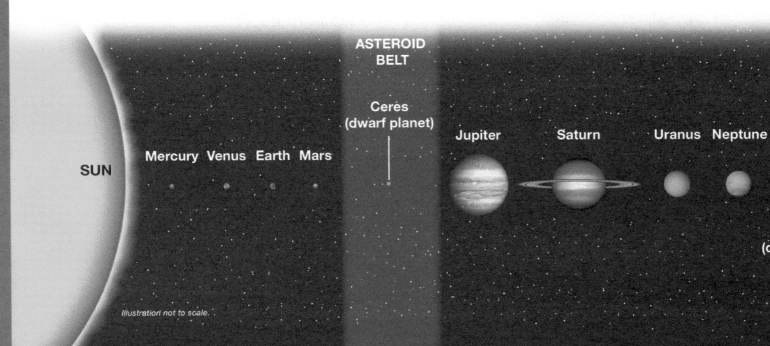

ASTEROID BELT

KUIPER BELT

Ceres (dwarf planet)

Jupiter   Saturn   Uranus Neptune

Eris (dwarf planet)

SUN

Mercury Venus Earth Mars

Pluto (dwarf planet)

Illustration not to scale.

Scattered disc

Throughout your text book you will see this icon, which stands for science, technology, engineering, and math (STEM). STEM is an integrated way to approach learning that connects academic disciplines to real-world situations.

Read the following scenario and try to identify the steps of the engineering cycle and the STEM disciplines used.

In today's changing world, new and improved products and processes are developed every day. For example, improvement in technology allows your cell phone to perform multiple tasks, such as texting, surfing the internet, and listening to music at the same time. Powerful computer chips have become smaller and smaller, allowing you to work on portable devices at any location.

The field of engineering is focused on creating and improving products and processes that people need or want. Engineers and designers use some or all of the STEM disciplines in their work. They also use a process called the engineering cycle to design and improve products and processes.

The engineering cycle has the following steps:

Identify a need or problem – What is the problem or process that needs to be solved or improved?

Design – Identify why this product or process is needed by making a list of everything your solution needs to accomplish. Identify the constraints or limitations that need to be taken into account such as the cost, time, materials, and size.

Create a prototype – Many ideas and a variety of solutions may be a result of brainstorming and research. Building prototypes or trying out new processes is necessary to work toward a solution.

Test the prototype – Test all the prototypes to see if they work or have flaws.

Evaluate the design – Complete an analysis by collecting data and testing the design against what needs to be accomplished. Analyze the results of the tests and make improvements to the design, or, if necessary, start all over again with a new design.

Your school has a recycling committee that ensures that all plastic bottles are recycled, but the school does not recycle paper and still produces too much waste.

Your teacher breaks the class into groups and asks each group to identify the reasons why the school does not recycle paper. The groups must research the recycling system and decide the constraints they need to take into account when recycling paper.

Each group develops a solution or prototype design to address the paper-recycling problem. The groups present their plans to the class.

Each team analyzes the various solutions and decides on one that will work or decides that all the plans are flawed.

The class makes a decision on one solution and checks it against the initial problem and constraints.

1

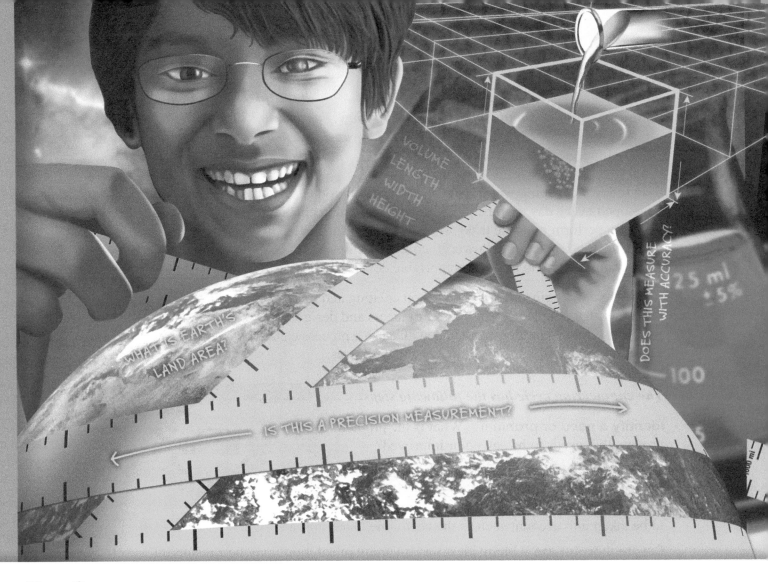

VOLUME
LENGTH
WIDTH
HEIGHT

WHAT IS EARTH'S LAND AREA?

IS THIS A PRECISION MEASUREMENT?

DOES THIS MEASURE WITH ACCURACY?

25 ml ± 5%

100

Exploring on Your Own

Earth science includes the studies of geology, meteorology, astronomy, and oceanography. Each field involves scientists and engineers using math and technology to answer scientific questions and solve problems. Pick one field and research how scientists and engineers work together in that field. Looking for the following information will help you in your research: what measurements are made, what tools are used, and what inventions and innovations have improved how research in the field is conducted? Record your research on a large poster.

Science Is Everywhere

Think about the title of this chapter. Is it true? The things you do every day are useful when you practice science. Your brain processes information all the time. You use this information to make choices and solve problems. You choose what you want to eat for lunch. You solve problems like finding a missing sock.

In this chapter, you will learn the basic skills needed for practicing all science, including Earth science. You will learn about making observations and learn how to follow the scientific process.

Key Questions:

1. *What is the difference between an observation and an inference?*

2. *What is an experiment?*

3. *What do you do if your hypothesis is incorrect?*

1.1 **Learning about Science**

How do you find a lost object? For example, what do you do if you can't find one of your favorite socks? Most likely you predict where it is based on your experience. A statement based on your experience is called an inference. You hear the clothes dryer running. Is your missing sock in the dryer? Asking questions and making inferences are important parts of science (Figure 1.1).

inference - a statement based on experience.

science - an orderly and reasoned process for answering questions.

hypothesis - a possible answer to a scientific question based on observations.

What is science?

Observe Science is an orderly and reasoned process for answering questions. You start by making observations. Look at the picture below. One observation is that the girl is reading a book. Another observation is that the girl is smiling.

Ask a question Once you've made your observations, you continue by forming a question. Why is the girl smiling?

Make a hypothesis Based on your observation, you might propose that the girl is smiling because she likes to read. A possible answer to a scientific question, based on observations, is called a hypothesis. A hypothesis is not necessarily correct though. How can you find out if your hypothesis is correct? Do an *experiment*!

Figure 1.1: *The science process is like looking for a lost sock.*

What is it like to be a scientist?

Looking through a keyhole   Jacques Cousteau, a famous marine biologist, described a scientist as "a curious person who looks through a keyhole." What did he mean? When you look through a keyhole, you can't see *everything*, only a few things (Figure 1.2). An experiment is like looking through a keyhole. The results of each experiment give you a small amount of information, not the answers to all your questions.

Experiments   An **experiment** is something you do to test a hypothesis. Scientists perform many experiments to understand how things work.

Applying knowledge   For example, scientists called *volcanologists* do experiments to learn how to predict volcanic eruptions. The knowledge from these experiments helped people evacuate in time when the Colima Volcano erupted in Mexico in June 2005.

Figure 1.2: *Can you tell what is happening on the other side of this keyhole? Performing an experiment is like looking through a keyhole. The results of the experiment give you only a small amount of information.*

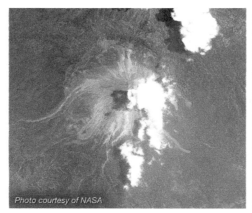

Photo courtesy of NASA

A bird's eye view of the erupting Colima Volcano, June 2005.

Photo courtesy of USGS/Cascades Volcano Observatory

Volcanologists performing experiments.

Fields of science

A list of sciences   Below you'll find descriptions of some fields of science (Figure 1.3). All scientists study interesting events and objects. Which field of science would you like to study?

Physics   Physics is the study of how and why things move. Physicists study motion, electricity, light, and sound. In a physics class, you might measure how fast something moves or learn how sound is made.

Chemistry   Chemistry is the study of matter. Examples of matter include air, water, a book, and you! Chemists do jobs like creating new medicines or figuring out the best way to refine oil to make gasoline. In a chemistry class, you might study the properties of water or learn to perform chemical reactions.

Biology   Biology is the study of living things. Living things include bacteria, plants, animals, and people. If you take a biology class, you might learn about your genetic material (DNA) or about how you digest your lunch!

Earth science   Earth science is the study of Earth's processes and is the main focus of this book. Branches of Earth science include geology, astronomy, meteorology, and oceanography. *Geology* is the study of Earth's surface. *Astronomy* is the study of stars, planets and other objects found in space. *Meteorology* is the study of Earth's weather and climates. *Oceanography* is the study of Earth's oceans.

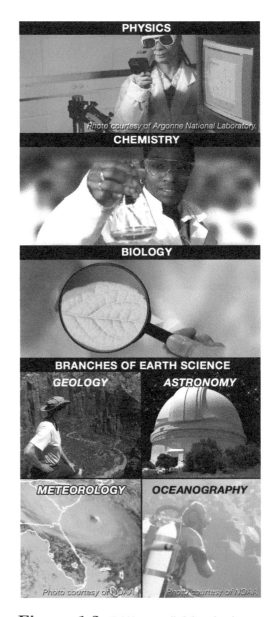

Figure 1.3: *Different fields of science.*

How science affects your life

Science in the morning
Brushing your teeth is an activity that involves science. The fluoride in your toothpaste strengthens your tooth enamel so that you get fewer cavities (Figure 1.4). A chemist figures out how much fluoride to add to your toothpaste. Too much fluoride can discolor your teeth and too little will not help keep them strong.

Science at school
Making the pencil you use in class involves many fields of science (Figure 1.4). The rubber for the eraser was probably made from petroleum. Earth scientists often work in the petroleum industry. The wood of your pencil was probably harvested from a forest. Biologists play an important role in studying forests used by the wood and paper industries. The "lead" of your pencil is a mixture of clay and graphite. The right mixture of these two materials was probably determined by a chemist.

Science after school
If you play a sport, you are affected by the motion laws of physics. If you have a doctor appointment, you are experiencing the science of biology. As you travel around your town you might see mountains, lakes, and forests. All of these are studied by a range of scientists including Earth scientists.

Science at meals
Do you eat a variety of foods each day? MyPlate (Figure 1.4) gives you guidelines on how to eat in a healthy way. The National Academy of Sciences helped develop these guidelines. MyPlate is science in action, helping you to eat well!

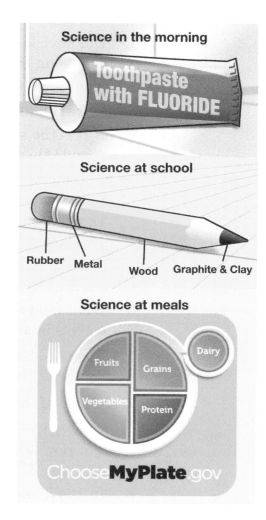

Figure 1.4: *Science during the day. To help you make healthy choices during meals, visit the website of the U.S. Department of Agriculture (USDA) at www.choosemyplate.gov.*

1.1 Section Review

1. You have lost your favorite jacket. How is finding a lost object like using the science process?

2. What is an inference?

3. Make inferences regarding the following situations.

   a. It is the start of a new school year. When will the school day end? On what experience is this inference based?

   b. Tomorrow is Saturday. What will you be doing at 10:00 a.m.? On what experience is this inference based?

4. You notice that the leaves on your houseplant are wilted. Why are the leaves wilted? Come up with a hypothesis.

5. Describe an experiment you have done on your own or in a science class. What was your hypothesis in this experiment?

6. What field of science would be used to study the way sound travels in an auditorium?

         a. biology   b. chemistry

         c. physics   d. oceanography

7. Which of these things might be studied in geology class?

   a. How volcanic rocks form   b. How clouds form

   c. How to improve the speed   d. What kinds of organisms
        of a race car   live in a pond

8. In 1847, Maria Mitchell discovered the Nantucket comet. It was the first time a comet had been discovered by a U.S. citizen and the first time a comet had been discovered by a woman. What kind of scientist was Maria Mitchell?

9. A scientist uses a high-powered computer program to help him predict where a hurricane will hit the United States' coastline. What kind of scientist is this person?

CHALLENGE

When you look at a slice of bread, you see little holes in it. Make a hypothesis about what causes these little holes.

Hint: Study a bread recipe to learn about the ingredients that are used to make a loaf of bread.

Question:
What causes these little holes in a slice of bread?

1.2 Observing the World

Chances are you have heard a person yell, "Watch me!" as he or she jumps off a diving board (Figure 1.5). Science involves observation, but most things that you study in science, like trees or fish, don't yell, "Watch me!" You can only discover the fascinating things that trees and fish do when you use your senses to observe them.

Powers of observation

Making observations

An observation is an accurate description. "The sky is blue" is an observation. However, if you look at the sky every day, you will observe that it is not always blue. Some days it is grey, or it may have shades of red during a sunrise or a sunset. "The sky changes color based on the weather or the time of day" is a more accurate observation.

Observations versus opinions

What happens when a weather report predicts rain? Most likely, you form an opinion. Farmers like rain because it helps water their crops. But a person who wants to have a yard sale might grumble, "I don't like rain!"

- An observation is: It's raining.
- An opinion is: I like rain!

When practicing science, it is important to make observations without making opinions. Why do you think this is important?

An observation example

It's "wear your favorite color" day at school. You make an observation: all of your friends are wearing purple. To see if the most popular color is purple, you count how many people are wearing each color. You discover that 50 students are wearing blue, 35 are wearing red, 30 are wearing green, and 20 are wearing purple. An observation based on evidence is that the most popular color is blue.

Figure 1.5: *People say "Watch me!" but fish, trees, and clouds, three things in nature that are worth studying, only say "Watch me!" in cartoons!*

Interview a scientist or read about one. Write a paragraph about something you have learned.

Using all of your senses

The five senses The five senses are seeing, hearing, touching, tasting, and smelling. Making observations requires the use of one or more of these senses. Modern instruments can extend our senses beyond our natural abilities. Ways that the senses are used by scientists are described below.

Seeing An astronomer looks through a telescope to see objects that are millions of miles away. A biologist looks through a microscope to study small organisms like bacteria that are millions of times smaller than you are.

Hearing *Acoustics* is the science of designing objects based on how sound travels. Hearing is important in this field of science. Hearing is also important in *ornithology,* the study of birds. Because birds are sometimes hard to see, they often have to be identified by their sound.

Touch Geerat J. Vermeij, Ph.D. is a marine biologist who is blind. He relies on his sense of touch to study the shells of mollusks (Figure 1.6). His observations, based on touch, have helped him understand how mollusks protect themselves from predators.

Taste and smell The senses of taste and smell are used when scientists develop new food products. How food tastes and smells determines whether it is enjoyable to eat.

Photo courtesy of Mary Doval Graziose

Figure 1.6: *Geerat Vermeij uses his sense of touch to study the shells of marine mollusks. Examples of mollusks include snails, clams, conches, and even some without shells like octopi!*

STUDY SKILLS

Use your powers of observation when you read. Look through the chapter for all the main titles and headings. Read those first before you begin reading paragraphs.

Each paragraph has a sidenote that highlights the main idea. Use this sidenote to form a question. Then, ask yourself if you can answer the question after you have read the paragraph.

Recording observations

Keeping a notebook
Observations from experiments are written in a notebook—an important tool in science. Figure 1.7 shows a science student writing in her lab notebook.

Format
A lab notebook contains questions, observations, hypotheses, experiments, graphs, and drawings (Figure 1.8). The notebook may also contain mistakes! Mistakes show a thought process. Some mistakes spark new ideas or discoveries. When a mistake is made, a single line is drawn through it so that the word or number is still readable (see below).

SPEED DATA   Draw a single line through mistakes.

DISTANCE (CM)	TIME (SECONDS)	SPEED (CM/SECOND)
16	0.1	160
32	0.3	~~170~~ 107

Photo courtesy of Molly Nix

Figure 1.7: *This student is writing in her lab notebook.*

What should I write?
The science process helps you know what to write. First you record your observations, a question, and a hypothesis. Then you record the experiment procedure and data. Data can be descriptions or measurements. (The table below lists measurements that you might make during an experiment. The table also lists the tools needed to make these different measurements.) You write your conclusions last. Now your experiment can be repeated by you or by other people because you have recorded everything you did!

If you want to measure...	Use a...
distance, length, or height	ruler, meter stick, or tape measure
mass or weight	balance or scale
volume	beaker or graduated cylinder
temperature	thermometer
time	stopwatch, watch, or clock

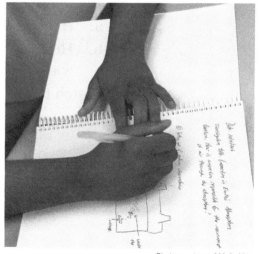

Photo courtesy of Molly Nix

Figure 1.8: *Here is a page from the student's lab notebook.*

1.2 Section Review

1. Choose an environment in which you can make observations. Write down as many observations as you can in one minute.

2. What is the difference between an observation and an opinion?

3. Think about your favorite food.

    a. Write an observation about your favorite food.

    b. Write an opinion about your favorite food.

4. List the five senses that you can use to collect data. List one observation for each sense.

5. Why is it important for a scientist to keep a notebook?

6. List two reasons why you should not erase mistakes from your science notebook. Discuss your ideas with a partner.

7. The word *science* is derived from a Latin word that means "to know."

    a. How does science help us know about the world?

    b. How is practicing science different from watching TV as a way to learn about the world?

8. Match the parts of the science process with their description.

1. observation	a. Is my dog hungry?
2. question	b. I put food in a bowl. My dog stopped barking and ate the food. He wagged his tail.
3. hypothesis	c. My dog was barking because he was hungry.
4. data	d. Maybe my dog is barking because he is hungry.
5. conclusion	e. My dog is barking.

SOLVE IT!

Mystery!

Being a scientist is like being a detective. How would you solve the following mystery using the scientific process?

The scene

You come home from school and discover that your room is a mess and one of your sneakers is missing.

The clues in your room

Your little sister's favorite glitter pen is on your desk. Muddy paw prints are on the carpet, and you find some clumps of fur on your bedspread.

The suspects

Annie, your little sister; Mom; Dad; Scruffy, the cat; Fran, your neighbor; and Waldo, Fran's dog

Extension: Write a short story that includes the above information and the scientific process you would use to figure out what happened. You get to choose the solution to the mystery!

1.3 Using the Scientific Method

The *scientific method* is a step-by-step procedure for practicing science. In this section, you will learn how to use the scientific method. You will also learn the difference between a scientific fact and a scientific theory.

Begin with an observation

An observation and a question
Your friend Sam notices that the grass on the school grounds is not green everywhere. In one place, where students wait for the bus, the grass is brown. Sam makes a diagram to illustrate his observations (Figure 1.9). His question is, "Why is the grass brown near the area where students wait for the bus?"

The hypothesis
Based on his observation, Sam states a hypothesis: *Students walk on the grass near the area where they wait for the bus*. Recall that a hypothesis is a possible answer to a scientific question based on observations. A hypothesis is tested to see if it is correct or not.

Collecting data
Pieces of information that are collected to test a hypothesis are called **data**. There are many different types of data. *Qualitative* data are in the form of words. *Quantitative* data are in the form of numbers. Here are some examples of data.

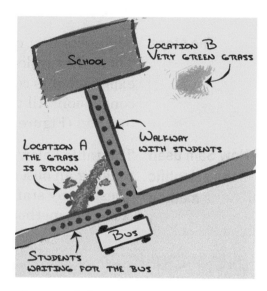

Figure 1.9: *Sam's diagram of the school grounds.*

data - pieces of information collected to test a hypothesis.

Examples of qualitative data	Examples of quantitative data
Students walk on the grass and the sidewalk.	10 students walked on the grass and 3 students walked on the sidewalk.
Red and green apples are in the bowl.	4 apples are red and 5 apples are green.
We caught a large fish.	The mass of the fish was 5 kilograms.
My dog ate his food.	My dog ate 2 cans of food.

The scientific method

The steps   Scientists first observe, form a question, and state a hypothesis. Then, they collect data by performing an experiment. After the experiment is complete, the scientists study the data and reach a conclusion. All together these steps are called the **scientific method** (Figure 1.10).

How Sam used the scientific method   The table below shows how Sam used the scientific method. After making an observation, he asked a question. He answered this question by stating a hypothesis. Sam completed the steps of the scientific method by collecting data and drawing a conclusion.

VOCABULARY

scientific method - a series of steps including observing, forming a question, stating a hypothesis, collecting data, and reaching a conclusion.

1. Make observations	The grass is brown at the area where students wait for the bus (Location A) and green in an area closer to the school building (Location B). *(Figure 1.9)*
2. Ask a question	Why is the grass brown near Location A where the students wait for the bus?
3. State a hypothesis	The grass is brown at Location A because students walk on the grass there.
4. Collect data 	For his experiment, Sam observes students for three days while they wait for the bus. During this time, he records that students walk on the grass at Location A, and no students walk on the grass at Location B.
5. Draw conclusions	Sam concludes that his hypothesis is correct. The grass is brown at Location A because students are walking on the grass.

 Make observations

Ask a question

 State a hypothesis

Collect data

Draw conclusions

Figure 1.10: *Basic steps in the scientific method.*

What is a good hypothesis?

Making a good hypothesis

Sam's hypothesis was good because it could be tested with an experiment. Sam tested his hypothesis by observing the students while they waited for the bus. Below are other testable hypotheses that Sam could have made.

The grass near the walkway is brown because:

1.   it is not getting enough water.

2.   it is not getting enough fertilizer.

Inference

A good hypothesis is based on your experiences. As you have learned, an *inference* is a statement based on your experiences.

Here are some examples of inferences.

- For five weeks, the cafeteria has served ice cream on Friday. My inference is that the cafeteria will serve ice cream next Friday.
- I have gone to 10 birthday parties. At each party, people sang "Happy birthday to you." My inference is that when I go to another birthday party, people will sing "Happy birthday to you."

What happens next?

Sam made a hypothesis. Then, he collected data. Sam's next step might be to report the results of the experiment in a lab report (Figure 1.11). A lab report follows the steps of the scientific method.

What if your hypothesis is incorrect?

An incorrect hypothesis is another piece of information that you can use to answer scientific questions. Let's say Sam wants to know why the grass near the school is so healthy. His hypothesis might be that the grass is fertilized. If this hypothesis is incorrect, Sam can make a new hypothesis about why the grass is healthy and run a new experiment.

MY JOURNAL

Pick one of the hypotheses listed at the left. Write a paragraph that describes the steps you would follow to test this hypothesis in an experiment.

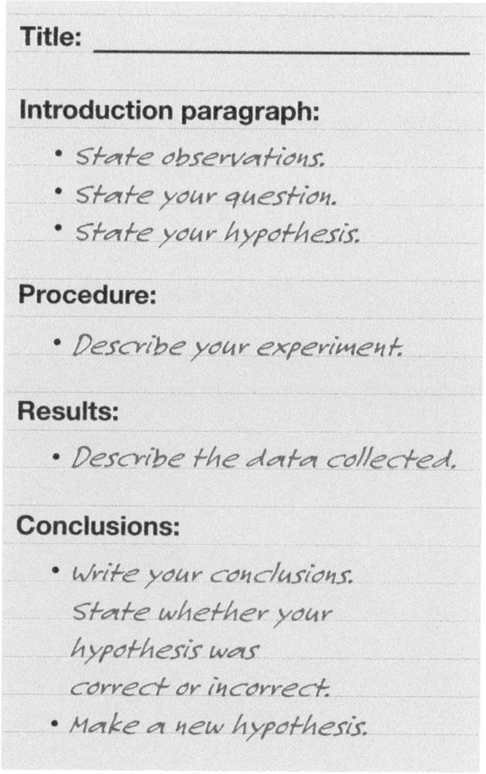

Title: _____

Introduction paragraph:

- *State observations.*
- *State your question.*
- *State your hypothesis.*

Procedure:

- *Describe your experiment.*

Results:

- *Describe the data collected.*

Conclusions:

- *Write your conclusions. State whether your hypothesis was correct or incorrect.*
- *Make a new hypothesis.*

Figure 1.11: *An example of a lab report. Note that the format of the lab report follows the steps of the scientific method.*

Scientific facts, laws, and theories

What is a scientific fact? Scientific facts are statements that are accepted as being true. These facts have been repeatedly measured or observed. Here are some scientific facts.

- The ocean is salty.
- It takes 365.25 Earth days for Earth to orbit around the Sun.
- Earth has one moon.

Scientific laws and theories Knowledge about a topic grows as more and more experiments are performed by many different people. Scientific laws and theories are statements that are supported by the observations and evidence from these experiments. Scientific laws describe, but do not explain, an observed phenomenon. An example of a scientific law is the *law of gravity*. Scientific theories address more complex ideas. An example of a scientific theory is the *theory of plate tectonics*. Even accepted scientific laws and theories are constantly tested by new experiments.

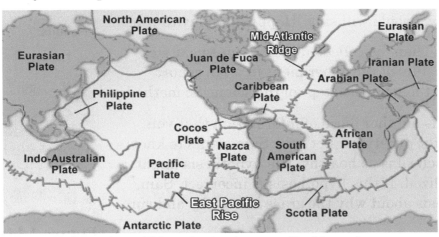

Location of lithospheric plates on Earth's surface.
The theory of plate tectonics describes how the plates move.

 VOCABULARY

scientific law - a statement that describes an observed phenomenon; it is supported by evidence collected from many observations and experiments.

scientific theory - a statement that explains a complex idea; it is supported by evidence collected from many experiments.

What is the law of gravity?

The law of gravity states that objects attract other objects. Your pencil falls to the ground when you drop it because the mass of the pencil and the mass of Earth attract each other!

What is plate tectonics?

The surface of Earth is broken into many pieces, like a giant jigsaw puzzle. These pieces are called lithospheric plates. The graphic at the left illustrates the location of the plates on Earth's surface.

The theory of plate tectonics explains how the plates move on Earth's surface. You'll learn about plate tectonics in Unit 4.

1.3 Section Review

1. Are you a scientist? The answer is yes! Each day you do things that are related to investigating the world in a scientific way. Respond to the following based on what you did today.

   a. List one observation you made about the weather.

   b. List one question you asked. What was your hypothesis for this question?

   c. List some qualitative data you collected. Example: It is cold outside.

   d. List some quantitative data you collected. Example: The temperature is 15°C.

   e. State a conclusion you made today.

2. You are about to leave for school. You look outside and see tall, puffy clouds covering a darkened sky. You hear a distant rumble of thunder, so you reach for your raincoat. What did you infer about the upcoming weather? On what experience did you base this inference?

3. Give an example of a question that you would like to answer by doing an experiment. State a hypothesis for your question.

4. Give an example of a scientific fact about the human body.

5. What is the difference between a scientific fact and a scientific theory?

6. A very well-known and important scientific law is the law of gravity. What is gravity? Do a test to see if gravity exists.

7. *Discussion*: The scientific method is a step-by-step model for conducting scientific investigations. However, sometimes scientists need to follow the steps out of order or skip certain steps. Discuss with your class situations where a scientist might not follow the scientific method exactly.

CHALLENGE

In the United Kingdom, there is a store that hires people to travel around the globe to buy the world's best chocolate. This person must be good at judging the chocolate by taste. The person has to taste about a pound of chocolate a day!

Imagine that your job is to taste samples of your favorite food. You have five samples to taste and you have to pick the best one.

Examples:

- Which candy maker makes the best chocolate?
- You are the judge in a pie-baking contest. Which pie is the best?
- Which pizza parlor in your town makes the best pizza?

Write a description that explains how you would use the scientific method to pick the best sample.

Hint: Are there other senses in addition to taste that might be useful for picking the best sample?

Which pizza parlor in your neighborhood makes the best pizza?

Dr. Rosaly Lopes—Volcano Scientist

What is it that you love? Playing baseball? Video games? Math? Spelling? Drama club? Singing? In-line skating? Volcanoes? Volcanoes! That just happens to be Rosaly Lopes' passion. She is a planetary volcanologist who searches for and studies volcanoes on Earth and elsewhere in the solar system. And at the National Aeronautic and Space Administration's Jet Propulsion Laboratory in Pasadena, California, she is considered an expert.

Dr. Rosaly Lopes standing on the Pu'u O'o eruption of the Kilauea volcano on Hawaii's Big Island.

Rosaly Lopes was born in Brazil and dreamed of being a scientist. As a child, she was fascinated by the study of space and the areas beyond Earth. At 18, she went to study astronomy at the University of London. Her original goal was to be an astronaut, but she found herself greatly influenced by a geology teacher who had visited Mount Etna, Europe's largest volcano, on the Italian island of Sicily. Lopes got hooked on the idea of traveling the world to study volcanoes.

She went on at the university to receive her doctorate degree in planetary geology and volcanology. In 1979, she found herself on Sicily doing fieldwork when Mount Etna erupted, killing several people. The experience taught her to truly appreciate and respect the power of volcanoes.

Thinking scientifically

Like most scientists, Dr. Lopes follows the scientific method in her research. The first step is to ask questions. For example, why are volcanoes important to understand? Scientists study volcanoes on Earth in order to improve their ability to predict eruptions. Millions of people live near volcanoes. Their eruptions can cause great harm to local communities and the wider region. A volcano's eruption can cause climate changes and affects not only people, but also plants and animals.

Volcanoes are an important feature on Earth and other planets. Our planet has the most volcanoes in the solar system. Yet for Dr. Lopes, studying volcanoes on Earth was not enough. She recognized that by studying volcanoes on other planets, she could ask even more questions, and different kinds of questions. Meaningful questions can lead to a better understanding of the universe in which we live.

Mt. Etna, Sicily, Italy

Gathering data

On Earth, a lot of volcanic data is gathered by using satellites and aircraft. In space, volcanoes are studied mostly by using space-craft, satellites, and radar images. NASA's Galileo mission to Jupiter provided information about that planet's moon, Io. Dr. Lopes learned that the lava temperature on Io is nearly 2,600 degrees Fahrenheit. She was amazed because this is almost 500 degrees hotter than lava here on Earth.

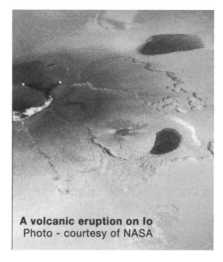

A volcanic eruption on Io
Photo - courtesy of NASA

Today, NASA's Cassini mission is gathering information about Saturn's largest moon, Titan. Dr. Lopes has learned that Titan has cold volcanoes with lava that is a slushy mixture of water, ice, and ammonia.

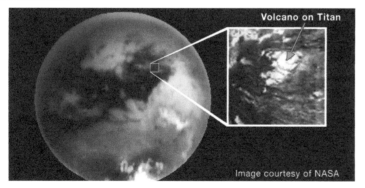

Volcano on Titan

Image courtesy of NASA

Presenting data

Scientists communicate their findings in many ways. Dr. Lopes writes papers that are published in scientific journals. She gives talks at scientific meetings. An important part of her job is speaking to the public and she often presents seminars at universities and astronomy clubs.

Television and books are ways to reach an even wider public. Dr. Lopes has appeared on the Discovery Channel and ABC News's "Nightline." She has filmed a program with National Geographic. She has written The Volcano Adventure Guide (Cambridge University Press, 2005) to advise people who want to safely explore some of the most famous volcanoes on Earth and explorers who may never get any closer to a volcano than in the pages of her book.

A record-breaking mom

Stop and think about what you could do to get in the Guinness World Records. Hop on one foot for a long time? Eat a lot of pies? What do you think Dr. Lopes did to get into the Guinness book?

She (not surprisingly) discovered volcanoes. Lopes' discovery of 71 active volcanoes on Io—which is about 500 million miles away from her Pasadena lab—is a world record. Her son thinks it is great to have his mom in the Guinness World Records.

When asked what is the best part of her work, Dr. Lopes says: "The knowledge that I am exploring new places and seeing places that nobody has seen before. The thrill of discovery drives many of us scientists. It is not always a 'Wow, look at that,' though there is certainly plenty of that. Often discovery is the painstaking analysis of data, not unlike a detective unraveling a mystery."

QUESTIONS

1. Why do scientists like Dr. Lopes study volcanoes?
2. How are volcanoes on Earth studied, compared with volcanoes on the other planets?
3. How does Dr. Lopes communicate her findings?
4. List the roles that Dr. Lopes has in her life.

Observing the World Around You

One thing that all scientists have in common is that they make countless numbers of observations in their work. In order to be a scientist, you must practice the skill of making observations. It is a good idea to leave space for writing observations in your lab notebook.

During this activity, you will be asked to make as many observations as you can of what your teacher does in front of the classroom. The classroom needs to be silent so that all students can concentrate and be the best scientists they can be!

What you will do

1. Make a table like the one on this page on a separate sheet of paper.

2. There are two cups in front of the room, labeled A and B. There is a liquid in each of the cups. Write down your observations about these two liquids in the first row of your table. These are your initial observations before your teacher has conducted tests.

Cup A   Cup B

3. Now, your teacher will begin a series of tests on each of the liquids.

4. For each test, record your observations in the correct column. In the column labeled Cup A, write observations about Cup A. In the column labeled Cup B, write observations about Cup B.

5. Share your observations as a class. Your teacher will write all observations on the board.

Events conducted by the teacher	Observations of Cup A	Observations of Cup B
Initial observations (before any tests)		
Test 1		
Test 2		
Test 3		

Applying your knowledge

a. How many senses did you use when making observations? Which sense/senses did you use the most?

b. How successful were you at making observations? What was your biggest problem?

c. What is the difference between an observation and an inference?

d. What are some inferences you could come up with about the various tests that were done in this experiment?

e. Was the liquid in Cup A the same as the liquid in Cup B? Explain your answer.

Chapter 1 Assessment

Vocabulary

Select the correct term to complete the sentences.

science	data	experiment
inference	scientific method	scientific theory
hypothesis	scientific law	

Section 1.1

1. You look up at the sky and see dark clouds. You predict that it might rain. A statement like this based on experience is called a(n) _____.

2. _____ is an orderly and reasoned process for answering questions. Astronomy is an example. Astronomy is a process for answering questions about stars and planets.

3. A(n) _____ is a predicted answer to a question based on observations. It must be testable and isn't always correct.

4. If you want to support or refute a hypothesis, you perform a(n) _____.

Section 1.2

There are no vocabulary words in this section.

Section 1.3

5. _____ are information that is collected in order to answer a question.

6. The _____ is a series of steps including observation, forming a question, stating a hypothesis, collecting data in an experiment, and reaching a conclusion.

7. A(n) _____ is a statement that explains a complex idea such as a process for how Earth's surface has changed over time.

8. A(n) _____ is a statement that describes an observed phenomenon such as why an object falls when you drop it.

Concepts

Section 1.1

1. In the morning, you see a full glass of water on the kitchen table. By nighttime, the glass is almost empty. Is this second statement a hypothesis or an observation?

2. In the morning, a jar is filled with water. By the afternoon, the water level is lower. You propose that the water level has gone down because it was evaporated by the Sun. Is this second statement a hypothesis or an observation?

3. Write a short paragraph that describes two characteristics that are important for a scientist to have.

Section 1.2

4. You are a judge at a contest to pick the best cake. Which senses do you use for making your observations? Explain how each sense that you list would be useful.

5. How is an observation different from an opinion? Give an example of an observation and an opinion.

6. You are conducting an experiment to see whether hot or cold water freezes fastest in a freezer. What information should you record in your science notebook during the experiment? On a piece of notebook paper, make a sample lab notebook page for this experiment.

Section 1.3

7. What are the different types of data that scientists collect during experiments? Give an example of each type of data.

8. While riding in a car on a highway, you notice rock formations near the road that have wavy layers. State a hypothesis for how you think the rock layers became wavy. Could you easily test this hypothesis by following the steps of the scientific method? Why or why not?

9. Identify each statement as an observation or inference. If a statement is an inference, write an observation on which it may be based. If a statement is an observation, write an inference based on that observation.
    a. John is wearing red.
    b. The students will work hard during class tomorrow.
    c. It is going to be hot and humid tomorrow.

10. What do these three terms have in common: scientific fact, scientific law, and scientific theory?

11. Why is it important to perform many experiments?

Math and Writing Skills

Section 1.1

1. Choose two things that you do every day and explain how science relates to these things.

2. Write a paragraph about a famous scientist or a scientist whom you may know! In what field of science does this person work? How are you similar to this person?

3. In Section 1.1, you will find a bird's-eye view of the erupting Colima volcano. This image shows what the volcano looks like from an airplane flying above it. Draw a sketch that shows what this volcano might look like from the side.

Section 1.2

4. Write a story about a nature experience you have had at school, home, or on a trip. After you have written your story, list three observations and three opinions in your story.

5. Choose an interesting object from your home and gather measuring tools (such as a ruler, scale, and a calculator).
    a. Observe the object for five minutes. Write down everything you observe.
    b. Then, make and record measurements of the object.
    c. Which task (a or b) produced qualitative data?

Section 1.3

6. Pretend you are Sam from Section 1.3. Write up a lab report based on the experiment he did.

7. Make an observation about something that happens in your classroom often. Formulate a hypothesis about why this thing or event happens. Design an experiment to test your hypothesis.

8. The text describes the law of gravity in words. What is the law of gravity in terms of a formula. See if you can find out the answer to this question by looking through resources including textbooks, the Internet, or in your school library. The complete name (to help you with your research) is the *Law of Universal Gravitation.*

Chapter Project—Observing Nature

Pick anything in nature at or outside your home to observe—the sky or a sunset, a tree, a puddle, a garden, or even soil. Your teacher will approve your choice before you begin. Observe your piece of nature for 10 minutes every day for one week. *Without stating what the object is*, record all observations in your science notebook as words and drawings. Also, write down any questions you have throughout the observation period.

After you have collected your observations, choose one of the questions you had, and answer it. Use evidence from all of your observations to form inferences. Also, make predictions (based on your observations) about what will happen to that piece of nature over the next couple of months.

At the end of the week, bring your notebook of observations to class. Your teacher will collect and redistribute them to other students. You will look at another student's notebook, and see if you can guess what the other student has observed!

The Science Toolbox

Many tools are used in science. What is the most important tool? It's your brain! Among other things, your brain allows you to ask questions and make hypotheses. Other science tools allow you to make measurements and collect data. An experiment is also a science tool. Some science tools are big and heavy like huge telescopes. Some are small like a ruler to measure distance or a graduated cylinder to measure volume. Let's go look in the science toolbox and see what else is in there.

Key Questions:

1. Why are units important?

2. What is the difference between accurate and precise measurements?

3. What is a model and why is it useful?

Foreground photo by Jack Dykinga, ARS/USDA.

2.1 Making Measurements

An important step in the scientific process is collecting data. Measurements are one form of data. Measurements tell you how big or how small something is. Measurements also help you compare objects.

What is a measurement?

A number plus a unit   A **measurement** is a number that includes a unit. A **unit** is a specific quantity that is counted to make a measurement. The unit provides information about the type of measurement.

Why are units important?   A basketball player might say, "I'm tall! I'm almost 2 high." You might think "almost 2" doesn't sound very tall.

The basketball player is not tall if his height is almost 2 *feet*. A medium-sized dog is about 2 feet tall. However, the basketball player *is* tall if he is almost 2 *meters* tall. Two meters equals a height of about 6 feet 6 inches (Figure 2.1).

The words *meters* and *feet* are units. Always include a unit when making measurements.

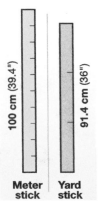

Meter stick   Yard stick

 VOCABULARY

measurement - a number that includes a unit.

unit - a specific quantity that is counted to make a measurement.

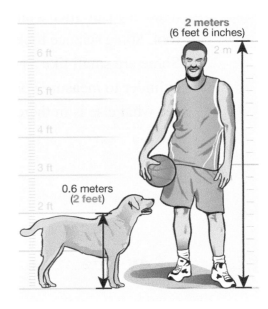

Figure 2.1: *A measurement includes a number and a unit. Two meters is much taller than 2 feet!*

Activity: How tall are you in feet and meters?

Find a partner. You and your partner will need two measuring tools: a yardstick and a meter stick. Use the yardstick to measure height in feet and inches. Use the meter stick to measure height in meters and centimeters. Measure your partner's height. Your partner will measure your height.

How tall are you in feet and inches?
How tall are you in meters and centimeters?

A history of measuring systems

English System of measurement   At one time, the English System of measurements (which is used in the United States) included nearly a dozen units just for weight. For example, a pharmacist weighed medicine in *grains*, a jeweler weighed gold and gems in *carats*, and a carpenter weighed nails in *kegs* (Figure 2.2). These units were hard to compare to each other.

The Metric System   During the 1800s, a new system of measurement was developed in Europe and Great Britain—the Metric System. The goal of this system was for all units of measurement to be related.

Comparing the systems   Centimeters (cm) relate to liters in the Metric System. A 10 cm × 10 cm × 10 cm cube holds exactly 1 liter of liquid. However, in the English System, feet do not relate easily to gallons. A cube that is 1 foot × 1 foot × 1 foot holds about 7.48 gallons of liquid.

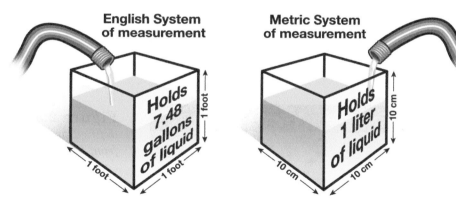

SI Units   The name Metric System was change to the International System of Units in 1960. From here on, we will refer to this system as SI units.

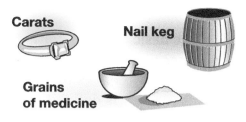

Figure 2.2: *Measurements in the English System.*

English and SI units

Imagine that you are working on your bicycle and find that the wrench that you have selected is one size too small. The graphic below shows that it is easier to pick the next larger size if you use SI units than if you use English units.

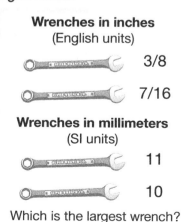

Which is the largest wrench?

The meter

The basic distance unit
The **meter** is the basic distance unit for the SI Units System of measurement. In 1791, a meter was defined as one ten-millionth of the distance from the North Pole to the equator. Today a meter is defined more accurately using the speed of light (Figure 2.3). The meter was used as a starting point for developing the rest of the SI Units System of measurement.

Useful prefixes
Prefixes are added to the names of basic units in the SI Units System. Prefixes describe very small or large measurements. There are many SI unit prefixes, but only three are used most of the time.

VOCABULARY

meter - the basic distance unit for the SI Units system of measurement.

Prefix	Prefix + meter	Compared to 1 meter
kilo-	kilometer	1,000 times bigger
centi-	centimeter	100 times smaller
milli-	millimeter	1,000 times smaller

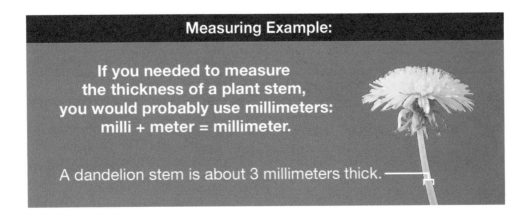

Measuring Example:

If you needed to measure the thickness of a plant stem, you would probably use millimeters: milli + meter = millimeter.

A dandelion stem is about 3 millimeters thick.

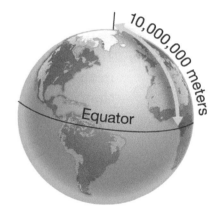

Figure 2.3: *In 1791, a meter was defined as 1/10,000,000 of the distance from the North Pole of Earth to its equator. Today a meter is defined more accurately as the distance that light travels in a fraction of a second.*

Measuring mass and weight

Atoms   You have learned how to measure distance in the SI Units System. Another important measurement has to do with the amount of matter in an object. Everything is made of *matter*. Matter is made of particles called **atoms**. Atoms are too small to see with your eyes. An atom is 10 million times smaller than a grain of sand.

Matter and mass   **Matter** also has mass and takes up space. The **mass** of an object equals the amount of matter it contains. A *gram* is the basic unit of mass in the SI Units System. It is defined on the next page.

Mass stays the same   Mass and weight are not the same thing. One apple has a mass of about 150 grams. If you flew in a spaceship to Mars, the apple would still have a mass of 150 grams. However, the weight of the apple would be different!

Weight   **Weight** is a measure of the force of gravity on an object's mass. The more mass an object has, the greater the force of gravity on that object. On Earth, 15 apples weigh about 5 pounds. On Mars, the force of gravity is less. Those same 15 apples would weigh only about 2 pounds (Figure 2.4)!

In science class, we will use the terms *grams* and *mass* instead of *pounds* and *weight*.

atom - a particle of matter.

matter - anything that has mass and takes up space.

mass - the amount of matter that an object contains.

weight - a measurement of the force of gravity on the mass of an object.

EARTH: 15 apples weigh about 5 pounds

MARS: 15 apples weigh about 2 pounds

pound = unit of weight	gram or kilogram = unit of mass
2.2 pounds on Earth = 1,000 grams = 1 kilogram	

Figure 2.4: *Fifteen apples on Earth weigh about 5 pounds. The same 15 apples weigh about 2 pounds on Mars! This is because the force of gravity is less on Mars.*

The gram and the liter

The gram   A **gram** is the basic unit of mass in the SI Units System. A gram is defined as the mass of one-thousandth of a liter of pure water. Using prefixes, we would say that 1 gram is the mass of 1 *milliliter* of water.

The liter   The **liter** is the basic SI unit of volume. The liter is based on the centimeter. The prefix *centi-* means 1/100. A centimeter is one-hundredth of a meter—about the width of a pencil. A liter is equal to the volume of a cube-shaped box that is 10 centimeters on each side (Figure 2.5).

Volume   **Volume** measures how much space is occupied by an object. The formula for the volume of a rectangular solid is length × width × height.

Cooking with grams   When you cook, you can measure the volume of each ingredient in grams, using an electronic scale. Wet and dry ingredients can all be measured in the same bowl. You simply set the scale back to zero after measuring each ingredient. Many wet ingredients are mostly water. We know that 1 milliliter of water equals 1 gram. Rather than using a measuring cup to measure 250 milliliters of milk, you can add 250 grams of milk to the mixing bowl on the scale. This means you only have one bowl to wash when you're done!

250 milliliters of milk equals 250 grams of milk

 VOCABULARY

gram - the basic unit of mass in the SI units measuring system; one-thousandth of a liter.

liter - the basic unit of volume in the SI units measuring system.

volume - a measurement of how much space is occupied by an object.

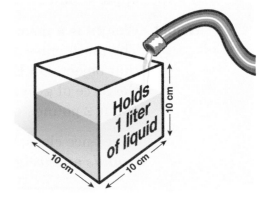

Figure 2.5: *A liter is equal to the volume of a cube-shaped box that is 10 centimeters on each side.*

Measuring volume with SI units

Measuring volume with distance

If an object is a solid cube or rectangle, you can measure its length, width, and height in SI units. These measurements are multiplied together to find the volume in cubic SI units. If the measurements are taken in centimeters, the result of the multiplication will be in cubic centimeters or cm^3. This way of measuring SI volume is best suited for solid objects with parallel sides, but is also used for large volumes. For example, the volume of a lake may be measured in cubic meters (m^3) (Figure 2.6).

Measuring small volumes of liquid

The volume of small amounts of liquids can be measured by pouring them into beakers or graduated cylinders (Figure 2.7). Volume measured this way is reported in milliliters (mL).

The graphic below illustrates the two ways to measure volume in SI units. Regardless of the method chosen, the result is the same!

Volume = 3,200,000,000 m³

Source: U.S. Geological Survey Photographer: C.D. Miller

Mono Lake, California

Figure 2.6: *Large volumes are measured in cubic meters. The volume of Mono Lake in California is about 3.2 billion cubic meters (measurement made in 2002).*

Two ways to measure volume in SI Units:

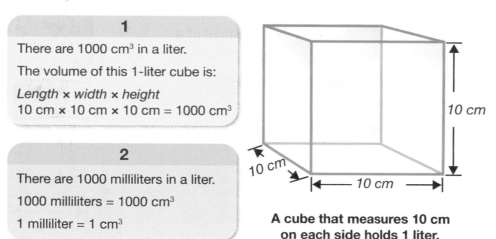

1

There are 1000 cm³ in a liter.

The volume of this 1-liter cube is:

Length × *width* × *height*
10 cm × 10 cm × 10 cm = 1000 cm³

2

There are 1000 milliliters in a liter.

1000 milliliters = 1000 cm³

1 milliliter = 1 cm³

10 cm

10 cm

10 cm

A cube that measures 10 cm on each side holds 1 liter.

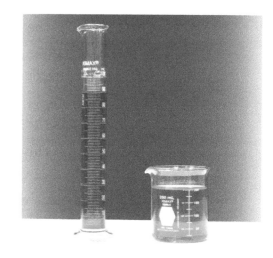

Figure 2.7: *A beaker (right) and a graduated cylinder (left) are used to measure small volumes.*

2.1 Section Review

1. What is the main difference between the SI units measuring system and the English System of measurement?

2. What is the relationship between a cubic centimeter and a milliliter?

3. What is the mass of a cubic centimeter of pure water?

4. How many milliliters are in a liter?

5. What is the mass of a liter of pure water in grams? In kilograms?

6. What prefix increases an SI unit 1,000 times?

7. If you were going to measure the length of your foot, would you use millimeters, centimeters, or meters? Explain your answer.

8. How many liters of pure water are in a cubic meter?

9. What is the mass of a cubic meter of pure water in kilograms?

10. A metric ton equals 1,000 kilograms. What is the mass of a cubic meter of pure water in metric tons?

11. A room is 8 meters wide, 5 meters long, and 4 meters high. What is the volume of this room?

12. What is the difference between mass and weight?

13. *Challenge*: Write a short story or describe a real-life story that illustrates why units are important.

SOLVE IT!

Use a metric ruler or a meter stick to measure the dimensions of your room at home. Record your measurements on a piece of paper. Make a map of your room on another piece of paper using a scale of 1 meter = 1 centimeter. Once you have drawn the shape of your room on the piece of paper, make the map. Where is your bed? Where do you keep your clothes? Where are your favorite things?

Example:

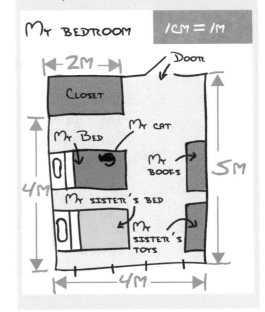

2.2 Measuring Time and Temperature

This section continues to address measuring techniques and tools. You will learn about measuring temperature and time. You will also learn the difference between measuring accurately versus measuring precisely.

Measuring time

Figure 2.8: *12:00 p.m. is lunchtime.*

What time is it? What time does your school start in the morning? What time does school end? What time is lunchtime? These questions ask about a specific moment in time (Figure 2.8).

Measuring time It is often important to measure time in experiments. For example, it is important to know how long it takes for something to move or grow. It might take 1 hour for a car to travel 80 kilometers on a highway. It takes about 156 days to grow a pumpkin from a seed (Figure 2.9).

Units for measuring time You are probably familiar with the common units for measuring time: seconds, hours, minutes, days, and years. The table below shows how these units are related to each other.

Time relationships
1 minute = 60 seconds
1 hour = 60 minutes
1 day = 24 hours
1 year = 365 days
1 century = 100 years

Figure 2.9: *It takes about 156 days to grow a pumpkin from a seed.*

Measuring temperature

Two temperature scales There are two commonly used temperature scales. If the temperature in England is 21 degrees Celsius, you can wear shorts and a T-shirt. If the temperature in the United States is 21 degrees Fahrenheit, you will need to wear a heavy coat, gloves, and a hat. The United States is one of few countries that still use the Fahrenheit scale. For this reason, it is useful to know both of these temperature scales (Figure 2.10).

Fahrenheit On the Fahrenheit scale, water freezes at 32 degrees and boils at 212 degrees. A comfortable room temperature is 68°F. The normal temperature for a human body is 98.6°F.

Celsius On the Celsius scale, water freezes at 0°C and boils at 100°C. The normal human body temperature on the Celsius scale is 37°C. Most temperature measurements used in science and engineering are in Celsius because 0° and 100° are easier to work with than 32° and 212°.

Converting between the scales You can convert between Fahrenheit and Celsius using these formulas.

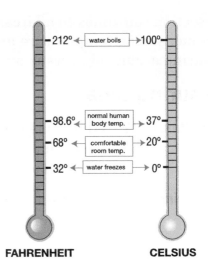

Figure 2.10: *The Fahrenheit and Celsius temperature scales.*

CONVERTING BETWEEN FAHRENHEIT AND CELSIUS

$$T_{Fahrenheit} = \left(\tfrac{9}{5} \times T_{Celsius}\right) + 32 \qquad T_{Celsius} = \tfrac{5}{9}\left(T_{Fahrenheit} - 32\right)$$

$T_{Fahrenheit}$ = Temperature in °F

$T_{Celsius}$ = Temperature in °C

SOLVE IT!

You are doing a science experiment with a Fahrenheit thermometer. Your data must be in degrees Celsius. If you measure a temperature of 86°F, what is this temperature in degrees Celsius?

How do you measure temperature?

Thermometers Accurate measurement of temperature requires a *thermometer*, an instrument that measures temperature. Some thermometers contain liquid alcohol. They measure temperature changes by showing a change in the volume of the alcohol.

When temperature increases As you have learned, matter is made of particles called *atoms*. Groups of atoms are called *molecules*. As the temperature rises, the alcohol molecules in a thermometer move faster and bounce off each other. As a result, the alcohol expands and takes up more space in the thermometer. The volume of the alcohol increases. When the temperature decreases, the molecules move less and take up less space. The volume decreases. Even a small change in volume inside the tube makes a visible change in the amount that the alcohol moves up or down (Figure 2.11).

Different thermometers All thermometers are based on some physical property that changes with temperature. Digital thermometers sense temperature by measuring the ability of electricity to pass through a part of the thermometer called a *probe*. Aquarium "sticker" thermometers use a chemical that changes color at different temperatures.

Digital
thermometer

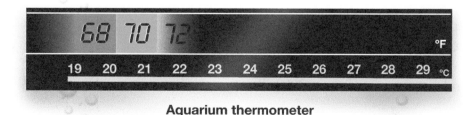

Aquarium thermometer

Particles move around more as the temperature increases. The same number of molecules takes up more space at a higher temperature.

50 alcohol particles at a lower temperature   50 alcohol particles at a higher temperature

Figure 2.11: *Alcohol particles move faster at higher temperatures and spread out. The volume of alcohol expands, or takes up more space.*

STUDY SKILLS

A mathematical formula is easier to use the more you practice using it. Practice converting Celsius degrees to Fahrenheit degrees at least once a day. Pretty soon this conversion formula will be easy to use!

Accuracy versus precision in measuring

An accurate measurement Imagine that you bring home a new air temperature thermometer. It reads 25.0°C (77°F). You check it against the always-correct digital thermostat on your living room wall. It says 25.0°C also. You decide that your new thermometer is **accurate**. An accurate measurement is one that is factual.

An inaccurate measurement You can also gauge temperature with your body. At 25°C, most people feel comfortable—neither too not nor too cold. Let's say you feel a chill in your house. You check your new thermometer. It still reads 25.0°C. You take another look at the always-correct digital thermostat on the wall, and it says 20.0°C. Now you know the new thermometer is sometimes *inaccurate*.

A precise measurement A good measuring tool is both accurate and precise. How do you know if a tool is precise? You measure the same thing several times. **Precise** measurements are close to the same value. The closer they are, the more precise the tool. Suppose your home stays exactly 20°C for 10 days. Your new thermometer reads:

Day	1	2	3	4	5	6	7	8	9	10
Temperature (°C)	25.1	25.2	25.0	25.0	25.1	25.2	25.1	24.9	25.0	25.1

Precise vs. accurate The measurements are precise because they all fall close to one value—25°C. But they are still inaccurate! Measurements can be accurate and precise, accurate and imprecise, inaccurate and precise, or inaccurate and imprecise. Figure 2.12 illustrates these types of measurements.

Increasing precision Often in an experiment, a measurement is made three times. Each time is called a *trial*. Taking the average of three measurements is more accurate and precise than just making one measurement.

VOCABULARY

accurate - a measurement that is factual.

precise - a measurement that is consistent although it may or may not be accurate.

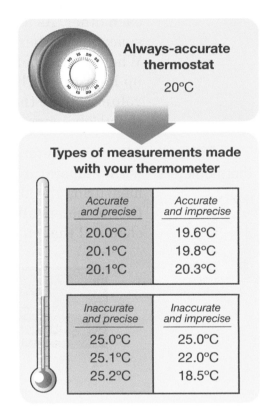

Always-accurate thermostat

20°C

Types of measurements made with your thermometer

Accurate and precise	Accurate and imprecise
20.0°C	19.6°C
20.1°C	19.8°C
20.1°C	20.3°C

Inaccurate and precise	Inaccurate and imprecise
25.0°C	25.0°C
25.1°C	22.0°C
25.2°C	18.5°C

Figure 2.12: *Types of measurements.*

2.2 Section Review

1. Describe three measuring tools that are used in science. The sidebar box at the right lists some of these tools.

2. The flow rate of a river is known to be 10 m³/s. Describe each of the sets of measurements in terms of accuracy and precision:

   a. 10.15 m³/s, 10.01 m³/s, 10.00 m³/s   c. 10.4 m³/s, 9.5 m³/s, 9.8 m³/s

   b. 12.0 m³/s, 15.5 m³/s, 20.2 m³/s   d. 12.0 m³/s, 12.1 m³/s, 11.9 m³/s

3. A mathematical formula is one kind of tool. Use the temperature conversion formula below to fill in the following table. The first one is done for you.

	Celsius degrees	Conversion formula	Fahrenheit degrees
a.	25°C	$(^9/_5 \times 25°C) + 32 = X°F$ Multiply: $(9 \times 25) = 225$ Divide: $225 \div 5 = 45$ Add: $45 + 32 = 77°F$	77°F
b.	100°C		
c.	5°C		
d.			40°F

CONVERTING BETWEEN FAHRENHEIT AND CELSIUS

$$T_{Fahrenheit} = (\tfrac{9}{5} \times T_{Celsius}) + 32 \qquad T_{Celsius} = \tfrac{5}{9}(T_{Fahrenheit} - 32)$$

$T_{Fahrenheit}$ = Temperature in °F $T_{Celsius}$ = Temperature in °C

MY JOURNAL

Write a short story about making an important scientific discovery. Include tools from the "science toolbox" in your story. Here is a list of important science tools:

- Your brain
- The scientific method
- An experiment
- Ruler, meter stick, tape measure
- Triple beam balance
- Beakers or graduated cylinders
- Thermometer
- Stopwatch
- Clock
- Calculator
- Graph paper
- Computer

SOLVE IT!

You want to cut a board so that it is 1.75 meters long. Which procedure would most likely result in a board of the most accurate length? Explain your answer.

a. You measure once and then cut.

b. You measure three times and then cut.

2.3 Systems and Models

VOCABULARY

system - a group of objects and the factors that affect the objects.

variable - a factor that affects an object; examples include mass, temperature, speed, and time.

The universe is huge and complex, so it is useful to think about only one small part at a time. A river flowing down a mountain to the ocean is a small part of the universe. In science, a group of objects—like a riverbed, the river water, and organisms in the river—is called a system.

What is a system?

A group of objects   A **system** is a group of objects and the factors that affect these objects. Some systems include:

* the respiratory system in the human body;
* a river system (Figure 2.13);
* a car engine; and
* a stream table used to model a river (see diagram below).

Variables   A factor that affects an object is called a **variable**. A system can be affected by many variables. In an experiment, only a few variables are studied. Figure 2.14 lists variables that are part of a stream table system. Additional variables include light, temperature, and the floor. These variables either stay constant or they do not affect the system.

NPS photo by J Schmidt

Figure 2.13: *What are the parts of this river system?*

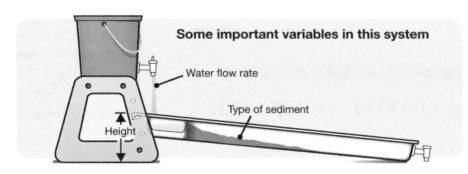

Some important variables in this system

Water flow rate

Type of sediment

Height

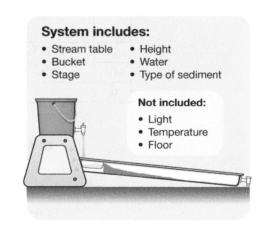

System includes:
* Stream table
* Bucket
* Stage
* Height
* Water
* Type of sediment

Not included:
* Light
* Temperature
* Floor

Figure 2.14: *A system includes objects and variables.*

Systems and experiments

Start with a question

Suppose you want to know how a river channel is affected when the landscape is changed from a gentle slope to a steep hill. You can set up an experiment using the stream table system to find out. An experiment investigates how one variable in a system affects another. Experiments usually start with a question such as, "How does the height of a stream table affect how a river forms?" To answer the question, we could change the stream table height three times and observe how a river forms at each of the heights (Figure 2.15).

Independent and dependent variables

The variable that is changed in an experiment is the independent variable. The variable that is affected by this change is the dependent variable. In Figure 2.15, height is the independent variable and the way the river forms is the dependent variable.

Change one variable at a time

An experiment should have only one independent variable. If you change more than one variable at a time, you won't know which one is responsible for the experiment's results. For example, to study what happens to a river channel when you change the slope, you need to use the same amounts of water and sediment each time. The quantities of water and sediment are control variables. Control variables are variables that are kept the same in an experiment. If you changed both the height of the ramp and the amount of sediment, how could you tell which variable affected the river formation?

State a hypothesis

A hypothesis describes how the independent variable will affect the dependent variable. It is important to remember that a hypothesis is not necessarily correct. The results of the experiment will either support or refute the hypothesis. One hypothesis for the stream table experiment is, "Wider rivers are formed in the stream table as the height of the stream table increases."

VOCABULARY

independent variable - a variable that is changed in an experiment. The independent variable is sometimes called the *manipulated variable*.

dependent variable - a variable that is affected by the change to the independent variable. The dependent variable is sometimes called the *responding variable*.

control variable - a variable that is held constant in an experiment.

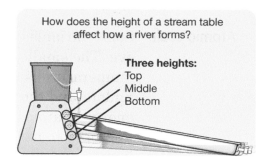

How does the height of a stream table affect how a river forms?

Three heights:
Top
Middle
Bottom

Figure 2.15: *In this experiment, height is the independent variable and the way the river forms is the dependent variable. A control variable is the amount of sediment in the stream table.*

The scale of a system

Large scale, human scale, and small scale
One characteristic of all systems is their scale. The word *scale* here refers to size. Figure 2.16 shows how things compare at different scales. It shows a road and a river at three different scales. On a large scale (bottom row), you can see the size of an object, but you can't see many details. For example, on a road map, you see the streets, but not the street signs. On a small scale (top row), you see a small section of the object up close so you can see more detail. On a human scale (center row), you see more detail than with a large scale, but not as much as with a small scale.

Macroscopic scale
Most of the things you measure in classroom experiments are large-scale, or *macroscopic*. Variables are on a large scale when you can see them with the naked eye, or measure them directly. The flow rate of a river and the temperature of the air are large-scale variables.

Atomic scale
Some variables are so small that they are not visible to the eye. The smallest scale involves atoms. For example, temperature is related to the energy of atoms. To understand the connection between temperature and the energy of atoms we need to investigate at the *atomic scale*. You need to use a special, high-powered microscope to see items on an atomic scale.

The scales of different systems

Small scale

Photo courtesy of NPS/DOI

HARTFORD

Photo courtesy of NASA

Large scale

Figure 2.16: *A road and a river seen at three macroscopic scales.*

Models

What is a model? A *model* explains the cause and effect relationships between variables in a system. For example, if you increase the height of a stream table, the speed of the water flow will increase. A model is a good science tool because it helps you think about how variables are related. There are many types of models.

Mental models If you wanted to kick a soccer ball into a goal, you could use a mental model. You imagine the ball going into the goal and that helps you know how hard to kick the ball (Figure 2.17).

Physical models A physical model (or scale model) is a small version of something big. For example, an engineer might make a small model bridge to learn how to build an actual bridge for a city. A scale model has to be proportional to the real object. A scale of 1 centimeter = 10 meters means that an object 100 meters long in real life would be 10 centimeters long in a small-scale model.

Conceptual models A conceptual model is a way of using your existing knowledge to understand or remember a new concept. Earth scientists use a conceptual model called the *theory of plate tectonics* to explain why earthquakes occur (see sidebar box). Comparing the Earth's plates to puzzle pieces makes the concept easier to understand.

Mathematical models An example of a mathematical model is $E = mc^2$. This mathematical model states that energy (E) equals mass (m) times the speed of light squared (c^2). Graphs are another type of mathematical model that you'll learn about in the next section. A graph is a picture that shows how two variables are related.

Energy Mass
$$E = mc^2$$
Speed of light

 VOCABULARY

graph - a picture that shows how two variables are related.

Figure 2.17: *Imagining how to kick a soccer ball to make a goal is a mental model.*

A conceptual model: The theory of plate tectonics

Earth's surface is like a giant puzzle with huge pieces called plates. The theory of plate tectonics describes how the plates move on Earth's surface. You will learn more about plate tectonics in Unit 4.

2.3 **Section Review**

1. In Section 2.3, you learned that systems, experiments, and models are types of scientific tools. Explain why each of these things can be considered a scientific tool.

2. What is the difference between an independent variable and a dependent variable?

3. You read about an experiment that related the height of a stream table to how a river formed. In the experiment, what kind of variable is the height of the stream table?

4. A fish aquarium is a system. List three parts of this system.

5. Is the stream table system a macroscopic scale system or an atomic scale system?

6. How would you make a physical model of a real car? The length of a real car is 4 meters long. If the physical model has a scale of 10 centimeters = 1 meter, how long would the model car have to be?

7. What kind of model is a graph?

8. What kind of model is a globe of Earth?

9. *Extension*: The height of a stream table (as show in Figure 2.15) affects the *slope* or how steep the stream table is. Come up with a hypothesis to answer this question: What happens to the rate of water flowing in the stream table if you increase the slope?

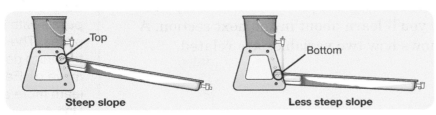

Steep slope   Less steep slope

Do an experiment

Following is an experiment for you to try. Be sure to state a hypothesis before you do the experiment, and follow the steps of the scientific method.

Does salty water freeze at a lower temperature than tap water? Here are some tips for this experiment. Place containers of salty water and tap water in a freezer. Use equal volumes of water. Observe the water samples at regular intervals and measure the temperature of each. Record the temperature at which ice forms on each sample.

Questions:

1. What was your hypothesis?

2. What was the independent variable in this experiment?

3. What was the dependent variable?

4. What tools did you use to do this experiment?

5. What was your conclusion?

2.4 **Graphs**

An experiment is an important scientific tool. When you do an experiment, you can use a graph as a mathematical model that helps you interpret the data you collect.

What is a graph?

A graph is a picture A *graph* is a picture that shows how two or more variables are related. Graphs are easier to read than tables of numbers, so they are often used to display data collected during an experiment.

Independent variable Most of the time, graphs are drawn with the *independent variable* on the horizontal or *x*-axis. Independent variables are controlled by the experimenter. The independent variable in Graph A is the amount of gas in the car (Figure 2.18).

Dependent variable The *dependent variable* usually goes on the vertical or *y*-axis. A dependent variable is affected by an independent variable. In Graph A, distance traveled depends the amount of gas the vehicle has.

Types of graphs Types of graphs include line, bar, and pie graphs. A line graph is used when one variable causes a second variable to increase or decrease in value (Graph A). A bar graph compares categories of information (Graph B). A pie graph is a circular graph that also compares categories of information (Graph C). The data in a pie graph is usually written in percentages. The values in a pie graph should add up to 100 percent.

(A) Line Graph

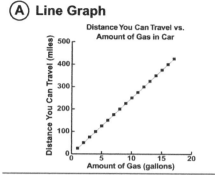

(B) Bar Graph

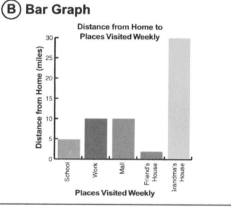

(C) Pie Graph

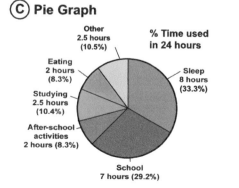

Figure 2.18: *Examples of graphs.*

Parts of a graph

A picture of information A graph is a picture of information. All of the space on the graph should be used so that the data "picture" is easy to understand.

Example A car wash is being held to raise money for a school trip. The data set (Table 2.1) and the line graph below show the relationship between the amount of money in the cash box and the number of hours spent washing cars.

Data for a line graph

Table 2.1 contains a data set. A data set is organized into pairs of values. For every value in the "*x*" column, there is a value in the "*y*" column. Each pair of values can be represented by writing (*x*, *y*). A pair of values (*x*, *y*) represents a certain location or point on a graph. The *x* and *y* values are the *coordinates* of the point. The "picture" of points for this data set is the graph at the left.

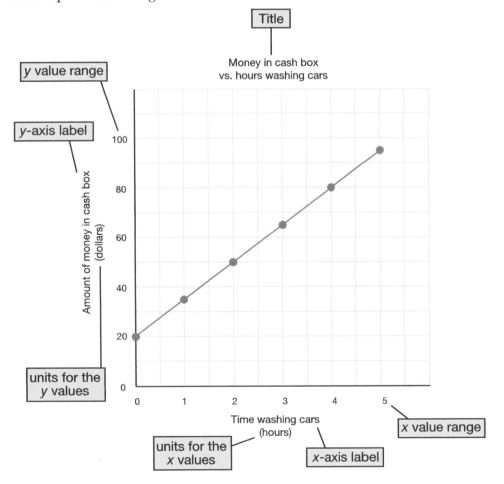

Title

Money in cash box
vs. hours washing cars

y value range

y-axis label

units for the
y values

Amount of money in cash box
(dollars)

Time washing cars
(hours)

units for the
x values

x-axis label

x value range

Table 2.1: Money in cash box vs. number of hours washing cars

x *# of hours washing cars*	*y* *Amount of money in cash box*	*(x, y)* *Coordinates*
0	20	(0, 20)
1	35	(1, 35)
2	50	(2, 50)
3	65	(3, 65)
4	80	(4, 80)
5	95	(5, 95)

How to make a line graph

Step 1   After you have collected your data, you compare independent and dependent variables. The independent variable usually goes on the *x*-axis of a graph. The dependent variable usually goes on the *y*-axis. Be sure to label each axis (see graph at right).

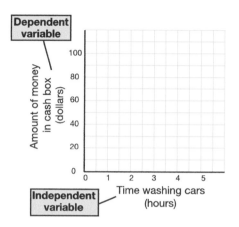

Step 2   The next step is to make a scale for each axis of the graph. When talking about a graph, *scale* refers to how each axis is divided up to fit the range of data values. Let's say we have a piece of graph paper that is 12 boxes by 12 boxes. The range of values for the *x*-axis is 0 to 5. The range of values for the *y*-axis is 20 to 95. To make a graph of this data, we need to figure out the value for each box on each axis.

To do this, you can use a formula:

Data range ÷ Number of boxes on the axis = Value per box

SOLVE IT!

Make a bar graph and pie graph

1) A bar graph compares categories of information. Use the following data set to make a bar graph.

Number of students who bring lunch to school each day

Day	Number of Students
Mon	30
Tue	30
Wed	30
Thurs	30
Fri	5

2) A pie graph also compares categories of information. Use the following data set to make a pie graph.

Percent of students in afterschool activities

Activity	% of Students
Soccer	25%
Dance	25%
Karate	25%
Drama Club	12.5%
Math Team	12.5%

The scale for the *x*-axis is easier to determine. You have 12 boxes and values from 0 to 5 hours. The data range is 5 hours.

Data range ÷ Number of boxes on the axis = Value per box
5 hours ÷ 12 boxes = 0.42 hour/box

One box equals 0.42 hour per box. Round 0.42 to 0.5. This means every two boxes equals 1 hour.

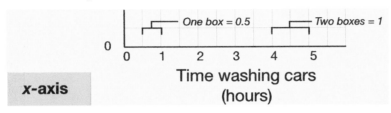

x-axis

For the *y*-axis, the data range is $20 to $95. To more easily calculate the scale, choose $0 to $100 as the data range. Calculate the scale this way:

Data range ÷ Number of boxes on the axis = Value per box
$100 ÷ 12 boxes = $8.3 per box or $8.3/box

Round $8.3 to $10. One box on the *y*-axis equals $10 (Figure 2.19).

Now, write the numbers of the data range on each axis at evenly spaced intervals. Label each axis with its corresponding variable and unit.

Step 3 Plot each point by finding the *x*-value and tracing the graph upward until you get to the correct *y*-value (Figure 2.20). Make a dot for each point. Draw a smooth curve that shows the pattern of the points.

Step 4 Create a title for your graph (see page 42).

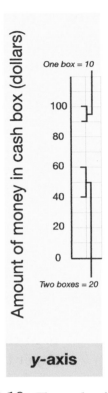

y-axis

Figure 2.19: *The scale of the y-axis for the graph.*

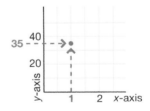

Figure 2.20: *Plot each point by finding the x-value and tracing the graph upward until you get to the correct y-value.*

2.4 Section Review

1. Why is it a good idea to make a graph of the data in a data table?

2. Questions and variables for different experiments are listed below. For each, determine which variable is independent and which is dependent.

	Question	Variables	Independent or dependent?
a.	Does getting more sleep help you do better on tests?	Test scores	
		Hours of sleep	
b.	Does the mass of a toy car affect its speed?	Mass	
		Speed of the car	
c.	Does the amount of sunshine increase the number of fruit per apple tree?	Amount of sunshine	
		Number of fruit per tree	

3. Below is a list of data sets. State what kind of graph you would use for each.

   a. Favorite foods of a group of 100 students: 10 percent prefer steak, 20 percent prefer french fries, 20 percent prefer spaghetti, 25 percent prefer ice cream, and 25 percent prefer pizza

   b. Speed of a toy car on a ramp versus the height of the ramp

   c. Books in a library: 2,000 non-fiction books, 1,500 fiction books, and 500 children's books

4. A blank graph is 10 boxes by 10 boxes (Figure 2.21). You want to plot a data set on this graph. The range of values for the x-axis is 0 to 20. The range of values for the y-axis is 0 to 10. Make a sketch that shows the scale that you would use for each axis.

Design three experiments to determine which of three chocolate chip cookie manufacturers makes the best cookie.

- One experiment should result in data that you can plot on a line graph.
- The second experiment should result in data that you can plot on a bar graph.
- And the third experiment should result in data that you can plot on a pie graph (or cookie graph)!

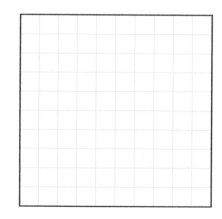

Figure 2.21: *A blank graph that is 10 boxes by 10 boxes.*

Hydrogeologists and Their Tools

Take a look at the topic word hydrogeology. *It is from the Greek word* hudor *meaning "water" and* logia *meaning "study of." So, a hydrogeologist is a scientist who studies water found beneath Earth's surface. This water is known as groundwater and is an important part of our lives.*

A water detective and doctor

A hydrogeologist is like a detective and a doctor all in one. She

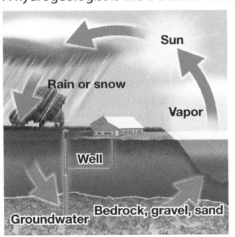

or he investigates how groundwater moves through soil and rock. The scientific method helps them to locate water and solve problems. These scientists are responsible for supplying and controlling groundwater. The water you drink today is safe because a hydrogeologist works to inspect and keep our groundwater safe.

Hydrogeologists protect local water quality from the effects of mining or construction projects. They monitor water quality, and write new laws to protect groundwater. They study groundwater flow and oversee the clean up of pollution before it affects our groundwater.

Going underground for water

You may already know that over 70 percent of Earth is covered with water, but 97 percent of this water is not drinkable. The remaining 3 percent of water is found in glaciers, icecaps, lakes, rivers, streams, and groundwater. How much groundwater do you think we have beneath Earth's surface? A good guess would be about 8,336,364 cubic kilometers. That sounds like a lot, but it's really a drop in the bucket. Only 0.61 percent of the Earth's total water is found in groundwater.

With so little available, it's clear that we need to protect this valuable resource. Hydrogeologists have a challenging role when it comes to protecting the quality and quantity of our water supply.

A ground breaking story

Hydrogeologists use a variety of different tools to collect data about a groundwater location. Let's look at how the tools of a hydrogeologist are used during a job.

The town of Seepio, New Hampshire, wants to build a landfill (a place to put garbage for the town). A hydrogeologist is hired to find out how the landfill would affect the town's groundwater. It is important that the landfill does not pollute the town's water supply.

Aerial and satellite images are used by hydrogeologists to find features called fracture zones or faults. These are cracks in Earth's crust. Large volumes of groundwater can be found in these areas. To locate a site for the landfill, the hydrogeologist wants to avoid places where there would be a lot of groundwater. After studying aerial and satellite images, the hydrogeologist found no fracture zones or faults in the location. This means that there might not be a lot of groundwater near the landfill location.

The search goes on

The hydrogeologist now needs to "look" below ground using electricity. How is that possible? Water conducts electricity. If the spaces in between the soil and rocks are filled with water, electricity will be conducted. This piece of evidence will help the hydrogeologist locate water.

Electric current testing was completed at the location in Seepio. The results showed poor electrical conduction. This piece of evidence leads the hydrogeologist to think that there isn't much water at the landfill location.

Next, a shallow hole is drilled into the ground. One or two dynamite sticks are placed in the hole. The dynamite explosion will cause seismic waves to travel through the rock and bounce back to a receiver. If the waves take a long time to travel, the bedrock is deeper. Bedrock is solid rock underneath loose ground. Water flows best through loose ground. At the site in Seepio, the waves have short arrival times, which means that the bedrock is closer to the surface. The evidence here means that there is not much soil through which water can travel. Little space beneath the ground is available to collect water.

Two other instruments can be used to figure out the depth of the bedrock. One is a ground-penetrating radar which sends and receive waves. The other is a magnetometer which measures changes in the magnetic field. By using these instruments, the hydrogeologist confirms that the bedrock is not far below the surface. If the landfill did pollute this water, the pollution would be only in this small area.

Test wells and maps

Test wells allow the hydrogeologist to sample soil and water below the surface. The samples indicate that the location has sandy soil and with high water quality. Water travels easily through sandy soil, so it is important to make sure that this area is not polluted.

Small diameter water wells called piezometers are placed at several locations at the site. They are used to track the movement and pressure of the water underground. The results show that the water is moving to the river system. This means that protecting

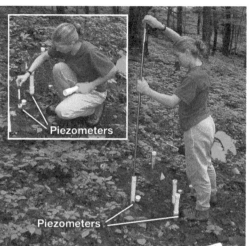

Piezometers

Piezometers

Photos courtesy of Naomi S. Hicks. Photographer Steve Hicks.

this underground water from pollution is even more important. The river is used for swimming and is home to many plants and animals.

The hydrogeologist also takes time to study maps of the soil and geology of the location. The map studies provide evidence that the water is moving through the sand down to a local river system.

Should a town build a landfill?

The hydrogeologist has made many observations and collected a great deal of data. The final step is to write a report that recommends whether or not to build the landfill. In this case, the hydrogeologist might say that the local environment is too important to risk having it polluted by the landfill. However, the hydrogeologist might also report that the sandy area underground would be useful for monitoring water quality quickly. The hydrogeologist would know about a pollutant moving through the location before serious damage could occur to the river system.

QUESTIONS

1. Write a report that answers this question: Should the town of Seepio build the landfill at the proposed location?

2. Imagine your report is presented to the town at a meeting. Write a short speech to summarize your report.

3. Pick one tool that was used in the groundwater story. Describe how this tool works and why it is important for studying groundwater.

Measurement Olympics!

During the Measurement Olympics, you and a partner will practice measurement and conversion skills.

What you will do

You will have 4 minutes at each event station. Your teacher will instruct you when it is time to move to a new station. Your partner will measure and record the results for you while you compete. Then, you will do the same for him/her.

Description of events

- **Straw Javelin:** During this event, you will be throwing a straw as far as you can, like it is a javelin. Your front foot may not cross the start line, and you must throw the straw like a javelin with only one hand. Measure the distance of your throw in meters and centimeters.

- **Paper Cup Challenge:** How much water can you move from a tank to a beaker in 10 seconds using just one paper cup? Use a graduated cylinder to measure the volume of water you successfully transferred. Be careful so you don't spill any water!

- **Pebble Grab:** Who can grab the greatest mass of pebbles? Use only one hand to grab as many pebbles as you can out of a container. Transfer them to a triple beam balance to measure the mass. Be sure the balance is zeroed before you begin!

- **Side Step:** How far is your leg span? From a starting point step as far as you can to the side. Your partner will measure the length of your step in meters and centimeters.

- **Hoppity Hop:** Who can hop 10 meters the fastest on one foot? Your teacher has marked 10 meters on the floor. Using the timers provided, time how long it takes your partner to hop 10 meters on one foot!

Olympic Results

1. Record your results below. Any result with missing or incorrect units will be automatically disqualified from the Measurement Olympics!

2. After you have recorded your results there will be a class discussion about the winners. Record the winner's results for each event.

Olympic Event	My Results	Winner's Results
Straw Javelin		
Paper Cup Challenge		
Pebble Grab		
Side Step		
Hoppity Hop		

Applying your knowledge

a. Calculate the difference between the winner's results and your results for each event. (Don't forget units.)

Olympic Event	Difference
Straw Javelin	
Paper Cup Challenge	
Pebble Grab	
Side Step	
Hoppity Hop	

b. Which measurement were you most familiar with before the olympics? Why?

c. Which measurement did you find easiest to do during the olympics? Why was it so easy for you?

d. Which measurement did you find to be the most difficult during the olympics? Why?

Chapter 2 Assessment

Vocabulary

Select the correct term to complete the sentences.

measurement	unit	atom
mass	gram	weight
dependent variable	variable	control variable
liter	independent variable	graph
meter	matter	system
volume	accurate	precise

Section 2.1

1. A(n) _____ includes a number and a unit.

2. My dog is 2 feet tall. The word "feet" in this sentence is an example of a(n) _____.

3. A(n) _____ is a distance measurement that is a little longer than a yard.

4. The _____ is the basic unit of volume in the SI system of measurement.

5. A formula for _____ is length ∞ width ∞ height.

6. One _____ is the mass of one milliliter of pure water.

7. Your _____ is the same on Earth and on Mars.

8. Your _____ is less on Mars than it is on Earth.

9. _____ has mass and takes up space.

10. A(n) _____ is a particle of matter.

Section 2.2

11. You buy a one-pound bag of sugar and then weigh it on a scale. The reading on the scale says "1.00 pound." The reading on the scale is a(n) _____ measurement.

12. Three people measure the mass of a box. Each person discovers the box is 1.5 kilograms. The measurements are _____.

Section 2.3

13. In my experiment I studied a(n) _____ that included a stream table, a bucket, and water.

14. The rate of water flow into the stream table is a(n) _____ in my experiment.

15. A(n) _____ is the variable that scientists change on purpose in an experiment.

16. The _____ is the variable in an experiment that changes as a result of how another variable is changed.

17. When doing an experiment it is important to keep one variable constant. This kind of variable is called a(n) _____.

18. A(n) _____ is a picture that allows you to see how two variables relate to one another.

Concepts

Section 2.1

1. What is a unit? In your answer, give an example of an SI unit and an example of a unit from the English System of measurement.

2. Which statement is correct? Explain why it is the only correct statement?

   (a) I am 2 tall.   (c) I am 2 meters tall.

   (b) I am 2 kilograms tall.   (d) I weigh 30 milliliters.

3. You learned about two systems of measurement. Which of these systems is based on the number 10?

4. An apple on the moon has the same mass as an apple on Earth, but the same apple weighs more on Earth than it does on the moon? Why?

5. The force of gravity on the moon is less than it is on Earth. Therefore, the weight of your body on Earth is _____ it is on the moon. Which statement goes in the blank: greater than, the same as, or less than?

Section 2.2

6. You want to do an experiment to find out how long it takes for a bean plant to grow from a seed. What units of time would you use?

7. Below are pictures of different measurement tools. Identify whether the tool is used to measure length, volume, or mass.

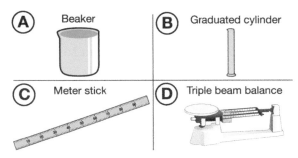

(A) Beaker (B) Graduated cylinder

(C) Meter stick (D) Triple beam balance

8. You use your watch to time how long it takes for a friend to run one kilometer. You know your watch is fast by 5 minutes. How would you describe this time measurement?

Section 2.3

9. Is an ant farm in an aquarium an example of a system? Use the definition of a system from the chapter to answer this question. Explain your answer in paragraph form.

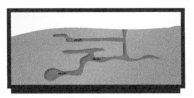

An ant farm

10. You want to find out if light affects the growth of plants. To do your experiment, you use two plants. One plant is a bean plant and the other is a spider plant. Both plants are in the same size pot and the same type of soil. You put the bean plant in a window, and you put the spider plant in a closet, where the light will be turned off for the duration of the experiment. The experiment lasts one week. Each day at 9:00 a.m. you measure the height of each plant and record your data using centimeters in your science notebook. At the same time, you water each of the plants with 500 mL of water. Is your experiment a good scientific experiment? Why or why not?

Does light affect the growth of plants?

Spider plant in a dark room

Bean plant on window sill

11. Identify the independent variable, dependent variable, and the control variable(s) in this experiment. Explain your reasoning.

Question: How does wheel size affect the speed of carts moving down a ramp?

In the experiment, there are five carts that are all identical, except for the wheels. Each cart had a different size wheel with diameters as follows: 5 cm, 7 cm, 9 cm, 11 cm, and 13 cm. The carts were placed one at a time on a ramp and released. The carts were released from the same starting point. The time for each cart to roll 2 meters down the ramp was recorded. There were three trials for each cart, and the same ramp was used for the entire experiment.

Section 2.4

12. There are three graphs below. Identify each type of graph.

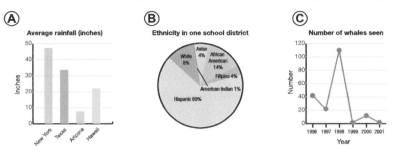

13. When graphing you should usually:

   a. put the independent variable on the *x*-axis.

   b. put the dependent variable on the *x*-axis.

   c. put the independent variable on the *y*-axis.

   d. put the control variable on the *y*-axis.

14. Below are three data sets. What kind of graph would you use to plot each data set? Explain your answer.

   a. Student grades on a science test

Grade	Percent of students who earned this grade
A	25%
B	35%
C	35%
D	5%
F	0%

   b. The favorite foods of students in a 6th grade class

Favorite food	Number of students who say that this food is their favorite
Pizza	10
Ice cream	3
Tacos	5
Chocolate	2
Spaghetti	3

   c. The height of a plant each day

Day number	Height (cm)
1	3
2	3.2
3	4
4	4.5
5	6

Math and Writing Skills

Section 2.1

1. How many meters does each value represent?

   a. 1,000 millimeters

   b. 300 centimeters

   c. 2 kilometers

2. A book is on a shelf that is 2.5 meters high. How high is the book in centimeters?

3. How long is this wrench in centimeters?

4. You have a box that measures 5 cm ∞ 5 cm ∞ 3 cm. How many milliliters of water would fit in this box?

5. Which box would hold 100 milliliters of water?

   a. A box that measures 2 cm ∞ 2 cm ∞ 2 cm

   b. A box that measures 4 cm ∞ 5 cm ∞ 5 cm

   c. A box that measures 20 cm ∞ 2 cm ∞ 1 cm

6. Your mother gives you 1,000 mL of your favorite soda and says "You are only allowed to drink half of a liter of that soda." How many milliliters are you allowed to drink? How much soda will be left over after you drink half a liter?

7. A grocery store wants to sell 100 pounds of bananas. What is the mass of these bananas in kilograms?

Section 2.2

8. Calculate how many seconds are in 2 hours and 5 minutes.

9. What is the typical body temperature of the human body in Fahrenheit? Now, convert this to Celsius and report typical human body temperature in Celsius.

10. Describe the ability of each of the following basketball players to make a basket. Use the terms *accurate* and *precise*.

    a. Ace makes 10 baskets in a row.

    b. Whoosh misses 10 baskets in a row but hits the backboard each time.

Section 2.3

11. Here are some examples of systems: the Earth and moon system, the digestive system in your body, and a fish in an aquarium. Choose one of these systems and write a paragraph about it that answers these questions.

    •What are the different parts of the system?
    •Why is it a system?
    •What variables affect the function of the system?

12. You are doing a presentation about the Golden Gate Bridge in your social studies class. Find out how long and wide the bridge is.

    a. If you were going to make a physical model of this bridge, what scale would you use?

    b. Would a physical scale model be easy to do? Why or why not?

Section 2.4

13. Make three graphs of the data that were reported in Concept question 14. Make one graph for each data set, and be sure it has all of the proper components.

14. Below is a bar graph for climate data in Los Angeles over one year. Answer the following questions about the graph.

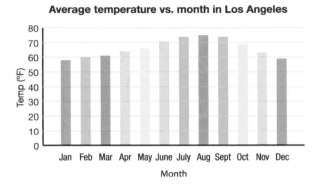

a. When was the highest average temperature?

b. When was the lowest average temperature?

c. What does the graph show about the trends in temperature in Los Angeles over one year?

d. What do you predict the average temperature will be in May of the following year?

Chapter Project—Conduct an experiment

Design and conduct your own scientific experiment. What do you want to find out? The experiment can take up to one week to perform, or can take only a couple of hours to perform. Here is what you need to keep in mind.

• Ask a question about which you are curious.
• Your hypothesis must be testable.
• You need an independent and a dependent variable.
• Are all other variables controlled?
• How are you going to collect data, make measurements, and record results?

Be sure to check with your teacher about your question and your hypothesis before continuing with your experiment.

Chapter 3

Physical Science Connections

In this chapter, you will learn about energy, heat, density, and buoyancy. You will also learn how they impact you and your surroundings. For instance, think about a hot-air balloon. How does it fly? You will learn the answer to this question in this chapter. Understanding how a hot-air balloon flies is part of learning Earth science. Energy, heat, density, and buoyancy are related to all sorts of interesting topics including hurricanes, ocean currents, plate tectonics, and the formation of stars.

Key Questions:

1. What is energy?

2. What is the difference between temperature and heat?

3. Why do some things float and other things sink?

3.1 Types of Energy

 **VOCABULARY**

One of the important variables in any system is *energy*. **Energy** is the ability to create change in a system. The Sun is the ultimate energy source for Earth. In addition to solar energy, some other types of energy include motion, height, and heat.

energy - the ability to create change in a system.

The ultimate source of energy

Surface heat energy
Most of Earth's surface heat energy comes from the Sun. About 5 million tons of the Sun's mass is converted to energy every second through nuclear reactions. This energy leaves the Sun as radiant energy that is mostly visible light. Visible light includes all the colors you see in a rainbow. Radiant energy also includes infrared radiation (heat) and ultraviolet light. Visible and ultraviolet light, and infrared radiation are part of the *electromagnetic spectrum*.

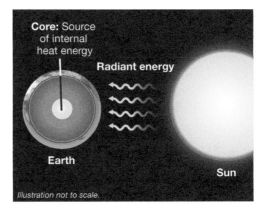

Figure 3.1: *Earth is warmed from the inside by heat from its core. Earth is warmed on its surface by radiant energy from the Sun.*

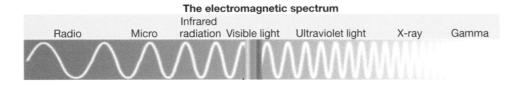

Internal heat energy
Earth's internal heat energy mostly comes from its *core* (Figure 3.1). Much of this heat energy is left over from when Earth first formed. Some of the core's heat energy comes from the breakdown of radioactive atoms. Radioactive atoms are unstable and undergo changes that produce heat and other products.

Energy makes things happen
Energy causes events to happen under and on Earth's surface. Figure 3.2 lists examples of energy and the changes caused by energy.

Figure 3.2: *Examples of energy and changes caused by energy.*

Energy at a small scale

Particles of matter move constantly   Matter is made of tiny particles called *atoms*. Atoms are too small to see with your eyes or even with a magnifying glass (Figure 3.3). Atoms move constantly. They move around in the water you drink and in the air you breathe. All of the atoms of your body are moving constantly, too—even when you are asleep!

Motion energy   Imagine what it would be like to live in an atom-sized world. If you were suddenly shrunk to the size of an atom, you would be pushed and shoved by all the atoms around you. Watch out! Atoms whiz by at fast speeds! The constant motion of atoms is a form of energy. The energy of motion is called kinetic energy. Faster atoms have more kinetic energy than slower atoms.

kinetic energy - motion energy.

Atoms are so small that 200,000 could fit across the thickness of a piece of aluminum foil.

Figure 3.3: *The thickness of a sheet of aluminum foil is about 200,000 atoms across. Atoms are too small to see with your eyes or even with a magnifying glass!*

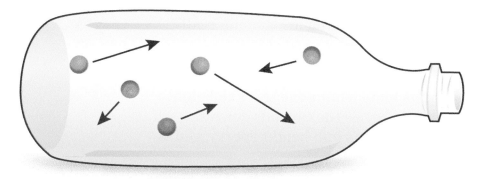

Imagine that atoms are big enough to see.

In this diagram, arrow length shows atom speeds. The longer the arrow, the faster the atom is moving. Which atoms have the most kinetic energy?

Height energy

Potential energy
Did you know that you can increase your energy by walking up a flight of steps? The higher you are relative to Earth's surface, the more height energy you have. Height energy is a type of potential energy. **Potential energy** is stored energy.

Examples
If you drop a ball from a high position, it will bounce higher than if you dropped it from a low position. The higher position gives the ball more potential height energy.

Height energy and Earth science
Height energy also affects how water runs off a mountain and over the land. Figure 3.4 shows an experiment that you can do to test how height affects water running over land.

Potential and kinetic energy
Imagine that you are riding a roller coaster. At the top of a the first hill you have a lot of potential energy, but not much *kinetic energy* (energy of motion). So you move slowly. Near the bottom of the hill, you have a lot of kinetic energy (you are moving really fast), but you have less potential energy (Figure 3.5).

Energy in systems
Systems tend to move from higher to lower energy. At the top of a roller coaster hill, the car has more height energy. The height energy is converted to motion energy as the car rolls down the hill. Once it reaches the bottom, the car has less height energy and is more stable.

potential energy - stored energy.

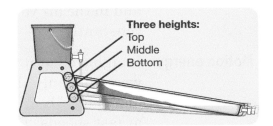

Figure 3.4: *How does the height of a stream table affect how water runs over sediment?*

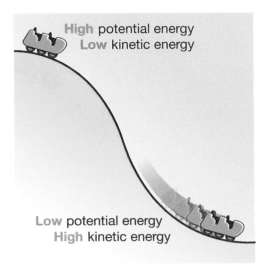

Figure 3.5: *Potential and kinetic energy on a roller coaster.*

Heat energy

From warmer to cooler objects

Heat is a form of energy. Heat moves from warmer to cooler objects. If you touch a hot dinner plate, heat from the plate moves to your cooler finger. Fast-moving atoms of the plate push against the slower atoms of your finger. The nerves in your finger send a warning message to your brain. Then, your brain sends a message to your hand to pull away from the plate.

The hot dinner plate will not stay hot forever. Eventually, as heat from the plate transfers to the cooler air around it, the plate cools down to the temperature of the room.

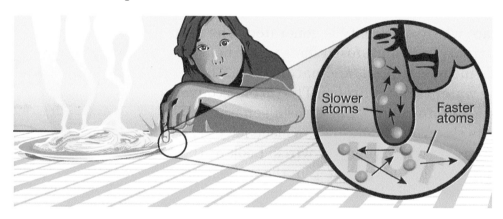

Usable energy and heat

We all eat to get energy. Some of that energy is used to do tasks like completing homework. The rest becomes heat energy. To get more energy to do more activities, you need to eat more food!

Friction

Energy is released due to *friction* when two objects rub against each other (Figure 3.6). The more friction there is between objects, the more energy builds up between them. Some of this energy is converted to heat. Rub your hands together really fast. You will feel heat from the friction. If you wet your hands, it will be harder to generate heat. The water reduces the friction between your hands.

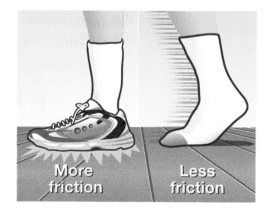

Figure 3.6: *There is more friction between a sneaker and a gym floor than between a sock and the gym floor.*

MY JOURNAL

1. Place an ice cube in a plastic sandwich bag and seal the bag tightly. What happens to the ice cube when you let it sit on the table (in the bag)?

2. Sketch a "before" and "after" picture in your journal. Record the time it took for the ice cube to melt.

3. What could you have done to speed up the melting process? List all possibilities.

Energy flow and heat loss

Heat and light bulbs   A light bulb produces energy in the form of light. The light bulb might feel hot to the touch after it has been lit for awhile. This is because only 2 percent of the energy produced by a regular (or incandescent) light bulb is light energy. Ninety-eight percent of the energy produced is heat (Figure 3.7)!

Heat and cars   The source of energy for a car is gasoline. For most cars, only about 20 percent of the gasoline burned by the engine is used to move the car. Eighty percent of the energy from the gasoline becomes heat energy (Figure 3.8).

Heat and fuels   A **power plant** is a place where electricity is generated. The first step in producing electricity is to burn fossil fuels to get heat to boil water. Fossil fuels include coal, oil, and natural gas. The steam from the boiling water turns a *turbine*. The turbine converts the energy from the steam into energy that turns a generator. The generator then converts this kinetic energy into electricity. The electricity is carried from the power plant by wires. Look at the diagram below. Some heat is lost at each step in the process of converting fuel energy into useful electricity.

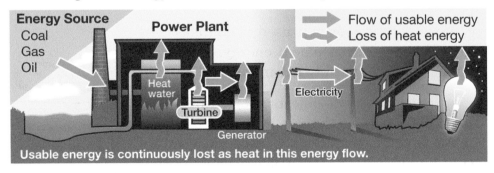

power plant - a place where electricity is generated.

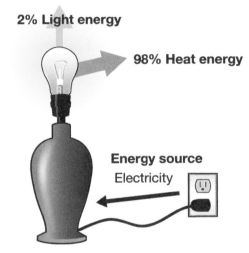

Figure 3.7: *Most of the energy used by a light bulb becomes heat energy.*

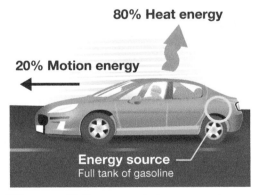

Figure 3.8: *Most of the energy from gasoline becomes heat energy.*

3.1 Section Review

1. How do you know that energy is involved when you see a plant grow? Name one kind of energy that is involved.

2. How do you know that energy is involved when you push a toy car? Name one kind of energy that is involved.

3. What are atoms?

4. How is kinetic energy related to the speed of atoms?

5. Fill in the blank. Faster atoms have _____ (more/less) kinetic energy than slower atoms.

6. Fast, rushing water flows in a channel at the base of the Andes Mountains in Argentina (Figure 3.9). The speed (and sound) of this fast-flowing water is very exciting. Explain in terms of potential and kinetic energy why this water moves so quickly.

7. In which direction is heat transferred—from warm to cool or from cool to warm?

8. In which situation would more friction occur? Why?

   a. A car tire contacts dry pavement

   b. The blade of an ice-skate contacts smooth ice

9. What kind of energy is used to keep a light bulb lit?

10. Describe the process by which electricity is made at a power plant that uses fossil fuels.

11. What type of energy is lost in a light bulb, car, and power plant?

12. Research the answers to these questions using your school library or the Internet. In terms of energy produced or used:

    a. what is the main difference between an incandescent light bulb and a compact fluorescent light bulb?

    b. what is the main difference between gasoline-powered and electric hybrid cars?

CHALLENGE

Compare this hydroelectric power plant to one that burns fossil fuels.

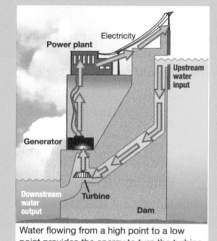

Water flowing from a high point to a low point provides the energy to turn the turbine.

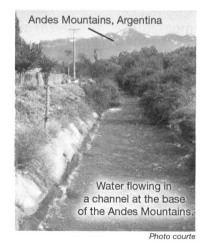

Andes Mountains, Argentina

Water flowing in a channel at the base of the Andes Mountains.

Photo courte

Figure 3.9: *Water flowing at the base of the Andes Mountains in Argentina.*

3.2 Heat

What happens to an ice cube when you hold it in your hand? The ice melts because heat flows from your hand to the ice cube. We've all experienced the effects of heat, but what exactly *is* heat?

Heat and temperature

What is heat?
Heat is a form of energy caused by the motion of atoms.* Heat is the sum of the kinetic energy of each atom in a sample. This means that a bucket of hot water has more heat than a cup of hot water. The bucket contains more fast-moving atoms than the cup. More fast-moving atoms create more heat energy.

What is temperature?
Temperature is related to heat, but it isn't the same thing. Temperature is a measure of the *average* speed of atoms in a sample. The average speed of the atoms in a hot object is fast. The average speed in a cold object is slower (Figure 3.10).

What is your temperature?
Sometimes when you are sick, a thermometer might show a temperature of 100°F or more. The normal temperature for the human body is 98.6°F. A thermometer measures the average kinetic energy of the atoms in your body.

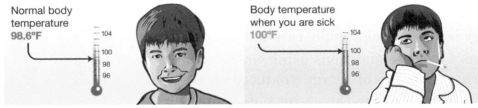

The average speed of atoms in your body is higher when you are sick.

* Footnote: This definition of heat was adapted to be appropriate for the level and content of this text.

 VOCABULARY

heat - a form of energy caused by the motion of atoms.

temperature - a measure of the speed of an individual atom or of the average speed of a sample containing lots of atoms.

Atoms in a hot object

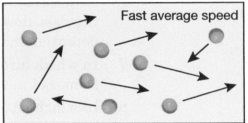

Fast average speed

Atoms in a cold object

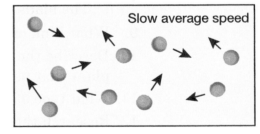

Slow average speed

Figure 3.10: *The average speed of atoms in a hot object is fast. The average speed of atoms in a cold object is slower.*

Summary of heat and temperature

An example   If you want to warm up the water in a swimming pool, you need heat energy. Which of the following methods for warming the water will work best?

- Warm the water by adding a teacup of water at 100°C, or
- Warm the water by adding a bucket of water at 50°C

The water in the teacup has a higher temperature, but there are fewer molecules than in the bucket. This means that the teacup water has less heat energy than the water in the bucket.

Even though the water in the teacup has a higher temperature, the water in the bucket is a better choice for warming the pool water because it contains more total heat energy!

 SOLVE IT!

When two equal volumes of water are mixed, the final temperature of the mixture is halfway between the two original temperatures.

This is because molecules collide and exchange energy. Fast molecules slow down while the slow ones speed up. Eventually, all the molecules are going at about the same speed.

Use this information to solve the following problem.

A cup of water with a temperature of 20°C is mixed with a second cup of water with a temperature of 80°C. Both cups contain the same amount of water. What will the temperature of the final mixture be?

What is the final temperature?

Two methods of heating the pool are shown.

Which is best?

Teacup of **100°C** water added to pool

Bucket of **50°C** water added to pool

It's cold!   Still cold!   Yeah! It's warmer!

Heat transfer by convection

 VOCABULARY

What is convection? Convection is the transfer of heat through the motion of gases and liquids such as air and water. Warm air rises and cold air sinks. Convection occurs naturally in Earth's atmosphere. Convection also occurs in buildings. To understand convection, let's think of how a room gets heated.

convection - transfer of heat through the motion of liquids and gases.

Convection is used to heat rooms Look at the illustration below. A radiator is a device used to heat a room. Heat from the radiator warms nearby air atoms. The warmed atoms move quickly and carry heat energy as they rise above the radiator. A curtain above the radiator flutters as fast-moving atoms collide with it. Eventually, the heat from the radiator combined with the convection of the air make the room comfortably warm.

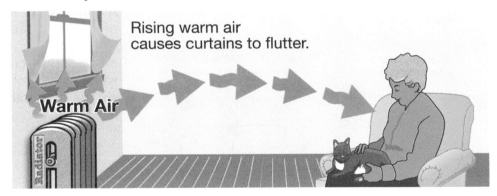
Rising warm air causes curtains to flutter.
Warm Air
Radiator

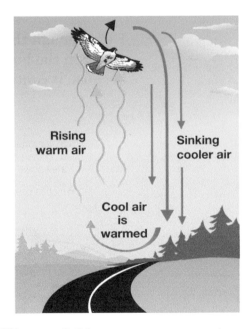
Rising warm air
Sinking cooler air
Cool air is warmed

Convection is used to fly Outdoors, convection of the air is driven by the Sun's energy. The Sun warms the air near Earth's surface. This warm air rises. Hawks make use of the rising air to soar in the sky (Figure 3.11). Eventually, the warm air cools down and sinks back to the ground where it may get reheated. Then, the convection cycle of air begins again.

Figure 3.11: *Hawks use convection to soar. They are lifted higher in the sky by rising currents of warm air.*

Heat transfer by conduction

 VOCABULARY

conduction - transfer of heat by direct contact of atoms and molecules.

What is conduction? Conduction is the transfer of heat by the direct contact of atoms and molecules. Heat is transferred from atom to atom by direct contact. If you hold an ice cube, warmer atoms in your hand will transfer heat by conduction to the cooler ice cube atoms.

Moving atoms Unlike the atoms in liquids and gases, the atoms in solids are anchored in place. They can wiggle and push each other, but they do not move freely. If you place a cold spoon into a mug of hot cocoa, you may notice that the handle of the spoon becomes warm. If atoms in a solid object can't move freely, how does the handle of the spoon get warm?

How conduction warms things up Imagine the spoon handle as a long line of atoms. At first, all of the atoms are moving at similar speeds. You know this because the whole handle is the same temperature. Soon the part of the handle closest to the surface of the cocoa heats up. The atoms close to the surface of the cocoa are now wiggling and pushing at a higher speed. As these atoms push other atoms further along the handle, the more-distant atoms speed up. Eventually, the atoms all along the handle speed up. Transferring heat this way is an example of conduction.

MY JOURNAL

Where does conduction take place in your house? Walk through your house. In each room, observe whether or not there are objects that are involved in conduction. Based on your observations, make a list of as many examples of heat transfer by conduction as you can. Remember, in solids, the atoms and molecules are touching each other. That's why heat transfer by conduction works best between solids.

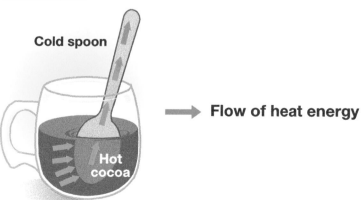

Cold spoon

Flow of heat energy

Hot cocoa

Heat transfer by radiation

What is radiation? The heat from the Sun is necessary for life to exist on Earth (Figure 3.12). This heat is not transferred to Earth by conduction or convection. The Sun's heat reaches Earth by a heat transfer process called radiation. Radiation is heat transfer through empty space. Heat transfer by radiation occurs without direct contact or movement of atoms.

Summary of convection, conduction, and radiation All three forms of heat transfer are often working at the same time to transfer energy from warmer objects to cooler objects. A pot of water being heated by a campfire is warmed through the combined processes of conduction, convection, and radiation!

VOCABULARY

radiation - heat transfer that involves energy waves and no direct contact or movement by atoms.

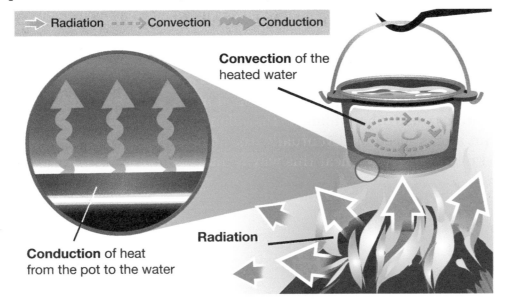

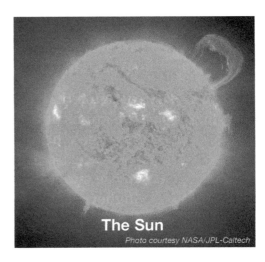
The Sun
Photo courtesy NASA/JPL-Caltech

Figure 3.12: *The Sun's heat is the product of nuclear reactions between atoms in the Sun. The Sun's heat reaches Earth by radiation.*

3.2 **Section Review**

1. Why does an ice cream cone melt on a warm day?

2. Figure 3.13 lists the speeds of student runners. Find the average speed of the students by adding the speeds and dividing by five. If the group of students represent a group of atoms, what does their average speed represent?

3. What is the difference between heat and temperature?

4. Will one liter of hot water have more or less heat energy than two liters of hot water? Explain your answer.

5. You mix 100 milliliters of 10°C water and 100 milliliters of 90°C water. What is the final temperature of the mixture?

6. State the type of heat transfer that is occurring in each situation.

   a. Warm air rises.

   b. You feel the heat on your feet as you walk barefoot across a driveway in the summertime.

   c. The Sun's heat makes you want to stand in the shade.

7. A hawk gets some help while flying by using convection currents (air currents created by rising warm air). How is the Sun involved in creating convection currents?

8. How would heat transfer occur in the following substances or objects?

   a. The atmosphere

   b. A metal rod

   c. Water in a pot

   d. An empty pot on a hot stove

   e. The air inside a hot-air balloon

Student	Speed (cm/s)
Alice	100
Bernard	150
Chloe	50
Dev	75
Eduardo	125
AVERAGE (sum of five speeds ÷ 5)	

Figure 3.13: *The speeds of five students running in a gymnasium.*

In this chapter, you learned that warm air rises and cold air sinks.

Imagine you have a group of 100 atoms and that you can change the temperature of the group.

Come up with a hypothesis to explain why this group of atoms would rise if it were warm. And why the group would sink if it was cold.

Hint: Refer to Figure 3.11.

3.3 Density and Buoyancy

It's impossible for a person to lift a real boulder because a boulder is too heavy (Figure 3.14). Why, then, can "superheroes" move huge "boulders" in the movies? It's because even though the fake boulders are the same size as real boulders, the fake boulders are less dense! The properties of density and buoyancy also cause some things to float and others to sink. Ice cubes float in a glass of water, but a pebble will sink. Why? You'll find out by reading this section.

Density

What is density?   Density describes the relationship between an object's mass and its volume. Density is the mass of an object divided by the volume of the object. A real boulder has a greater density than a fake boulder made of plastic foam.

Density depends on two things   The density of a material depends on two things:

1.   The mass of the atoms that make up the material, and
2.   The volume or amount of space the material takes up. This is related to how closely the atoms are "packed" in the material.

A material like plastic foam has low density. Plastic foam has molecules that are low in mass and not packed very close together. Additionally, plastic foam has air pockets. A material like rock has molecules that are higher in mass than the molecules of plastic foam, and they are packed more closely together. This means rock has a higher density than plastic foam (Figure 3.14).

Solids, liquids, and gases   Liquids and gases are also made up of atoms and molecules and have mass and volume. As with solids, you can find the density of a liquid or a gas too!

VOCABULARY

density - the mass of an object divided by the object's volume.

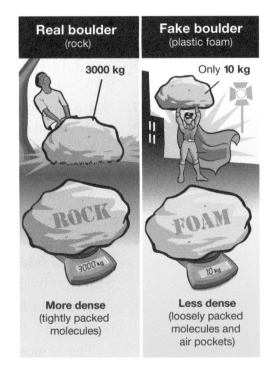

Figure 3.14: *The density of a real boulder versus the density of a fake boulder.*

Finding density

Doing the math The density of an object is found by measuring the object's mass and volume then dividing the mass by the volume. Division can be shown with a slash mark (/). The slash is read as the word *per*. A density of 2.7 g/cm^3 is read as: two point seven grams per cubic centimeter.

SOLVE IT!

Use the mass and volume data for a steel cube and a steel nail to calculate the density of these objects.

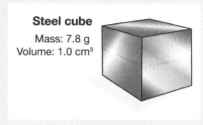
Steel cube
Mass: 7.8 g
Volume: 1.0 cm³

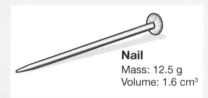
Nail
Mass: 12.5 g
Volume: 1.6 cm³

How does the density of the steel cube compare to the density of the steel nail?

DENSITY

$$Density\ (g/cm^3) \longrightarrow D = \frac{m}{V} \begin{matrix} \longleftarrow Mass\ (g) \\ \longleftarrow Volume\ (cm^3) \end{matrix}$$

What is the density of an aluminum metal block that has a mass of 27.0 g and a volume of 10.0 cm³ ?

D = m/V
D = 27.0 g/10.0 cm³
D = 2.7 g/cm³

The density of a material is always the same The density of a material is always the same under the same conditions of temperature and pressure. This is true regardless of how much of the material you have. For example, the density of aluminum metal is always 2.7 g/cm^3 (or 2.7 g/mL, see Figure 3.15). Aluminum foil, aluminum wire, or an aluminum brick all have the same density. This is true as long as your sample is not hollow and does not have any other materials mixed with it.

Remember:

1 cubic centimeter = 1 milliliter (1 cm³ = 1 mL).

Therefore,

2.7 g/cm³ = 2.7 g/mL.

Figure 3.15: *Volume units.*

Reviewing mass and volume

Mass vs. weight What is the mass of your body? You are probably familiar with measuring your weight, but not your mass. Mass and weight are not the same thing. *Mass* is the amount of matter in an object. *Weight* is a measure of the pulling force of gravity on mass. In the English system, weight is measured in pounds. The SI unit is called a *newton*. It takes 4.448 newtons to make one pound.

Weight on other planets The force of gravity is different on every planet. As a result, your weight would change if you visited another planet. A boy who weighs 445 newtons (100 pounds) on Earth would weigh 1,125 newtons on Jupiter! However, his mass stays the same on both planets (Figure 3.16). This is because mass measures the amount of matter a body contains, not how much that matter is pulled by gravity.

A solid cube or rectangle *Volume* is the space that an object takes up. To find the volume of a solid cube or rectangle, you measure the length, width, and height of the object. Then you multiply the length, width, and height together. If your measurements are in centimeters, the volume unit will be cubic centimeters, or cm^3.

Odd-shaped objects You can find the volume of an odd-shaped object, like a key, by placing it in water. This *displacement method* can be done in a graduated cylinder (Figure 3.17). First, the volume of water in the graduated cylinder is noted. Then, the key is placed in the graduated cylinder. The key pushes aside an amount of water equal to its volume, causing the water level to rise. The volume of the key is equal to the volume of the water with the key in it (28 mL) minus the volume of the water without the key (25 mL). The volume of the key is 3 mL.

	Mass (kg)	Weight (newtons)
Earth	45.5	445
Jupiter	45.5	1,125

Figure 3.16: *Mass versus weight on Earth and Jupiter. Weight changes from place to place, but mass stays the same.*

What is the volume of the key?

28 mL
- 25 mL
―――――
3 mL

Volume of key =
3 mL or 3 cm³

Figure 3.17: *Measuring the volume of an odd-shaped object.*

Sinking and buoyant force

A 400 cm³ rock displaces 400 cm³ of water

The illustration below shows a rock with a volume of 400 cm³ that has sunk to the bottom of a pond. When the rock is completely underwater, it displaces (pushes aside) an amount of water that is equal to its volume. The rock displaces 400 cm³ of water.

VOCABULARY

buoyant force - an upward lifting force that acts on an object when it pushes aside a fluid.

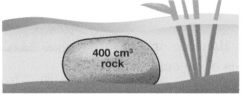
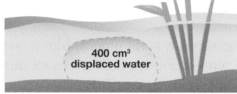

The rock weighs 9.8 newtons

On Earth, this 400 cm³ rock weighs 9.8 newtons. This means that if you are holding the rock, you use 9.8 newtons of force to support it.

The water weighs 3.9 newtons

On Earth, the 400 cm³ of water displaced by the rock weighs 3.9 newtons. This means that it takes 3.9 newtons of force to support the displaced water.

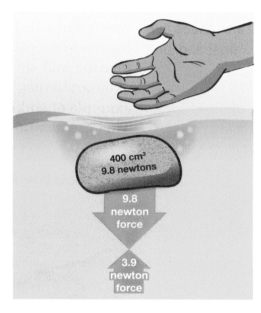

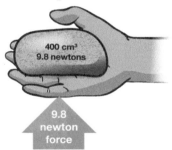
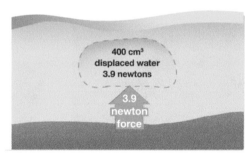

The water pushes on the rock with a 3.9 newton force

When the rock is dropped into water, the water pushes back on the rock with a force *equal to the weight* of the displaced water. The upward force shown in Figure 3.18 is called buoyant force. The buoyant force is always equal to the weight of the displaced fluid.

Why does the rock sink?

The rock sinks because its weight is greater than the displaced water's weight. The 9.8-newton downward force acting on the rock is greater than the water's 3.9-newton upward force.

Figure 3.18: *The buoyant force of the water displaced by this rock is not enough to support it and make it float. Therefore, the rock sinks!*

Floating and sinking

Fluids Matter that can flow is called a **fluid**. Liquids and gases are both fluids. Under the right conditions, solid matter that is made of small particles can also flow. The ground shaking during an earthquake can turn soil into a fluid! When this happens, cars and other solid objects can sink into the ground.

Solids, liquids, and gases can float and sink We are used to talking about a solid object, like a boat, floating or sinking in a fluid like water. Figure 3.19 gives examples of objects that help people float safely in water. But other examples of floating and sinking exist. Vinegar sinks to the bottom of a bottle of oil-and-vinegar salad dressing. This is a liquid-in-a-liquid example of sinking. A balloon filled with helium gas floats in air. This is a gas-in-a-gas example of floating.

Floating and sinking in fluids

Solid in liquid   Gas in gas   Liquid in liquid

Oil

Vinegar

How a hot-air balloon flies The air in a hot-air balloon is heated. The air expands as it is warmed. When the balloon is full, some air is forced out of the opening at the bottom because the balloon doesn't stretch. The mass of the remaining air is less, but the volume is about the same. This makes the density of the balloon less, so the balloon is more buoyant. The less-dense, warm air in the balloon floats in the denser, cooler surrounding air. This is how a hot-air balloon flies.

VOCABULARY

fluid - matter that can flow, usually a liquid or a gas.

MY JOURNAL

Make a list of five objects (all made of different materials) that float in water, and a list of five objects (all made of different materials) that sink in water.

Several ways to help people float better in the water

Figure 3.19: *A foam life preserver, a life vest, and a raft all help people float!*

3.3 Section Review

1. Which of the follow substances are fluids?

a. light	b. hardened concrete	c. water
d. air	e. orange juice	f. helium

2. Give an example of an object (solid, liquid, or gas) that floats on a fluid.

3. What is buoyancy? Against what other force does it act?

4. An object that weighs 10 newtons displaces 12 newtons of water. Will this object sink or float?

5. Ben's model boat weighs 4 newtons. When he places it in the water it sinks! Explain what happened and what he can do to make it float.

6. What makes an object float rather than sink? Use the terms *weight, density,* and *buoyant force* in your answer.

7. A beach ball that is full of air floats in a swimming pool. However, a ball that is not inflated sinks to the bottom of the pool. Why?

8. You read how a hot-air balloon floats in the sky. (a) What could a pilot do to cause the balloon to sink back to the ground? (b) What could the pilot do to make the balloon go higher?

9. Use the Internet or other research materials to answer these questions.

   a. If you went for a swim in the Dead Sea in Israel, you would discover that it is very easy to float! Find out why.

   b. What percent of an iceberg is below water? Why?

 SOLVE IT!

Concrete Canoe Competition

Concrete is a heavy construction material made from sand, gravel, and stone. If you toss a piece of concrete into a pond, it sinks. So, how can you make concrete float? The American Society of Civil Engineers (ASCE) sponsors an annual contest for college-level engineering students. The goal is to build a concrete canoe that displaces enough water so that up to four adults can be in it without it sinking. The contestants race the canoes to win scholarships. In order for a concrete canoe to float, it must be shaped so that it pushes aside enough water to create enough buoyant force to support the boat's weight.

Make a sketch that explains why a block of concrete sinks, but a concrete canoe floats!

Photo © Bart Boatwright, courtesy of the American Society of Civil Engineers

Full of Hot Air

Do you know what the oldest form of aircraft is? You may think it is the airplane flown by the Wright brothers in 1903. The hot air balloon dates back much earlier than the Wright brothers. In 1783, the first passengers in a hot air balloon were a duck, rooster, and a sheep.

Several months later, the Montgolfier brothers of France made a balloon of paper and silk. This flight carried two men for 25 minutes across 5½ miles. Ballooning has come a long way since that historic flight. Balloons are used to forecast weather, explore space, perform science experiments, and flying in them is considered a sport.

The science behind hot air balloons

Hot air balloons have three major parts: envelope, basket, and burner. The envelope is the colorful part of the balloon. It is made of heat resistant nylon with a special liner to hold in the heat. The basket is made of strong wicker that will not crack upon landing. Before takeoff, inflator fans are used to fill the envelope with air. Once the envelope is filled with air, burners heat the air. Just as smoke rises, the heated air makes the balloon rise.

An increase in the temperature of a gas causes an increase in the movement of gas atoms. When atoms move around more, they move further apart. Gas atoms that are farther apart decrease gas density.

In a hot air balloon, the heat from the burners makes the envelope air less dense. The air inside the envelope is now lighter than the air outside. These temperature and density differences create a force called buoyancy. Buoyancy is an upward force.

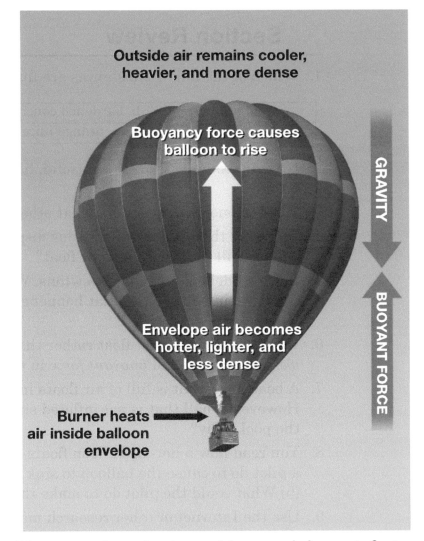

Outside air remains cooler, heavier, and more dense

Buoyancy force causes balloon to rise

GRAVITY

BUOYANT FORCE

Envelope air becomes hotter, lighter, and less dense

Burner heats air inside balloon envelope

When you are in a swimming pool, buoyancy helps you to float. For hot air balloons, buoyancy pushes the lighter, hotter air up. The result is the hot air balloon rises.

Hot air balloons depend on the wind to travel. The pilot controls the burner to raise or lower the balloon to catch these winds. Balloons move wherever the wind blows!

Chapter 3 Connection

Hot air balloons used for science

The National Scientific Balloon Facility in Palestine, Texas, is a National Aeronautics and Space Administration (NASA) facility. NASA launches about 25 science balloons each year. Science balloons do not carry people, but carry a "payload." The payload carries equipment for experiments and may weigh up to 8,000 pounds. These experiments help scientists study earth and space. Airplanes usually fly five to six miles above the ground. Science balloons fly up to 26 miles high!

An Ultra Long Duration Balloon (ULDB)

Photo - courtesy of NASA

NASA is developing an Ultra-Long Duration Balloon (ULDB). The ULDB envelope is made of a material that is as thin as sandwich wrap. Scientists hope the ULDB will be able to fly up to 100 days. Longer balloon flights will let scientists carry out more advanced science experiments.

Steve Fossett

Steve Fossett is the first person to fly solo around the world in a hot air balloon. He is an adventurer who worked 10 years to achieve this goal. On June 19, 2002, Fossett completed his trip. His journey lasted 14 days, 19 hours, and 51 minutes. Fossett did run into problems during his great balloon adventure. At one point, he had to fly as low as 500 feet to avoid very high winds.

Although Fossett was alone in the balloon, he did not work alone to complete the trip. He had a team that included meteorologists, engineers, scientists, and balloonists. Fossett's balloon was equipped with computers, telephone, radio, and almost 20 pounds of maps. He also had oxygen available for high altitudes. The air at high altitudes is very thin and does not have enough oxygen for normal breathing.

Balloon festivals

In the United States, there are more than 4,000 balloon pilots. Pilots from around the world love to gather, race, and fly. The Albuquerque International Balloon Fiesta in New Mexico has been held annually for over 30 years. This fiesta is the largest balloon festival in the world with over 500 balloons. The Helen to the Atlantic Balloon Race and Festival in Georgia is the oldest in the south. It is also the only long distance hot air balloon race in the United States.

Imagine floating above some of the most spectacular views from coast to coast. Ballooning in New Hampshire offers views of the White Mountains. The Sonoma County Hot Air Balloon Classic, held in Windsor, California, offers balloonists early morning rides over the vineyards of Northern California. Hot air ballooning is not just full of hot air. The wind welcomes the balloonists and provides an experience unlike any other of its kind.

QUESTIONS

1. How does heat affect air density?
2. Describe buoyancy and its effect on a hot air balloon.
3. How do you steer a hot air balloon?

Chapter 3 Connection

Energy at the Surface of Earth

In this activity you will model radiation of heat energy from the Sun to Earth.

Materials

- Two 16- or 24-ounce soda bottles with some sand for stability
- Two digital thermometers and paper towels
- Light source
- Black paper and white paper
- Stopwatch (or use the CPO Science timer)
- Tape, pencil, scissors, and a metric ruler

What you will do

1. Pour a handful of sand into each of the soda bottles. The sand steadies the empty bottle by adding a little weight.

2. Wrap a strip of paper towel around the thermometers at the zero degree mark. Insert a thermometer into each bottle so that it snugly fits into the neck.

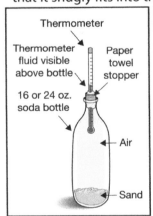
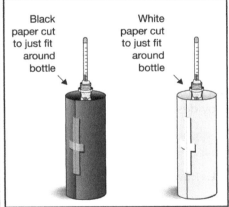

3. Practice fitting a piece of black paper around one of the bottles so that the bottle is completely surrounded, but with no overlap. Mark the paper with a pencil, and cut the paper as necessary so that there is no overlap.

4. Tape the black paper to the bottle. Wrap the paper snugly around the bottle, and tape it in place.

5. Repeat steps 3 and 4 for the other bottle, substituting the black paper with the white paper.

6. Place each bottle 10 cm away from the light source.

7. Record the initial temperature of the bottles in Table 1.

8. Turn on the light source and record temperatures in both bottles every minute for 10 minutes in the table.

9. Graph your data. Use the time as the x-axis data and the temperature as the y-axis data.

10. Make a legend to indicate the curves for the black bottle and white bottle. Don't forget to label your axes, to use units, and to title your graph.

Table 1: Radiation data

	Temperature at each minute (°C)										
	0	1	2	3	4	5	6	7	8	9	10
Black bottle											
White bottle											

Applying your knowledge

a. What form of heat transfer occurs between the light source and the bottles?

b. Which of the bottles reached a higher temperature?

c. What was the difference in the final temperatures of the two bottles?

d. Which bottle absorbed more energy from the light source? How do you know this?

e. Describe what happened to the energy from the light source when it reached the black bottle and the white bottle. Think about how the two bottles each absorbed and reflected radiation.

f. Based on your results, what types of surfaces on Earth would absorb more radiation from the Sun? What is the light source modeling in the Earth-Sun system?

Chapter 3 Assessment

Vocabulary

Select the correct term to complete the sentences.

energy	heat	conduction
kinetic energy	temperature	density
potential energy	convection	buoyant force
radiation	power plant	fluid

Section 3.1

1. A child on a sliding board has more _____ at the top of the slide than at the bottom.

2. A place that produces electricity is called a(n) _____.

3. _____ is the energy of motion.

4. Systems tend to move from higher to lower _____.

Section 3.2

5. Twenty five grams of hot water has more _____ energy than 15 grams of hot water.

6. _____ is heat transfer through empty space.

7. The transfer of heat by the direct contact of atoms is called _____.

8. _____ is the transfer of heat through the motion of gases and liquids.

9. The _____ of a sample is related to the average speed of atoms in that sample.

Section 3.3

10. Matter that can flow is called a(n) _____.

11. An object which has a weight (downward force) of 20 newtons displaces a volume of water that weighs 8 newtons. This object will sink because the _____ is not enough to help it float.

12. The _____ of warm air is less than cold air so warm air rises.

Concepts

Section 3.1

1. What is the main source of energy on Earth?

2. You ride down a hill on your bicycle and come to a stop. At the top of the hill, you had more height energy. What happened to this height energy as you rolled down the hill?
    a. The height energy increased.
    b. The height energy decreased and was converted to other forms of energy.
    c. The height energy stayed the same.

3. Which of the following would be an example of kinetic energy?
    a. Energy stored in the muscles of a cat
    b. Energy from the wind
    c. Energy in a battery

4. Give an example of heat moving from a warmer object to a cooler object.

5. Computers get warm as they are used. Small fans are built in computers to keep them cool. Sometimes you can hear the fan when you use a computer. Why do you think the computer gets warm when you use it?

Section 3.2

6. An iceberg has more heat in it than a cup of boiling water. Explain why this is true based on what you understand about heat energy.

7. Saucepans are made of metal so they heat up quickly. This takes advantage of the process of:

   a. radiation.
   b. convection.
   c. conduction.

8. Birds use this type of heat transfer to lift them in the air.

   a. radiation
   b. convection
   c. conduction

9. The transfer of heat energy through space from the Sun comes in the form of:

   a. radiation.
   b. convection.
   c. conduction.

Section 3.3

10. Density is the ratio between which two properties of an object (see box below)? Write the formula for density.

mass	temperature	weight
heat energy	volume	buoyant force

11. Fill in the blanks using the terms *mass* or *weight*.

    a. Your _____ is always the same regardless of gravity.
    b. Your _____ on Earth is different than on the moon because of the moon's weaker gravitational force.
    c. On Earth the _____ of an object is 10 newtons.
    d. On Jupiter the _____ of an elephant would be greater than it is on Earth, but its _____ would be the same.

12. The _____ (mass, weight, or density) of a material is the same no matter how much of the material you have.

13. When talking about buoyant force, why is the weight of an object talked about instead of its mass?

14. If the weight of an object was 500 newtons and the buoyant force was 75 newtons, would the object sink or float?

15. Define the term fluid and give three examples of fluids.

16. True or False: This is an example of a gas floating on another gas—warm air rising above cooler air because it is less dense.

17. True or False: You can increase the volume of a liquid or air by increasing its temperature. Explain your answer.

Math and Writing Skills

Section 3.1

1. Using what you have learned about energy, describe an event or a regular day in your life in terms of energy. Include at least three types of energy in your description.

Section 3.2

2. A cup of water at 5°C is mixed with a cup of water at 25°C. Both cups have the same amount of water. What will the temperature of the final mixture be?

3. The final temperature of a mixture is 60°C and the volume of the mixture is 200 milliliters. To make the mixture, a 100-milliliter sample of water at 30°C water was used. What was the temperature and volume of the other sample of water that was used to make the mixture?

4. What would the temperature in Celsius be if you mixed 50 milliliters of water at 32°F with 50 milliliters of water at 0°C? Explain your answer.

5. You want to heat a cold room. You place a space heater in a corner. Make a sketch that describes the motion and temperature of the air in the room when the space heater is turned on.

Section 3.3

6. The volume of a solid 4 cm ∞ 6 cm ∞ 10 cm is:

    a. 24 cm.

    b. 240 cm.

    c. 240 cm^3.

    d. 100 cm^3.

7. What is the volume of a box that measures 10 meters long by 5 meters wide by 2 meters high?

8. You know that a box can contain 150 cm^3 of water. Give an example of what the dimensions of the box might be.

9. The volume of a 20-gram object is 5 cm^3. What is its density?

10. On Great Skies Airlines a carry-on suitcase can be no more than 12 kg and 30,000 cm^3. Does the following suitcase qualify as a carry-on? Explain your answer.

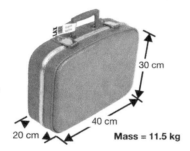

30 cm
40 cm
20 cm
Mass = 11.5 kg

11. Describe how you would find the volume of these two objects: (a) a cardboard box, and (b) a marble.

12. At the top of the highest mountain on Earth, the force of gravity is a little less than it is at sea level. Would your weight be a little greater or a little less at the top of the highest mountain on Earth?

13. The density of water is 1.0 g/cm^3 and the density of wax is 0.9 g/cm^3. Would wax float or sink in water?

14. Use the densities of these common substances to identify which illustration is correct.

	Density (g/cm^3)
air	0.001
wood	0.9
water	1.0
glass	2.3
mercury	11.0

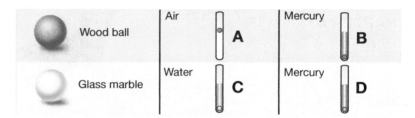

Wood ball — Air — A — Mercury — B

Glass marble — Water — C — Mercury — D

15. If an object has a buoyant force acting on it of 320 newtons, would the weight of the object have to be more or less than 320 newtons in order to float?

16. Neutral buoyancy is when an object stays in one position underwater. It doesn't sink or float. An object weighs 135 newtons. What would the buoyant force have to be in order for the object to have neutral buoyancy?

Chapter Project—Solar Radiation

Use a digital thermometer to record air temperatures in different areas of your school. Measure temperature: (1) over shady and sunny surfaces, (2) over different types of surfaces such as a parking lot, a sidewalk, and a grassy field, (3) at different times of the day, and (4) on the north-, south-, east-, and west-facing sides of the building. What does your data tell you about the amount of solar radiation that is absorbed in and around your school by different types of surfaces? Present your data as a poster.

UNIT 2

WATER AND WEATHER

WHAT CAUSES LIGHTNING?

WHAT IS THE WATER CYCLE?

WHAT IS A GYRE?

Exploring on Your Own

Predicting the weather is based on understanding weather patterns. Because so many variables are involved in weather patterns, weather and storm prediction involves computer modeling and simulations. Interview a local meteorologist or visit a local science museum to learn how computers are used in weather forecasting. Also find out about the latest technology used in weather forecasting and what is used to present weather reports to the public.

Chapter 4

Water and the Water Cycle

The amount of water on Earth is about the same now as it was during the age of the dinosaurs, 65 to 220 million years ago. With about 70 percent of its surface covered with water, Earth is truly a water planet. However, only a small amount of this water is available for household, agricultural, and industrial use. Since Earth has been around for such a long time, why haven't we run out of water? In this chapter, you will learn how water moves naturally around Earth so that it is available to use year after year.

Key Questions:

1. *Where is most of Earth's water found?*

2. *How is a mud puddle part of the water cycle?*

3. *What is the difference between an aquifer and a watershed?*

4.1 Water on Earth's Surface

About 70 percent of Earth's surface is covered with water. This water is found in oceans, rivers, lakes, under the ground, and as ice.

The hydrosphere

What is the hydrosphere? All the water on Earth is part of a large system called the hydrosphere (Figure 4.1). A set of processes called the *water cycle* keeps water moving from place to place on Earth. You will learn about the water cycle in the next section.

Water phases on Earth In Chapter 2, you learned that *matter* is anything that has mass and takes up space. Phases of matter include liquid, solid, and gas. On Earth, water occurs in all three phases. Most of the water on Earth is liquid. The estimated volume of liquid water on Earth is 1.386 billion cubic kilometers. The next most common phase of water is ice. If all the ice on Earth melted, the level of the oceans would rise about 70 meters!

Water in the atmosphere Gaseous water is located in the atmosphere, the layer of gases that surrounds Earth. Moisture in the atmosphere replenishes our water supplies when it becomes rain or snow and returns to Earth.

VOCABULARY

hydrosphere - an Earth system that includes all the water on the planet.

atmosphere - the layer of gases that surrounds Earth.

Image courtesy of NASA.

Figure 4.1: *Earth's hydrosphere includes all the water on the planet. The clouds in the picture are also part of the hydrosphere. Can you find the hurricane? It's part of the hydrosphere too.*

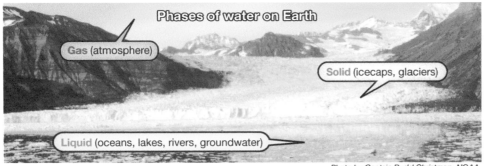

Phases of water on Earth

Gas (atmosphere)

Solid (icecaps, glaciers)

Liquid (oceans, lakes, rivers, groundwater)

Photo by Captain Budd Christman, NOAA.

The distribution of water on Earth

Salt water and a little fresh water

About 97 percent of Earth's water is salt water found in oceans. Almost 2 percent of Earth's water is frozen at the North and South Poles and on mountain tops. Finally, less than 2 percent of the water on Earth is fresh water that humans, plants, and animals can consume. If all the water on Earth could fit into a one-liter container, the amount of fresh water would equal only about 17 milliliters (Figure 4.2).

An important resource

Water is an important resource. Most living things rely on fresh water. The hydrosphere and the water cycle allow our limited supply of fresh water to be recycled.

Where do we find water?

This table lists how water is distributed on Earth.

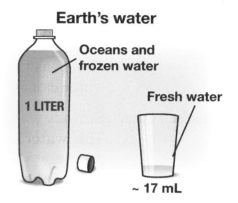

Earth's water

Oceans and frozen water

1 LITER

Fresh water

~ 17 mL

Figure 4.2: *If all the water on the Earth could fit into a one-liter container, the amount of fresh water available for human consumption would be equal to about 17 milliliters.*

Water source	Water volume, in cubic kilometers	Percent of total water
Oceans, seas, bays	1,338,000,000	96.5%
Icecaps, glaciers, permanent snow	24,064,000	1.74%
Groundwater	23,400,000	1.7%
Ground ice and permafrost	300,000	0.022%
Lakes (fresh & saline)	176,400	0.013%
Soil moisture	16,500	0.001%
Atmosphere	12,900	0.001%
Swamp water	11,470	0.0008%
Rivers	2,120	0.0002%
Biological water	1,120	0.0001%
Total water volume	1,386,000,000	100%

SOLVE IT!

How big is a cubic kilometer? One cubic kilometer is 1,000 m × 1,000 m × 1,000 m or 1,000,000,000 m^3 (one billion cubic meters)!

If the volume of a swimming pool is 1,000 m^3, how many swimming pools fit inside one cubic kilometer?

To find out how many swimming pools equal all the world's rivers, you would have to multiply the number you just got by 2,120!

Places where water is found

Where water collects

After a rainstorm, water collects in low areas on the ground. On a small scale, these low areas form mud puddles. On a large scale, low areas that collect water include oceans and rivers. Earth's water can also be found frozen in glaciers and underground.

Surface water

Surface water on Earth refers to water that collects on the ground. This water includes oceans, lakes, rivers, streams, and reservoirs. A reservoir is a protected artificial or natural lake that is used to store water.

Frozen water

Frozen water is found at the poles and on mountain tops as glaciers and ice sheets. A glacier is a huge mass of ice that forms on land when snow and ice accumulate faster than they melt (Figure 4.3). Most of Earth's fresh water is in the form of glacier ice.

Groundwater and the water table

Groundwater is water that collects underground. Some of the water on Earth's surface moves down through the soil to the water table. The water table is the upper level of underground water. Below this level, the spaces between particles of soil and rock are saturated (filled) with groundwater. The water table changes depending on the season. A well's water level indicates the water table for an area.

VOCABULARY

surface water - water found on Earth's surface in places like oceans, lakes, rivers, and reservoirs.

reservoir - a protected artificial or natural lake that is used to store water.

glacier - a huge mass of ice that forms on land when snow and ice accumulate faster than they melt.

groundwater - water that collects underground.

water table - the upper level of water underground; below the water table, all spaces are filled with groundwater.

Photo by Rear Admiral Harley D. Nygren, NOAA Corps (ret.)

Figure 4.3: *A glacier.*

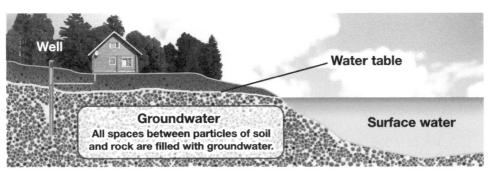

Well

Water table

Groundwater
All spaces between particles of soil and rock are filled with groundwater.

Surface water

Water as a resource

Water for life The temperature range on Earth's surface is just right for water to exist in all three phases—liquid, solid, and gas (Figure 4.4). Most water on Earth is in the liquid phase. Liquid water is extremely important for living things. For example, a human body is 60 percent to 75 percent water (Figure 4.5). You need water to keep your blood, brain, and lungs working properly.

Water dissolves many things One of the reasons why water is so useful is that it can dissolve many things. When you eat food, water in your body dissolves nutrients so they can be carried through your bloodstream. Oxygen is another important substance that is dissolved in your blood. Oxygen dissolved in rivers and lakes keeps fish alive and healthy. Water also dissolves the minerals that make up rocks. Over long periods of time, water changes Earth's surface by dissolving and wearing down rocks and mountains. For example, the Grand Canyon was formed when the water of the Colorado River wore down the rocks in its path.

Sun	Surface Temperature Range (°C)	
Mercury	-170 to 390	Too cold and too hot
Venus	45 to 480	Too hot
Earth	-88 to 56	**Just right for liquid water!**
Mars	-89 to 20	Too cold

Planet sizes and distances not to scale.

Figure 4.4: *Mercury, Venus, and Mars are too hot or too cold for water to exist in all three phases. But Earth is just right!*

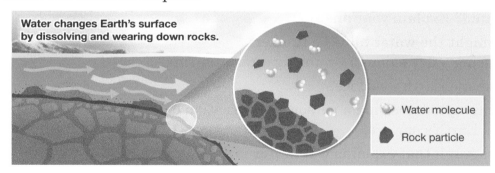

Water changes Earth's surface by dissolving and wearing down rocks.

Water molecule

Rock particle

Additional water uses Water is necessary for all forms of agriculture and farming. For example, water is needed to grow grain for bread and to grow fruits and vegetables. Water is also used in industry and in many ways in your home.

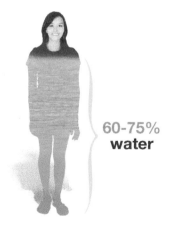

60-75% **water**

Figure 4.5: *The human body is 60 percent to 75 percent water.*

4.1 Section Review

1. Earth is often called a "water planet." Why?

2. How much of Earth's surface is covered by water? How much is covered by land?

3. The hydrosphere contains all the water on Earth. Name four locations where you find water.

4. How is Earth's atmosphere part of the hydrosphere?

5. In what phase of matter is most water found on Earth—gas, solid, or liquid?

6. The second most abundant form of water on Earth is ice. Where can most of this frozen water be found?

7. What would happen if all of the frozen water on Earth melted? How would this event affect people living in coastal areas?

8. Compare surface water and groundwater.

9. What is the water table?

10. In which place—desert or rainforest—would the water table be further underground? Explain your answer.

11. In which season might the water table be further underground—during a dry summer or during a rainy spring?

12. How does water shape Earth's surface?

13. Write a short paragraph describing a personal observation of how water shapes Earth's surface.

14. Write a short paragraph that explains why water is so important for human beings.

15. Like people, animals depend on water. Identify the water environment in which each animal in Figure 4.6 lives. You may need to do research to find the answers.

Water in the universe

As far as scientists know, Earth is the only place in our solar system that has liquid water.

Find out why! After performing your research, write a short paragraph that describes your findings.

Photo "A" by Kathy Crane, NOAA Arctic Research Office;
Photo "C" by Eric Engbretson, USFWS;
Photo "D" by William W. Hartley, USFWS.

Figure 4.6: *Question 15.*

4.2 The Water Cycle

The Sun keeps water moving through the hydrosphere by providing energy. In this section, you will learn about the water cycle and where water goes so that it is available for people, animals, and plants.

Recycling water

Sharing water with the dinosaurs For millions of years, only a small percentage of fresh water has been available to meet the basic needs of life on Earth. Remember that our total water supply today is the same as when the dinosaurs were around. Therefore, the water you drink was probably used by other organisms during the past millions of years. A set of processes called the **water cycle** keeps our water continuously recycled and naturally filtered. The water cycle is sometimes called the *hydrologic cycle*.

The Sun drives the water cycle The Sun is the source of energy that drives the water cycle. Wind, weather, and gravity are additional natural forces that keep water moving from place to place (Figure 4.7). Of course, people also play a role in transporting water on Earth.

Wind and weather Wind and storms provide forces that cause water to be blown or moved from once place to another. For example, wind blowing clouds moves water vapor from one place to another. Precipitation (rain or snow) is a way water moves from the sky to the ground.

Gravity In Chapter 2, you learned that the more mass an object has, the greater the force of gravity is on that object. Water has mass and is affected by gravity. For example, when raindrops get big enough in a rain cloud, gravity causes them to fall to the ground. Gravity also causes water to run down mountains to the coast (Figure 4.7). And gravity is the primary force that moves water from Earth's surface, through the ground, to become groundwater.

water cycle - a set of processes energized by the Sun that keep water moving from place to place on Earth; also called the hydrologic cycle.

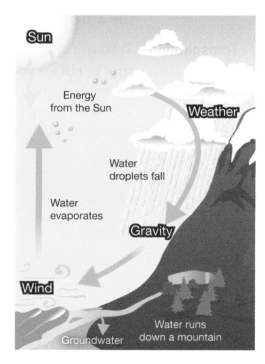

Figure 4.7: *The Sun, wind, weather, and gravity drive the water cycle.*

Water cycle processes

Four main processes

The four main processes of the water cycle are *evaporation, transpiration, condensation,* and *precipitation.*

Evaporation

Evaporation occurs when liquid water has enough energy to leave the liquid phase and become a gas called water vapor. The source of this energy is heat from the Sun. The Sun warms the surfaces of mud puddles, lakes, rivers, and oceans. As a result, water obtains enough energy to evaporate and become water vapor in the atmosphere.

Transpiration

Transpiration is the process in which plants lose water through tiny pores on their leaves. The pores open to gain carbon dioxide. Once the pores are open, the plants lose water, and release oxygen. The water vapor contributes to the water cycle. All living organisms benefit from the released oxygen. It's what we breathe!

VOCABULARY

evaporation - the process by which a substance in its liquid phase gains energy and enters its gaseous phase; a phase of the water cycle.

water vapor - water in gas form.

transpiration - the process by which plants lose water through tiny pores on their leaves; a phase of the water cycle.

The water molecule

You have probably heard water called "H-two-O" and written as H_2O. This way of talking about water refers to a water molecule that is made of two hydrogen atoms and one oxygen atom. In this text, we represent the water molecule like this:

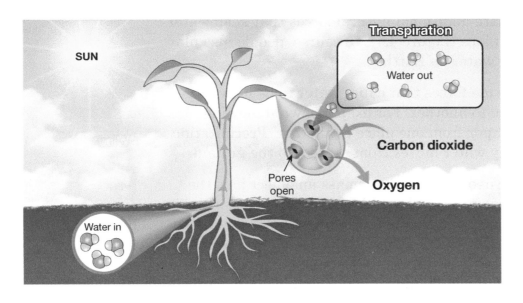

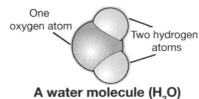

A water molecule (H_2O)

Condensation

Condensation occurs when water in its gaseous phase loses energy. This tends to happen high in the atmosphere as the molecules cool down. Water molecules cool and slow down so much that they group and form droplets of liquid. When these droplets are heavy enough, they fall to Earth as rain.

Precipitation

Precipitation is any form of condensed water vapor in the atmosphere falling back to Earth. This includes rain, snow, sleet, and hail.

Following the water cycle

The diagram below illustrates the water cycle. Trace the path of water from the ocean to groundwater and back to the ocean. What other paths do you see in the water cycle?

condensation - the process by which a substance in its gaseous phase loses energy and enters its liquid phase; a phase of the water cycle.

precipitation - condensed water vapor in the atmosphere falling back to Earth in the form of rain, hail, sleet, or snow; a phase of the water cycle.

The Water Cycle

Condensation
Water vapor transport
SUN
Water droplets
Precipitation
Evaporation   Transpiration
Evaporation
River
Lake
Land and trees
Percolation
Groundwater Flow
Ocean

Imagine you are a snowflake in an icecap on the top of a mountain. Describe what happens to you as the seasons change starting with winter. Describe your path through the water cycle. Also, describe any points along your journey where you might interact with human beings!

How water moves in the water cycle

Surface runoff   Precipitation that reaches Earth's surface often flows over the land. This water, called **surface runoff**, eventually reaches lakes, rivers, and oceans. Surface runoff dissolves and collects minerals and nutrient-rich soil as it flows. Many of the minerals and nutrients in fresh water and salt water come from surface runoff.

Percolation   Water that flows over the land can percolate through the soil to become groundwater. **Percolation** is the process of liquid moving through a substance that is porous (has many tiny holes or "pores"). Groundwater can move through soil because the soil is porous.

Aquifers   The destination for percolating groundwater can be an underground area of sediment and rocks called an **aquifer**. When groundwater is removed from an aquifer for human consumption, it can take 300 to 1,000 years or more to replenish the supply. Groundwater that is not collected from an aquifer will continue to flow through sediments and may eventually enter the ocean, thus continuing the water cycle.

The importance of aquifers   Aquifers are important water sources. For example, the water obtained from the Ogallala Aquifer in the mid-western United States has made agriculture profitable in this dry region. The Ogallala is one of the largest aquifers in the world. Its underground area (450,000 km^2) is in parts of South Dakota, Nebraska, Wyoming, Colorado, Kansas, Oklahoma, New Mexico, and Texas. With such a demand on its water supply, the Ogallala Aquifer is in danger of becoming depleted because the water is being used faster than it can be replenished.

VOCABULARY

surface runoff - water that flows over land until it reaches lakes, rivers, and oceans.

percolation - the process of liquid moving through a porous substance.

aquifer - a underground area of sediment and rocks that is filled with groundwater.

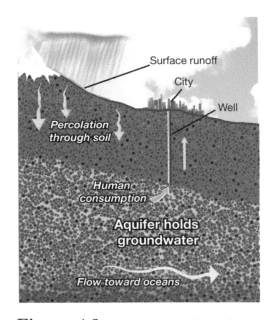

Figure 4.8: *Surface runoff reaches surface water locations or percolates into an aquifer. Groundwater that is not collected from the aquifer by cities flows to oceans.*

Watersheds

What is a watershed? A **watershed** is an area of land that catches all precipitation and surface runoff. This water is collected in a body of water such as a river. Eventually, all this water flows to an ocean (Figure 4.9). The boundaries of a watershed are often steep mountain ridges.

Watersheds The water in a watershed is directly connected to the groundwater. Water collects in a place like a river, but some of the surface runoff becomes groundwater. The water that comes to many homes in the United States originates in a watershed that can be local or from another region.

Natural resources In addition to supplying our drinking water, watersheds also provide habitat for plants and animals, areas of natural beauty, and bodies of water for recreation. As communities grow and change, it is important to protect these natural resources.

Watershed

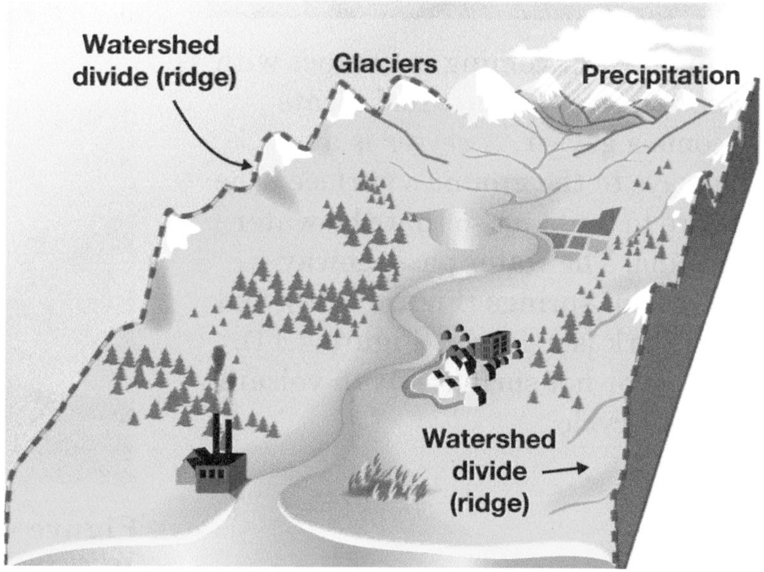

watershed - an area of land that catches all precipitation and surface runoff and collects it in a body of water such as a river.

Ocean	Some sources of water
Atlantic	St. Lawrence River, the Great Lakes, eastern North America, South America east of the Andes, northern Europe, western-Sub-Saharan Africa, Caribbean Sea basin, Mediterranean Sea basin
Pacific	China, southeastern Russia, Japan, Korea, South America west of the Andes, Pacific Islands, and western North America
Indian	eastern coast of Africa, India, Burma, Australia, Indonesia, southeast Asia
Arctic	Most of Russia and Northern California
Southern	Antarctica

Figure 4.9: *Some sources of water for the world's oceans. See if you can find these places on a globe!*

The water cycle and volcanoes

Water in hot rock You may be surprised to learn that volcanoes are part of Earth's water cycle. This is because water is an ingredient in the hot, molten rock that is inside a volcano. Inside the volcano, this hot, molten rock is called *magma*. Outside the volcano, it is called *lava*. You will learn more about volcanoes in Chapter 12.

Water vapor from eruptions When a volcano erupts, water is released as water vapor into the atmosphere. The water vapor eventually condenses and falls as rain or another form of precipitation.

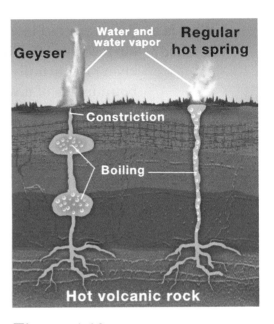

Figure 4.10: *A diagram of a geyser and a hot spring.*

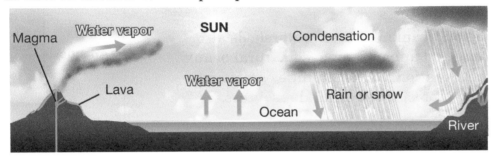

Hot springs and geysers Hot springs are the result of groundwater coming in contact with hot rock or magma below Earth's surface. The hot rock heats the water. A hot spring can become a geyser. A *geyser* is a hot spring with constricted passageways to the ground's surface. The constriction causes water pressure to build up so that the water eventually explodes from the ground. The water passageway is not constricted for other types of hot springs (Figure 4.10). Old Faithful in Yellowstone National Park is a geyser (Figure 4.11). Water that evaporates from geysers or hot springs—both volcanic features—becomes part of the water cycle.

Figure 4.11: *Old Faithful in Yellowstone National Park is a geyser.*

4.2 Section Review

1. List the sources of energy and forces that drive the water cycle.

2. Give an example of how people participate in the water cycle.

3. All the water on Earth is recycled. What does that mean about the water you drank today? Give an example of where your drinking water could have been in the past.

4. What has to happen for liquid water to become water vapor?

5. Plants need water but they lose water by opening pores on their leaves. Why do they open their pores?

6. Which process of the water cycle is similar to water droplets forming on a bathroom mirror when you take a shower? Pick the correct answer and explain your choice.

    a. condensation   b. precipitation

    c. evaporation   d. transpiration

7. Which of these items is porous under normal conditions?

    a. a cotton shirt   b. a piece of steel

    c. a raincoat   d. a plastic cup

8. In which of these situations is percolation occurring?

    a. A mud puddle dries   b. You pour a glass of orange juice

    c. Water goes through coffee grounds to make coffee   d. Snow melts outside on a hot, sunny day

9. What is the difference between an aquifer and a watershed?

10. You learned that it might take 300 to 1,000 years or more to replenish any groundwater that is removed from an aquifer. Why do you think it would take so long?

11. How are volcanoes part of the water cycle?

MY JOURNAL

Research the answers to these questions for your town.

1. What is the name of the watershed or aquifer that your town uses for drinking water?

2. Is there a local organization that monitors the water quality of your watershed?

STUDY SKILLS

Learning new words

You can learn and remember the definitions of new words by using them in a sentence.

For each of the vocabulary words in this chapter, write a sentence that uses the word correctly. You may want to make a drawing that helps you remember the new word. For example, make a drawing of the water cycle and fill in the terms you know!

The Wild World of Caves

Caves are one of the natural wonders of our world. You'll find that they exist in many areas around the globe. In the United States alone, there are over 200 caves that are open to the general public. People of all ages are fascinated by caves and the many legends and stories that have been told over the years. Why are we drawn to caves? Maybe it's because caves are known to be secret hiding places. They are dark and dangerous and often mysterious. Yet many are places of spectacular beauty. All are home to many bat species and other creepy crawling cave animals that dwell in the darkness.

There are more than 40,000 known caves in the United States. Mammoth Cave in Kentucky is the world's longest cave with more than 350 miles of passageways.

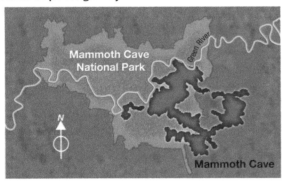

Types of caves

The formation of a cave is dependent on the material from which it is made. The process evolves slowly over millions of years and changes constantly. Basically, there are four main types of caves: ice caves, sea caves, lava caves, and limestone caves.

Ice caves form when the Sun melts the ice on a glacier. The water seeps down into cracks of the glacier. The warm water melts away the ice inside. The cracks, also known as *fractures*, increase in size. These caves often appear blue in color from the light passing through the ice.

Sea caves are formed by the action of water. A cave forms when an area of rocky shore has a weak spot like a fracture. Constant waves wear away the rock at the weak spot causing a cave to form. Over time it can become a large underwater cave system.

Lava cave

Photo courtesy of NPS

Lava caves, often called lava tubes, form quickly compared to other cave types. They form from molten lava that spills over during a volcanic eruption. Tubes form when the outer layer of lava hardens into rock and the hot molten lava continues to flow like a river inside. The tubes drain of all the lava when the molten flow stops and the result is a tube-like cave.

Limestone caves—like Mammoth Cave—are by far the largest and most common caves in the world. Most limestone caves are created when surface water seeps into cracks and dissolves the limestone underground. Surface water includes rivers, lakes, and oceans. Carbonic acid is largely responsible for the chemical weathering of rocks and the formation of caverns in limestone.

Mammoth Cave, Kentucky

Photo courtesy NPS

Show caves versus wild caves

A cave in its natural untouched state is called a wild cave. Wild caves can be explored freely, but are extremely dangerous. You must be well equipped and knowledgeable to explore wild caves on your own. In order to avoid the hazards and dangers of wild caves, show caves were developed and many are maintained by the National Park Service. Show caves allow the public to safely view the beauty of a cave. These caves have guides, established paths, lighting, a place to eat lunch, and bathrooms—all far beneath Earth's surface. The most famous show caves in the United States are located at Carlsbad Caverns National Park in Carlsbad, New Mexico.

Carlsbad Caverns
Photo courtesy NPS

Carlsbad Caverns contains one of the world's largest underground chambers called the Big Room. The Big Room is the largest room in the cavern. It is also the largest cave chamber in the United States. It is located 754 feet below the surface, is 25 stories high, and about a third of a mile wide. Just how large is the Big Room? According to the National Park Service, this room is about the size of six football fields. Visitors travel to the chamber by elevator. Once there, they can walk a one-mile path that circles the room.

Formation of the Big Room

How did the large chambers of Carlsbad Caverns form?

Groundwater, mixed with carbon dioxide (and other gases) from the air, and soil forms an acid which dissolved the limestone to create underground chambers. Acidic water alone did not do all of the work. Oil and gas deposits located underground contain hydrogen sulfide. Hydrogen sulfide mixed with groundwater created sulfuric acid which dissolved the limestone and created large pathways. Then, the mountainous land surrounding the cave rose upwards causing the whole area to be above the water table. The water drained away leaving behind the spectacular caves and chambers.

Cave dwellers

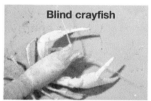
Blind crayfish
Photo courtesy NPS

Organisms that spend their entire lives living only underground in caves are called troglobites. This term is from the Greek word *troglos* which means "cave." These organisms can not live outside the cave environment. Troglobites include blind crayfish, blind salamanders, blind fish, and blind shrimp. These organisms are white because they lack pigmentations.

Trogloxenes are organisms that move freely in and out of caves. The suffix -*xenos* means guest. These cave dwelling guests include bats, raccoons, bears, and bobcats. The third group of cave-dwelling organisms are called troglophiles. The word origin is Greek and means "cave lover." These organisms like to live in caves, but can also survive outside the cave environment. They include different species of beetles, crickets, spiders, and salamanders.

QUESTIONS

1. Why have many caves in the United States become national parks?

2. What role does water play in the formation of caves?

3. Explain how lava tubes are formed.

4. Why might a cave animal be blind or have poor eyesight?

Conserving Water While You Brush

Currently, underground water is being used at a faster rate than it can be replenished. In the United States, about 50 percent of the population depends on underground aquifers for their water. In addition, energy is necessary to treat water before and after it is used and returned to the environment. Wasting clean water often leads to emptying valuable underground aquifers we depend on and wastes the energy necessary to treat the water.

In this activity, you will determine just how much water is wasted if the faucet is left running each time you brush your teeth. You will learn that you can conserve a lot of water by turning off the faucet while you brush!

Materials

- Toothbrush and toothpaste
- One or more containers that fits in your sink under the faucet
- Metric measuring cup (with milliliter markings)
- Calculator

What you will do

1. Prepare your toothbrush to clean your teeth.

2. Place the container beneath the faucet to catch the water.

3. Begin brushing your teeth but do not turn off the faucet. Take the regular amount of time it takes for you to brush. When the container in the sink is nearly full, remove it and place another, empty container under the faucet.

4. Do not spit out the toothpaste foam from your mouth into the containers!

5. Be sure to turn off the faucet once you are done brushing and have rinsed your mouth.

6. Now, use the measuring cup to determine how much water was used. Copy Table 4.1 into your notes and record your results. Convert your measurements to milliliters. (*Conversion*: 1 cup = 237 milliliters.)

7. Once you have finished, attempt to reuse the water by pouring it in a plant, drinking it, or using it to clean dishes.

8. In school, share your data with others. Record the class average in the Table 4.1.

Table 4.1: Amount of water used

	Amount of water collected when the faucet is left running while brushing (milliliters)
You	
Class average	

Applying your knowledge

a. Calculate the difference between your results and the class average. Was there a big difference or not? Why do you think so?

b. If the average person uses only 125 milliliters of water to brush their teeth (when they don't leave the faucet running), how much water is lost if the faucet is left running? Use the class average to calculate your results.

c. If a person brushes their teeth twice a day, how much water could they save, per day, by turning the faucet off while brushing?

d. How much water could be saved in a week, if a person turned off the faucet while brushing?

e. How many people live in your town? How much water can be saved weekly in your town? (Only answer this question if you are provided with your town population.)

f. Now, come up with a catchy slogan to help people remember to turn off the faucet while they brush and conserve water!

Chapter 4 Assessment

Vocabulary

Select the correct term to complete the sentences.

hydrosphere   glacier   groundwater

surface water   water cycle   water table

reservoir   evaporation   transpiration

condensation   precipitation   surface runoff

aquifer   watershed   percolation

atmosphere   water vapor

Section 4.1

1. All the water on Earth is included in the _____.

2. _____ is water that collects underground.

3. A(n) _____ forms when more ice accumulates than melts.

4. A(n) _____ is a protected lake that is used to store water.

5. An ocean, lake, or river is an example of _____.

6. Gaseous water is found in Earth's _____.

7. The upper surface of the saturated zone underground is the _____.

Section 4.2

8. Evaporation is one of four processes in the _____.

9. Rain and snow are forms of _____.

10. Water in gaseous form is called _____.

11. _____ occurs when water goes from being a *gas* to a *liquid*.

12. _____ occurs when water goes from being a *liquid* to a *gas*.

13. _____ is the release of water from plants.

14. A(n) _____ is an underground area filled with groundwater.

15. A(n) _____ is an area of land that catches and collects water.

16. _____ is water that flows over land.

17. _____ occurs when liquid water moves through a porous substance.

Concepts

Section 4.1

1. How is Earth's atmosphere a part of the hydrosphere?

2. The amount of water on Earth has remained about the same for millions of years. How is this possible?

3. If all the water on Earth could fit in a one gallon container, the amount of frozen water would be equal to about one-third of a cup. How does this amount of water compare to the amount of freshwater and ocean water on Earth.

4. True or False: The water table level stays the same year round? Explain your answer.

5. Why is Earth a good place to find ice, liquid water, and water vapor?

Section 4.2

6. List a way that you could participate in the water cycle.

7. Compare and contrast condensation and evaporation.

8. When plants open the pores on their leaves:

   a. water enters the plant.   b. sugar enters the plant.

   c. water and oxygen leave and carbon dioxide enters.   d. sunlight enters the plant.

9. If you were to do an analysis of what is in groundwater, what might it contain? Why?

10. What land area is the watershed for the Southern Ocean?

11. Use a map of the United States to find the St. Lawrence River. It is located by the Great Lakes.

   a. In what direction does it flow?

b.   Into what body of water does it flow?

12. Name one process of the water cycle that is involved in a volcanic eruption. Explain your answer.

13. What is the difference between a geyser and a hot spring?

Math and Writing Skills

Section 4.1

1.   Match these water resources with their percentage of Earth's total water resources:

Freshwater	a. 0.001%
Soil moisture	b. 1.7%
Ocean (salt water)	c. 96.5%

2.   Pick a freshwater lake that you know about and research it. Make a colorful brochure that highlights the benefits of this lake to people. Include photographs if you have or find them.

3.   Select one of your favorite foods or products and find out how water is involved in making it. Make a poster to display your findings.

Section 4.2

4.   In a short paragraph, explain how the Sun, wind, and gravity are involved in the water cycle.

5.   Explain how water could go from precipitation, to surface runoff, to groundwater, to an aquifer, to the ocean.

6.   Imagine you are a raindrop.

a.   Write a paragraph that explains what could happen to you after you fall to the ground in a desert environment.

b.   Now, write a paragraph that explains what could happen to you after you fall to the ground in an environment that is below 0°C. *Note*: Icy ground is not porous.

7.   *Evapotranspiration* is evaporation from surface water plus transpiration from plants. This graph shows evapotranspiration over one year. Come up with a hypothesis to explain the data shown in the graph.

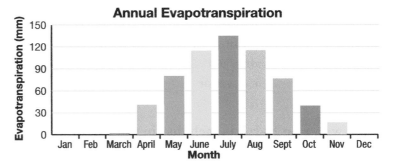

Section 4.3

Chapter Projects—Snow-making and the Water Cycle

During the winter, some people like to go skiing. However, the weather doesn't always cooperate and ski resorts have to make their own snow. In other words, the ski resorts participate in the water cycle by forcing liquid water to become snow (frozen snow).

- Making snow takes a lot of water. For example, it takes about 285,000 liters of water to create a 6-inch blanket of snow covering 61 meters × 61 meters. The system in a good-sized ski slope can convert 18,927 to 37,854 liters of water to snow every minute!
- Making snow also takes a lot of energy. Snow-making machines use fossil fuels and cause pollution.

Research and write a report on how snow-making affects the environment in snow resort towns. Find out how ski resorts work to minimize their impact on the environment.

If you go skiing in the winter, find out how the ski resort you visit makes snow. Find out if the ski resort takes steps to protect the environment!

Earth's Atmosphere

In Chapter 4, you learned about Earth's hydrosphere. In this chapter, you will learn about another important system—the atmosphere. Earth's atmosphere is a blanket of gases that surround the planet, protecting and sustaining life. The atmosphere contains the carbon dioxide needed by plants for photosynthesis, and the oxygen that most organisms need to breathe. Earth stays warmer at night because of the atmosphere. The ozone layer, in the stratosphere (a layer in the atmosphere), protects us from the Sun's ultraviolet rays. These rays can cause eye and skin damage. Every time you breathe, you are benefiting from the atmosphere. Read on to find out more about it!

Key Questions:

1. What gases are in the atmosphere?

2. What are the layers of the atmosphere?

3. Why is Earth neither too cold nor too hot?

5.1 The Atmosphere

An **atmosphere** is a blanket of gases that surrounds a planet. As you will learn here, Earth's atmosphere protects and sustains life. The mixture of gases in the atmosphere is called **air**. Air is what we breathe. Air is what causes our weather. Read on to find out more about air and our atmosphere.

What's in Earth's atmosphere?

Nitrogen   You may be surprised to learn that the most abundant gas in Earth's atmosphere is nitrogen. Nitrogen gas makes up about 78 percent of the atmosphere (Figure 5.1). Nitrogen is released into the air by volcanoes and decaying organisms.

The nitrogen cycle and living things   Nitrogen is an important component of protein. Protein is an essential substance in the body tissues of all living things. The nitrogen used to make protein in living things can't be absorbed directly from the air. Instead, nitrogen is changed into nitrogen-containing molecules by bacteria in the soil. Plants absorb these molecules from the soil and use them to make proteins. Animals and people eat plants to obtain these proteins. The bacteria in the soil eventually return nitrogen to the atmosphere (Figure 5.2).

Oxygen   The second most abundant gas is oxygen, which makes up 21 percent of Earth's atmosphere. When we take a breath of air, the most important gas that we breathe in is oxygen. Humans and other living things need oxygen to survive.

Trace gases   The remaining 1 percent of Earth's atmosphere is made up of 0.93 percent argon and 0.04 percent carbon dioxide. There are also tiny amounts of neon, helium, methane, krypton, and hydrogen, which we call *trace gases*.

VOCABULARY

atmosphere - a blanket of gases that surrounds a planet.

air - the mixture of gases that make up Earth's atmosphere.

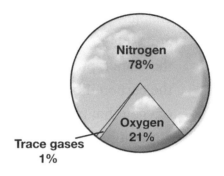

Figure 5.1: *Gases in Earth's atmosphere*

Nitrogen in the atmosphere

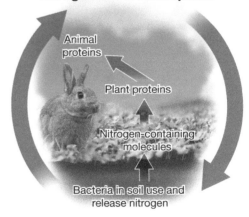

Figure 5.2: *The nitrogen cycle.*

The story of Earth's atmosphere

Earth is just right   In the last chapter, you learned that Earth's surface temperature is just right for all phases of water to exist. This is because Earth is not too close or too far from the Sun. Earth's special atmosphere exists because our planet has the right balance of mass and distance from the Sun (Figure 5.3).

Why Earth has an atmosphere   Earth's atmosphere formed early in its geologic history. Heat from the Sun drove off most of the lightweight elements like hydrogen and helium. Earth would have remained a rocky, airless world except that as it cooled, earthquakes and volcanoes spewed out heavier gases like nitrogen and carbon dioxide. Earth's gravitational pull held on to these gases, creating the atmosphere.

No atmosphere on Mercury   The planet Mercury is too small and too close to the Sun to have retained an atmosphere during its formation. Venus, Earth, and Mars, however, are far enough away and have enough gravitational pull to hold on to their atmospheres.

Venus, Earth, and Mars   The atmospheres of Venus, Earth, and Mars contain similar elements. Table 5.1 compares the atmospheres of these planets.

Sun	Does the planet have an atmosphere?	
Mercury	No	Too small, too close to the Sun
Venus	Yes	Mostly carbon dioxide
Earth	Yes	**Just right for life!** Mostly nitrogen and oxygen
Mars	Yes	Mostly carbon dioxide

Planet sizes and distances not to scale.

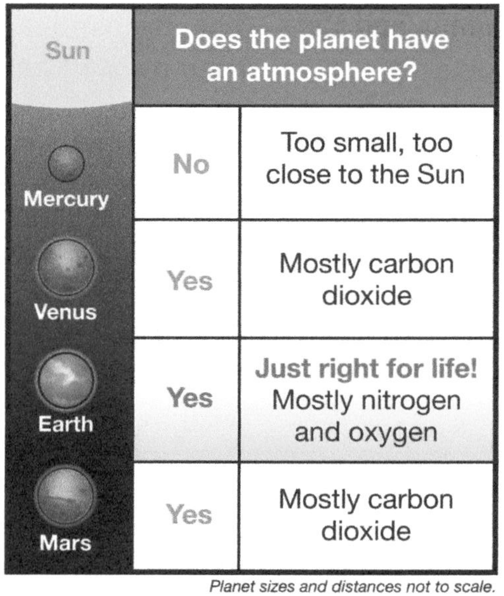

Figure 5.3: *Atmospheres of some of the planets.*

SOLVE IT!

Use the data in Table 5.1 to make a pie graph that shows the composition of the atmosphere on Venus. Assume the percentage for "other gases" equals 1 percent.

How does this pie graph compare to the pie graph in Figure 5.1?

Table 5.1: The atmospheres of Venus, Earth, and Mars.

Planet	Major gases in atmosphere			
	Carbon dioxide	**Nitrogen**	**Other gases**	
Mercury	No atmosphere			
Venus	96%	3%	0.1% water vapor	
Earth	0.04%	78%	21% oxygen	0.93% argon
Mars	95%	3%	1.6% argon	

Earth's unique atmosphere

Venus and Mars   The atmospheres of Venus and Mars are mostly carbon dioxide with a small amount of nitrogen. Earth's atmosphere is different. Ours is the only planet with a large amount of oxygen and just a tiny amount of carbon dioxide. Why is Earth's atmosphere unique?

Oxygen enters Earth's atmosphere   During Earth's ancient history, some of the earliest forms of life began to use the Sun's energy to survive. The process used by these early life forms and still used today by all plants is called *photosynthesis*. Plants use carbon dioxide and release oxygen in this process. As a result, Earth's atmosphere changed and filled with oxygen.

Storing carbon   The bodies of living things are made mostly of carbon atoms. For example, plants take in carbon from the atmosphere to build tissues. Carbon enters the atmosphere when organisms exhale carbon dioxide and when organisms decompose. If all of this carbon used by life processes returned to Earth's atmosphere, it would be unavailable for living things. Fortunately, long-living organisms, like trees, store carbon for long periods of time. Also, when organisms die and decompose, some of the carbon from their bodies becomes stored in the ground. *Fossil fuels* (oil, coal, and natural gas) are created when carbon from decaying plants and animals is stored in the ground.

How Earth stores carbon   The White Cliffs of Dover (see sidebar) provide a visual example of how carbon is stored on Earth. These cliffs are made of the shells of tiny, water-dwelling organisms. The organisms use carbon and calcium to form shells of calcium carbonate, or chalk. When the organisms die, the shells sink to the ocean floor. Piles of calcium carbonate build up over many centuries. Due to certain geological events, the calcium carbonate ocean floor off the coast of England became a land structure, the White Cliffs of Dover.

One way that Earth stores carbon

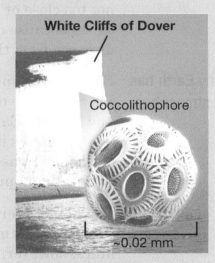

White Cliffs of Dover

Coccolithophore

~0.02 mm

Single-celled organisms like this coccolithophore use carbon dioxide dissolved in seawater for photosynthesis. They also use the carbon to form intricate calcium carbonate shells like the one shown above. Although each organism is only 0.002 to 0.02 millimeters across, these and other calcium carbonate shells pile up over the centuries, creating beautiful chalk structures like the White Cliffs of Dover in Britain.

Pressure in the atmosphere

A giant pile of cotton balls Earth's gravity prevents the nitrogen and oxygen molecules in our atmosphere from flying off into space. Imagine these molecules are like a giant pile of cotton balls. The cotton balls at the top of the pile are loosely spread out, but they press down on the ones below. The cotton balls at the bottom of the pile are packed together much more tightly than the ones at the top because of the pressure.

Pressure at sea level In the atmosphere, the molecules closest to Earth's surface are packed together very densely. This is because the weight of the molecules above presses down, creating *atmospheric pressure*. This pressure is greatest at sea level (the bottom of the atmosphere).

Altitude and pressure Altitude is a measure of the distance an object is above sea level. As the altitude of an object increases, the density of the air molecules around it is less, because there are fewer molecules above the object pushing down. This means that pressure decreases as altitude increases (Figure 5.4).

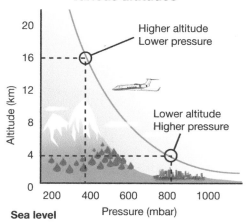

VOCABULARY

altitude - a measure of the distance an object is above sea level; usually the object is airborne.

Atmospheric pressure at various altitudes

Figure 5.4: *As altitude (height above sea level) increases, atmospheric pressure decreases (mbar = millibars of pressure).*

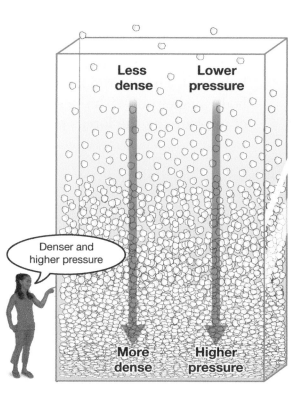

Less dense   Lower pressure

Denser and higher pressure

More dense   Higher pressure

What is atmospheric pressure?

Air molecules exert pressure
You have learned that our atmosphere is composed of air molecules. These molecules press down and create greater pressure close to Earth's surface (lower altitude). At high altitudes, there is less pressure. Atmospheric pressure is a measure of the force per unit area of air molecules in the atmosphere at a given altitude.

VOCABULARY

atmospheric pressure - a measure of the force per unit area of air molecules in the atmosphere at a given altitude.

Holding up under pressure
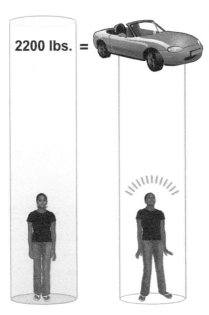

2200 lbs. =

At sea level, the weight of the column of air above a person is about 9,800 newtons (2,200 pounds)! This is equal to the weight of a small car. Why aren't we crushed by this pressure? Why don't we feel pressure pushing down on us? The answer is that the forces inside and outside the body are balanced. The air and tissue inside our body pushes out with the same amount of pressure as the forces pushing in!

Deep-sea fish
Depth: 600 meters

Photo courtesy NOAA

Figure 5.5: *Deep-sea fish are adapted to living at the high pressures found under water.*

How undersea animals withstand pressure
Deep-sea creatures that live at a depth of 3,000 meters below sea level have 300 times more pressure than we have at Earth's surface. These creatures survive because they generally lack air pockets and have body tissues that are jelly-like. At underwater pressure, the jelly-like body tissue holds its shape and functions properly (Figure 5.5).

How is atmospheric pressure measured?

What is a barometer? A **barometer** is an instrument that measures atmospheric pressure. Long ago, mercury barometers were used (Figure 5.6). They consisted of a tube sealed at one end and partially filled with mercury. The open end of the tube was placed in a dish containing more mercury. As air pressed down on the mercury in the dish, it forced the liquid in the tube to rise. The mercury in this kind of barometer rises 29.92 inches at sea level. This is equivalent to 1 atmosphere or 1,013 millibars of pressure (see chart below).

Aneroid barometers Since mercury is a poisonous liquid, *aneroid barometers* are used today (Figure 5.7). They have an airtight cylinder made of thin metal. When pressure increases, the walls of the cylinder squeeze inward. At lower pressures, the walls bulge out. A pointer attached to the cylinder moves as the cylinder changes shape, indicating the change in atmospheric pressure (Figure 5.7).

barometer - an instrument that measures atmospheric pressure.

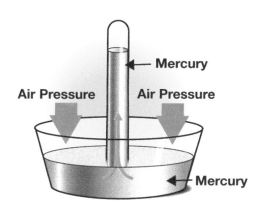

Figure 5.6: *A mercury barometer.*

Unit of pressure	Description	Relationship
inches of mercury (in Hg)	Unit describing the height of a column of mercury in a barometer.	29.92 in Hg = 1 atm
atmospheres (atm)	One atmosphere is the standard atmospheric pressure at sea level. Used by divers to compare pressure under water with surface pressure.	1 atm = 1.013 bars = 1,013 millibars
pounds per square inch (psi)	English unit commonly used to measure pressure of air in a container, like a tire or an inflatable ball.	1 psi = 6,895 Pa
pascals (Pa)	Metric unit commonly used to measure pressure of air in a container.	1 Pa = 1 newton/m^2
bars	Metric unit used to measure atmospheric pressure, most often in the form of millibars.	1 bar = 100,000 Pa

Figure 5.7: *An aneroid barometer. The units on this barometer are inches of mercury and millibars.*

5.1 Section Review

1. What are the two main gases in Earth's atmosphere?

2. Why is nitrogen an important element for sustaining life?

3. Give one reason why life exists on Earth and not on other planets.

4. How are these two things related: the White Cliffs of Dover and the gasoline you put in your car?

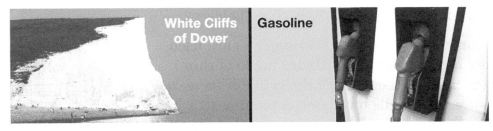

5. As a person moves higher above sea level, how does:

   a. the density of air molecules change?

   b. the atmospheric pressure change?

6. Mountain climbers who try to reach the summit of Mount Everest carry oxygen tanks. Why do you think they do this?

7. What does the term *altitude* mean?

8. Indicate where you would find higher water pressure and lower water pressure in Figure 5.8. Explain your answer.

9. In Earth's atmosphere and even under water, molecules press on objects. What prevents the human body and a deep-sea fish from being crushed by all this pressure?

10. How does an aneroid barometer work?

11. Convert an atmospheric pressure of 2 atmospheres to:

    a. inches of mercury (in Hg).

    b. bars.

Imagine that you are a science writer at a local newspaper. Each week, readers ask questions and you try to answer them. Here's this week's question:

Why do my ears sometimes hurt and "pop" during airplane takeoffs and landings?

Research and then answer the question. Remember, you are responding to a reader of your newspaper, so begin with "Dear reader," and make your response interesting!

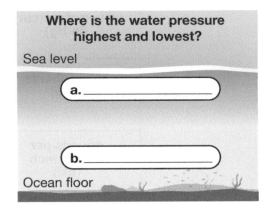

Figure 5.8: *Question 8.*

5.2 Layers of the Atmosphere

You probably know that temperature at the top of a high mountain is usually colder than at the base. But did you know that the temperature doesn't just keep decreasing as you go farther and farther up in the atmosphere? Actually, the temperature first decreases, then increases, then decreases, and then increases again. Scientists divide Earth's atmosphere into layers based on these zigzags in temperature (Figure 5.9).

The troposphere

The troposphere   We live in the troposphere, the layer that extends from 0 to approximately 11 kilometers (36,000 feet) above Earth's surface. About 75 percent of the atmosphere's mass is found in the troposphere. Almost all of Earth's water vapor, carbon dioxide, dust, airborne pollutants, and terrestrial life forms exist here.

Temperature decreases as you go up   The Sun warms Earth's surface. Heat radiates from the surface and warms the troposphere. As a result, the troposphere is warmest closest Earth's surface. The temperature drops about 6.5°C for every 1 kilometer you go up in the atmosphere. The temperature at the top of the troposphere is about –60°C.

Weather in the troposphere   The name *troposphere* contains the Greek root *tropo*, meaning "to turn or change." The troposphere is the region where clouds form and where all weather happens. When you hear about airplanes "flying above the weather," this means that they are flying above the troposphere.

VOCABULARY

troposphere - a layer of atmosphere that occurs from 0 to about 11 kilometers above Earth's surface; where all weather occurs.

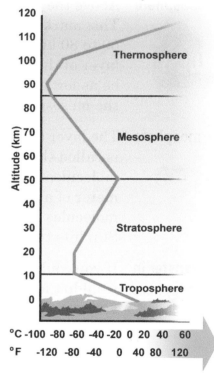

Figure 5.9: *Earth's atmosphere is divided into layers based on temperature.*

The stratosphere, mesophere, and thermosphere

Stratosphere

Above the troposphere lies the stratosphere, extending from about 11 to 50 kilometers above Earth's surface. The temperature *increases* as you go up in the stratosphere because of a thin layer of ozone. The *ozone layer* absorbs the Sun's high-energy ultraviolet (UV) radiation. As a result, the stratosphere is warm and we are protected from the skin and eye damage caused by UV radiation.

Mesosphere

Above the stratosphere, the temperature begins to drop again. This marks the beginning of the mesosphere, which extends from 50 to 80 kilometers above Earth. The mesosphere is the coldest layer of the atmosphere. At its outer reaches the temperature can be as low as −90°C. Most meteors or "shooting stars" burn up in the mesosphere.

Thermosphere

The layer that begins at about 80 kilometers above Earth's surface is called the thermosphere. This layer has a low density of air molecules—there are 100,000 times more air molecules in a cubic meter of air at Earth's surface than in the thermosphere. These molecules have a lot of kinetic energy, because the energy from the Sun hits them first. Temperatures in this layer can reach 1,800°C.

Heat transfer in the thermosphere

If you could hop out of a space shuttle into the thermosphere, you wouldn't feel hot. Temperature, as you remember, measures the average kinetic energy of the particles (atoms and molecules) of a substance. Heat, on the other hand, involves the transfer of energy from one object to another. Because the air molecules in the thermosphere are so far apart, very few of them would collide with you, so there would be very little heat transferred.

The exosphere and the ionosphere

The exosphere The **exosphere** begins at about 500 kilometers above Earth and does not have a specific outer limit (Figure 5.10). Lightweight atoms and molecules escape into space from this region.

Satellites in the exosphere Satellites orbit Earth in the exosphere. Most satellites that we rely on orbit 36,000 kilometers above the equator and travel at the same speed that Earth rotates. This orbit path is called the Clarke Belt. Communication on Earth depends on satellites. Satellites transmit information used for television shows, radio broadcasts, data and photos used in weather reports, and long distance telephone calls.

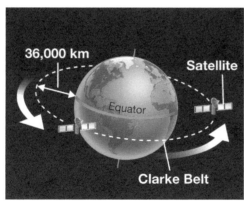
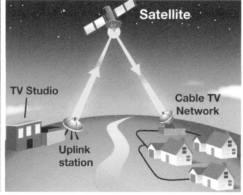

The ionosphere The **ionosphere** is part of the thermosphere and is where the Sun's ultraviolet light creates charged atoms and molecules called *ions* (Figure 5.10). The energy released in this process causes the high temperatures in the thermosphere. Ions easily transmit electricity and electromagnetic waves. The ionosphere makes it possible for you to tune into shortwave radio stations that originate 1,000 or more miles away. The radio signals are rebroadcast by the ions in the ionosphere back to Earth.

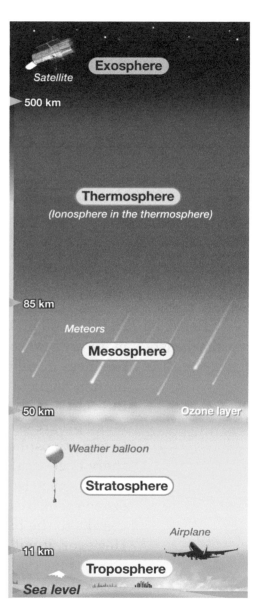

Figure 5.10: *The layers of the atmosphere.*

Chlorofluorocarbons and the ozone layer

The thinning ozone layer In the 1970s, scientists noticed that the ozone layer in the stratosphere above Antarctica was thinning. The detection of chlorine in the stratosphere led to the discovery that human activity was responsible for the loss of ozone. The culprit, it turns out, was a group of chemicals called chlorofluorocarbons (or CFCs).

CFCs CFCs were once commonly used in air conditioners, in aerosol spray cans, and for cleaning machine parts. While most airborne chemicals break down in the troposphere, chlorofluorocarbons stay intact until they travel up to the stratosphere. This journey can take anywhere from 6 to 26 years! In the stratosphere, the CFCs break down and release chlorine. The chlorine reacts with ozone molecules, leaving behind ordinary oxygen, which does not block incoming ultraviolet radiation (Figure 5.11).

Repairing the damage In the London Agreement of 1991, more than 90 countries banned the production and use of CFCs except for limited medical uses. Through international cooperation, we can make progress in repairing damage to our atmosphere. Currently, there is general agreement among scientists that loss of ozone seems to be slowing down thanks to the ban on CFCs. However, it will take many decades for the existing CFCs to break down.

The largest hole in the ozone layer ever observed. (September 24, 2006)

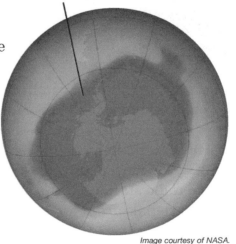

Image courtesy of NASA.

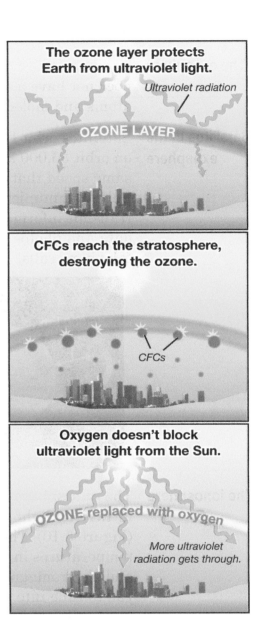

Figure 5.11: *CFCs and the ozone layer.*

5.2 Section Review

1. Almost all of Earth's weather occurs in which layer of the atmosphere?

2. In which layer of the atmosphere is the ozone layer located? How does this affect the temperature of this layer?

3. Why is the ozone layer important for life on Earth?

4. Which layer of the atmosphere is the coldest?

5. In which layer do most meteors or "shooting stars" occur?

6. In which atmospheric layer would you encounter 1,800°C temperatures? Would you feel hot? Why or why not?

7. What is the Clarke Belt?

8. Explain how you and a friend could demonstrate the term *geostationary*.

9. Which layer of the atmosphere is responsible for transmitted AM radio waves? How is this possible?

10. Oxygen is a molecule made up of two oxygen atoms. Ozone is a molecule made up of three oxygen atoms. In what other ways is oxygen different from ozone?

11. What are CFCs?

12. Why does the ozone layer seem to be recovering?

13. Research weather satellites. You may want to talk to a meteorologist to find out the answer to these questions.

    a. What kind of things can you see in a satellite photograph?

    b. How are satellite photographs helpful to people?

    c. What kind of technology is used to record this information?

    d. *Bonus Question*: What is the name of the first successful weather satellite?

STUDY SKILLS

Now that you have learned all about the layers of Earth's atmosphere, you need a way to organize the information.

Design an information table that lists and describes all the layers of Earth's atmosphere.

Things to include in your information table:

- Name of the layer
- Distance from Earth's surface
- Thickness of the layer
- Special facts about the layer

CHALLENGE

Make up a game or activity that you can play with friends to help you remember the different layers of the atmosphere.

5.3 Earth is Just Right

Earth is "just right" because its temperature is not too hot or too cold (Figure 5.12). Metals like lead melt on the hot surface of Venus, but not on Earth. Some gases freeze solid on Neptune, but not on Earth. Earth's temperature is especially nurturing for living things. This section is about how Earth's temperature stays "just right."

The importance of Earth's atmosphere

Temperature range   Earth's surface temperature stays within a narrow range—it is not too hot or too cold. The average temperature of Earth's surface is about 15°C. This temperature is maintained because Earth has an atmosphere that traps some of the Sun's energy. Without an atmosphere, Earth's surface temperature would be about –18°C.

	Surface temperature (°C)
Mercury	–170 to 390
Venus	450 to 480
Earth	–88 to 56
Mars	–89 to 20
Jupiter	–108
Saturn	–139
Uranus	–197
Neptune	–201

Figure 5.12: *The surface temperatures for planets in our solar system.*

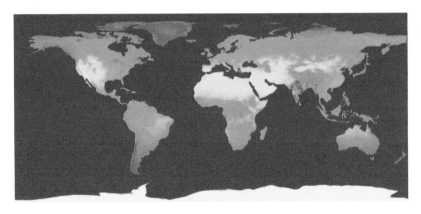

Land Surface Temperature (°C)

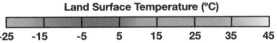

-25   -15   -5   5   15   25   35   45

July 2003. Image based on data from
NASA's Moderate Resolution Imaging Spectroradiometer (MODIS) Sensor. Credit: NASA

STUDY SKILLS

How to "read" diagrams

How do you read a diagram?

1. Read the caption and title.
2. Study the diagram to determine what information it is showing you.

Question: Refer to the diagram at the left. In your estimation, what was the most common land surface temperature for July 2003?

Heat transfer and water

The Sun's energy Most of the heat energy on Earth's surface comes from the Sun. At the same time that the Sun adds heat to Earth's surface, heat is being lost to space. The balance between the Sun's heat and heat lost into space is what determines Earth's surface temperature.

Heat transfer The Sun's heat reaches Earth by a heat transfer process called *radiation*. Radiation is heat transfer through empty space. Once heat has arrived on Earth, there are three ways that it moves through the atmosphere: radiation, convection, and conduction (Figure 5.13). You learned about these processes of heat transfer in Chapter 3. Heat transfer by *radiation* occurs without direct contact or movement of atoms. *Convection* is the transfer of heat through the motion of gases and liquids such as air and water. *Conduction* is the transfer of heat by the direct contact of atoms and molecules.

Heating Earth's surface When solar radiation reaches Earth, it is either absorbed or reradiated by the surfaces it encounters. When solar radiation is absorbed by a surface, the surface gets warmer. Land gets warm quickly during the day, and quickly loses this heat at night. Water, on the other hand, warms up and loses heat more slowly.

Water and specific heat Compared to land surfaces, water has a high specific heat. Specific heat is the amount of energy needed to raise the temperature of 1 gram of a substance by 1 degree Celsius. Having a higher specific heat means that it takes more energy to raise a substance's temperature, but once the substance is warm, it takes longer to cool off (Figure 5.14). The large amount of water on Earth prevents the planet from getting too hot or cold.

specific heat - the amount of energy needed to raise the temperature of 1 gram of a substance by 1 degree Celsius.

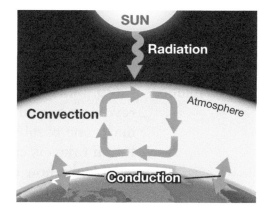

Figure 5.13: *Heat transfer on Earth.*

Figure 5.14: *The specific heat of water is higher than the specific heat of land.*

Earth's motion

Motion and temperature The motion of Earth also helps to balance its surface temperature. Read on to find out how two of these motions, rotation and revolution, affect the temperature of every place on Earth.

Rotation Rotation is the turning motion of a planet as it spins on its axis (Figure 5.15). It takes one day for Earth to make one complete spin. For half of a day, your side of Earth faces the Sun and experiences daytime. For the other half of the day, your side of Earth faces away from the Sun and experiences nighttime.

Revolution Revolution is the motion of a planet around its star. Earth revolves around the Sun. It takes about 365.25 days for Earth to make one revolution, or one trip, around the Sun. The path that Earth takes is called its *orbit* (Figure 5.15). Later in this chapter we'll learn how the revolution of Earth is related to the seasons.

 VOCABULARY

rotation - the motion of Earth spinning on its axis; one rotation is called a *day*.

revolution - the motion of Earth moving around the Sun; one revolution is called a *year*.

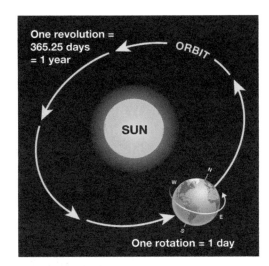

Figure 5.15: *Earth rotates on its axis and revolves around the Sun.*

This basketball is rotating.

This race car is revolving around the pit stop in the middle of the track.

 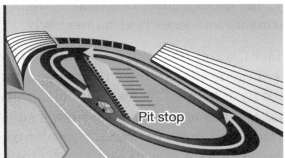

Pit stop

Temperature and Earth's rotation

Mercury is too hot and too cold! What happens if you put a burger on a hot grill and forget to turn it? The bottom will be burned to a crisp, and the top will be under-cooked. The planet Mercury is like that. One day on Mercury lasts for about 58 Earth days! The long day causes the temperature on the Sun-facing side of Mercury to reach about 390°C. Something made out of the metal lead would melt at this temperature! At the same time, the dark nighttime side plunges to −170°C. That's extremely cold!

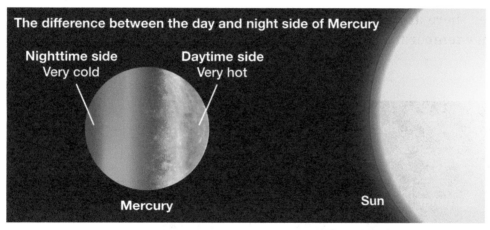

The difference between the day and night side of Mercury

Nighttime side
Very cold

Daytime side
Very hot

Mercury

Sun

The Earth is just right—not too hot or too cold! Even though Earth is farther away from the Sun than Mercury, our night side never gets as cold as Mercury's night side. Why not? Think about burgers again. A good chef turns the burger so it browns nicely on both sides. Similarly, the Earth turns rapidly enough so that there isn't enough time for our night temperature to sink too low. There also isn't enough time for Earth's day temperature to rise too high.

Greenhouse Gases

A greenhouse is a glass building where plants can be grown in a warm, moist environment. Scientists use the term "greenhouse gases" to describe certain gases in Earth's atmosphere. Like the glass in a greenhouse, greenhouse gases can slow down Earth's natural heat-loss processes. These gases are useful because they keep Earth warm. However, the amount of these gases is increasing in our atmosphere. Because of this increase, less heat energy will be able to leave Earth. Scientists are concerned that the resulting rise in Earth's average surface temperature might alter climates and other natural systems in our environment.

Revolution and Earth's seasons

Why does Earth have seasons?
The diagram below shows Earth at four different places in its revolution around the Sun. Why is it warmer in summer and cooler in winter in the northern hemisphere? In other words, why do seasons occur?

Earth is tilted
One guess might be that Earth is closer to the Sun during summer. But this isn't the correct answer. Earth has seasons because it is tilted on its axis. During our summer, the northern hemisphere receives sunlight that is more direct than it is in the winter, and in summer there are more hours of daylight. This means we have warmer temperatures in summer than we do in winter.

Earth's axis

Earth rotates about an imaginary axis that goes through its center. This axis is drawn on the images of Earth in the diagram on this page. The diagram shows that Earth is tilted at 23.5° as it revolves around the Sun.

The axis connects the North Pole and the South Pole. The north end of the axis points toward the North Star throughout the year.

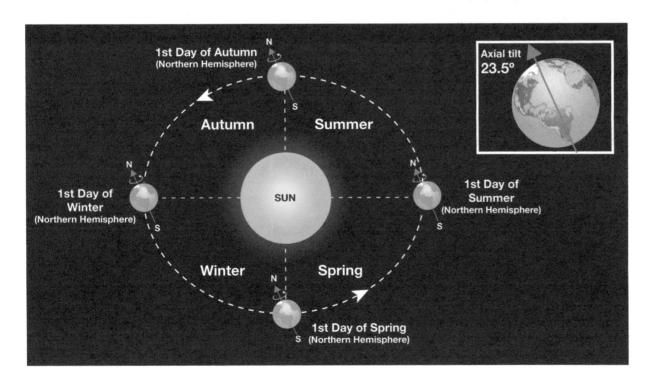

SOLVE IT!

Make your own sketch of the diagram at the left. Based on today's date, indicate on your diagram where Earth is on its path around the Sun.

5.3 Section Review

1. Describe two reasons why Earth's climate is "just right" for life.

2. What is the source of most of Earth's heat energy?

3. Some of Earth's heat energy is lost to space. Why is this important?

4. What are the three ways that heat energy moves through the atmosphere?

5. How does water help keep Earth from getting too cold or hot?

6. Define the term *rotation*. How long is one rotation of Earth?

7. Define the term *revolution*. How long is one revolution of Earth around the Sun?

8. Earth's surface does not get too hot or too cold compared to Mercury's surface. What differences between the two planets makes this possible?

9. What role do greenhouse gases play in keeping Earth warm?

10. Why does Earth have seasons?

11. During winter in the northern hemisphere, is the southern hemisphere tilted toward or away from the Sun?

12. How many degrees is Earth's axis tilted?

13. There are more hours of sunlight and more direct sunlight during summer. How does winter compare to summer in terms of hours of sunlight?

14. *Research*: You will need to do research on the Internet or at the library to answer these questions.

    a. What are the main greenhouse gases?

    b. Which planet—Venus or Earth—exhibits a stronger greenhouse effect? Why?

What are the seasons like where you live?

Write about how the seasons change over the year where you live. Describe your favorite part of each season.

Why is January a winter month in the northern hemisphere but a summer month in the southern hemisphere?

Hurricane Hunters

If there's a hurricane to be hunted, it's usually done by one of the specially-equipped NOAA (National Oceanic and Atmospheric Administration) planes. Two of the world's most popular research planes are based in Tampa, Florida.

NOAA hurricane hunter WP-3D Orion and Gulfstream IV aircraft in flight.
Photo courtesy of NOAA

They are both Lockheed WP-3D Orion planes and are commonly known as Kermit and Miss Piggy. In fact, the noses of both planes are painted with the pictures of these famous Muppet characters. These hurricane-hunting planes log between 300 and 400 hours of flight time each year. The primary purpose of their missions is to help forecast hurricanes. Information like the intensity and strength of a storm and when it will make landfall is gathered. A typical flight aboard Kermit or Miss Piggy can last up to eight hours and cover over 2,000 nautical miles. One nautical mile is equal to 1,852 meters. It's not your typical vacation fight.

Hurricane Katrina's large eyewall taken by a NOAA P-3 hurricane hunter pilot on August 28, 2005.
Photo courtesy of NOAA

Flying a hurricane mission

You could think of Kermit and Miss Piggy as flying meteorological laboratories. The planes are equipped with state-of-the-art instrumentation. On a typical hurricane mission, the plane will be occupied by 18 highly-qualified individuals. Hurricane-hunting crew members include pilots, flight engineers, navigators, scientists, and meteorologists. The pilots have a difficult job trying to keep the plane level. They fly through high winds and pounding rains filled with turbulence. Turbulence is any irregular atmospheric motion. In simpler terms, it's more of an up-and-down motion, or the feeling of bumpiness. The crew flies through a lot of turbulence before they reach the storm's eye wall and finally the eye (the center of the hurricane). The eye is often a calm and clear area. The eye wall surrounds the eye and has the highest wind speeds of the storm. As you can imagine, everything must be bolted down securely to withstand all the turbulence. Just about everything on the plane is tied down or velcroed, even the pencils and pens!

Plane instrumentation

Detailed pictures and data of the weather systems in the upper atmosphere are collected during a mission. The NOAA planes are equipped with many cameras and sensing instruments to accomplish this task. The mass of the plane is approximately 61,235 kilograms (135,000 pounds) when it is fully loaded with people, fuel, cameras, and all the instruments. That's one big load flying into those hurricanes!

The dropsonde is one of the most important instruments on board. It's a tube-like canister the size of a paper towel tube.

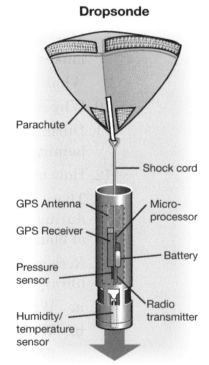
Dropsonde

Parachute

Shock cord

GPS Antenna

GPS Receiver

Micro-processor

Battery

Pressure sensor

Humidity/ temperature sensor

Radio transmitter

These canisters contain several sensors used to measure air temperature, humidity, and atmospheric pressure at different places in the storm. They are dropped from the bottom of the plane through a chute. A parachute attached to the canister allows it to drop downward slowly. As it falls, data are collected and transmitted back to the plane. A GPS (global positioning system) receiver is used to monitor the location and wind speed of the storms. Scientists can drop as many as 50 dropsondes during a hurricane mission.

Hurricane facts

Hurricanes are tropical cyclones, which are warm, low-pressure storms that form in the tropics. They rotate counter-clockwise (to the left) in the Northern Hemisphere, and clockwise (to the right) in the Southern Hemisphere.

You can see the direction in the NOAA satellite image that tracked hurricane Katrina in 2005. When these storms reach a wind speed between 63 and 118 km/h (39 and 73 mph), they are known as a tropical storm and are given a name by the National Hurricane Center (NHC) in Miami, Florida. A tropical storm becomes a hurricane when the winds become 119 km/h (74 mph) or greater. The NHC uses the Saffir-Simpson Hurricane Scale to categorize the hurricanes. The scale goes from 1 through 5 and is based on wind speed.

Hurricane Katrina, 2005

Photo courtesy of NOAA

Forecasting hurricanes

Isaac Ginis is a professor of oceanography at the Graduate School of Oceanography at the University of Rhode Island. He is considered to be one of the most accurate hurricane forecasters in the world.

Isaac Ginis, Professor of Oceanography University of Rhode Island

Photo courtesy of Nora Lewis/URI.

According to Ginis, ocean water temperature is the key factor in forecasting hurricanes. Warm ocean water causes hurricane winds to intensify. However, the winds stir up the water so that deeper, cooler water rises to the ocean surface. The cooler water can reduce the intensity of the hurricane. This information helped Ginis develop an ocean model that shows ocean currents and temperature. It is used today by the NOAA to help predict hurricane intensity. Ginis's ocean model and an atmospheric model created by NOAA are considered some of the most accurate models in hurricane forecasting since 2001.

QUESTIONS

1. If a hurricane-hunting plane flew an 8-hour mission that covered 2,000 nautical miles, how many meters would the crew have traveled?

2. What conditions are needed to form a hurricane?

3. Explain the major difference between a hurricane in the Northern Hemisphere and the Southern Hemisphere.

4. Why is it important to accurately forecast hurricanes?

Bernoulli's Principle

Our atmosphere and golf balls

In addition to providing us with air to breathe, the air in our atmosphere is useful for playing sports, travelling, and all sorts of things. Because of air and how it flows around objects, a baseball pitcher can throw a "sinker," an airplane can fly, and a golf ball can soar for long distances.

A short history of golf balls

In the 1840s, a golf ball was made from the heated and molded parts of a Malaysian tree—the gutta-percha gum tree. The balls were called *gutties*. Golf players at the time realized that old gutties with nicks (little dents or scratches) went further than new ones. So, golfers started to nick the gutties on purpose. In the early 1900s, balls were made of rubber and coated with a latex. Circular depressions called dimples were made in the balls. By 1930, a standard weight and size was established for golf balls and approximately 400 dimples were put on each ball.

Standard golf balls are made with approximately 400 dimples.

What is Bernoulli's principle?

Bernoulli's principle states that as air moves faster, its pressure decreases. If a golf ball were smooth, air would flow over it at the same speed at the top and bottom. Because of the dimples and the backspin caused by hitting the ball with the golf club, the air flowing over the top is moving faster than the air flowing under the ball. The faster air creates a low pressure so the ball experiences a "lift." Bernoulli's principle was developed by Daniel Bernoulli, a Swiss mathematician and scientist. Now, try to create Bernoulli's principle using three methods.

Materials

(A) Cheeseball snack food and bendable straw, (B) ping-pong ball and blow dryer, and (C) paper strip (3 inches × 9 inches)

What you will do

A: Put the bendable straw in your mouth with the short section bent at a 90° angle up into the air. Place the cheeseball on the end of the straw. Blow through the straw. Can you get the cheeseball to be suspended in the air above the straw? Keep trying. It can be done.

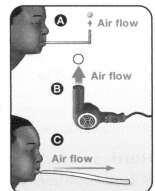

B: Use a blow dryer and ping pong ball for the same effect. Hold the blow dryer up vertically so that the ball can be supported by the air flow.

C: Hold the paper strip with your hand so that the 3-inch side is just below your lips and the length of the paper strip is hanging below your lips. Blow over the paper strip.

Applying your knowledge

a. Explain why the activities demonstrated Bernoulli's principle. You may diagram your answer if you want.

b. One of the diagrams below represents a baseball called a "sinker" thrown by a pitcher. The other represents a golf ball. High pressure (H) and low pressure (L) regions, and the direction of air currents around the balls are indicated. Identify which ball is the "sinker" and which ball is the golf ball. Explain your reasoning. *Hint*: Identify where the air is flowing faster over each ball.

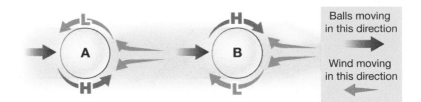

Chapter 5 Assessment

Vocabulary

Select the correct term to complete the sentences.

air   altitude   atmospheric pressure

barometer   stratosphere   troposphere

mesosphere   thermosphere   exosphere

ionosphere   specific heat   rotation

revolution

Section 5.1

1. Our atmosphere is composed of _____, a mixture of gases.

2. The _____ of an airplane rapidly increases as it takes off.

3. At sea level, _____ is equal to about 9,800 newtons.

4. A(n) _____ measures atmospheric pressure.

Section 5.2

5. Shooting stars occur in the _____.

6. The _____ extends into space.

7. The _____ has a very low density of air molecules.

8. The ozone layer occurs in the _____.

9. All weather on Earth occurs in the _____.

10. AM radio waves are transmitted in the _____.

Section 5.3

11. Water has a higher _____ than land.

12. It takes one day for Earth to make one _____.

13. The time for one _____ on Earth is one year.

Concepts

Section 5.1

1. Why doesn't Mercury have an atmosphere?

2. Nitrogen is 78 percent of the atmosphere. How is nitrogen important to living things?

3. Why is there more carbon dioxide in the atmosphere on Mars and Venus than on Earth?

4. Explain what happens to the following factors as you go from sea level up to the top of a mountain.

    a. Atmospheric pressure

    b. The density of air molecules

    c. The elevation

5. Compare and contrast how humans and deep-sea creatures survive under pressure.

6. How is a mercury barometer different from an aneroid barometer?

Section 5.2

7. Explain what happens to temperature as you go from sea level to the top of the thermosphere.

8. You are an airplane pilot and the weather is really bad, causing a bumpy plane ride. What could you do to make the flight more comfortable for your passengers?

9. What is the ozone layer?

10. What does the term *geostationary* mean? Why are many satellites geostationary?

Section 5.3

11. What are the three ways that heat is transferred in Earth's atmosphere?

12. Temperatures on Mercury can be much colder than on Earth, but Mercury is closer to the Sun. How is this possible?

13. What are greenhouse gases?

14. Explain how these factors help keep Earth's temperature within a narrow range that is good for life on the planet.

    a. The distance from the Sun.

    b. The atmosphere.

    c. The water on the planet's surface.

15. Earth is tilted at an angle of 23.5° as it revolves around the Sun. How does this tilt affect the amount of daylight that North America receives in the summer versus the winter?

Math and Writing Skills

Section 5.1

1. Imagine you are a space tourist guide. Some space tourists want to take a vacation on Earth. Make a one-page flyer that advertises why Earth is a good place to visit. Your flyer should include information about the atmosphere, the temperature range, other details, and drawings.

2. Find out the atmospheric pressure for today. You can find this value by listening to a local TV weather report or by going to a weather Web site on the Internet. Convert this pressure reading so that you have the value in inches of mercury, atmospheres, and in millibars.

3. In the chapter, you learned about the atmospheres of some planets. Now find out about the atmosphere of one of these planets: Jupiter, Saturn, Uranus, and Neptune.

Section 5.2

4. You are an expert speaker on Earth's atmosphere and have just given a talk. Now, someone from the audience asks you this question: Why does Earth's atmosphere have layers? What do you say to the audience member?

5. *Research*: How does the density of air molecules in the mesosphere compare to the density of air molecules in the thermosphere?

    a. Come up with a hypothesis.

    b. List a way you could test your hypothesis.

Section 5.3

6. How long does each event take? Give your answer in days.

    a. Five Earth rotations

    b. Two Earth revolutions

Chapter Project—Mile High City Baseball

Denver, Colorado, is the Mile High City because it is one mile above sea level. At this location, rumor has it that hitting baseballs a long way is easier than in other cities and it is hard to throw curve balls or sinkers.

1. Come up with a hypothesis for why this rumor might be true in the Mile High City.

2. If the rumor is true, how might a game played in the Mile High City be different from a game played at sea level in terms of:

    a. number of runs earned by a team during a game?

    b. number of hits and home runs earned by a team during a game?

3. See if the rumor is true by researching this effect called "The Coors Field Effect" after the field, Coors Field, where the Colorado Rockies professional baseball team plays. Then, write up your finding in a report!

Weather and Climate

How is the weather predicted? What factors influence whether you will see sunshine, clouds, or precipitation on any given day? In this chapter, you will learn how temperature, pressure, and water content in the atmosphere work together to produce different kinds of weather. You'll explore cloud formation, precipitation, air masses, and fronts. You'll also learn what the symbols on a weather map mean, and how different kinds of storms develop.

Key Questions:

1. What causes wind?

2. What do clouds tell you about the weather?

3. Why do different parts of Earth have different climates?

6.1 Introduction to Weather

Weather is a term that describes the condition of the atmosphere in terms of temperature, atmospheric pressure, wind, and water. The major energy source for weather events is the Sun. Weather events tend to happen when air masses interact or change locations. An air mass is a large body of air (sometimes covering thousands of square kilometers) with consistent temperature and moisture content throughout. In this section, you will learn how weather happens. You will also learn important terms used for talking about weather.

Weather factors

Temperature The temperature of air determines whether it rises or sinks. The Sun warms Earth's surface. As air near the surface is warmed, it expands and becomes less dense. The less-dense air rises. Eventually the warm, less-dense air that rose from the surface cools. The same chain of events that made the air rise now works in reverse and the air sinks back to the ground (Figure 6.1).

Pressure When warm air rises from Earth's surface, an area of low atmospheric pressure is created. This lower-pressure area draws in air from surrounding higher-pressure areas. Eventually the warm air that rose from the surface cools and becomes denser. This dense, cool air sinks back to the surface, causing an area of high atmospheric pressure.

What is wind? Wind is the horizontal movement of air that occurs as a result of a pressure difference between two air masses. The greater the difference in pressure, the greater the speed of the air flow. Most of these pressure differences are due to unequal heating of the atmosphere.

weather - the condition of the atmosphere as it is affected by temperature, atmospheric pressure, wind, and water.

air mass - a large body of air with consistent temperature and moisture content throughout.

wind - the horizontal movement of air that occurs as a result of pressure differences between two air masses.

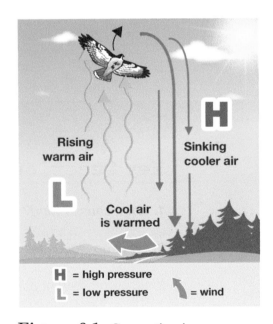

Figure 6.1: *Convection in the atmosphere.*

Convection in the atmosphere

Thermals

A **thermal** is a small, upward flow of warm air. Gliding birds like hawks often ride a thermal as they hunt for food. Pilots of sailplanes (which lack an engine) also ride thermals (Figure 6.2). Thermals usually come and go over a short period of time.

Breezes and specific heat

Convection near coastlines causes *sea breezes* during the day and *land breezes* at night. These breezes occur because water has a higher *specific heat* than land. This means that water warms and cools more slowly than the land.

Sea breezes

During the daytime, the land heats up faster than the ocean. Rising warm air over the land creates a low-pressure area. Eventually the rising air moves out over the sea, cools, and sinks toward the sea surface. The cooling, sinking air mass creates a high-pressure area. Air flows from high- to low-pressure areas. So, during daytime hours, there is a cool sea breeze from sea to land.

Land breezes

During the evening hours, a land breeze occurs because the ground cools rapidly during this time but the ocean remains warm. At night, warm air rises over the sea, creating a low-pressure area. The air sinks over the land creating a high-pressure area. The breeze then flows from land to sea.

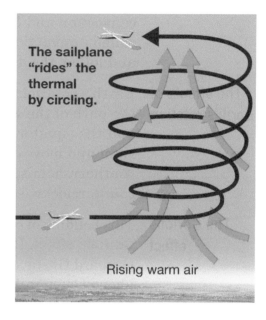

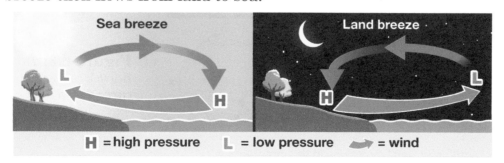

H = high pressure   L = low pressure   ➡ = wind

Figure 6.2: *A thermal is a rising column of warm air. Gliding birds and sailplanes "ride" thermals. In fact, the pilots look for gliding birds to find these invisible air currents.*

The Coriolis effect

Global convection Convection also occurs on a global scale. Warm, less-dense air at the equator tends to rise and flow toward the poles. Then, cooler, denser air from the poles sinks and flows back toward the equator.

Convection cells Due to Earth's rotation, rising warm air from the equator doesn't make it all the way to the poles. The combination of global convection and Earth's rotation sets up a series of wind patterns called convection cells in each hemisphere. Look at Figure 6.3 and follow the arrows. Do you see where air is rising and sinking?

The effects of Earth's rotation Earth's rotation also changes the direction of airflow. This causes the path of the wind to be curved as it moves between the poles and the equator. In the northern hemisphere, winds bend to the right and move clockwise around a high pressure center (H). In the southern hemisphere, winds bend to the left and move counterclockwise around a high pressure center (H).

The Coriolis effect This bending of currents of air due to the Earth's rotation is called the Coriolis effect. It is named after the French engineer-mathematician Gaspard Gustave de Coriolis (1792–1843), who first described the phenomenon in 1835.

VOCABULARY

convection cells - large wind patterns in Earth's atmosphere caused by convection.

Coriolis effect - the bending of currents of air or water due to Earth's rotation.

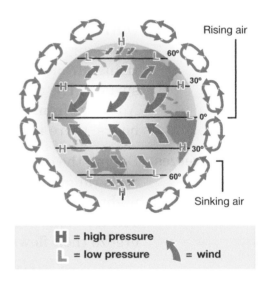

Figure 6.3: *This diagram shows Earth's convection cells and how winds curve due to the Coriolis effect.*

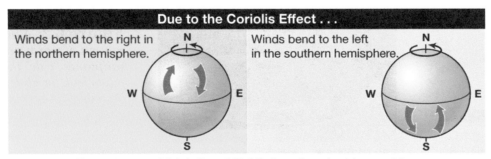

Due to the Coriolis Effect . . .

Winds bend to the right in the northern hemisphere.

Winds bend to the left in the southern hemisphere.

To understand "right" and "left" directions in this graphic, imagine you are standing at the base of each arrow on the globes.

Global surface wind patterns

Wind and human history
Three important global wind patterns exist in each hemisphere (Figure 6.4). Sailors have used these winds to travel to and explore new lands throughout human history.

Trade winds
The *trade winds* are surface wind currents that move between 30° north or south latitude and the equator. Remember, the air around the equator warms, rises, and flows toward the poles. At about 30° N and 30° S, it cools, sinks, and flows toward the equator again. The Coriolis effect bends the trade winds so that they flow from northeast to southwest in the northern hemisphere and from southeast to northwest in the southern hemisphere.

Prevailing westerlies
The trade winds set up a high-pressure area at about 30° N latitude. Air along the surface between 30° N and 60° N moves northward, from high to low pressure. The air bends to the right due to the Coriolis effect, creating the *prevailing westerlies*. Most of the United States is between 30° N and 60° N, so most of our weather patterns move from southwest to northeast. In the southern hemisphere, the weather patterns between 30° S and 60° S tend to move from the northwest to the southeast.

Polar easterlies
Polar easterlies form when the air over the poles cools and sinks, creating a high-pressure area. Like the other global winds, this polar wind is bent by the Coriolis effect. The air flows from northeast to southwest in the northern hemisphere, and from southeast to northwest in the southern hemisphere.

The polar front
At about 60° latitude, the polar easterlies meet the prevailing westerlies at a boundary called the *polar front*. Here, the dense polar air forces the warmer westerly air upward. Some warmer air flows toward the poles, and some flows back toward the 30° latitude line.

STUDY SKILLS

Which way does the wind blow?

Here are some facts about winds to help you study.

-Winds are described by the direction from which they originate. That means that a west wind blows from the west, for example.

-Trade winds are named after trade routes used by sailing merchants.

-Prevailing westerlies are so named because they blow from the west.

-Polar easterlies are so named because they come from polar regions and blow from the east.

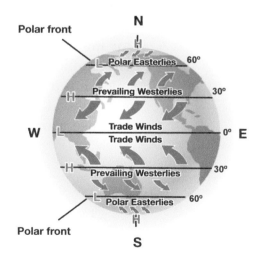

Figure 6.4: *Global surface wind patterns.*

Air and water vapor

Water vapor You have just learned how air temperature and atmospheric pressure influence weather. Now, let's look at a third factor: water vapor in the air. Water vapor is the result of liquid water *evaporating*. Liquid water from oceans, rivers, and even puddles changes to water vapor and mixes with the air (Figure 6.5).

How much water vapor can air hold? An air mass can be compared to a sponge. Warm air is like a big sponge that can contain a lot of water vapor. Cold air is like a small sponge that can contain less water vapor. Air that contains the maximum amount of water is *saturated*. Like a soggy sponge, saturated air can't hold more water vapor. When more water vapor is added, it condenses and forms droplets.

Relative humidity *Relative humidity* is a measure of how much water vapor an air mass contains relative to the total amount of water vapor it could contain at a certain temperature. Let's say we have two air masses with the same number of air molecules. The warm air mass has a greater volume because the molecules are more spaced out. Both air masses contain 50 percent of the total amount of water vapor they could contain. The graphic below shows that the warm air mass has a greater capacity to hold more water vapor than the cool air mass. It feels more humid on a warm day than on a cool day because warm air can hold so much more water.

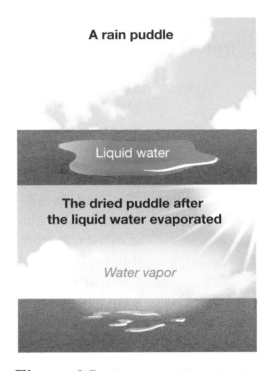

A rain puddle

Liquid water

The dried puddle after the liquid water evaporated

Water vapor

Figure 6.5: *When a puddle dries, the water can become water vapor in the atmosphere. However, water in a puddle can also seep into the ground.*

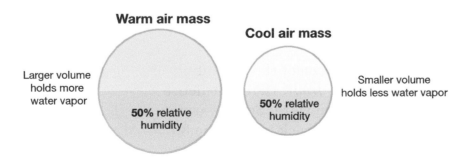

Warm air mass

Cool air mass

Larger volume holds more water vapor

50% relative humidity

Smaller volume holds less water vapor

50% relative humidity

6.1 Section Review

1. Define wind. Draw a diagram that illustrates how wind is created.

2. How does convection help birds and sailplanes to fly?

3. Why is the path of the wind curved as it moves from the poles to the equator?

4. Why are there three different wind patterns in each hemisphere? What are the names of these wind patterns?

5. Which wind pattern most affects the United States?

6. Which holds more water vapor, a warm or a cold air mass?

7. When the air is filled to capacity with water vapor, it is said to be _____.

8. What does it mean for an air mass to have 70 percent relative humidity?

9. An air mass cools to the point where it becomes saturated. What might happen next?

10. A cool (10°C) air mass warms to 30°C.

    a. Does the volume of the air mass decrease or increase when the temperature goes up?

    b. If the amount of water vapor in the air mass stays the same, does the relative humidity increase or decrease when the temperature goes up?

MY JOURNAL

Throughout human history, sailors have used global wind patterns to travel to and explore new lands.

Research one of the more famous ship captains—Capt. James Cook (1728–1779). Who was he? What is he known for?

Write a short report about one or more of Captain Cook's adventures or achievements.

A replica of Captain Cook's ship the *HMS Endeavor*.

Photo by John Hill

6.2 Weather Patterns

As you have learned, our weather is part of Earth's atmosphere. We can learn about today's or tomorrow's weather by listening to a meteorologist. You can also find out about weather on your own by looking at clouds in the sky and by taking your own weather data. This section is all about observing weather patterns.

Meteorology

What is a meteorologist?

A **meteorologist** is a person who uses scientific principles to explain, understand, observe, or forecast Earth's weather. Many meteorologists have college degrees in physics, chemistry, or mathematics. Radio and television weathercasters are often professional meteorologists.

Tools used by meteorologists to help people

Meteorologists use satellite and computer technology to inform people about the weather. For example, meteorologists can use data to predict hurricanes. Before 1960, a hurricane could hit without warning. Since 1960, weather satellites have helped predict and track hurricanes. Figure 6.6 shows a satellite image of Hurricane Hugo about to make landfall on the coast of South Carolina in 1989. Government organizations like the National Hurricane Center (NHC) monitor storms that might become hurricanes. The NHC issues hurricane watches and warnings so that people can evacuate a threatened area.

Weather map courtesy NOAA.

 VOCABULARY

meteorologist - an individual who uses scientific principles to forecast the weather.

Figure 6.6: *A weather satellite image of Hurricane Hugo making landfall on the coast of South Carolina in 1989.*

 MY JOURNAL

What is it like to be a meteorologist? Find out by interviewing a meteorologist or by researching the job of a meteorologist on the Internet. Write about your findings in a report. Include photographs or pictures in your report.

Water in the atmosphere

Water in the atmosphere
Rain, snow, sleet, and hail occur because water exists in the atmosphere. Even when the skies are blue, there is water present. The amount varies from just 0.1 percent in the atmosphere above Antarctica to as much as 3 percent above a tropical rainforest.

Three phases of water in the atmosphere
Water in the atmosphere exists in all three phases (solid, liquid, and gas). Ice crystals occur high in the troposphere. Tiny water droplets, much too small to see, are suspended throughout the troposphere virtually all the time. They are considered liquid water and not gas because they are made of microscopic "clumps" of water molecules. Water in the atmosphere also occurs as water vapor—water in the gas phase.

Temperature and pressure
As temperature *increases*, the rate of evaporation *increases* (Figure 6.7). Higher temperatures cause the liquid water molecules to move fast so they have enough energy to break free of their bonds with each other. These water molecules become water vapor in the atmosphere. In contrast, as atmospheric pressure *increases*, the rate of evaporation *decreases* (Figure 6.7). This is because the pressure makes it harder for water molecules to escape from the liquid to the gas phase.

Dew point
Both condensation and evaporation occur in the atmosphere all the time. However, each process may happen at different rates. When the rate of evaporation is greater than the rate of condensation, we see clearing skies. When the rate of condensation exceeds the rate of evaporation, we say that the air's **dew point** has been reached. This is the temperature at which more water vapor is condensing than evaporating in an air mass. The water in the air mass is getting colder, slowing down, and forming "dew" or droplets.

As temperature increases, evaporation increases.

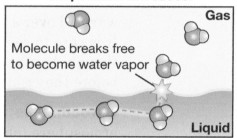

As atmospheric pressure increases, evaporation decreases.

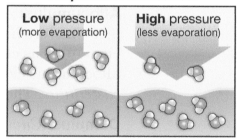

Figure 6.7: *The relationship between temperature and pressure when evaporation occurs.*

Cloud formation

What is a cloud? When more water in the atmosphere is condensing than evaporating, we begin to see clouds. A **cloud** is a group of water droplets or ice crystals that you can see in the atmosphere. The flat bottom of the cloud marks the level of the atmosphere where condensation first exceeds evaporation. Clouds are divided into two broad categories: cumuliform clouds (*cumulus* means "piled up") and stratiform clouds (*stratus* means "layer").

Cumuliform clouds *Cumuliform clouds*, which look like heaps of popcorn, form as an air mass rises because of convection (Figure 6.8). Air is commonly warmed over a dark surface (like a road) that absorbs a lot of heat. It is rare to see a line of these clouds right above a dark surface though, because wind currents blow the rising air masses around before they condense and form clouds.

Cirrocumulus: Small, puffy, "cotton-ball" type clouds high in the atmosphere (above 6,000 meters) are called *cirrocumulus*. They usually indicate fair weather.

Altocumulus: *Altocumulus clouds* form between 2,000 and 6,000 meters high. They usually form larger, darker puffs than cirrocumulus clouds. Sometimes they appear in rows. If the altocumulus clouds look like towers, they are called *altocumulus castellatus*. These clouds often appear before a storm.

Cumulus: *Cumulus clouds* are the tall, puffy clouds that form when the air over land is heated. As a result, these clouds often break down as the Sun sets. Often, cumulus clouds have a flat base. They are found below 2,000 meters.

Cumulonimbus: A dark and stormy cumulus cloud is called *cumulonimbus*. Thunderstorms develop from cumulonimbus clouds. These clouds are between 2,000 and 15,000 meters high.

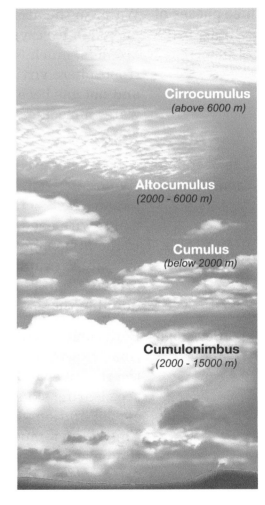

Figure 6.8: *Cumuliform clouds.*

Stratiform clouds *Stratiform clouds* form when a large mass of stable air gradually rises. As this air rises, it expands and cools, allowing condensation to spread evenly throughout the layer. Stratiform clouds look like smooth, flattened blankets (Figure 6.9). They can cover as much as 300,000 square miles! A sky with stratiform clouds appears uniformly gray.

Cirrostratus: *Cirrostratus clouds* look like a translucent white coating across the sky. They are high clouds, located at least 6,000 meters above the ground. These clouds are made of ice crystals. As a result, sunlight shining through the crystals is refracted (bent) causing a halo-like effect around the Sun.

Altostratus: *Altostratus clouds* are the most easily recognizable stratiform clouds. If the sky looks like a smooth gray sheet and no shadows form on the ground, you are seeing altostratus clouds located between 2,000 and 6,000 meters high.

Stratus: *Stratus clouds* form below 2,000 meters. Stratus clouds look like fog that doesn't quite reach the ground.

Nimbostratus: When a stratus cloud turns dark gray, it signals the approach of rain. These rain clouds are called *nimbostratus*.

Stratocumulus clouds *Stratocumulus clouds* have aspects of both cumuliform and stratiform clouds (Figure 6.10). They form when convection occurs inside a stratiform cloud. As rising air cools, the water in the cloud condenses, creating a cumuliform cloud within the stratiform cloud. This causes the smooth cloud to look lumpy.

Cirrus clouds *Cirrus clouds* are thin lines of ice crystals high in the sky, above 6,000 meters (Figure 6.11). A curved cirrus cloud is commonly called a "mare's tail." The curving is due to a change in wind direction, and as a result may indicate that the weather is going to change.

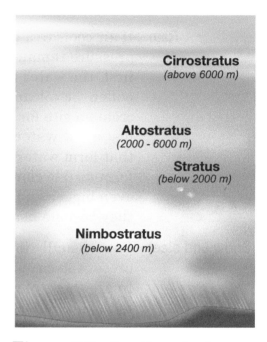

Figure 6.9: *Stratiform clouds.*

Figure 6.10: *Stratocumulus clouds.*

Figure 6.11: *Cirrus clouds.*

Precipitation

Rain   If air cools to a temperature lower than the dew point, and the pressure remains constant, water vapor condenses into liquid. At first, the water molecules condense on particles such as dust, pollen, or volcanic ash. Once a few water molecules condense, they create a site for other molecules to condense too. What starts as just a few water molecules quickly grows to millions of molecules that form water droplets. If the droplets become big enough, they form visible clouds. Clouds will produce *rain* when the drops get even bigger and have a volume of about 1 milliliter. At this size, they become heavy enough to fall as raindrops.

Snow and sleet   *Snow* usually forms when both ice crystals and water droplets are present in the sky. The water droplets attach to ice crystals and freeze there. When the ice crystals are large enough, they will fall to the ground as snow. However, if the air temperature near the ground is warm, the crystals will melt and the precipitation will fall as rain. Sometimes very cold air lies below warmer air, causing the water to refreeze and hit the ground as *sleet*.

Dew and frost   Because the ground cools quickly, the temperature of the ground is often below the dew point late at night or early in the morning. Air near the ground gets cooled and some water vapor condenses in the form of *dew*. If the temperature is low enough, the dew freezes and turns to *frost*.

Fog   If air within a few hundred meters of the ground is cooled below the dew point, *fog* will form. Fog can form under two conditions. Warm moist air could move over a cooler surface, or the ground below could cool below the dew point at night. Either way, fog consists of suspended water droplets. Fog is a ground-level cloud.

Condensation warms the air

Condensation is actually a warming process. Why? Energy was needed when the water changed from a liquid to a gas. This energy is released when the water changes back into the liquid form. As a result, if it is not too windy, you can sometimes feel the air warm up a few degrees when precipitation begins to fall.

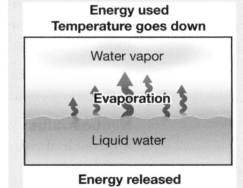

**Energy used
Temperature goes down**

Water vapor

Evaporation

Liquid water

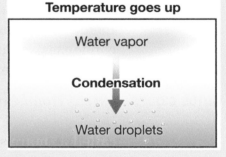

**Energy released
Temperature goes up**

Water vapor

Condensation

Water droplets

Fronts

Large bodies of air

As you learned in Section 6.1, air masses are large bodies of air sometimes covering thousands of square kilometers. Air masses form when air is stationary over an area long enough to take on the characteristics of the surface below. Two common air masses affecting the United States are the *continental polar air mass*, which forms over the Canadian plains, and the *maritime tropical air mass*, which forms over the Gulf of Mexico (Figure 6.12). The continental polar air mass contains cold, dry air. In contrast, the maritime tropical air mass contains warm, moist air.

Moving air and fronts

Changing atmospheric conditions and global wind currents cause air masses to move. The continental polar air mass tends to slide south or southeast, while the maritime tropical air mass tends to slide north or northwest. When two different moving air masses collide, the border between them is called a front.

Cold fronts

A cold front occurs when cold air moves in and replaces warm air. The warm air is forced sharply upward by the cold, denser air. The rising warm air cools. This causes condensation. Often rain or snow showers accompany a cold front. As a cold front moves through an area, the temperature and water content of the air decrease rapidly. The temperature can sometimes cools as much as 15°F in one hour.

VOCABULARY

front - the border between two different air masses.

cold front - a front that occurs when a cold air mass moves in and replaces a warm air mass.

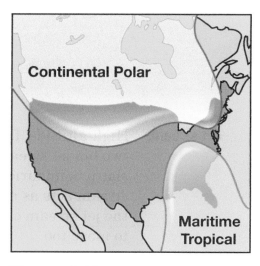

Figure 6.12: *Two air masses that affect the weather in the United States.*

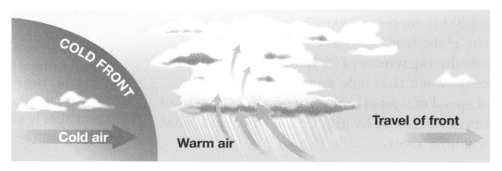

Warm fronts A **warm front** occurs when warm air moves in and replaces cold air. The warm air slides up over the colder air. The warm air rises and cools, but in this case the lifting is very gradual and steady. As a result, long bands of light precipitation often move ahead of a warm front. As a warm front moves through an area, there will be a noticeable increase in temperature and moisture in the air.

VOCABULARY

warm front - a front that occurs when a warm air mass moves in and replaces a cold air mass.

jet streams - high-altitude, fast-moving winds.

Jet streams High-altitude, fast-moving winds are called **jet streams**. There are two big jet streams in each hemisphere, formed where there are sharp boundaries between cold and warm temperatures. A jet stream acts as a border between cold and warm air masses. When the jet stream changes its path, air masses to either side of it tend to move too.

Speed and path of a jet stream The jet stream winds are found near the top of the troposphere, and have speeds of at least 87 kilometers (54 miles) per hour, and sometimes as great as 320 kilometers (200 miles) per hour. The jet streams flow around the globe from west to east. A jet stream attains its fastest speeds during winter of its hemisphere when the temperature difference between that pole and the equator is greatest. The path and speed of a jet stream can be altered by land features such as mountain ranges, or by giant cumulus clouds that act like boulders in a rushing river.

Weather Map Symbols for Fronts

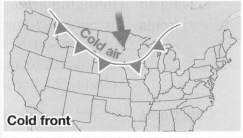

Cold front

Warm front

On a weather map, a cold front is shown using a line marked with triangles. The triangles point in the direction the front is moving. A warm front is shown using a line marked with semicircles.

Low- and high-pressure areas

Low-pressure centers When a cold front moves into a region and warm air is forced upward, a low-pressure center is created near Earth's surface at the boundary of two air masses (Figure 6.13). Cold air rushes in to fill that low-pressure region. This cold air forces more warm air to be pushed upward. A cycle begins to develop. Due to the Coriolis effect, the air masses move in curved paths. As a result, the moving air begins to rotate around the low-pressure center (Figure 6.13). In the northern hemisphere, the moving air rotates counterclockwise, while in the southern hemisphere, the air rotates clockwise. Strong winds and precipitation often accompany these rotating systems.

High-pressure centers A high-pressure center tends to be found where a stable, colder air mass has settled in a region. Colder air is denser than warm air, and therefore creates higher atmospheric pressure. Sinking air in a high-pressure center inhibits the development of the upward air movement needed to create clouds and precipitation. High-pressure centers, therefore, are associated with fair weather and blue skies. Winds rotate clockwise in the northern hemisphere and counter-clockwise in the southern hemisphere. This is the opposite of what happens in a low-pressure center.

Isobars The wavy lines on a weather map are often associated with high- (H) and low- (L) pressure centers. Each line, called an isobar, connects the places that have the same atmospheric pressure. Isobars help meteorologists pinpoint the location of high- and low-pressure centers, and provide information about the movement of weather systems.

VOCABULARY

low-pressure center - a low-pressure area created by rising warm air.

high-pressure center - a high-pressure area created by sinking cold air.

isobar - a line on a weather map that connects places that have the same atmospheric pressure.

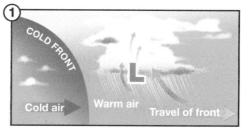

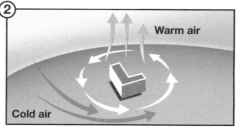

Figure 6.13: *(1) Warm air is forced upward when a cold front moves into an area. A low-pressure center is created. (2) The cold air moving toward the low- pressure center begins to rotate around it in a counterclockwise direction.*

Thunderstorms

Storm cells

Thunderstorms occur because of convection in the atmosphere. Warm air rises from the ground to the top of the troposphere. This is called an *updraft*. As the updraft rises, it cools and condenses, forming a towering cumulonimbus cloud. Eventually, some of the cloud droplets become large enough to fall as rain. Cold air from the top of the troposphere is dragged down along with the rain. This cold, dense air is called a *downdraft*. The downdraft and updraft form a type of convection cell called a **storm cell** within the cloud. A storm ends when cool air from the downdraft replaces all the warm air on the ground. The updraft stops flowing. Next, the rain stops and the thunderstorm ends.

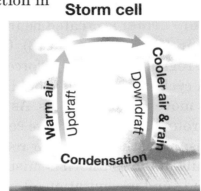

Storm cell

Warm air Updraft
Cooler air & rain Downdraft
Condensation

Lightning and thunder

Lightning is a bright spark of light that occurs within a storm cloud, between a cloud and Earth's surface, or between two storm clouds. Lightning occurs when the bottom of a storm cloud becomes negatively charged (–) and the top becomes positively charged (+). The negative charges on the bottom of the cloud repel negative charges on the ground so the ground becomes positive (Figure 6.14). In this situation, a spark can travel between the negatively- and positively-charged surfaces. **Thunder** is the sound we hear that is associated with lightning. Thunder is caused by the rapid heating and expanding of air that is near lightning.

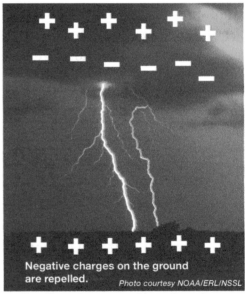

Negative charges on the ground are repelled. *Photo courtesy NOAA/ERL/NSSL*

+ Positive charges – Negative charges

Figure 6.14: *Lightning occurs when a spark travels between negative and positive charges.*

Hurricanes

Cyclones and hurricanes

A cyclone is a low-pressure center that is surrounded by rotating winds. The Coriolis effect causes these winds to rotate counterclockwise in the northern hemisphere and clockwise in the southern hemisphere. A hurricane is a tropical cyclone with wind speeds of at least 119 kilometers (74 miles) per hour. The Saffir-Simpson Hurricane Scale is one scale used for rating hurricanes (Figure 6.15).

How hurricanes form

Warm, moist air over the tropical ocean provides the initial energy source for a hurricane. As the warm air rises, the water vapor in it condenses. Clouds and thundershowers form. The condensation releases heat, warming the surrounding air even more. As all of this air expands and rises, it creates an area of low pressure at the surface of the water. This pressure difference causes the surrounding air to rush toward the center. The path of this rushing air curves due to the Coriolis effect, and a rotating system forms.

Hurricane conditions

Several conditions must be present for a rotating system to become a hurricane. First, the ocean water must be warm (about 27°C). Second, the layer of warm ocean water must be deep enough so that cooler water does not get stirred up to the surface by the storm. Cooler water decreases the strength of the storm. Next, the air must be warm and moist to a point high above sea level. Water vapor from high-level air is pulled into the storm. When it condenses, heat is released, and the storm strengthens. Finally, the wind conditions must also be just right. Winds blowing from different directions or at different speeds can break the storm apart.

VOCABULARY

cyclone - a low-pressure center surrounded by rotating winds.

hurricane - a tropical cyclone with wind speeds of at least 74 miles per hour (119 kilometers per hour).

Saffir-Simpson Hurricane Scale

Name	Wind Speed	Damage	Storm Surge
Tropical depression	< 63 km/h	Little	None
Tropical storm	63–117 km/h	Minor flooding	Very minor
Category 1 hurricane	119–153 km/h	Minimal damage	1.2–1.5 m
Category 2 hurricane	154–177 km/h	Moderate	1.6–2.4 m
Category 3 hurricane	178–209 km/h	Extensive	2.5–3.7 m
Category 4 hurricane	210–249 km/h	Extreme	3.8–5.5 m
Category 5 hurricane	> 250 km/h	Catastrophic	> 5.6 m

km/h = kilometers per hour

Figure 6.15: *The Saffir-Simpson Hurricane Scale.*

Tornadoes

Comparing hurricanes and tornadoes

A **tornado**, like a hurricane, is a system of rotating winds around a low-pressure center. An average tornado is less than 200 meters in diameter—tiny, compared with the 640 kilometer (640,000 meter) average diameter of a hurricane! However, the wind speeds of a tornado are much greater than those of a hurricane. A tornado's wind speed can reach 400 kilometers per hour.

How tornadoes form

A tornado begins to form when the updrafts in a storm cell reach more than 160 kilometers per hour. Winds near the top of the cumulonimbus cloud begin rotating at a high speed. As more air flows in to the low-pressure center of the storm, the rotation extends downward. The diameter of the rotating wind pattern narrows, causing the wind to speed up. As the rotating wind pattern narrows and lengthens, it forms a *funnel cloud* (Figure 6.16). If the funnel cloud reaches the ground, it becomes a tornado.

High wind speeds cause damage

The rushing wind of a tornado can flatten houses and even lift cars completely off the ground. A tornado in Broken Bow, Oklahoma, once carried a motel sign 48 kilometers and dropped it in Arkansas! Most tornadoes last around 10 to 20 minutes, although the strongest tornadoes can last an hour or more. They travel along the ground at speeds of about 40 to 60 kilometers per hour.

tornado - a system of rotating winds around a low-pressure center; a tornado is smaller than a hurricane, but has faster winds.

How a Funnel Cloud Forms

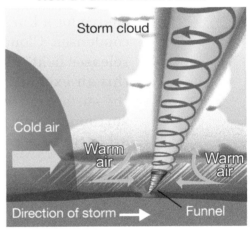

Figure 6.16: *A funnel cloud forms when updrafts in a storm cell reach high speed and begin to rotate. As the diameter of the rotation narrows and extends downward, a funnel cloud takes shape.*

A funnel cloud

Photo courtesy NOAA/OAR/ERL/NSSL.

El Niño Southern Oscillation

A storm pattern in the Pacific Storm patterns across the globe can happen in cycles. One such pattern is in the tropical Pacific. Usually, the trade winds blow warm water from east to west across the Pacific Ocean, from Peru on the ocean's eastern coast toward Indonesia on the western coast (Figure 6.17). As a result, the average water temperature off the coast of Indonesia is 6°C warmer than the average water temperature off the coast of Peru. The warm water of the western Pacific typically generates thunderstorms of greater frequency and intensity than what is normally seen near Peru.

El Niño Southern Oscillation For reasons not fully understood, every so often the trade winds weaken and the warm water reverses direction, flowing from the western Pacific toward South America (Figure 6.17). Along with that warm water comes greater thunderstorm activity across the Pacific. Indonesia and other western Pacific nations experience drier-than-normal conditions, while the eastern Pacific countries get more precipitation. This change in wind flow, air pressure, and thunderstorm activity is known as the *El Niño Southern Oscillation*.

El Niño Peruvian fishermen were among the first to notice the change in water temperature along their shores. When the warm water from the west flows toward South America, it cuts off a normal pattern in which cold water from the ocean depths flows up to the surface along the coast of Peru. The upwelling cold water brings nutrients necessary for fish and other aquatic life to flourish. During an El Niño event, the warm water flowing over the cold water acts like a lid (Figure 6.18). It prevents the cold water from reaching the surface. As a result, nutrients are not available for aquatic life and the fish population declines.

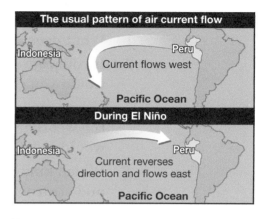

Figure 6.17: *The usual pattern of air current flow compared to what happens during El Niño.*

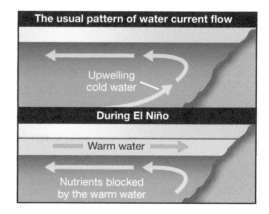

Figure 6.18: *The usual pattern of water current flow compared to what happens during El Niño.*

6.2 Section Review

1. What does a meteorologist do?

2. If you wanted to increase the rate of evaporation of water, how would you change the temperature and pressure?

3. Name one type of cloud you would expect to see on a day when the weather is cool, dry, and clear. Name one type of cloud you would see if a thunderstorm were about to happen.

4. Which kind of cloud has the characteristics of both cumuliform and stratiform clouds? Describe this cloud.

5. What causes frost to form?

6. How is the weather associated with a cold front different from the weather associated with a warm front?

7. Indicate which characteristics below apply to a high-pressure center and which apply to a low-pressure center.

   a. rising warm air

   b. sinking cold air

   c. wind rotates counterclockwise around this pressure center in the northern hemisphere

   d. precipitation

   e. dry and clear

8. How is convection of air involved in the development of a thunderstorm?

9. What conditions are needed for a hurricane to develop?

10. List three differences between a hurricane and a tornado.

11. On the Saffir-Simpson Hurricane Scale, what is the difference between a Category 1 hurricane and a Category 5 hurricane?

12. Fish populations decline as a result of the El Niño Southern Oscillation. Why?

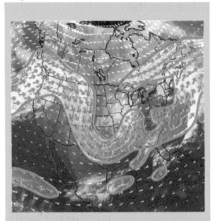

This photo of the jet stream was taken by the GOES-8 satellite in orbit 36,000 kilometers above Earth. Arrows were added to indicate wind direction.
Research one important aspect of the jet stream and write a short report on it.

SOLVE IT!

When Hurricane Andrew hit Florida in 1992, its winds were 265 km/h and it produced a storm surge of 5.2 meters. What category was Hurricane Andrew on the Saffir-Simpson Scale?

Research the answer to the following question. How does Hurricane Katrina, which hit New Orleans in 2005, compare to Hurricane Andrew?

6.3 Climates and Biomes

Imagine that someone gave you an airplane ticket to travel to Africa to see Serengeti National Park in Tanzania. If you like adventures, you might say "Great! When do I leave?" Then you would want to pack your suitcase. But what would you take? What is the climate like in Africa?

Climate

Factors that affect climate

Climate is the type of weather patterns that a place has, on average, over a long period of time. If you wanted to know about the climate in a place you were about to visit, you might ask questions like "How hot and how cold does it usually get? Does it rain a lot? How often is the temperature below freezing?" Climate depends on many factors, including latitude, precipitation, elevation, topography, and distance from large bodies of water.

The Serengeti region is in Tanzania and Kenya.

VOCABULARY

climate - the long-term record of weather patterns and includes the temperature, precipitation, and wind for a region.

MY JOURNAL

Packing for an adventure in the Serengeti

1. On a world atlas, find the Serengeti. Describe where it is located.

2. Make a prediction about the kind of weather the Serengeti will have next week.

3. Then, research the seasonal weather on the Internet or in the library. Were you correct in your prediction?

4. Using what you learned, make a list of things you would need to pack in your suitcase to visit the Serengeti.

Characteristics of biomes

What is a biome? Scientists divide the planet into climate regions. Each region is called a biome. Earth has six major biomes: deserts, grasslands, temperate deciduous forests, rainforests, taigas, and tundras. These biomes generally differ in their latitude, weather and relative humidity, amount of sunlight, and topography. Each biome has a unique set of plants and animals that thrive in its climate.

Latitude, humidity, and biodiversity Recall that *relative humidity* is a measure of how much water vapor an air mass contains relative to how much it can contain. From the poles to the equator, humidity, and the biodiversity of plants and animals increase. *Biodiversity* refers to the measure of the variety and number of organisms that live in an area.

Sunlight at the equator vs. high latitudes Earth is hottest near the equator where the Sun is closest to being directly overhead year round. At the north and south poles, temperatures are much colder. This effect is related to the fact that light travels in straight parallel lines. To demonstrate what is happening, imagine shining a flashlight on a sheet of paper (Figure 6.19). The light makes a bright, small spot. By tilting the paper, you can make the light spot bigger and less intense.

Latitude and solar radiation At the equator, sunlight is direct and intense. Earth's north and south poles are tilted away from or toward the Sun depending on the time of year. The locations of the poles relative to the Sun and Earth's spherical surface mean that sunlight reaching these areas is spread out and less intense (Figure 6.19). As a result, the average yearly temperature at the equator is 27°C (80°F), while at the North Pole it is −18°C (0°F). Generally, as latitude (or distance from the equator) increases, the amount of incoming solar radiation decreases.

biome - a major climate region with particular plants and animals. Earth has six major biomes.

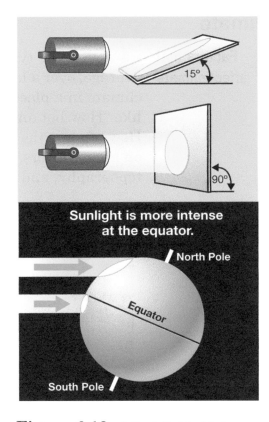

Figure 6.19: *A flashlight shining on a piece of paper represents solar radiation reaching Earth. If you tilt the paper, the spot of light spreads out and becomes less intense, like at the poles.*

Other factors besides latitude can affect climates

Temperatures in inland regions Have you ever wondered why cities near the ocean don't get as hot in the summer or as cold in the winter as inland cities at the same latitude? Portland, Oregon, and Minneapolis, Minnesota, are two cities near the same latitude (Figure 6.20). Look at Table 6.1 below to see the average daily temperature ranges for these cities.

Table 6.1: Average daily temperature ranges for Portland and Minneapolis.

Month	Average daily temperature range	
	Portland	Minneapolis
January	1 to 7°C, (34–45°F)	–16 to –6°C (3–21°F)
July	14 to 27°C (57–80°F)	17 to 29°C (63–84°F)

Water helps regulate temperature The differences in temperature between the two cities have to do with water. Because of its higher specific heat, water warms up and cools down slowly. In contrast, land warms up and cools down quickly because of its lower specific heat. Therefore, regions near water—like Portland—do not have extremely hot or cold weather.

Elevation Latitude is an important factor in defining a biome. However, elevation is also a factor. *Elevation* is the height or distance of an object or area from sea level. The range of biomes that exist on Earth from the equator to the poles also exists if one goes from the bottom of a mountain to the top of a mountain (Figure 6.21).

Minneapolis is hotter in the summer and colder in the winter than Portland.

Figure 6.20: *Portland and Minneapolis are near the same latitude but they have different climates.*

SOLVE IT!

Questions about Table 6.1:

1. It is January 3 and –10°C outside. Where am I?

2. It is July 4 and 20°C. Can you figure out from the table where I am? Why or why not?

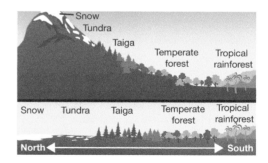

Figure 6.21: *Latitude versus elevation for the Northern Hemisphere.*

Earth's biomes

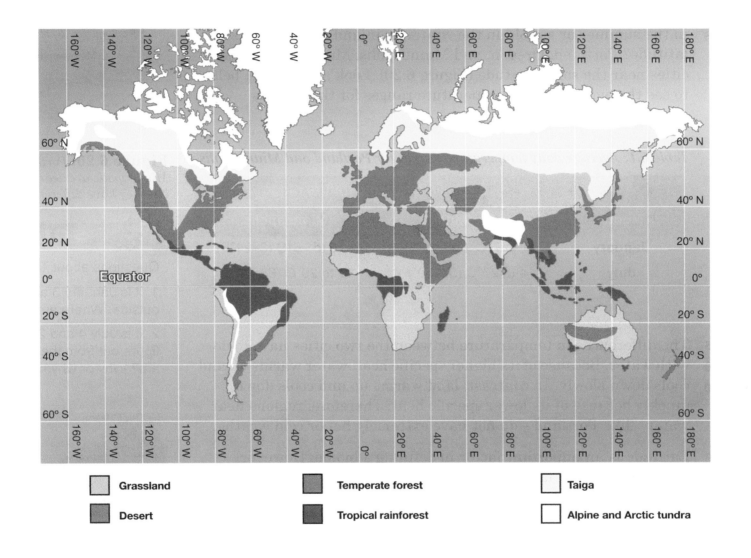

☐	Grassland	☐	Temperate forest	☐	Taiga
☐	Desert	☐	Tropical rainforest	☐	Alpine and Arctic tundra

Types of biomes

Deserts A desert averages less than 35 centimeters of rainfall per year. Most deserts are found around the latitudes of 30° N and 30° S. Deserts have large variations in daily high and low temperatures.

Grasslands Grasslands are on every continent except Antarctica. There are two types: tropical grasslands, known as *savannas*, and *temperate grasslands*. Savannas occur where there is not enough rainfall to create a rainforest. Temperate grasslands are in the mid-latitudes and receive most of their precipitation in the spring and summer.

Temperate deciduous forests Temperate deciduous forests are found in middle-latitude regions, where there are four distinct seasons. Average yearly rainfall is 75 to 150 centimeters, enough to support the growth of broad-leafed, deciduous trees like oak and maple. *Deciduous* means these trees lose their leaves at the end of the growing season.

Rainforests Tropical rainforests are near the equator—between the latitudes of 23.5° N and 23.5° S. They have an average rainfall of at least 200 centimeters per year. The temperature of these rainforests is nearly constant and in a narrow range—20 to 25°C. Temperate rainforests, another kind of rainforest, are in the middle-latitude regions, and experience about 250 centimeters of rain per year.

Taiga The taiga is the largest biome. The taiga can be found between the latitudes of 50° N and 70° N in North America, Europe, and Asia. The average temperature in the taiga is below freezing for at least six months of the year.

Tundras The tundra is the coldest biome on Earth. The word *tundra* comes from a Finnish word for "treeless land." There are two types of tundra—Arctic tundra, found in a band around the Arctic Ocean, and alpine tundra, found high in mid-latitude mountains.

 VOCABULARY

desert - a climate region that averages less than 35 centimeters of rainfall per year.

grasslands - climate regions with too little rainfall to support a forest. Grasslands have grasses as the main vegetation.

temperate deciduous forests - climate regions in the mid-latitudes that have four seasons.

tropical rainforests - climate regions found near the equator that have a lot of rainfall and high biodiversity.

taiga - the largest climate region, found in the higher latitudes; also known as a boreal or coniferous forest.

tundra - a climate region located in high latitudes; the coldest land biome.

Plants and animals in biomes

Communities A biome is characterized by its plant and animal communities. The plants and animals in a community interact with each other and survive in a shared environment. The plants and animals in the environment have adaptations that allow them to obtain enough resources (such as food, water, or sunlight) to survive.

Adaptations Jackrabbits have an adaptation to keep cool in the hot desert—enormous ears with many blood vessels near the surface (Figure 6.22). Blood running through the vessels speeds up heat transfer from the jackrabbit's body to the air so the jackrabbit stays cooler.

Ecosystems Biomes are large geographic areas. Within a biome, there are many interrelated ecosystems. An *ecosystem* is made up of the plants and animals that live there, plus nonliving things like soil, air, water, sunlight, and nutrients. The living and nonliving parts of an ecosystem work together, and each organism plays an important ecological role.

How many roles? The number and types of organisms that an ecosystem can support depends on the resources available (food sources) and on environmental factors. Environmental factors include the amount of available sunlight, water, and the temperature. The roles within a biome ecosystem depend on the quantity and type of resources. Each ecosystem of a particular biome type has organisms that play similar roles. For example, both a rainforest in South America and a rainforest in Australia have predators, herbivores (plant eaters), and decomposers (organisms that "eat" decaying plants and animals such as fungi and bacteria).

Jackrabbit
Photo by George Harrison, USFWS

Figure 6.22: *The large ears of a jackrabbit help this desert animal to cool down.*

MY JOURNAL

Biodiversity

Does this statement surprise you? Why or why not?

The biodiversity of the desert is greater than for all other biomes with the exception of the tropical rainforest.

Why is biodiversity in an ecosystem important?

Write your response as a short essay.

6.3 Section Review

1. What are three factors that affect climate?

2. Are climate and weather the same thing? If not, explain how these terms are different.

3. What happens to the intensity of solar radiation and Earth's average yearly temperature as you move from the equator to the South Pole or North Pole?

4. Find San Francisco, California, and Topeka, Kansas, on a map of the United States. How would the weather in the these two places compare? Explain your answer.

5. Refer to the Earth's biome map on page 144. What kind of biome occurs at 30° S and 150° E? Describe what this biome is like.

6. Alpine and Arctic tundra occur at a mid-latitude location near India (25° N 80° E). Why do you think this biome occurs here? (*Hint*: Find out what land form occurs at this location.)

7. A photograph of an Arctic hare is shown in Figure 6.23. This animal lives in cold environments.
   a. What adaptations do you see that this animal has?
   b. How does the appearance of this animal compare to the jackrabbit in Figure 6.22?

8. The main grass in a grassland in North America is prairie grass. The main grass in a South American grassland is pampas grass. Would you expect the ecological role of these grasses in these two locations to be the same or different? Explain your answer.

CHALLENGE

What's your climate?

1. From the reading, list the factors that affect the climate of an area.

2. Use these factors to describe the climate where you live.

Arctic hare

Photo courtesy of U.S. Fish and Wildlife Service

Figure 6.23: *An Arctic hare.*

Meteorologists Weather it All

Neither rain nor sleet nor cold shall keep a mail carrier from doing his or her job (or you from walking the dog). The same can be said of your local meteorologist. Every day meteorologists broadcast weather reports. Millions of people plan what they will wear, what they will do after work or on the weekend, and if they will carry their umbrellas based on those reports.

But only a very few meteorologists in the United States wear a microphone or appear on camera at work. Most meteorologists work for the National Weather Service (NWS), a government agency that is part of the National Oceanic and Atmospheric Administration (NOAA).

NOAA was formed in 1970, and its mission is to predict changes in the atmosphere and ocean environments. This task includes predicting the weather.

Meteorologists observe and study Earth's atmosphere and its phenomena. Many work to forecast the weather and changing climate conditions, while others do scientific research. They try to understand how the atmosphere affects the environment. They study the constant changes in our atmosphere. They create computer models to predict how storms will form, when rivers will flood, and what areas will suffer droughts. Their work can go far beyond telling an audience whether it will be sunny or cloudy tomorrow.

Meteorologists at work

Julie Dian is a meteorologist who works at the National Weather Service Ohio River Forecast Center in Wilmington, Ohio. One of her responsibilities is to compare readings of temperature, winds,

atmospheric pressure, precipitation patterns, and other variables. She draws conclusions and makes predictions about local weather with these data.

Dian and other meteorologists use many tools of their trade. They gather information in many different ways.

- More than 11,000 volunteers from all over the United States and beyond provide daily reports. They phone their reports to warning and forecast centers.
- Satellites collect data and record images. The TV images you see of hurricanes in the Gulf of Mexico or Caribbean Sea, for instance, are provided by cameras on satellites high above Earth.
- Ground-based radar scans for precipitation and clouds.
- Weather balloons are launched to gather data.

Up, up, and away

Wind direction, air pressure, temperature, and humidity of air masses high in the sky all affect our weather down on the ground. Weather balloons can monitor these conditions.

Weather balloons are released at least twice a day from a structure (like the one at right) at the National Weather Service office in Wilmington. Additional balloons are released more often during severe weather.

The balloons are filled with helium. When they are inflated on the ground, they are about 2 meters across. As they rise, they grow to a diameter of about 6 meters. This is because the air pressure is lower at higher altitudes, so the gas inside the balloon expands.

Chapter 6 Connection

One type of balloon carries a *radiosonde*, which is a miniature radio transmitter with instruments on it. The balloon rises 27,400 meters (90,000 feet) or higher. All along the way, the radiosonde measures data such as temperature, air pressure, and humidity, and transmits the measurements to a ground receiver or a satellite.

Dian uses a theodolite to track balloons that have been launched from her center. A *theodolite* is a surveyor's instrument for measuring angles and, in this case, for following the altitude and movement of the balloon. In this photo, Dian shows a student the radio theodolite at the NWS office. In her left hand, she holds an unopened weather balloon. The theodolite in the photo shows the wind speed at different altitudes. Some theodolites contain telescopes, and others have radio receivers.

Methods for predicting

There are several different ways to predict the weather. All of the information collected—from volunteers, radar, satellites, and weather balloons—is used in different models. Some of the older methods use historical information to predict future weather events. The most complex of these involves finding very similar conditions at some point in the past. Then the weather is predicted based on what happened in the "same" situation back then.

Today, computers have made forecasting much more successful. Numerical weather prediction, or NWP, is used to create computer models of the atmosphere. With NWP, many variables are considered. Air temperatures at different altitudes, wind speeds, humidity, high and low pressure areas—all of this is fed into a computer. The computer creates a complex model of the atmosphere and provides the most accurate forecasts available.

QUESTIONS

1. What is the mission of the National Oceanic and Atmospheric Administration?

2. What causes weather balloons to expand in diameter from 2 to 6 meters?

3. Why are today's weather forecasts more accurate than in the past?

Rainy Day Mystery

It's summertime and raining in Savannah, Georgia. You call your friend in Los Angeles, California, and find out it's sunny. During the summer it hardly ever rains in Los Angeles. You decide to do some investigative meteorological work to find out why the climates of these two cities are so different.

What you will do

1. Find out the latitude for each city using a globe, atlas, or an Internet mapping web site. Also, be sure to find both of these cities on a map.

Climate Data for Savannah and Los Angeles

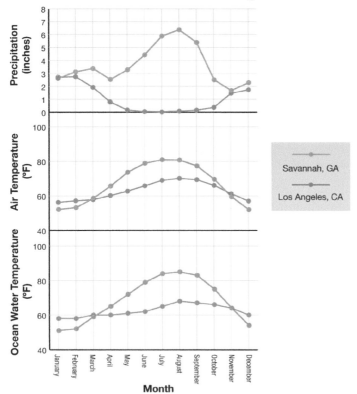

2. Imagine that you have collected data and made the graphs on this page. Write a paragraph that describes each graph and answers these questions: (a) What does the graph show for Savannah, Georgia? (b) What does the graph show for Los Angeles, California?

3. Based on the graphs, you can identify relationships. On a separate piece of paper, copy and fill in this table.

What relationship do you see between...	
... ocean water temperature and air temperature?	
... ocean water temperature and precipitation?	
... air temperature and precipitation?	

4. Based on your work so far, write one hypothesis to explain why it rains more in Savannah than in Los Angeles.

Applying your knowledge

a. Do you think latitude explains the difference in climate of these two cities? Why or why not?

b. Which city has ocean water whose temperature varies a smaller amount during the year?

c. In what two months were the ocean water temperatures nearly the same?

d. Which city has air temperatures which vary the smallest amount during the year?

e. In what two months were the air temperatures approximately the same?

f. What do you notice about the answers to questions c and e?

g. Do you think that there is a relationship between ocean water and the climates of coastal cities?

Chapter 6 Assessment

Vocabulary

Select the correct term to complete the sentences.

convection cells	weather	wind
cloud	air mass	Coriolis effect
high pressure center	thermal	dew point
thunder	meteorologist	warm front
low pressure center	front	jet streams
climate	isobars	storm cell
grasslands	cyclone	lightning
tundra	hurricane	tornado
temperature deciduous forests	desert	biome
tropical rainforest	taiga	cold front

Section 6.1

1. Any condition of the atmosphere can be called _____.

2. A(n) _____ is a large body of air.

3. _____ is the flow of air from higher to lower pressure.

4. Birds can "ride" a(n) _____ which is an upward flow of air.

5. _____ are air patterns caused by global convection.

6. Earth's rotation causes the _____.

Section 6.2

7. _____ is the temperature at which water vapor is cool enough to condense.

8. A group of water droplets that you can see in the atmosphere is called a(n) _____.

9. A(n) _____ is the border between two different air masses.

10. A(n) _____ occurs when a cold air mass replaces a warm air mass.

11. When warm air moves in and replaces cold air it is called a(n) _____.

12. A(n) _____ studies and predicts the weather.

13. The _____ is a, high-altitude, fast-moving current of air that serves as a border between air masses.

14. _____ is a spark that occurs between the bottom of a cloud and the ground due to negative and positive charges.

15. A(n) _____ connects places on a weather map that share the same atmospheric pressure.

16. Wind moves counterclockwise around a(n) _____ in the northern hemisphere.

17. A(n) _____ is associated with sinking air.

18. The sound of expanding heated air during a storm: _____.

19. A thunderstorm ends when there is no longer an updraft or a downdraft of a(n) _____.

20. A(n) _____ is a low pressure center that is surrounded by rotating winds.

21. A storm with a Saffir-Simpson Scale rating of Category 1–5 is called a(n) _____.

22. A(n) _____ is smaller than a hurricane, but has faster winds.

Section 6.3

23. A(n) _____ is a major climate region with particular plant and animal communities.

24. _____ are characterized by grasses and a dry climate.

25. This biome is the coldest on Earth: _____.

26. A(n) _____ receives less than 35 centimeters of rain a year.

27. _____ have four distinct seasons.

28. This biome is the largest land biome: _____.

29. This biome is found at about 23.5° N and S: _____.

30. _____ refers to the long-term weather patterns of a location.

Concepts

Section 6.1

1. What causes wind?

2. A weather map shows a high pressure area located over Town A and a low pressure area located over Town B. Which direction will the wind blow? From Town A to Town B or from Town B to Town A?

3. Explain the difference between a land and a sea breeze.

4. Why is atmospheric pressure low at the equator?

5. What causes the Coriolis effect?

6. In what direction would you expect a global wind pattern to be blowing at 15° S latitude? What is the name of this global wind pattern?

7. A weather report states that the relative humidity is 40 percent. What does this value mean?

Section 6.2

8. Explain how temperature and pressure affect the amount of water in Earth's atmosphere.

9. Copy this table on to your own paper and fill it in.

Cloud category	How it forms	Types
Cumuliform		
Stratiform		

10. When precipitation occurs, does air temperature get warmer or cooler? Why?

11. You hear a weather report that a warm front is moving through your town. What kind of weather do you expect?

12. Would a hurricane form under these conditions? Why or why not? The conditions: The ocean water temperature is 30°C, the wind is blowing from one direction, the layer of warm ocean water is 50 meters deep, and the air is warm and moist up to 5,750 meters.

13. The Coriolis effect is minimal along the equator. As a result, what might you expect at the equator?
    a. Sinking cold air   b. Few or no cyclones forming
    c. A high pressure center   d. A tornado

14. What is the weather like in Indonesia during an El Niño event? Why?

Section 6.3

15. Identify whether these comments are talking about the weather or about the climate for an area.
    a. A cold front is moving into the area.
    b. A region has two main seasons—a wet and a dry season.
    c. My region averages only 20 centimeters of rain a year.
    d. Tomorrow will be windy and sunny.

16. What is a biome and how many main biomes are on Earth?

17. Explain why the average yearly temperature at the equator is hot (27°C) and the average yearly temperature at the North Pole is cold (–18°C).

18. To travel to a different climate from the one you are in now, what would you need to do?

19. You can expect to find tundra in the high northern latitudes of the northern hemisphere. Where would you expect to find a tundra ecosystem on a mountain?

20. How many seasons are there in temperate deciduous forests?

Math and Writing Skills

Section 6.1

1. You are a pilot who wants to fly an airplane from St. Paul, Minnesota, 700 miles south to Little Rock, Arkansas. If you set your compass and try to fly straight south, you will probably end up in New Mexico! Why?

2. The trade winds were named by sailors who crossed the North Atlantic in the 17th and 18th centuries in search of goods to bring back to Europe. The trade winds provided a helpful push on their journey west. Find out more about famous global winds. Research one of the following topics.

   a. Horse latitudes

   b. Alize

   c. Roaring forties

3. A warm (25°C) air mass contains 80 percent of the water it could contain. The air mass warms to 30°C.

   a. Does the volume of the air mass decrease or increase when the temperature goes up?

   b. Does the relative humidity of the air mass increase or decrease when the temperature goes up? (Assume that the amount of water in the air mass stays the same.)

Section 6.2

4. Locate an image of a weather map in a newspaper or find one on the Internet. Copy a portion of the map and identify a high pressure center, a low pressure center, one or more isobars, a warm front, and a cold front.

5. Read this paragraph and then answer the question.

   Warm, moist air crosses over the Pacific Ocean and reaches the Washington coast. At first, the air mass flows up the western side of a mountain which has a lot of trees and plants. Cool temperatures at the top of the mountain on the west side cause the mass to decrease in size so that water vapor becomes first a cloud and then rain droplets. The resulting cool, dry air mass sinks down the eastern side of the mountain into warm temperatures. The land that this dry air passes over will have a dry climate.

   Now, look at the illustration below. Which city would receive more rain per year—Olympia or Yakima? Explain your answer. Go to the Internet and find out what the average rainfall actually is for each of these cities. This data will help you determine if your answer is correct!

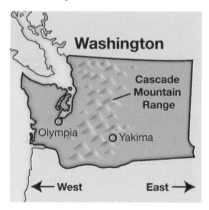

Section 6.3

6. The desert is home to more different types of animals than any other place except the rainforest. How can animals survive in such a hot climate? Use the library or Internet to learn how animals are able to survive in a desert climate or one of the other climates.

7. Study the following map showing population density and the Earth's biomes map from the chapter.

   a. Which biomes have the most densely populated areas?

   b. Which biomes have the least densely populated areas?

   c. Propose an explanation as to why different biomes have such different population densities.

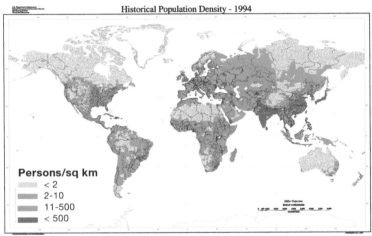

Historical Population Density - 1994

Persons/sq km
- < 2
- 2-10
- 11-500
- < 500

Courtesy of NASA, NRCS, USDA

8. Answer these questions using the Earth's biome map.

   a. What biome is located at 60° N and 100° E?

   b. What biome is located at 0° and 60° W?

   c. What biome is located at 40° N and 80° W?

   d. Give the latitude and longitude for one grassland biome.

   e. Give the latitude and longitude for one desert biome.

9. Use this table to answer the questions below.

| Biome | Temperature range | |
	Low temp (°C)	High temp (°C)
Tropical rainforest	20	25
Tundra	−34	12

   a. Which biome has the largest range of temperature?

   b. Which biome gets the warmest?

   c. Which biome gets the coldest?

   d. Using the data above, construct a bar graph that shows the average high temperatures and the average low temperatures for the rainforest compared to the tundra.

Chapter Projects—Demonstrating the Coriolis Effect

Place a large foam ball on a wooden skewer. Use a marker to draw the north and south poles and the equator on the ball. Ask a partner to rotate the skewer so that the ball turns in a counterclockwise direction as seen from the north pole. Using a permanent marker, try to draw a line from the north pole toward the equator. Next, start at the equator and try to draw a line straight up. What happened?

Now turn the ball over and switch roles. Your partner should demonstrate the way air currents would flow in the southern hemisphere from the south pole to the equator. The ball needs to be turned clockwise in this position.

Oceans

Imagine you are an astronaut in a space shuttle looking back at Earth. What does it look like? You probably know that it is mostly blue. That blue color comes from the five oceans that cover most of Earth's surface.

The United States has two oceans at its east and west borders: the Atlantic Ocean and the Pacific Ocean. Have you seen either of these oceans? When you see an ocean, it is easy to appreciate what a massive body of water it is.

Aside from being big, what characteristics does an ocean have? You might know that ocean water is salty and that waves form in oceans. In this chapter, you'll learn much more about oceans, waves, beaches, and the features of the deep ocean floor!

Key Questions:

1. How many oceans does Earth have?

2. What factors affect the size of ocean waves?

3. Where does sand come from?

7.1 Introduction to Oceans

About 97 percent of Earth's water is contained in five oceans. The oceans cover most of Earth's surface and are important to life on the planet. However, we can't drink ocean water. It's too salty! In this section you will learn why the oceans are salty. You'll also learn about ocean currents.

Salt water

Salt in ocean water Ocean water is about 3.5 percent salt. The word **salinity** is used to describe the saltiness of water. Most of the salt in ocean water is sodium chloride. You use sodium chloride, or table salt, on your food. Sodium chloride is found in nature as the mineral *halite* (Figure 7.1). In some places, special ponds called *salt evaporation ponds* are set up to harvest salt from the ocean (Figure 7.2).

Sources of salt The salt in the oceans comes from minerals in the ocean floor, from gases released by volcanoes, and from rivers that carry dissolved minerals from land to sea. These dissolved minerals come from chemical weathering of rocks on the continents.

VOCABULARY

salinity - a term that describes the saltiness of water.

Halite
(Sodium chloride)

Photo courtesy U.S House Subcommittee on Energy and Natural Resources

Figure 7.1: *Sodium chloride, or table salt, comes from the mineral halite.*

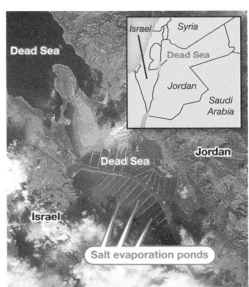

Photo courtesy of NASA

Figure 7.2: *Salt evaporations ponds in the Dead Sea are used to harvest salt for human consumption.*

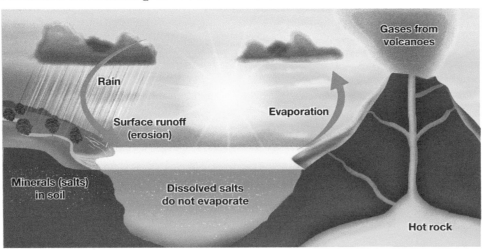

Earth's oceans

Earth from space Astronauts are amazed when they see our blue planet from space. Earth is mostly bright blue because of its vast oceans.

Five oceans Four of Earth's oceans are easy to identify because of the shape of the surrounding continents. These four oceans are the Atlantic, Pacific, Indian, and Arctic Oceans. The fifth ocean, the Southern Ocean, is composed of the waters surrounding Antarctica. The Southern Ocean includes the water south of 60° S latitude.

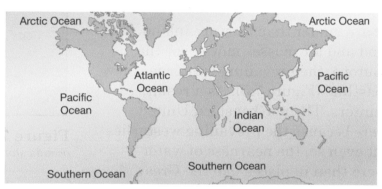

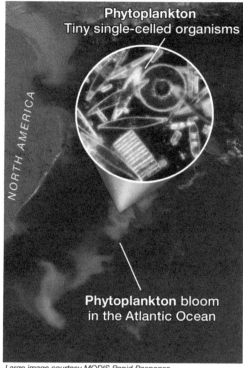

Large image courtesy MODIS Rapid Response Project at NASA/GSFC. Inset image courtesy NOAA.

Figure 7.3: *Tiny, single-celled ocean organisms called phytoplankton produce most of the oxygen in the atmosphere.*

The importance of Earth's oceans Oceans are an important source of water for the water cycle. They also help maintain Earth's heat balance. Because water has a high specific heat, the oceans do not heat up or cool down quickly. As a result, our climate does not become too hot or too cold. Also, oceans spread energy and heat from the hot equator to the colder poles through ocean currents and waves. In addition to moving heat, ocean currents help propel ships as they navigate the globe. The oceans are also important because tiny, single-celled ocean organisms called *phytoplankton* that live in the oceans produce most of the oxygen in the atmosphere (Figure 7.3).

Oceans and Earth's climate

Storing heat in the oceans

Earth's oceans are warmed by the Sun during daylight hours and that heat energy is stored. The oceans are able to store heat energy for two reasons. First, water has a high specific heat, so it takes a long time for it to cool down once it is warm. Second, solar radiation penetrates the water surface and allows the Sun's heat energy to be stored many meters deep (Figure 7.4). Because of this heat storage, the water on Earth prevents the planet from getting too hot or too cold.

Where do you find milder climates?

The climates on the coastline are milder than they are inland. This is because ocean-warmed wind and air masses move over the oceans toward the land. In Europe, the prevailing westerlies blow over the ocean toward the coastline (Figure 7.5). As a result, Europe tends to have mild winters. The northeastern United States has more severe winters because the prevailing westerlies blow away from its coast. But even so, the nearness of water makes the winters milder there than in places like the Great Plains of the United States. This area can be extremely cold because it is far from the ocean.

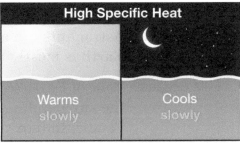

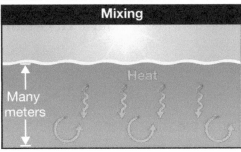

Figure 7.4: *Two reasons why the oceans store heat energy.*

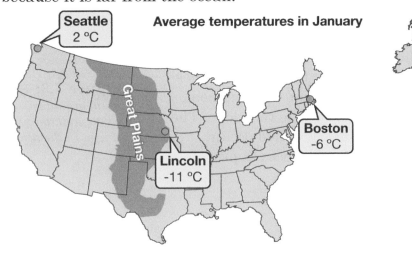

Average temperatures in January

Seattle 2 °C

Great Plains

Lincoln -11 °C

Boston -6 °C

London 1 °C

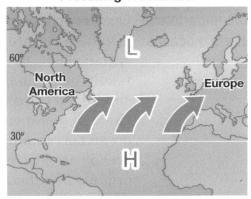

Figure 7.5: *The prevailing winds between 30° and 60° N latitude.*

Surface currents and gyres

Wind drives surface ocean currents
The Sun's unequal heating of Earth and the Coriolis effect cause permanent global wind patterns (see Chapter 6). As they blow across the ocean, these winds push water in the direction they are moving. This creates surface ocean currents that can travel for long distances. Small "pushes" to the surface ocean currents also come from the tides as they move in and out along coastlines.

Surface currents transport heat energy
Surface currents move enormous quantities of water. The Gulf Stream is a surface ocean current that transports 80 million cubic meters of water per second past Cape Hatteras (Figure 7.6). Because the Sun heats this water, the currents also transport heat energy. The heat transported by the Gulf Stream is equivalent to the output of 1 million power stations! Surface ocean currents usually carry heat from regions near the equator toward the poles.

Gyres
The Coriolis effect and the shape of the coastlines cause surface ocean currents to form large rotating systems called gyres. Gyres north of the equator—like the North Atlantic gyre—turn in a clockwise direction. The North Atlantic gyre is composed of four surface ocean currents. Gyres south of the equator turn in a counterclockwise direction.

 VOCABULARY

surface ocean currents - wind-driven currents that move at the ocean surface, often for long distances.

gyres - large rotating ocean current systems.

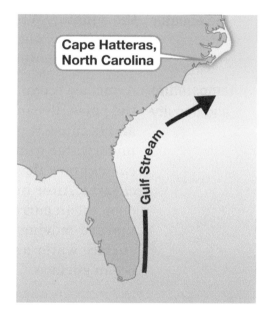

Figure 7.6: *The Gulf Stream is a surface ocean current. The Gulf Stream is part of the North Atlantic gyre.*

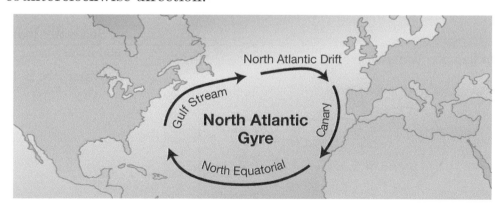

Deep ocean currents

What is a deep ocean current? Deep ocean currents move below the surface of the ocean. They are slower than surface ocean currents. Deep ocean currents are driven by density differences. Denser water sinks and less-dense water floats. Since temperature and salinity affect the density of water, the currents are also called *thermohaline currents*. *Thermo* means temperature and *haline* means salt.

Evaporation near the equator Global wind patterns and heat speed up evaporation of water near the equator. When ocean water evaporates, the water leaves and the salt stays behind. When this happens, surface ocean currents near the equator become saltier.

Temperature and density A surface ocean current cools as it moves from the equator toward the poles. Because this water is saltier than surrounding water and because it is now cooler, it sinks to the ocean floor as a huge underwater waterfall. What was once a warm *surface ocean current* now flows along the ocean floor as a cold *deep ocean current*. After hundreds to thousands of years, the slow-moving deep ocean current water returns to the surface in a upward-moving *upwelling*. Upwellings return the original surface water and nutrients from the ocean bottom back to the ocean surface.

ă VOCABULARY

deep ocean currents - density- and temperature-driven currents that move slowly within the ocean; also called thermohaline currents.

SOLVE IT!

Will an object float or sink?

On average, salt water has a salinity of 3.5 percent (also written as 35 parts per thousand or 35 ppt). Determine if the following fluids would sink or float in average salt water that is 25°C.

a. Salt water that is 35 ppt and 50°C.

b. Salt water that is 35 ppt and 4°C.

c. Salt water that is 40 ppt and 25°C.

d. Water that is 10 ppt and 25°C.

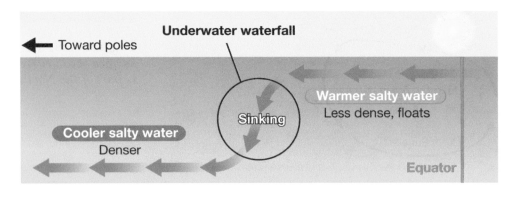

7.1 Section Review

1. What does the term *salinity* mean?

2. Where does the salt in the oceans come from?

3. Name Earth's five oceans.

4. List two reasons why Earth's oceans help make the planet suitable for life to exist.

5. In which of these places would winter be the most extreme: central Asia or western Canada? Explain your answer. If necessary, look at a globe to answer this question.

6. What keeps surface ocean currents moving?

7. Name the four currents of the North Atlantic Gyre.

8. What characteristics of deep ocean currents affect their motion?

9. At a coastline, freshwater flows into salty water. Which two of these events might be occurring at a coastline? Explain your answer.

    a. The freshwater floats on top of the salt water.   b. The freshwater sinks in the salt water.

10. *Challenge*: How does the Coriolis effect influence the movement of surface ocean currents in both hemisphere?

11. *Challenge*: Pick one of these terms and find out its meaning. Write a short paragraph about each term based on your research. Include a diagram with your paragraph to help explain each term.
    a. thermocline
    b. estuary

CHALLENGE

In this section, you learned the average temperatures in January for certain cities.

- Describe what winter is like in your city. Do you live near an ocean or a large body of water?
- What is the average January temperature for your city?
- How does this average temperature compare to those listed in the text?

SOLVE IT!

Predict which mass of water will sink and which will float in a mass of water that is 10°C with a density of 1.0260 g/cm^3.

a) 15°C, density = 1.0255 g/cm^3

b) 10°C, density = 1.0270 g/cm^3

7.2 Waves

This section is about waves. It is easy to see waves in water. After throwing a stone into a pond, you will see water periodically bobbing up and down on the surface. This bobbing motion represents a wave. Read on to learn more about waves.

Making waves

A disturbance moving forward   Waves are caused by a *disturbance* moving forward (Figure 7.7). To understand this, think about making a wave with a piece of rope. If you snap the rope sharply up and down, waves will travel toward the other end of the rope while your end of the rope stays in your hand. In the case of water waves, the water moves up and down as the disturbance moves forward.

Waves occur as a repeating pattern of *crests* and *troughs*. A **crest** is the high point of a wave. A **trough** is the low point. The **amplitude** of a wave is the distance between a wave crest or trough and the average level of motion (see diagram below). **Wavelength** is the length of one complete wave. It is measured from any point on a wave to the same point on the next wave. The time that it takes for one wavelength to pass a single point is called the **period** of a wave.

VOCABULARY

crest - the high point of a wave.

trough - the low point of a wave.

amplitude - the vertical distance between a wave crest or trough and the average level of motion.

wavelength - the distance between two wave crests, or the distance between two wave troughs.

period - the time it takes for one wavelength to pass by a single point.

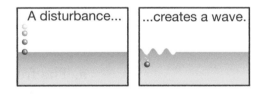

Figure 7.7: *A disturbance is a movement that begins in one location and sets things in motion farther away.*

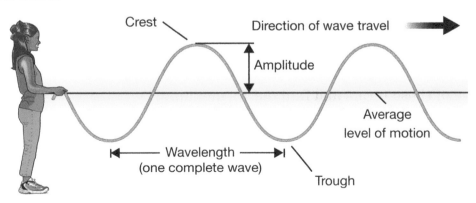

More about waves

Circular motion A wave causes a circular motion in the water as it passes by. In the graphic below, you see the water before the wave arrives (A). Then, the wave approaches (B). Next, the trough of the wave arrives (C). The water rises as the crest approaches (D). Finally, the water is pushed forward at the top of the crest (E).

Observations about waves The seagull and the dolphin in the graphic below both trace a circular path, but the dolphin's path is smaller than the seagull's. Also, the wave has no effect on the water below the wave base. The *wave base* is located at a depth that is half the wavelength of the wave. Submarines avoid being affected by waves by traveling below this level. Figure 7.8 summarizes these observations.

Wave Observations	
Size of wave motion	Decreases below the ocean surface.
Depth of wave motion	There is no water motion below the wave base. The wave base occurs at a depth that is is about half the wavelength of the wave.

Figure 7.8: *A summary of wave observations.*

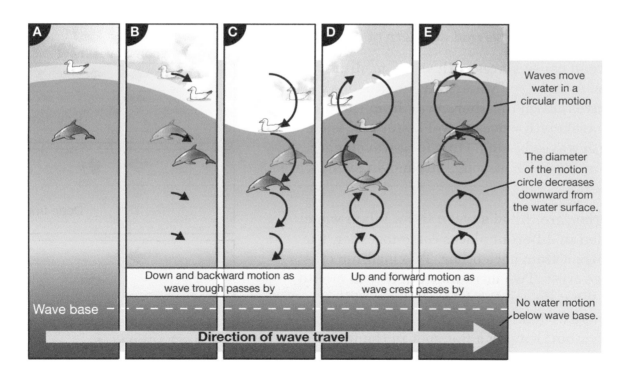

Waves move water in a circular motion

The diameter of the motion circle decreases downward from the water surface.

No water motion below wave base.

Down and backward motion as wave trough passes by

Up and forward motion as wave crest passes by

Wave base

Direction of wave travel

Wind causes waves

How does wind cause waves?
Most ocean waves are caused by friction between the wind and the ocean surface. At first, small ripples form as the wind begins to blow. The ripples allow the wind to "grip" the water. As the wind gets stronger, the ripples become bigger waves with more height, longer wavelengths, and longer periods. The size of ocean waves formed by wind depends on wind speed, the amount of time the wind blows, and fetch (Figure 7.9). **Fetch** is the amount of open water over which wind blows. The greater the fetch, the larger the waves that are created.

The Beaufort Wind Force Scale
The Beaufort Wind Force Scale is used to describe the intensity of wind. The scale goes from 0 to 12. Each level of the scale refers to a particular wind speed and its effects. The Beaufort Scale is used on land to record wind speed as a measure for weather conditions. It can also be used to predict the size and strength of ocean waves.

Waves and swells
Storms in the open ocean cause waves with short, medium, and long wavelengths. A variety of water wavelengths makes the sea rough. The waves travel together, away from the storm, but the long-wavelength waves travel faster and leave the shorter-wavelength waves behind. Only long-wavelength waves occur far from a storm. These long, fast-moving waves are called **swells**.

Wave trains
Waves traveling together are called a **wave train**. When wave trains that were formed in different places come together, the waves add to and subtract from each other. Two medium crests will form a single large crest. Two medium troughs will create a really deep trough. What do you think would happen if a high crest came together with an equally deep trough? They would cancel each other out, leaving a flat spot in the water (Figure 7.10).

The size of ocean waves depends on...	Wind speed
	The length of time that the wind blows
	Fetch

Figure 7.9: *Factors that affect the size of waves.*

When waves meet

High crest

Deep trough

Flat spot

Figure 7.10: *What happens when waves meet?*

Tsunamis compared to wind waves

What is a tsunami?
A tsunami is a huge wave made by a large disturbance like an underwater earthquake, landslide, or volcanic eruption. The energy from these movements on the sea floor spreads as a wave on the ocean surface. Figure 7.11 compares wind waves and tsunamis.

Tsunamis in the open ocean
In the open ocean, wind-driven waves and tsunamis are about the same height. But the wavelength of a tsunami is much longer than the wavelength of a wind-driven wave. The wavelength of a wind-driven wave may measure 10 to 200 meters from crest to crest. It may take 5 to 20 seconds or so for a wind-driven wave to pass by. Wind-driven waves are small splashes compared to tsunamis. The wavelength of a tsunami can be thousands of meters long! Because the surface of Earth is curved, you can't see enough of it to detect the crest of a tsunami as it approaches. If a tsunami approached a ship you were in, you would see only a flat sea. As it passed under the ship, the tsunami would cause the ship to rise gently, about 10 meters, and then gently settle back after several minutes.

Waves in shallow water
When a wind wave or a tsunami approaches land, the wave base begins to drag on the shallow bottom. As the front of the wave slows, the back of the wave catches up. This shortens the wavelength making the wave crest higher. Eventually, the result is a breaking wave and surf. In the case of a tsunami, the crest of water can be up to 35 meters high or more. A tsunami crashing on shore may destroy buildings and wash ships inland. A huge tsunami occurred in the Indian Ocean in 2004.

VOCABULARY

tsunami - a huge wave made by a large disturbance like an underwater earthquake, landslide, or volcanic eruption.

	Wind wave	Tsunami
Period (seconds)	5–20	300–3,600
Wavelength (meters)	10–200	100,000–700,000
Speed (km/h)	< 50	500–1,000
Height (m)	0–14+	~35

Figure 7.11: *How a wind wave compares to a tsunami.*

SOLVE IT!

1. Convert the wavelengths of a wind wave and a tsunami to kilometers.

2. The period of a tsunami is 600 seconds. What is the period in minutes?

3. The height of a single story building is about 3 meters. How many stories high is a tsunami?

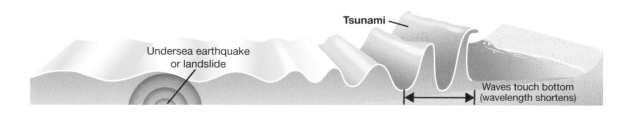

Tsunami

Undersea earthquake or landslide

Waves touch bottom (wavelength shortens)

7.2 **Section Review**

1. Name each labeled part of the wave diagram below.

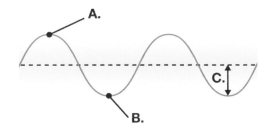

2. How long is the wave in the diagram? Give your answer in wavelengths.

3. What is fetch?

4. Which situation described below would produce the biggest wave? Explain your answer.

   a. The fetch is 0.5 mile, the wind blows for 5 minutes, and the wind speed is 10 km/h.

   b. The fetch is 1 mile, the wind blows for 10 minutes, and the wind speed is 10 km/h.

5. A boat is floating in the open ocean. A wave passes beneath the boat. Describe how the boat moves when this happens.

6. Describe how wave motion changes as you go from the ocean surface to below the wave base.

7. Two waves with the same amplitude meet.

   a. What happens when the crest of the first wave meets the trough of the second wave?

   b. What happens when two crests meet?

8. What causes a tsunami?

Surf while you study

You can improve how fast you learn by applying your knowledge to new situations.

For example, big waves are found at the shore lines of the Hawaiian Islands. These big waves are why the sport of surfing is very popular there.

Do some Internet surfing and apply what you've already learned from reading this chapter, to find out why Hawaii is such a good spot for big breaking waves.

7.3 Shallow Marine Environments

If you ask someone about their favorite place to visit, they might say, "The beach!" They probably wouldn't say, "A shallow marine environment!" But shallow marine environments, which you will learn about in this section, include beaches and other locations that are marine, or related to the ocean.

The parts of a beach

Beach zones   A beach is an area of coastal sand between the low tide line and the line of permanent vegetation. The backshore is the part of the beach above the high tide line which is only submerged during storms. The foreshore of a beach lies between the high and low tide lines (Figure 7.12). Marine biologists have a different name for the foreshore. They call it the *intertidal zone*.

Onshore and offshore regions   Below the foreshore is the *shoreface*. The shoreface is always underwater because it is below the low tide level. Passing waves affect the sediments of the shoreface, especially the upper part nearest the beach. Waves smooth land surfaces. Because waves have little effect on the lower part of the shoreface, the surface of this region is bumpy. Anything that is on the beach, foreshore, or shoreface is considered to be "onshore." Anything beyond the shoreface is "offshore."

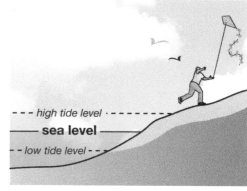

Figure 7.12: *The range of land between the high and low tide lines is called the foreshore. Sea level is the average ocean height between the high and low tide levels.*

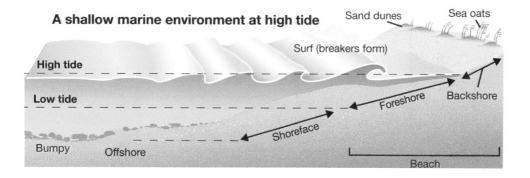

A shallow marine environment at high tide

Sandy beaches and tidal flats

Beaches have sand Sand is the most obvious feature of a beach. The light-colored, rounded grains slip easily through your hands. (Figure 7.13). Sand is not sticky. Blankets and towels only need a quick shake to remove dry sand.

Tidal flats have mud Tidal flats, which are often part of *salt marshes,* are also located in the intertidal zone (Figure 7.14). However, tidal flats are different from beaches. Tidal flats commonly have sandy areas, but most of a tidal flat is dark, sticky mud. And the sticky mud can smell very bad!

Why are tidal flats and beaches different? Tidal flats and beaches are both covered by sediment. Streams and rivers carry the sediment down from the mountains and other high places. The sediment includes particles of various sizes when it arrives at both areas. What happens to the sediment after it arrives is what makes tidal flats and beaches different.

VOCABULARY

tidal flat - a flat, muddy area in the foreshore.

Figure 7.13: *People enjoy the clean, light-colored, rounded sand grains that slip easily through their hands.*

This is a tidal flat in a salt marsh. You can see dark mud clinging to the students' shoes.

This is a beach. Sand covers every surface and no rocks are exposed.

Photos courtesy of Jim Sammons, Sammons' INK.

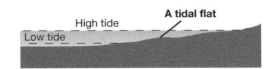

Figure 7.14: *A tidal flat is in the same area as a beach, yet the sediment found on tidal flats and beaches is very different.*

Waves and sand

Waves affect particles Waves are the key difference between tidal flats and beaches. Beaches are affected by strong wave action. Tidal flats are not. Waves change the size of sediment particles. A sample of tidal flat mud contains different kinds and different sizes of sediment particles.

Sand grains If you have ever stood on a beach, you know that waves seem to come in and go out from the edge of the beach. Swimming at the beach is a thrilling experience. As each wave passes over you, you feel the strong rush of water. This same rush and crash of the waves churns the sandy ocean floor. Sand grains are rounded by wave action.

Quartz

What is sand?

Feldspar

The largest particles of sediment are heavy enough to settle to the ocean floor. The smallest particles and broken grains are carried out to sea with the waves and ocean currents. The remaining particles, called *coarse sand,* build the beach (Figure 7.15). The coarse sand grains tumble over each other with every passing wave. The tumbling action wears away any sharp edges. It also polishes the grains. Some grains that are hard enough to withstand this harsh treatment are minerals called quartz and feldspar. Both quartz and feldspar contain silica. Beach sand in many locations is made mainly of rounded grains of the minerals quartz and feldspar.

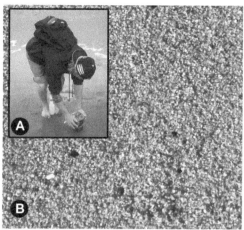

Photo A courtesy of U.S. Geological Survey

Figure 7.15: *(A) Scientists use special digital cameras to photograph and then measure the size of sand grains on a beach. (B) This image is of sand grains in a one-centimeter section of sand on a beach. By studying sand grains on a beach over time, scientists can determine how much wave energy affects the beach.*

Beaches in winter and summer

Winter versus summer beaches

Fast-moving water will move both small sand grains and large, heavy particles. Slow-moving water will drop these particles. During the winter, waves are stronger on the coasts of the United States than during the summer. Gentle summer waves tend to carry sand from deeper water onto the beaches. The stronger winter waves carry the sand back to deeper water (Figure 7.16). This back-and-forth action creates two distinctly different environments on the same beach: a summer beach and a winter beach (Figure 7.17). See page 168 for a photo of a summer beach.

Beaches change over time

Waves that create summer and winter beaches are not the same year after year. Just like one summer may have a little more or less rain than another, waves may be more or less energetic from year to year. During the winter, the sand that is removed from the beach winds up in sandbars, not far out from shore. During a harsh winter, the beach may be eroded by a series of very strong storms. High-energy waves carry away more sand than usual, carrying the sand further out from the shore. After a harsh winter, it may take years for the beach to recover from the erosion.

How does a beach get too much sand?

On the other hand, the gentle waves of a mild winter may not remove all of the summer sand. In this case, when the next summer arrives, the beach may start out with an extra amount of sand, and the summer waves will build up even more sand. After several mild winters, the sand may reach unusually high levels.

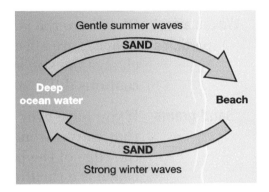

Figure 7.16: *Gentle summer waves carry sand from deep ocean water to beaches. Strong winter waves carry the sand from the beaches to deep ocean water.*

Figure 7.17: *This is a winter beach.*

Moving sand

Beaches and headlands
By moving sand and wearing away rock, waves change beaches. For example, more sand tends to be lost in winter from a beach than is returned in summer. This is because sand is carried too far from shore for gentle waves to return it. Over time, beaches lose more and more sand. Some places along a beach resist being changed by the waves. *Headlands* are places where the shore sticks out from the coast. Waves will cut away the softer rock at a headland and leave behind more durable rock. Eventually, a headland may become a sea stack (Figure 7.18).

Rivers and streams bring new sand
Beaches never completely wear away because rivers and streams bring new sand from the mountains to the beaches. But this sand doesn't stay in one location. Instead, it flows along the coast.

Longshore drift
A **coast** is the boundary between land and a body of water like the ocean. The movement of sand along a coast is called **longshore drift**. The beach sand that is lost to deep water is replaced by new sediments transported by a rivers and streams.

VOCABULARY

coast - the boundary between land and a body of water like the ocean.

longshore drift - the flow of sand along a coast.

Sea stacks

Photo courtesy of Jim Sammons, Sammons' INK.

Figure 7.18: *Some sediment is taken from beaches by the action of waves against the shore. In some places the shore resists wearing away. Waves cut away the softer rock on both sides of these more durable places. Eventually, the durable places, called sea stacks, will stand in the water separated from the shore.*

Small stream

Stream mouth

Here is a small stream flowing from a reservoir into the ocean. Longshore drift has carried sand from left to right along the coast. Longshore drift has shifted the stream mouth so far to the right that the stream flows along behind the beach.

Photo courtesy of Jim Sammons, Sammons' INK.

How does longshore drift work?

Waves carry sand in the direction they move

Longshore drift shapes beaches. Waves carry sand grains in same direction that the waves move. For example, as a wave moves toward and away from the beach, it drags sand grains forward and backward. If a wave came in a straight line to the beach, sand would go up and back the same path. The sand grains would end up just about where they began before the wave broke. Longshore drift occurs because waves approach the beach at an angle. This means the waves come in at one direction (the *upwash*) and then leave the beach at a different angle (the *backwash*). This process causes sand grains to move along the coastline of a beach.

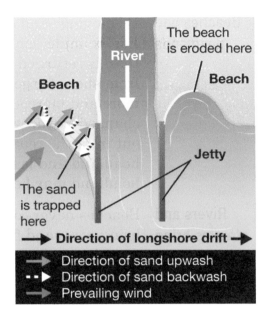

Figure 7.19: *A jetty is a barrier to longshore drift. Sand gets trapped on one side of the jetty, but the beach erodes on the other side.*

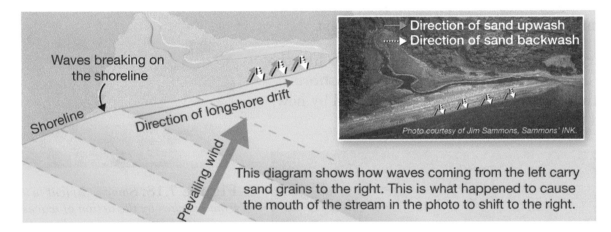

This diagram shows how waves coming from the left carry sand grains to the right. This is what happened to cause the mouth of the stream in the photo to shift to the right.

Barriers to longshore drift

Because the sand of a beach is constantly coming and going, a beach is like a river of sand. Evidence of the flow of sand at a beach can be seen wherever there are barriers to longshore drift. A *jetty* is a barrier that is built to control or slow down ocean currents along a coast (Figure 7.19). Another barrier is a *breakwater*, which protects a harbor from waves.

What happens to sand at a jetty

When a jetty is located along the coast of the ocean, longshore drift will be disrupted. Sand will quickly build up on the side of the barrier where the waves first hit. At the same time, the beach will erode away on the other side of the barrier.

Breakwaters lead to a new problem

Many breakwaters have been built in front of marinas or harbor entrances to protect them from high waves. But soon after solving the problem of high waves, a new problem appears. The water behind the breakwater is calmer than it used to be. The calm water drops its sediment and the marina or harbor entrance fills with sand (Figure 7.20). The only solution is to remove the breakwater or use pumps, called *dredges*, to remove the sand.

Continental shelves and canyons

Eventually, beach sand may find its way to the edge of the continental shelf and drop off into very deep water. Sand drifting down the steep face of a continental shelf cuts into the shelf just like streams cut into valleys. These cuts are called *submarine canyons*. As a canyon is cut, the cut grows in the direction of the shore. Some canyons are so close to the shore that sand moving along the coast by longshore drift lands in the canyon and gets deposited directly into the deep ocean basins. Beaches can lose a lot of sand quickly at submarine canyon locations.

VOCABULARY

continental shelf - the ocean bottom that extends from a coast or shoreline to the continental slope.

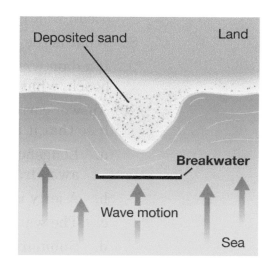

Figure 7.20: *A breakwater is a barrier to longshore drift that protects harbors. Excess sand can build up near a breakwater.*

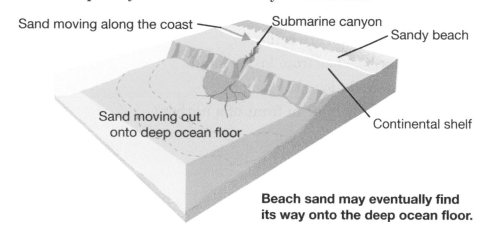

Beach sand may eventually find its way onto the deep ocean floor.

7.3 Section Review

1. Describe the parts of a beach.

2. What are the two names given to the area that lies between the high and low tide lines?

3. What is different about the sediment you find at a beach versus what you find at a tidal flat?

4. How do waves affect the smoothness of sand grains?

5. Name two minerals that are common in beach sand.

6. How do seasonal waves affect the shape of a beach?

7. Is the amount of sand moved between the beach and deep ocean water the same over time? Explain.

8. What is the main source of beach sand?

9. If a dam was built to block a river from flowing toward a beach, what might happen to this beach over time?

10. Answer correct or incorrect. If a statement is incorrect, rewrite it so that it is correct.

    a. Longshore drift occurs because waves move toward and away from a beach along the same path.

    b. A jetty is a barrier that disrupts longshore drift.

    c. The water behind a breakwater is very calm.

    d. Submarine canyons prevent beaches from losing sand.

11. How does longshore drift move sand along the beach?

12. What happens when a breakwater is built in front of a harbor?

Tidal flats and beaches are special environments. Use the Internet or reference books to find out what kinds of plants and animals live on tidal flats. Then, find out what kinds of plants and animals live on beaches. Make a poster to display what you learn.

Tidal flat

Beach

7.4 The Ocean Floor

It is possible that scientists know more about space than about the oceans on Earth. This is because scientists can use telescopes to see far-away space objects. But many of the important features of the oceans, especially the ocean floor, are hidden in deep water. In this section, you will learn about these hidden features.

Features of the ocean floor

The continental margin

The ocean floor can be divided into the continental margin and the deep ocean floor. The **continental margin** is the region around continents that includes the *continental shelf, continental slope,* and *continental rise.* The continental slope begins where the sea floor slopes toward the deep ocean floor. The continental rise is made of sediments that have washed down from the continental shelf and slope. Continental shelves surround many continents. They are shallow extensions of the continent, covered by 100 or so meters of ocean water (Figure 7.21).

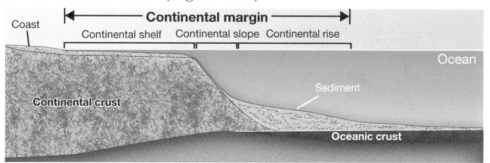

Features of the continental shelf

A *barrier island* is a low, sandy island that lies parallel to the shoreline. It blocks waves that come into shore and provides sheltered water between the island and the shore. A *bank* is a low, flat region on the continental shelf. Its surface is relatively close to the ocean surface. These features are shown on the diagram on page 176.

continental margin - the region around continents that includes the continental shelf and continental slope.

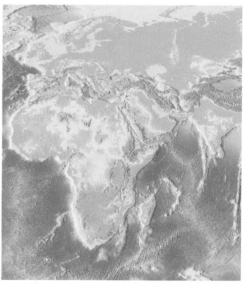

Map courtesy of National Geophysical Data Center (NGDC)

Figure 7.21: *The light blue color around the continents shows the continental shelf.*

The deep ocean floor

The abyssal plain The true ocean floor is called the *abyssal plain*. It is flat and smooth because a thick layer of sediment covers its features. It lies between 2,200 and 5,500 meters deep.

Mountains, trenches, and islands A *seamount* is a steep-sided mountain that rises from the ocean floor. Seamounts begin life as volcanoes over hot spots, but most become inactive as plate tectonics moves them off of the hot spot. Some are tall enough to reach the surface and form a volcanic island. A *guyot* is a seamount that has eroded so that it has a flat top and is underwater. *Mid-ocean ridges* mark places where two tectonic plates are separating and new ocean crust is being made. Mid-ocean ridges are a system of tall mountain ranges that pass through the world's oceans. *Deep-ocean trenches* are the deepest parts of the ocean. The deepest trench is the Mariana Trench near Guam in the North Pacific Ocean. A *volcanic island arc* is a string of volcanic islands that lies in a curving line along a trench.

CHALLENGE

Each feature of the deep ocean floor was a cool discovery. For example, guyots were discovered by Harry Hess, an important scientist in the development of plate tectonics.

Pick one feature of the deep ocean floor and go on a "knowledge hunt" to find out more about it.

Note: Guyot is pronounced "gee-oh."

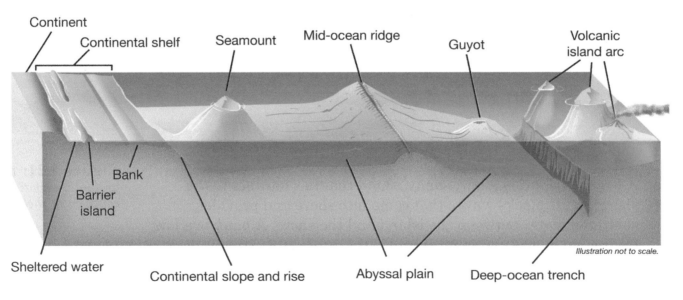

Continent
Continental shelf
Seamount
Mid-ocean ridge
Guyot
Volcanic island arc
Bank
Barrier island
Sheltered water
Continental slope and rise
Abyssal plain
Deep-ocean trench

Illustration not to scale.

7.4 Section Review

1. It is possible that scientists know more about space than they do about Earth's ocean floor. Why?
2. What three parts of the ocean floor are included in the continental margin?
3. What is the difference between a barrier island and a bank?
4. Why is the abyssal plain so smooth?
5. The abyssal plain is 2,200 to 5,500 meters deep. Convert this range to kilometers and miles. Conversion factors: 1,000 meters = 1 kilometer = 0.62 mile, or 1.61 miles = 1 kilometer.
6. What is a guyot?
7. What is the difference between a seamount and a mid-ocean ridge?
8. Many features of the deep ocean floor are volcanic. Why do you think this is so?
9. What is a volcanic island arc?
10. Research questions:

    a. Look at a globe and see if you can find an example of a volcanic island arc. Here's one example: the Lesser Antilles in the Caribbean Sea is a volcanic island arc (Figure 7.22).

    b. You learned that the Mariana Trench is the deepest one on Earth. Find out how deep it is!

    c. If you could go down and explore a mid-ocean ridge, what would you find?

    d. Find out about Marie Tharp. Who was she and what important contribution did she make to our understanding of the ocean floor?

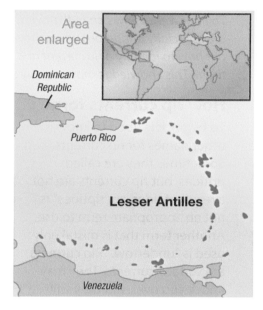

Figure 7.22: *Question 10a.*

Rip Currents

Have you ever been at the beach and noticed currents moving away from the shore? These currents are usually a darker color due to the sand and sediments mixed into the water from the bottom. These currents are called rip currents, *and they are good to know about. Their powerful flow can pull a swimmer away from the shore. They are especially dangerous when they are hard to see. Read on to find out how to identify a rip current and to know how to escape from them. This knowledge may one day save your life!*

How rip currents form

To begin, it is good to know other names for rip currents. Sometimes they are called riptides, but rip currents are not a result of tides, so "riptides" is not an appropriate term to use. Another term that is mistakenly used is "undertow." Rip currents are surface currents. They may knock you over, but they will not pull you under. Rip currents cause a swimmer to be pulled out to sea.

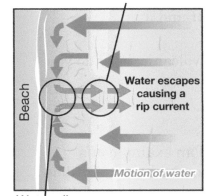

How a rip current forms

Break in sandbar

Beach

Water escapes causing a rip current

Motion of water

Water piles up

A rip current forms when water piles up near the shore and moves away from the shore all at one time. There are different ways that this can happen, but one of the most common is the result of a break in a sandbar.

Sandbars are long, narrow hills of sand that usually run parallel to the shore. Some sandbars are higher than the water surface and can easily be seen. Other sandbars are not tall enough to break through the water's surface and can't be seen from the shore.

As the waves come in from the ocean, the pass over the sandbar and lose energy in the process. Because the water has lost energy, it piles up between the sand bar and the shore. Then piled up water returns to the ocean by the fastest route available. Many times, the water rushes through the break in a sandbar. That's when the rip current is formed. The flow of a rip current can go on for several minutes or continue for hours since the waves from the ocean keep bringing more water in to this area.

Where rip currents occur

Rip currents can occur at any beach with breaking waves. They can also happen along jetties or under piers. In these places, the rip currents can actually be permanent.

Rip currents are strongest when the surf is rough or the tide is low. They can be seen as a break in the wave pattern coming towards shore and by the color of the water. Remember, the rip currents are darker in color because of the sediment they are carrying. Polarizing sunglasses are a good way of cutting down on the glare from the surface of the water in order to see the currents better.

Sandbar

Rip current

Rip current

Photos courtesy Dennis Decker, NWS Melbourne, Florida

What to do if you get stuck in a rip current

If you find yourself quickly being moved out to sea in a rip current, don't ever fight it and try to swim back through the current to shore. By doing that, you will waste a lot of needed energy and not get very far. You should always swim parallel to the shore until you are out of the rip current and then swim back to shore. Sometimes, it is hard to swim out of the rip current when it is very strong. In this case, you should float or tread water and wave for help.

You may notice that you are getting pulled sideways and then straight out. That can happen as water is being pulled from all directions through the opening in the sandbar.

You usually just find yourself in a rip current without noticing right away. But, once the current meets up with water at its level, past the opening in the sandbar, it will return to normal.

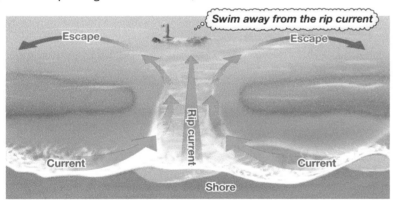

Rip currents do have some benefits. Surfers can hitch a ride on a rip current to catch an incoming wave. Lifeguards can use them to rescue someone out from the shore much faster than paddling through the waves.

Safe swimming

Going to the beach is a lot of fun. However, it is important to be safe while you are enjoying sunshine, sand, and waves. Rip currents are the number one reason for deaths at beaches. People caught in a rip current try to swim against it, get tired, and then drown!

You can keep yourself and others safe *and* have fun at the beach by knowing and following these safety tips!

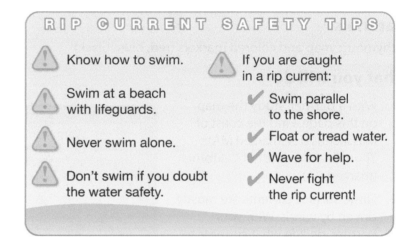

QUESTIONS

1. Why is "rip current" a better term than "riptide" and "undertow"?

2. What does a swimmer experience when he or she is caught in a rip current?

3. Describe how a rip current forms in your own words.

4. Make a safety poster to help people know how to avoid rip currents and how to escape from them.

Circumnavigating the Globe

The map on this page shows the world surface ocean currents. Currents that are relatively cold are marked in blue. Warm currents are marked in red. Currents the are shaded red/blue have an intermediate temperature. You will use this map to plot a sailboat route for *circumnavigating* the globe from the coast of Massachusetts to the coast of California. This means you can't just go around North America. You need to go around the world!

Materials

Bathymetric map and colored markers (red, blue, black)

What you will do

1. With a partner, study the map on this page. Find the coast of Massachusetts (marked MA). Then, find the coast of California (marked CA).

2. Large surface currents are mostly driven by winds. With your partner, decide what currents to use so that your sail takes you from Massachusetts to California. Before you get started on "sailing around the world," come up with a name for your sailboat.

3. As you choose currents, draw them on your bathymetric map. Use a red to indicate a warm current, blue to indicate a cold current, and red/blue shading to indicate other currents. Also use your black marker (or a pencil) to label each current you draw.

Applying your knowledge

a. Do the warm currents flow towards or away from the equator? Do the cold currents flow towards or away from the equator?

b. On which side of the ocean basins are warm currents found? On which side of the ocean basins are cold currents found?

c. List any uninterrupted currents. They flow around the globe without being blocked by land.

d. How many currents did you need to use to sail from Massachusetts to California? How does your route compare with the routes used by other teams?

e. How would you sail back to Massachusetts?

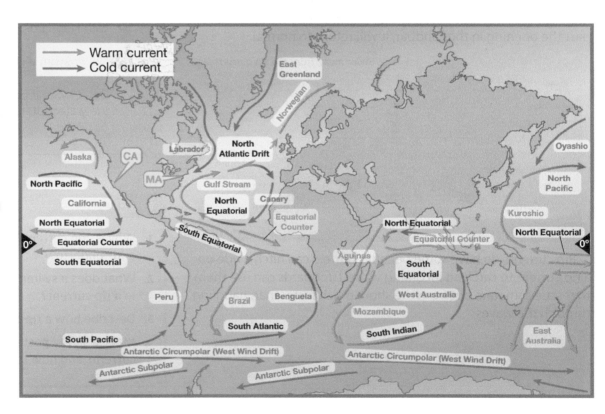

Chapter 7 Activity

Chapter 7 Assessment

Vocabulary

Select the correct term to complete the sentences.

salinity	surface ocean current	gyres
amplitude	deep ocean current	crest
tsunami	wavelength	trough
marine	continental margin	period
coast	continental shelf	tidal flat
foreshore	longshore drift	beach
backshore	swells	fetch
wave train		

Section 7.1

1. A circular ocean current system is called a(n) _____.

2. A density-driven current that moves slowly within the ocean is called a(n) _____.

3. The Gulf Stream is an example of a(n) _____.

4. _____ describes the saltiness of water.

Section 7.2

5. _____ is the amount of open water over which the wind blows.

6. _____ is the distance between two wave crests.

7. Many waves traveling together form a(n) _____.

8. The low point of a wave is the _____, while the high point of a wave is the _____.

9. A sudden movement of the sea floor created by an underwater earthquake could cause a(n) _____.

10. Long, fast-moving waves are called _____.

11. The _____ of a wave is the distance between a wave crest or trough and the average level of motion.

12. The time it takes for one wavelength to pass a single point is the _____ of a wave.

Section 7.3 and 7.4

13. Between the low and high tide lines, the _____ can be found.

14. The movement of sand along the coast is _____.

15. The term _____ refers to objects that are related to the ocean.

16. The part of the ocean floor that extends from the coast to the continental slope _____.

17. The boundary between a body of water and land is the _____.

18. The area that is between the low tide line and the line of permanent vegetation is called a(n) _____.

19. The continental shelf, slope, and rise make up the _____.

20. The part of a beach that is above high tide is called the _____.

21. A(n) _____ is a muddy area in the foreshore region.

Concepts

Section 7.1

1. What makes the oceans salty?

2. Why are the oceans able to store heat energy?

3. The interior of a continent is more likely to be extremely cold in the winter than a coastal areas. Why?

4. How do surface ocean currents affect the movement of heat at Earth's surface?

5. List the factors that affect how:

   a. surface currents move.

   b. deep ocean currents move.

6. What two factors cause gyres?

7. Why are deep ocean currents also called thermohaline currents?

Section 7.2

8. Draw a diagram of a wave. Include crest, trough, wavelength, and amplitude.

9. What is the difference between the amplitude and the wavelength of a wave?

10. A huge storm can affect boats and ships at the ocean surface. However, a submarine can avoid the effects of a storm by travelling deep underwater. Why doesn't the storm affect the submarine?

11. What three factors affect the size of ocean waves?

12. What is the Beaufort Wind Force Scale?

Section 7.3

13. List two names for the region between low tide and high tide.

14. What is the difference between a tidal flat and a beach?

15. From where does most of the sediment for tidal flats and beaches come?

16. Why do particles of sand tend to be round and polished-looking?

17. How does a beach get too much sand?

18. Can longshore drift be stopped? Why or why not?

Section 7.4

19. What are the three parts of the continental margin?

20. What function do barrier islands naturally perform?

21. What is the difference between a seamount and a guyot?

Math and Writing Skills

Section 7.1

1. You have a sample of ocean water that is 20°C and has a salinity of 35 ppt. If you poured a sample of 20°C that was 37 ppt, would that sample of water sink or float in the first sample?

2. A sample of ocean water in a beaker is allowed to sit outside in the Sun so that water in the sample can evaporate.

   a. What would happen to the salinity of the sample over time?

   b. Would the amount of salt change in the sample over time? Why or why not?

   c. What would happen to the salinity of the sample if it started to rain into the beaker?

3. Answer these questions about Earth's oceans. Review Chapter 4 to help you answer these questions.

   a. Name Earth's five oceans.

   b. How much of Earth's surface is covered by oceans?

   c. How much of Earth's water is in the oceans?

4. One of the deep ocean currents is called the Antarctic Circumpolar Current. It is so called because it circles Antarctica. It aids in the circulation of deep and middle-range waters between the Atlantic, Indian, and Pacific Oceans. The average speed is about 10 cm/s. How many kilometers would this represent for a day's time?

5. If upwellings bring nutrient-rich water to the ocean surface, then why might areas where upwellings occur be important to humans?

Section 7.2

6. Is a tsunami similar to a water wave caused by wind? Write a short paragraph in response to this question.

7. If the period of a wave is 15 seconds, how many wavelengths pass a certain point in 2 minutes?

8. If the wavelength of a wave is 20 meters, at what depth is its wave base?

9. If two wave troughs approach each other, what happens when they meet?

10. What happens when the crests of two large waves meet?

11. If the maximum speed of a commercial jet at cruising altitude is about 600 mph, how does this compare to the speed of a tsunami? Conversion factor: 1 km = 0.62 miles.

12. Why does the wavelength of a water wave or a tsunami shorten as it reaches a shoreline?

Section 7.3 and Section 7.4

13. What kinds of plants and animals might you find living on a beach? How do they survive in this environment? Research the answer to these questions or visit a beach a make a list of the organisms you see.

14. Structures called sea arches are featured in the photo at the right. How do you think these structures were formed? Write your answer as a short paragraph.

Photo courtesy NOAA

15. Imagine you could walk from a sand dune on the east coast of the United States all the way to the Mid-Atlantic Ridge in the Atlantic Ocean. Describe what you would see on your journey.

Chapter Projects—A Water Trick

See if you can setup two jars inverted on one another such that the liquid in one jar does not mix with the liquid in the other. *Important hints*: Ask an adult to help you. Work in a tray to catch any spills. Use two same-sized baby food jars that have been cleaned. Fill them to the rims with water. Make choices about the temperature and saltiness of the water in each jar. Add red food coloring to jar A and blue food coloring to jar B. Place an index card over the mouth of the jar B. Using both hands to hold the card to the rim of jar B, invert it on top of jar A. Gently pull out the card.

a. Do the two volumes of water initially mix or stay separated?

b. What will happen to the two volumes of water over time in a room that is at constant temperature?

c. Write up a short report that describes what you did and the results.

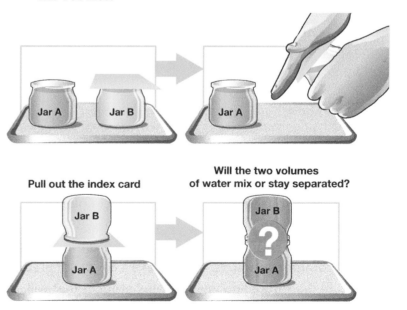

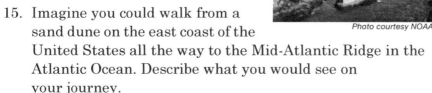

Exploring on Your Own

GPS (Global Positioning System) technology has transformed daily life ever since it was first available to the public in 1983. Find out about the history of GPS and create a historical timeline. On your timeline, include the appearance of GPS in common products. Then, make a couple of predictions for how GPS may be used in the future and invent a new product that will utilize GPS. Add this future of GPS to your timeline.

Chapter 8

Mapping Earth

Earth is an enormous network of systems. Studying large systems can be difficult. Through observations, explorers and scientists have come up with techniques to make the study of Earth easier. One technique for studying Earth is to make a map. There are many kinds of maps. Some maps, like road maps, show Earth as a flat surface. But Earth has mountains and valleys, even on the ocean floor! Topographic and bathymetric maps illustrate Earth's three-dimensional surface on a flat piece of paper. Read on to find out how this is done.

Key Questions:

1. *What is the prime meridian?*

2. *What does the topographic map of a mountain look like?*

3. *How are bathymetric maps made?*

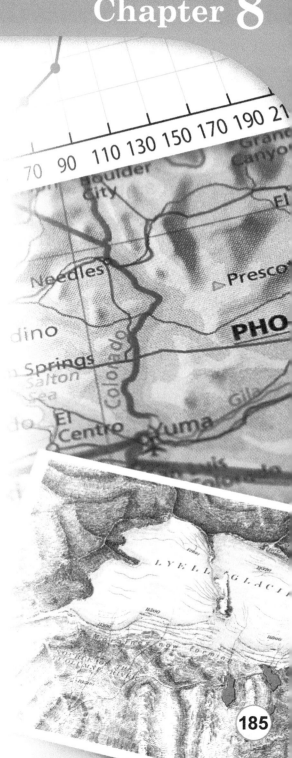

8.1 Maps

A map is a representational drawing of a location. You may be familiar with road maps or state maps. On a local weather report, you might see a map of the United States. There are also world maps. A globe is an example of a world map.

What's on a globe?

A model of Earth   A globe is a model of Earth. By looking at a globe you can see the oceans and continents on Earth's surface. Because a globe is a sphere, Earth's land masses are represented accurately. Key features of a globe are shown below.

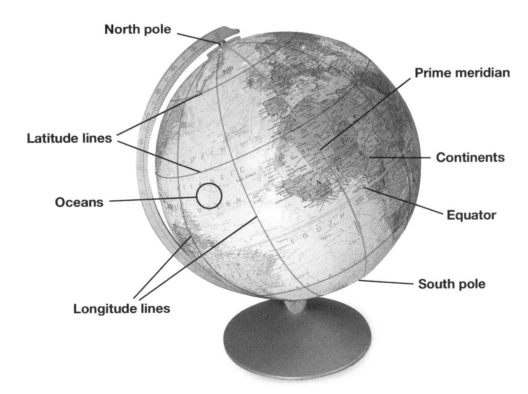

North pole

Prime meridian

Latitude lines

Continents

Oceans

Equator

South pole

Longitude lines

 VOCABULARY

map - a representational drawing of a location.

globe - a map of Earth that models its shape, and the locations and relative sizes of oceans and continents.

 SOLVE IT!

Eartha™—the World's Largest Revolving and Rotating Globe

Eartha™, the world's largest revolving and rotating globe, is located in Yarmouth, Maine, at the DeLorme headquarters (a company that makes maps). If you go to DeLorme headquarters, you can see Eartha™ in its three-story glass room. The globe's diameter is 41 feet 1.5 inches (0.01 km). The diameter of our planet is 12,756 km. How much bigger is Earth compared to Eartha™?

a. About 10 times bigger

b. About 1 million times bigger

c. About 1,000 times bigger

Latitude

What are those lines?

Horizontal and vertical lines on a globe or map form a grid that is useful for identifying the location of any place on our planet. Let's first look at the most well-known horizontal line—the equator.

The equator

The **equator** is an imaginary line around Earth's middle that lies between the north and south poles. Earth's equator is 40,075 kilometers (24,901.5 miles) long. Places located at or near the equator experience about 12 hours of daylight and 12 hours of night every day of the year. In some places around the globe, the location of the equator is marked with signs for tourists (Figure 8.1). The equator is at 0° latitude.

Latitude lines

The equator is a line of *latitude*. **Latitude** lines appear horizontal on a map. They are east-west lines that are north or south of the equator (Figure 8.2). Lines of latitude are also called *parallels*.

Degrees, minutes, and seconds

Each line of latitude represents one degree on Earth's surface. The average distance between each degree is 111 kilometers (69 miles). Each degree is divided into 60 minutes and each minute is divided into 60 seconds. Minutes and seconds in this context represent distances, not time! Figure 8.1 shows how to write the latitude of the equator. Minutes are represented with an apostrophe (') and seconds are represented with a double apostrophe (").

Latitude lines with names

The equator is one line of latitude you know about. Other latitude lines that you may have heard about are listed below. Can you find these on a globe?

Name of latitude line	Approximate location
Arctic Circle	66.5° N
Tropic of Cancer	23.5° N
Tropic of Capricorn	23.5° S
Antarctic Circle	66.5° S

VOCABULARY

equator - an imaginary line around Earth's middle; lies between the north and south poles.

latitude - east-west lines that are north or south of the equator.

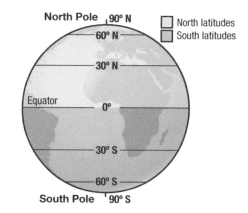

Figure 8.1: *This picture shows a sign that marks the location of the equator.*

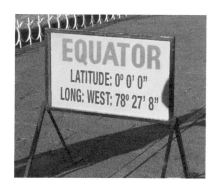

Figure 8.2: *Latitude lines.*

Longitude

Prime meridian

Longitude lines (or *meridians*) run north-south and are east or west of the prime meridian, which is an imaginary line that goes through Greenwich, England, and is perpendicular to the equator. The prime meridian is the 0° line of longitude (Figure 8.3).

The international dateline

The international dateline is an imaginary longitude line located mainly at 180°. Each new day begins at 12:00 a.m. at this line. As a result, you lose a day when you travel east across the line. For example, just before you cross the line it might be 3:00 p.m. on Sunday, but when you cross it, the time is 3:00 p.m. on Monday! If you travel westward across the line, you gain a day. Since this situation can be confusing, the international dateline zig-zags to avoid crossing through countries or territories.

Time zones

For every 15° of longitude past the international dateline, time changes by one hour. For example, when it is 2:00 a.m. at the international dateline, it is midnight in Sydney, Australia (about 30° west of the line).

longitude - north-south lines that are east or west of the prime meridian.

prime meridian - an imaginary line through Greenwich, England and perpendicular to the equator; 0° longitude.

international dateline - an imaginary longitude line located at 180° from the prime meridian.

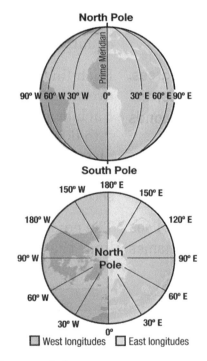

Figure 8.3: *Longitude lines.*

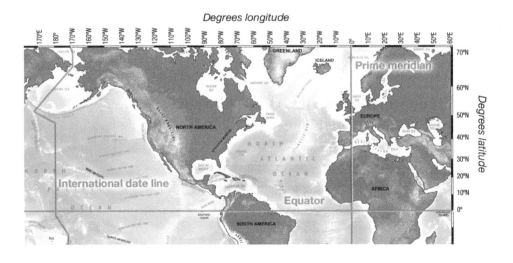

Projections

Globes   On a globe, you can see how the size of Greenland compares to the size of South America (Figure 8.4). Greenland is much smaller. But, look at the map below. What do you notice about the size of Greenland compared to the size of South America?

From a globe to a flat map   If you were traveling, it would be hard to use a globe to find your way. Because globes are an inconvenient size and shape, people prefer flat maps. However, it is difficult to show longitude and latitude on flat maps. To show this grid of lines accurately on a two-dimensional map, map makers have to distort the sizes of the landforms and oceans.

Mercator projection   A Mercator projection converts a section of a globe to a rectangular flat map. A Mercator projection map shows a section of the world as though it were projected on a cylinder. Mercator projections are most accurate where the cylinder touches the globe. Near the equator, landforms and oceans are accurate in size and shape. Near the poles, the landforms are distorted and appear much larger than they actually are.

Figure 8.4: *The image above shows how the size of Greenland compares to the size of South America in reality and on a globe.*

Mercator Projection
Converting a 3-D map to a 2-D map

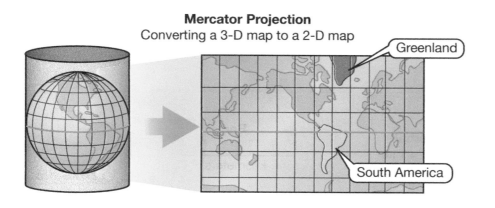

Features of maps

Direction symbols On maps, there is usually a symbol that indicates direction—north, south, east, and west. An example of this direction symbol is shown at the right. Sometimes only the arrow pointing north is shown.

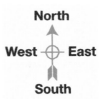

(ă) **VOCABULARY**

legend - a special area on a map that lists and explains the symbols that are used.

A map legend Maps usually have a **legend** that lists and explains the symbols that are used on the map. For example, the legend on a globe may include special lines to indicate the boundaries between countries, and circles of different sizes to represent the population sizes of cities. A legend on a road map might include special lines to indicate different kinds of roads (Figure 8.5) and the locations of places like parks, airports, and hospitals.

Scale of maps The *scale* of a map helps you relate the distances on the map to the larger, real-life distances. There are three kinds of map scales. A *fractional scale* shows the ratio of the map distance to the real-life distance as a fraction. The scale 1/100,000 means that one unit on the map is equal to 100,000 units in real-life. A *verbal scale* expresses the relationship in words, for example, "1 centimeter is equal to 1 kilometer." A *bar scale* is simply a bar drawn on the map with the size of the bar proportional to a distance in real life.

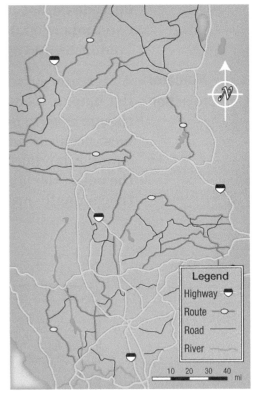

Figure 8.5: *A road map with a legend and a bar scale.*

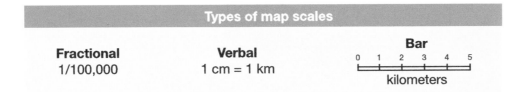

Types of map scales		
Fractional 1/100,000	**Verbal** 1 cm = 1 km	**Bar** 0 1 2 3 4 5 kilometers

8.1 **Section Review**

1. A globe is a more accurate map of the sizes and shapes of landforms on Earth's surface than a flat, paper map. Why?
2. What is the difference between latitude and longitude lines?
3. How is the prime meridian like the equator?
4. How is the prime meridian different from the equator?
5. Give the degree location for the international dateline.
6. You can find Omaha, Nebraska, at 41° 18' north and 95° 54' west. You can find Poughkeepsie, New York, at 41° 38' north and 73° 55' west. Are Poughkeepsie and Omaha near the same line of longitude or near the same line of latitude?
7. What is a Mercator projection?
8. Answer the following questions using the map below.
   a. Using only two-lane roads, how many kilometers is it from point A to point B?
   b. Which point is the furthest east on the map—A, B, C, or D?
   c. Which of the map locations would be most likely to have few or no cars—A, B, C, or D?

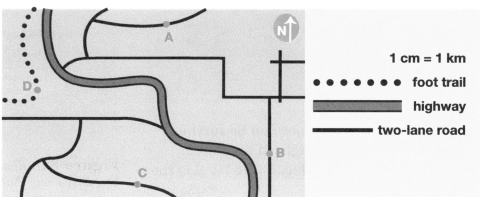

 SOLVE IT!

The location of the Tropic of Cancer is 23.5° N.

How far is the Tropic of Cancer from the equator?

Use this conversion factor:

one degree latitude = 111 km

STUDY SKILLS

Remembering the definitions of terms is an important task in science. One way to make this task easier is to come up with a unique way to remember them.

For example, can you think of a way to remember the difference between *latitude* and *longitude*? Give it a try!

Suggestions: Latitude lines are like the rungs on a ladder (ladder and latitude both start with *la-*). Longitude lines run the long way from one pole to the other.

8.2 Topographic Maps

How can you show a mountain on a flat map? In this section, you will learn about special map lines called *contour lines* that show mountains and other land features. Relief maps and topographic maps are used to show mountains and valleys.

Relief and elevation

Relief Relief describes the distance between high and low places on a map. Shaded relief maps (see below) show mountains and other land features using bumps and colors. For example, the western edges of North and South America would have bumpy ridges on a relief map, indicating mountain ranges. If you can feel bumpy ridges on the continents of a globe, that globe is a relief map.

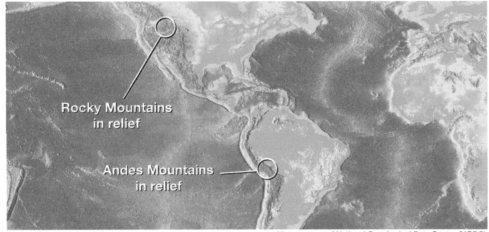

Rocky Mountains in relief

Andes Mountains in relief

Map courtesy of National Geophysical Data Center (NGDC)

Elevation The high, low, and flat places on Earth's surface can be further described using numbers. Elevation is the height of an object measured from a reference level, usually sea level. Sea level is the average level of the ocean (Figure 8.6).

VOCABULARY

relief - the distance between a high and low place on a map.

elevation - the height of an object measured from a reference level such as sea level.

sea level - the average level of the ocean; the halfway point between high tide and low tide.

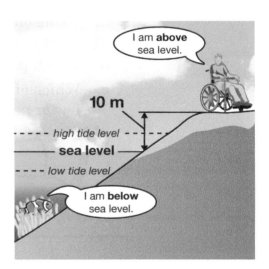

I am **above** sea level.

10 m

high tide level
sea level
low tide level

I am **below** sea level.

Figure 8.6: *Elevation and sea level. You may know that oceans experience tides—sea level is the halfway point between high tide and low tide.*

What is a topographic map?

Mapping the height of a mountain

Bumps or ridges can show mountains on a map. But let's say you wanted to know exactly how high a mountain is. Then, the best kind of map to look at would be a topographic map. A topographic map is a map that uses *contour lines* to show elevation.

Contour lines

Contour lines indicate all points where the elevation is the same. The zero contour line on a topographic map indicates all the points on the map that are at sea level. A 100-meter contour line indicates points that are 100 meters above sea level (Figure 8.7). Contour lines also show the slope of land. Slope (also called *gradient*) is a measure of how steep land is.

Legends for topographic maps

The legends for topographic maps (and other maps) use a range of symbols to show rivers and lakes, roads and railroad tracks, airports, types of vegetation, buildings, and many other things.

Topographic contour	*6000*	River	
Campground	▲	Lake	
Railroad track	┼──┼──┼	Highway	
School	⚑	Woodland	
Many buildings	▮▮	Orchard	

National Map Accuracy Standards

The United States Geological Survey (USGS) publishes about 57,000 topographic maps of the United States. These maps are drawn according to the National Map Accuracy Standards. The standards define accurate measurements for mapmaking so that any map you read can be compared to another map. The scales of most USGS topographic maps are 1:24,000, 1:100,000, 1:250,000, or 1:500,000.

topographic map - a map that uses contour lines to show elevation.

contour lines - curved lines on a map that indicate all the points where the elevation or depth is the same.

slope - a measure of how steep land is; also called gradient.

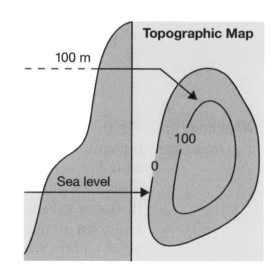

Figure 8.7: *The 0 contour line is always at sea level. A 100-meter contour line shows all places on the map where the elevation is exactly 100 meters above sea level.*

Making a topographic map

Drawing contour lines To understand how contour lines relate to the shape of a land form, imagine that you have a three-dimensional form in a box. The form represents an island. You pour water into the box to a starting level that represents sea level or the 0-meter contour line. By adding more water to the box, the edges of the island get covered. If you look down at the form from above, you will see the shape of the island at an elevation of 10 meters (Figure 8.8).

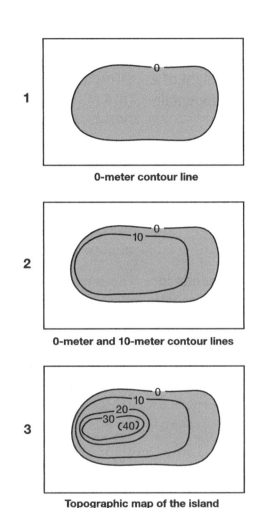

0-meter contour line

0-meter and 10-meter contour lines

Topographic map of the island

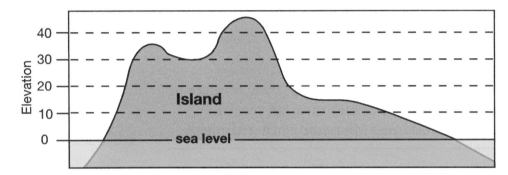

What does the map look like? Figure 8.8 illustrates how contour lines are used to make a topographic map. The 0 contour line shows the outline of the island at sea level. At the 10-meter mark, the outline of the island is smaller and lies inside the 0-meter contour. Only the highest of the two peaks is shown on topographic Map 3. The second peak is less than 40 meters high but taller than 30 meters. A contour line at 35 meters would be needed to see this peak.

Showing the slope of land The spaces between the 0-, 10-, and 20-meter contours are wider on the right side of the map than on the left. This shows that the right side of the island is not as steep as the left side. When contour lines are close together, you know that the land is steep. When contour lines are farther apart, the land is not as steep—it slopes gradually.

Figure 8.8: *Drawing contour lines to make a topographic map. Note that the space between the 10- and 20-meter contour lines is narrower on the left than the right. This shows that the left side of the island is steeper.*

Technology and making a topographic map

The birth of the USGS In 1879, the United States Geological Survey (USGS) was created by an act of the U.S. Congress. The USGS was given the task of mapping public lands. Early employees of the USGS had to travel to places that were often difficult to reach to carry out this task. Their means of transportation was often a team of pack mules.

Plane table surveying Of course, mapmakers in the 1800s did not have computers, electronic equipment, or airplanes to help them make their maps. They used a technique called *plane table surveying*. The plane table includes a horizontal table on a tripod. From the plane table, a surveyor uses a viewing instrument to gauge the height of land at a particular distance. To help with measurements of elevation, another surveyor holds up a tall measuring stick at the area being measured. This technique was used up until the 1970s.

A scientist doing a plane table survey (1941).

Photo by Captain Francis X. Popper, C&GS. Courtesy of NOAA.

Topographic mapping today Starting in the 1940s, scientists began using aerial photographs and other techniques to make topographic maps. Today scientists have computers, electronic devices, and airplanes to help them make maps. Although these tools make it easier to draw an accurate map, it is still a complex process. Today, overlapping aerial photographs are used to create a 3-D image of an area. Special software, computer technology, and stereo glasses are used to make topographic maps (Figure 8.9).

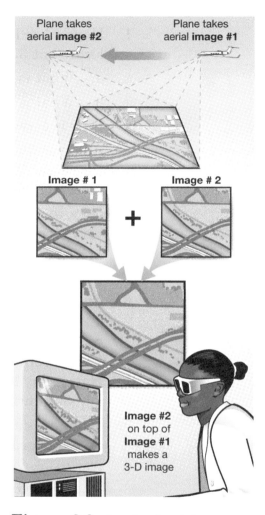

Figure 8.9: *A pair of aerial photographs is used to make a 3-D image that can be translated into a topographic map. Stereo glasses allow the mapmaker to see 3-D images.*

8.2 Section Review

1. House A is located at 100 meters above sea level. House B is located at 350 meters above sea level.

   a. What is the elevation of House B?

   b. What is the relief between House A and House B?

2. How is elevation related to sea level? What is sea level?

3. Answer correct or incorrect. Contour lines are lines on a map that show locations of equal relief. If this statement is incorrect, rewrite it to make it true.

4. On a topographic map, what clue tells you that the land has a very steep slope?

5. Match these islands (A, B, and C) with their topographic map.

6. The scale of a topographic map is 1:24,000, which means one centimeter on the map equals 24,000 centimeters on land. How many kilometers is 24,000 centimeters?

7. What does a scale of 1:500,000 mean on a topographic map?

8. *Challenge*: The most common type of topographic map created by the USGS is a 7.5 minute by 7.5 minute quadrangle map (Figure 8.10). This means that each side of the map is 7 minutes and 30 seconds. Each minute of latitude is 1,852 meters and each second of latitude is 31 meters. How many meters does this map cover in a north-south direction?

CHALLENGE

Mapping challenges

1. Make a map that includes a legend and a scale. Your map can be of your town, school, street, or home.

2. Find a map (in a book or atlas) that has a legend and that shows the scale of the map. Write directions for getting from one place to another, using real-life measurements (miles or kilometers) and indicating landmarks along the way.

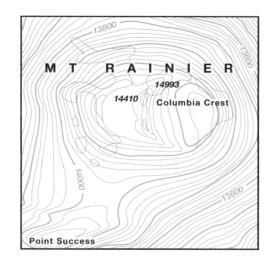

Figure 8.10: *Question 8. These blue contour lines represent the elevation of ice on the mountain top!*

8.3 Bathymetric Maps

You just learned how mountains and valleys on land are represented on a topographic map. In Chapter 7 you learned that mountains and valleys also occur on the bottom of the ocean. A bathymetric map shows the depths of a body of water, such as an ocean, and indicates mountains and valleys where the water is shallower or deeper.

Showing depth

Contour lines   As with elevation, the depth of a body of water is compared to sea level. Bathymetric maps often use contour lines to show depth. Look at Figure 8.11. Can you tell which part of the lake is deepest? Keep in mind that the numbers you see in this graphic are meters *below* sea level!

Using color   Color is also used to show depth in a lake or an ocean. In the image below, shallow areas are light blue and deep areas are darker blue. Find the long undersea mountain chain in the middle of the North Atlantic Ocean. This is called the Mid-Atlantic Ridge. You'll learn more about this ridge in Chapter 11.

bathymetric map - a map that shows the depths of a body of water such as a lake or an ocean.

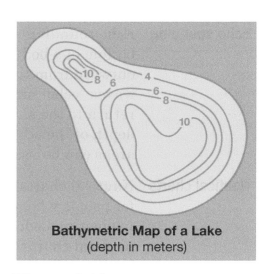

Bathymetric Map of a Lake
(depth in meters)

Figure 8.11: *A bathymetric map of a lake. Where is the lake the deepest? Where is the lake the shallowest?*

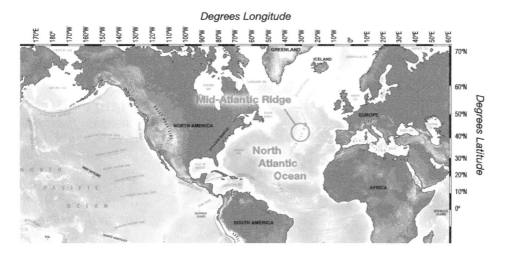

Degrees Longitude

Degrees Latitude

Technology and making bathymetric maps

How do you map the bottom of the ocean? A bathymetric map is a map that shows a body of water with all the water missing. You can't drain all the water out of an ocean or a lake. So, how do scientists make a bathymetric map?

How deep is the ocean? The average ocean depth is 3,711 meters (12,175 feet) and the deepest place of all is the Mariana Trench (located in the Pacific Ocean, near Guam) which is 10,923 meters (35,838 feet). Scientists measure these depths using a technology called *echo sounding* or *sonar*.

Echo sounding Echo sounding uses sound waves to measure the distance to the bottom of a body of water. A device on a ship sends sound waves outward from the bottom of the ship (Figure 8.12). The sound waves "echo" off the ocean floor. The time it takes for the echo to return to the ship and the speed of sound in water indicate the depth of the ocean in that location. The combined data for many areas can be used to map the ocean floor (Figure 8.13).

Nautical charts Nautical charts are important tools for people who are interested in navigating bodies of water. The nautical chart to the right shows a harbor of Puerto Rico. Land is indicated in yellow and water in blue. The contour lines on the yellow region show elevation on land. The contour lines in the blue region show depth of the water. Depths at single locations are indicated by numbers.

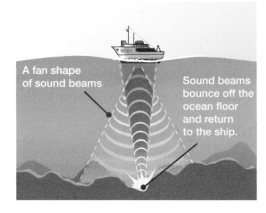

Figure 8.12: *Echo sounding.*

Image courtesy of USGS

Figure 8.13: *A bathymetric map of the ocean floor. Color is used to show elevation and depth. The islands are green and mountains on these islands are yellow. The deep Puerto Rico trench is purple and the other parts of the ocean floor are bright blue. See if you can find this location on a globe!*

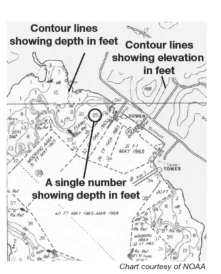

Chart courtesy of NOAA

8.3 Section Review

1. Name two ways that you could show depth on a bathymetric map.

2. Describe how sound waves are used to map the bottom of a lake. What is this technique called?

3. Look at the bathymetric map below.

    a. Which region is 200 meters deep on average at its edge?

    b. What single feature is 4,000 meters deep on the abyssal plain?

    c. What is the range of depth for the region of the ocean floor called the continental rise?

    d. Which ocean is featured in this bathymetric map?

    e. Which coast of the United States is featured on this map—the east or the west coast?

Write a paragraph that compares and contrasts a bathymetric and a topographic map.

Search a local or national newspaper for articles about the bottom of the ocean. Gather your articles and any other information you find into a folder. Use the facts you find to write a story about the ocean floor.

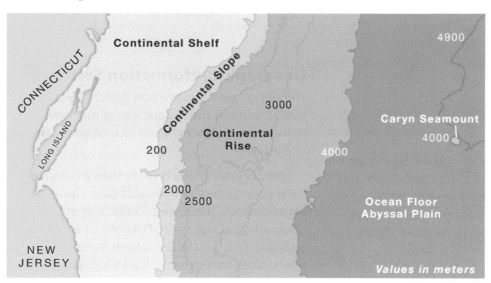

Continental Shelf

CONNECTICUT

Continental Slope

LONG ISLAND

3000

200

Continental Rise

Caryn Seamount

4000

4000

2000
2500

4900

Ocean Floor
Abyssal Plain

NEW JERSEY

Values in meters

Modern Mapmaking

Can you imagine trying to sail around the world without a map? The first Europeans to reach North America did just that. According to archaeologists, mapmaking is thousands of years old. The early maps are rough, but amazingly accurate drawings of surroundings. Some of the first maps showed hunting and fishing areas with detailed drawings.

Mapmaking is known as *cartography*. The early European cartographers were often painters and artists. In the past, cartography was considered more of an art than a science. A picture is really worth a thousand words when it comes to finding your way.

Library of Congress, Geography and Map Division

How things have changed

The first maps were probably drawn on animal skins. Later maps were made using hand-made brushes and parchment paper and then with pens and paper. Early maps were based on what people saw and what they were told. They were not nearly as accurate as they are today. However, they were able to measure distances between points on Earth's surface.

Now, thanks to sophisticated measuring devices, computers, and satellites, cartography is truly a science. One thing that hasn't changed is the importance and the need for maps.

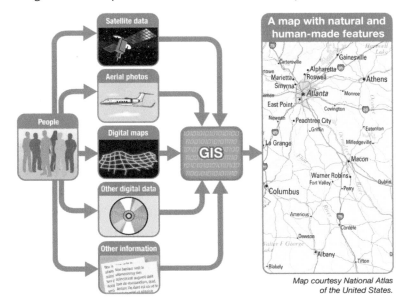

Map courtesy National Atlas of the United States.

Geographic Information System

The Geographic Information System (GIS) is a computer system that automates the production of mapmaking. GIS has the ability to measure distances. It can also calculate the area and borders of features.

The GIS technology is more than a computer system; it is a large collection of people, software, computers, information, and organizations. The system collects, stores, analyzes, and displays information about Earth. Data about Earth's surface are constantly added to GIS. It includes natural features, such as mountains, rivers, lakes, and streams. It also includes things that people have built, such as roads, buildings, and bridges.

Chapter 8 Connection

CAD and cartography

A map being drawn on a computer

Photo courtesy of Catherine Reed

Maps today are drawn on computers, often using computer-aided design (CAD). CAD systems are designed to show geographical features as drawings in a computer. Line thicknesses and colors can be changed easily. For example, a blue line might indicate water. These drawings are handled as separate layers that can easily be found and displayed for viewing alone or together. Because there are "layers" in the computer's files, they can be updated individually as well. For example, CAD allows you to update just the water features of an area or you can work with the water and land features combined!

Technology moves mapping forward

The use of aerial photographs and satellite imagery are ways in which mapmaking has changed. Today remote sensing is used to gather information about Earth from a distance. Remote sensing devices can be used on airplanes as they fly above Earth's surface. Satellites are also used to gather information as they orbit around Earth.

Now, the view from the air or even from space gives mapmakers the ability to make every map as exact as possible. Modern maps can be interactive and are easily updated. The best maps are just a mouse click away. In fact, you can view The National Map at http://viewer.nationalmap.gov/viewer. A few clicks of the mouse allow you to interactively view, customize, and print a map of your choice. The National Map is a topographical map of the nation that provides the public with high quality data and information.

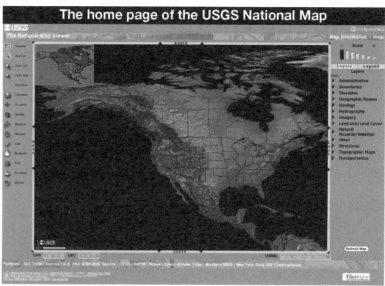

Image courtesy USGS.

Where to go for answers

The National Map, maintained by the United States Geological Survey (USGS), provides critical up-to-date and accurate data. The USGS works with other federal, state, academic, and private mapmaking agencies. Maps are essential tools in the field of geology in that they can record natural resources such as water, minerals, wildlife, and natural hazards such as earthquakes and volcanic activity.

QUESTIONS

1. What is cartography?
2. Describe the Geographic Information System (GIS).
3. In what ways are GIS and CAD systems different?
4. What is an advantage of having the National Map?

Circle the Globe

In this activity you will create a model of Earth. Using a compass, you will orientate your planet and label the major lines of latitude and longitude.

Materials

five-ounce tub of clay, navigational compass, 4¾ inch magnets, three thick rubber bands, permanent marker

What you will do

Part 1: Building your model

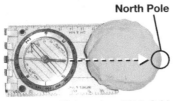

North Pole

Photo courtesy of Kristin Dolci

1. Place all four magnets on top of each other. Place them next to the compass to make sure that they have enough strength to pull the arrow in the compass.

2. Create a ball of clay and place the four magnets inside the center of the ball. This is meant to create a magnetic field similar to the one on Earth, however, it is not an accurate representation of the inside of Earth.

3. Lay the compass flat on the table. Move the ball of clay close to the compass until the compass needle moves freely. Be careful that the needle does not get stuck.

4. Continue to turn the ball of clay until the arrow on the needle (usually a red arrow) is pointing to the ball of clay. The arrow is now pointing in the direction of north for your ball of clay.

5. Using your marker, put a dot on the topside of the ball of clay, furthest from the compass. This is an estimate of the north pole. Note the north pole and magnetic north on Earth are close to one another but are not the same spot.

Part 2: Labeling your model

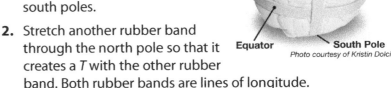

International Dateline (180°)
North Pole
90°W   90°E
Prime Meridian
Equator   South Pole
Photo courtesy of Kristin Dolci

1. Stretch one rubber band around your ball of clay so that it runs across your north pole. Use the marker to label the north and south poles.

2. Stretch another rubber band through the north pole so that it creates a *T* with the other rubber band. Both rubber bands are lines of longitude.

3. Label the bottom arm of the *T* prime meridian, 0° longitude.

4. Label the top arm of the *T* international dateline, 180° longitude.

5. Look at the prime meridian. Everything to the left of the prime meridian all the way to the international dateline is the western hemisphere and everything to the right is the eastern hemisphere.

6. Label the unmarked rubber band to left (west) of the prime meridian as 90° W. And label the unmarked rubber band to the right (east) of the prime meridian as 90° E.

7. The third rubber band is your equator. Stretch your equator around the center of your Earth so that it is perpendicular to your other rubber bands. Label the third rubber band the equator.

Applying your knowledge

a. All lines of latitude would be parallel to which of the rubber bands you labelled?

b. What other major lines of latitude could you have added to your Earth model?

c. What are the benefits of using lines of longitude and latitude when mapmaking?

Chapter 8 Assessment

Vocabulary

Select the correct term to complete the sentences.

legend	bathymetric map	topographic map
equator	contour line	elevation
latitude	map	sea level
longitude	prime meridian	globe
international dateline	relief	slope

Section 8.1

1. A(n) _____ is a representational drawing of a location.

2. Because a(n) _____ is a sphere, Earth's landforms are represented accurately.

3. The _____ is a line that falls between the north and south poles on Earth and that represents 0° latitude.

4. _____ lines are imaginary, horizontal lines on Earth's surface that run east-west and represent north and south locations.

5. _____ lines are imaginary lines on Earth's surface that run north-south and represent east and west locations.

6. The _____ is a line that is perpendicular to the equator and that represents 0° longitude.

7. You are halfway around the world from the prime meridian at the _____.

8. A(n) _____ is list of symbols used on a map.

Section 8.2

9. On a mountain top, the _____ is higher than at sea level.

10. The average water level of the ocean along a coastline is called _____.

11. _____ describes the distance between high and low places on a map.

12. A(n) _____ is a map that shows the surface features of an area and shows elevation by using contour lines.

13. A flat region of land has a(n) _____ of zero.

14. A(n) _____ on a topographic map shows a region of equal elevation.

Section 8.3

15. A(n) _____ is a map that shows the depths of bodies of water.

Concepts

Section 8.1

1. What do latitude and longitude lines represent?

2. The word *hemisphere* means "half a sphere." Which latitude divides Earth into the northern and southern hemisphere?

3. On what continent is this sign located?

4. Lines of latitude are parallel to which imaginary line?

   a. prime meridian   c. international dateline

   b. equator   d. the Mid-Atlantic Ridge

5. Fill in the blanks. All the places in Australia have _____ (north or south) latitude lines and _____ (east or west) longitude lines.

6. If you wanted to see an accurate representation of the sizes of the continents, would you use a Mercator projection map? Why or why not?

7. Why is a legend an important part of a map? What would happen if a map did not include a legend?

8. A verbal scale is 1 centimeter = 1 meter. Use this information to make a bar scale that shows a distance of 4 meters.

Section 8.2

9. Look at this diagram and label it using these terms. One term will not be used.

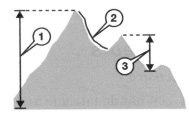

   a. slope   c. elevation
   b. relief   d. sea level

10. How are plane table surveying and photogrammetry similar and different? Answer this question as a short paragraph.

11. Look at the topographic map below.

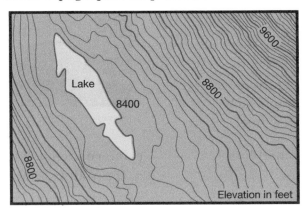

   a. Where are the steepest slopes on the map?
   b. Where is the lowest elevation shown on this map?
   c. What is the lowest elevation?
   d. Where are the gentlest slopes?

Section 8.3

12. List two differences between a topographic and a bathymetric map.

13. Briefly describe how scientists measure the depth of parts of the ocean.

14. A topographic map of a mountain with one high peak would look most like which type of bathymetric map?

   a. A map of a circular lake that is very deep
   b. A long, shallow river
   c. A harbor on the west coast of the United States
   d. A mountain stream

15. Why are nautical charts good safety tools?

Math and Writing Skills

Section 8.1

1. Look at a globe or another kind of world map. Pick a place that you have never been. Answer the following questions.
   a. What is the name of this place?
   b. What is its location in latitude and longitude?
   c. What hemisphere is it in—the north or south; the east or the west?
   d. Make a hypothesis about the kind of weather that is common in this place. Justify your answer.
   e. Write a short, fictional story about this place.
   f. Then, do some research on the Internet or in your library to find three facts about this place.

2. The location of the Tropic of Cancer is about 23° north of the equator. The location of the Tropic of Capricorn is about 23° south of the equator. About how far apart are these two lines of latitude in kilometers? Helpful information: Each degree of latitude represents 111 kilometers.

3. When it is 4:00 a.m. at the international dateline, at which longitude will a new day be beginning?

   a. 30° west
   b. 15° east of the international dateline
   c. 60° north of the equator
   d. 60° west of the international dateline

4. A map is drawn with 1 centimeter equal to 2 miles.

   a. How many centimeters equal 10 miles?
   b. How many miles does 4 centimeters represent?

5. Use the world map on the next page to answer the following questions.

   a. Where would you be at Lat. 0° Long. 0°—on water or land?
   b. Through what continent does the international dateline cross?
   c. Give the locations of the marked cities to the closest whole degree. Use this format for writing the locations—New York, Lat 41°N Long 74°W. The space between each line represents 10 degrees.
   Atlanta, Chicago, San Francisco, Honolulu, São Paulo, Paris, Moscow, Cape Town, Sydney

Section 8.2

6. The scale of a topographic map is 1:250,000 which means one centimeter on the map equals 250,000 centimeters on land. How many kilometers is 250,000 centimeters?

7. Look at the topographic map from Concepts question 11. How many feet does each contour line represent? (*Hint*: Subtract 8,400 from 8,800 and divide the answer by the number of lines between these two elevations.)

8. Make a sketch that shows a topographic map of a mountain. Use four contour lines to make your sketch.

9. Make a sketch that shows a topographic map of a mountain that has a very steep slope on one side and a very gradual slope on the other side.

Section 8.3

10. Imagine you want to know the depth of a lake. You have a really long pole and a measuring tape. How could you use these tools to find out how deep the lake is?

11. Make a sketch of a bathymetric map of your bathtub at home or a sink. The map should show the shape of your tub or sink. The map does not have to include measurements.

Chapter Project—Making maps

Now it's your turn to make maps.

   a. You want your friends to come to a party at your house after school. They have never been to your house before, so you have decided that the best way to give them directions is to create a map from school to your house. Include all important features along the route. Be sure your map is to scale, has a legend, symbols and other important map features. Remember, it must be accurate and easy to read!

   b. You decide that you want your party to have a pirate theme. You hide a treasure and draw a map for your friends to use to find it. Make your treasure map easy to follow.

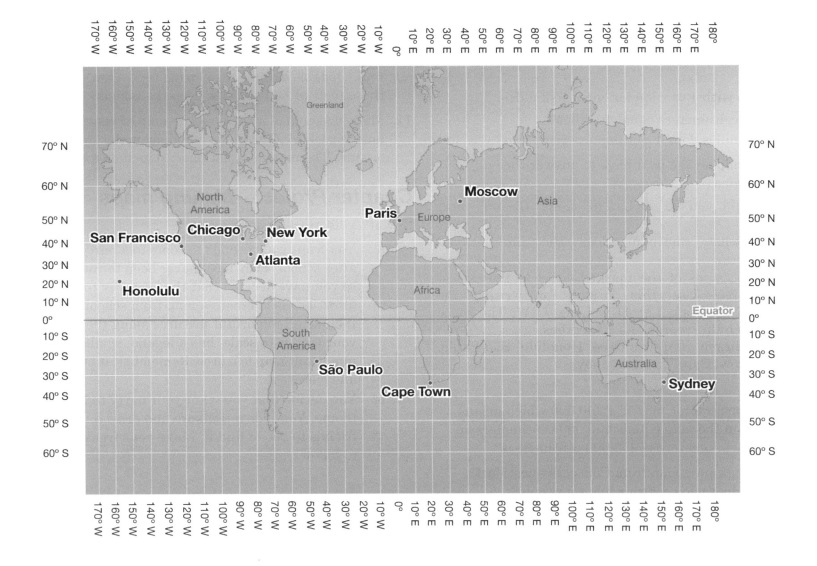

Earth and Time

If you wanted to learn about people and places that existed 50 years ago, what would you do? Most likely, you would read a history book. You might also talk to your grandparents to find out about how things were a long time ago.

Fifty years is a long time for people, but in terms of our planet, 50 years is not a long time. Our planet is 4.6 billion years old! How do you think scientists learn about Earth's ancient past? For starters, they might look at the layers of rock underfoot. Fortunately, there are places on Earth where the layers are above ground for all to see. One such place is the Grand Canyon. In this chapter, you will learn how scientists "read" Earth's history from layers of rocks and fossils.

Key Questions:

1. How is the Grand Canyon like a history book?

2. How old is Earth?

3. What is the difference between relative and absolute dating?

9.1 Relative Dating

Earth science is a large field of science that includes geology, the study of rocks and rock formations (Figure 9.1). This section is about geology and the scientific processes used to study it.

ā VOCABULARY

geology - the study of rocks and rock formations.

The beginnings of geology

Shark's teeth In 1666, Nicolas Steno, a Danish anatomist, studied a shark's head and noticed that the shark's teeth resembled mysterious stones called "tonguestones" that were found inside of local rocks. At that time, people believed that tonguestones had either fallen from the moon or that they grew inside the rocks. Steno theorized that tonguestones looked like shark's teeth because they actually *were* shark's teeth that had been buried and became fossils!

How did teeth get inside a rock? Steno realized that when an animal dies it is eventually covered by layers of sediment. The animal's soft parts decay quickly, but bones and teeth do not. Over a long period of time, the sediment around the dead animal becomes rock, with the bones and teeth inside.

Figure 9.1: *Examples of rock formations.*

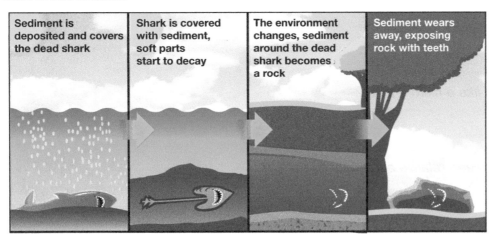

What is relative dating?

Steno's ideas
Steno's observations helped him develop ideas about how rocks and fossils form. His ideas are still used today in the study of geology as a technique called relative dating. Relative dating is a method of putting events in the order in which they happened.

What is a fossil?
Relative dating is used to learn the age of a fossil—the remains or traces of a dead animal or plant that has been preserved for a long time. A paleontologist is a scientist who studies fossils.

How is relative dating used?
Relative dating is used to determine the general age of a rock, rock formation, or fossil. Relative dating does not try to determine the exact age of an object, but instead uses clues to figure out the order of events over time. For example, you could use relative dating to figure out which event in the graphic at the right—the foot step, tire track, or snow fall—occurred first.

Snow depth

The present explains the past
Like Steno, Scottish geologist James Hutton (1726–1797) was an important figure in the development of modern geology. Hutton found that if you understand processes that are happening now, you can use that knowledge to explain what happened a long time ago. The short form of his idea is *the present explains the past.*

Comparing the present and past
When it rains really hard you might see flowing water washing away sediment (Figure 9.2). When the rains stops, you might observe that grooves were left behind by the flowing water. Observations of common, small-scale events in the present like this are helpful for understanding how large land features formed. For example, the Grand Canyon was formed by the Colorado River (see next page).

(see next page)

 VOCABULARY

relative dating - a method of putting events in the order in which they happened.

fossil - the remains or traces of a dead animal or plant that has been preserved for a long time.

paleontologist - a scientist who studies and identifies fossils.

Photo by Jack Dykinga, ARS/USDA.

Figure 9.2: *The way water affects land is seen every time it rains.*

Identifying clues using relative dating

Identifying clues   Steno's ideas for relative dating include superposition, original horizontality, and lateral continuity. These ideas help identify the clues you need to put events in the order in which they happened.

What is superposition?   *Superposition* means that the bottom layer of a rock formation is older than the layer on top, because the bottom layer formed first. A stack of old newspapers illustrates superposition (Figure 9.3).

Original horizontality   Sediment particles settle to the bottom of a body of water, such as a lake, in response to gravity. The result is horizontal layers of sediment. Over time, these layers can become layers of rock. This principle is called *original horizontality*. As you see in the graphic below, sometimes horizontal layers of rock may become tilted by a geological even and are found in a vertical position.

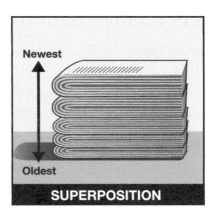

Figure 9.3: *A stack of old newspapers illustrates superposition. The oldest newspaper is on the bottom of the stack and the more recent newspapers are piled on, with the most recent on top.*

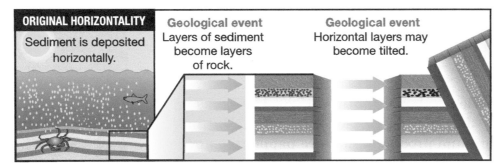

Lateral continuity   *Lateral continuity* is the idea that when layers of sediment are formed, they extend in all directions horizontally. Later, a separation may be caused by a geological event such as *erosion* (the breaking down of rock as it is moved by water) or an earthquake. The Colorado River created the gap that is now the Grand Canyon. If you were to compare rock layers in the Grand Canyon, you would find that the layers on one side of the canyon match up with the layers on the other side (Figure 9.4).

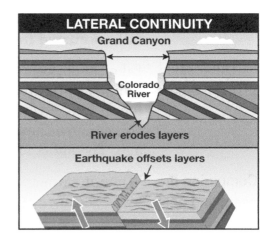

Figure 9.4: *Layers of rock are continuous unless a river erodes the layers or an earthquake moves them.*

The order of events and relative age

Cross-cutting relationships The theory of *cross-cutting relationships* states that a vein of rock that cuts across a rock's layers is younger (more recent) than the layers. Figure 9.5 shows a rock formation with three layers and a cross-cutting vein. The rock layers formed first. The vein formed when molten rock oozed into a crack in the original rock, cutting across the layers. The bottom layer is the oldest part of the rock formation and the vein is the youngest. The middle and top layers formed after the bottom layer, but before the vein.

Inclusions Sometimes rock pieces called *inclusions* are found inside another rock. During the formation of a rock with inclusions, sediments or melted rock surrounded the inclusions and then solidified. Therefore, the inclusions are older than the surrounding rock (Figure 9.5). A rock with inclusions is like a chocolate chip cookie. The chocolate chips (inclusions) are made first. Then they are added to the batter (melted rock or sediment) before being baked (hardened) into a cookie (rock).

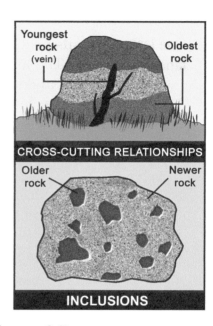

Figure 9.5: *Cross-cutting relationships and inclusions.*

Faunal succession *Faunal succession* means that fossils can be used to identify the relative age of the layers of a rock formation (Figure 9.6). For example, dinosaur fossils are found in rock that is about 65 to 200 million years old because these animals lived that long ago. The fossils of modern human beings (*Homo sapiens*) are found in rock that is about 40,000 years old, but not in rock that is 65 to 200 million years old. And dinosaur fossils are not found in rock that is 40,000 years old. This means that human beings did not live at the same time as the dinosaurs. How could you learn which plants and animals *did* live at the same time as the dinosaurs?

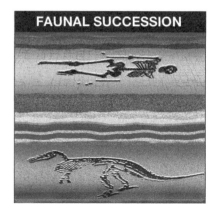

Figure 9.6: *Faunal succession.*

Fossils and Earth's changing surface

One large landmass Fossils provide evidence for how Earth's surface has changed over time. The left side of the graphic below shows the way Earth looked about 250 millions of years ago. Much of the land was part of a large landmass called Pangaea. The colors on the map show regions where various animals and plants lived. What would the climate have been like in the regions close to the South Pole?

Earth today Eventually, pieces of Pangaea separated and moved away from the South Pole. The right side of the graphic shows the way land is distributed today. The colors show where you would find the fossils of the organisms featured in Figure 9.7. The black dotted line marks where glaciers used to be.

Cynognathus ("Dog jaw")
Primitive mammal

Glossopteris (*Glossa* means "tongue" in Greek; this plant had tongue-shaped leaves)
Seed fern

Lystrosaurus ("Shovel lizard")
Primitive mammal

Mesosaurus ("Middle lizard")
Freshwater reptile

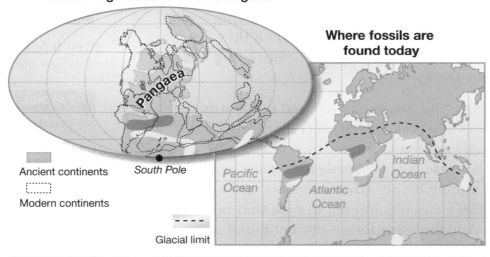

Where organisms lived on Pangaea

Pangaea

Ancient continents

Modern continents

South Pole

Glacial limit

Where fossils are found today

Pacific Ocean

Atlantic Ocean

Indian Ocean

Range of organisms

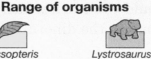
Cynognathus

Glossopteris

Lystrosaurus

Mesosaurus

Figure 9.7: *These organisms lived on Earth when the land was connected as one large landmass, Pangaea.*

9.1 **Section Review**

1. Describe Nicolas Steno's contribution to modern geology.

2. How are a vein of rock and an inclusion similar? How are they different? Describe a vein and an inclusion in your answer.

3. What idea is represented in the illustration at the right? Which organism is oldest? Which is youngest? How can you tell?

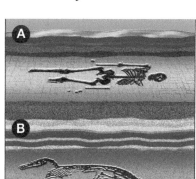

4. True or False: Superposition states that rock layers near the surface of Earth are younger than rock layers further from the surface. Explain your reasoning.

5. How is the Grand Canyon like a history book?

6. Why is there evidence of glaciers in Africa?

7. Why do fossils in South America match fossils in Africa?

8. Study the following picture. Which is the oldest layer of rock? Which layer is the youngest?

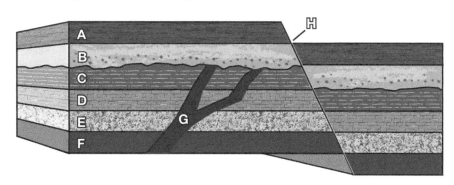

CHALLENGE

Use classroom resources, home resources, or the Internet to research the geology of the Grand Canyon. Then, answer the following questions.

1. When was the Grand Canyon formed?
2. How was it formed?
3. What are the different rock layers found in the Grand Canyon?
4. How old is the oldest rock layer?
5. How is the Grand Canyon changing today? Why is it changing?

SOLVE IT!

Look at the graphic to the left at the bottom of the page. In question 8, you identified the oldest and youngest layer of rock. Now, place the layers in order from oldest to youngest.

9.2 Geologic Time

The **geologic time scale** is a model of Earth's history. This section describes Earth's history from 4,570 million years ago (mya) until now. Parts of Earth's history are divided into eras that are determined by the main life forms that were present at the time. Each era is divided into smaller blocks of time called periods. Periods are determined based on the fossils found within each era.

Earth's earliest history

Precambrian   The Precambrian lasted from 4,570 to 542 mya. The first primitive living cells appeared more than 3,000 mya. Single-celled and soft-bodied organisms appeared toward the end of this time. Later, photosynthetic bacteria evolved and began to add oxygen to Earth's atmosphere. Some of that oxygen reached Earth's upper atmosphere and formed the ozone layer. The ozone layer blocked harmful radiation from the Sun. This allowed life to move out of the water and onto dry land.

Paleozoic Era   The Paleozoic Era lasted from 542 to 251 mya. *Paleozoic* is a Greek word meaning "ancient life." Rocks from the Paleozoic Era contain fossils of snails, clams, corals, and trilobites (Figure 9.8). New life forms developed early in this era. Later, in the Ordovician Period, glaciers covered Earth, causing many of these organisms to become extinct. In the Late Silurian–Early Devonian Periods, modern bony fishes appeared. Next, plants and air-breathing animals began to populate the land. Toward the end of the Paleozoic Era, much of the land was covered with forests of palm trees and giant ferns. Therapsids are a group of animals that dominated the land in the Permian Period. Scientists have determined that mammals evolved from therapsids (Figure 9.9).

Figure 9.8: *A trilobite fossil.*

Figure 9.9: *Examples of primitive mammals called therapsids.*

The Mesozoic Era to the present

Mesozoic Era The Mesozoic Era lasted from 251 to 65 mya. *Mesozoic* is a Greek word meaning "middle life." At the beginning of this era, Earth's continents were connected in one "supercontinent" called Pangaea. During the Triassic Period, pieces of Pangaea moved apart. The Mesozoic Era is often called the Age of Reptiles. Dinosaurs are the best-known reptiles of this era and dominated Earth for about 150 million years. The Jurassic Period was marked by the appearance of the first birds. During the Cretaceous Period, the Rocky Mountains in the western part of the United States began to form. Flowering plants also evolved during the Cretaceous Period. At the end of the Mesozoic Era, 65 mya, dinosaurs and many other animal and plant species abruptly became extinct. Geologic evidence indicates that a giant asteroid may have hit Earth, causing the extinctions.

Cenozoic Era to the present The Cenozoic Era began 65 mya and continues today. *Cenozoic* means "recent life." The two periods of this era are the Palaeogene and Neogene. The periods are divided into smaller periods of time called epochs. For example, the Neogene Period includes the Miocene, Pliocene, Pleistocene, and Holocene Epochs. The Holocene Epoch, which started about 10,000 years ago, is still going on today. Fossils from the Cenozoic Era are closest to Earth's surface, making them easier to find. Therefore, scientists have the most information about life in this era. The Cenozoic Era is often called the Age of Mammals because mammals diversified into a variety of species including land mammals, sea mammals, and flying mammals (Figure 9.10). The first ancestors of humans appeared about 4 million years ago. Modern humans appeared in the geologic record 40,000 years ago. The continents moved into the positions that they are in today during this era.

Mammoth

Smilodon

Eohippus

Figure 9.10: *The Age of Mammals.*

MY JOURNAL

Imagine you could go back in time and visit any period of Earth's geologic history. Which period would you want to visit? Why would you want to visit this time in geologic history?

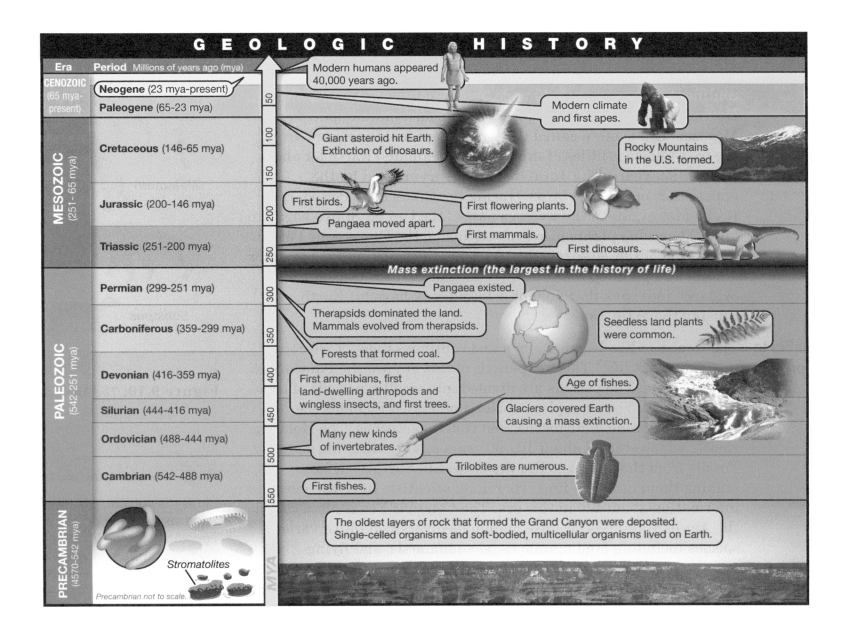

GEOLOGIC HISTORY

Era	Period	Millions of years ago (mya)
CENOZOIC (65 mya-present)	**Neogene** (23 mya-present)	
	Paleogene (65-23 mya)	
MESOZOIC (251-65 mya)	**Cretaceous** (146-65 mya)	
	Jurassic (200-146 mya)	
	Triassic (251-200 mya)	
PALEOZOIC (542-251 mya)	**Permian** (299-251 mya)	
	Carboniferous (359-299 mya)	
	Devonian (416-359 mya)	
	Silurian (444-416 mya)	
	Ordovician (488-444 mya)	
	Cambrian (542-488 mya)	
PRECAMBRIAN (4570-542 mya)		

Modern humans appeared 40,000 years ago.

Modern climate and first apes.

Giant asteroid hit Earth. Extinction of dinosaurs.

Rocky Mountains in the U.S. formed.

First birds.

First flowering plants.

Pangaea moved apart.

First mammals.

First dinosaurs.

Mass extinction (the largest in the history of life)

Pangaea existed.

Therapsids dominated the land. Mammals evolved from therapsids.

Seedless land plants were common.

Forests that formed coal.

First amphibians, first land-dwelling arthropods and wingless insects, and first trees.

Age of fishes.

Glaciers covered Earth causing a mass extinction.

Many new kinds of invertebrates.

Trilobites are numerous.

First fishes.

The oldest layers of rock that formed the Grand Canyon were deposited. Single-celled organisms and soft-bodied, multicellular organisms lived on Earth.

Stromatolites

Precambrian not to scale.

MYA

Absolute dating

What is absolute dating? Absolute dating is a method of measuring the age of an object such as a rock or fossil in *years*. Scientists use both absolute and relative dating to develop the geologic time scale. Absolute dating requires the use of a natural "clock." That clock is the *radioactive decay* of certain naturally-occurring elements like uranium and carbon.

Radioactive decay Radioactive decay refers to how unstable atoms lose energy and matter over time. Unstable atoms are called *radioactive isotopes*. As a result of radioactive decay, an isotope turns into another element over a period of time. An element is a substance composed of only one kind of atom. Uranium-238 is an radioactive isotope of uranium that decays in several steps, eventually becoming lead, a stable, nonradioactive element.

The half-life of uranium It takes 4.5 billion years for one half of the uranium-238 atoms in a specimen to turn into lead. We say that 4.5 billion years is the *half-life* for the radioactive decay of uranium-238 (Figure 9.11). Half-life is the amount of time it takes for half of the unstable atoms in a sample to decay. If a rock contains uranium-238, scientists can determine the rock's age by the ratio of uranium-238 to lead atoms in the sample. Understanding radioactive decay has allowed scientists to determine the age of rocks and fossils found on Earth.

Earth is around 4.6 billion years old The oldest rocks found on Earth so far are around 4 billion years old. Scientists can't determine Earth's exact age by dating Earth's rocks because the oldest rocks have been destroyed. But scientists have found moon rocks and meteorites that are around 4.6 billion years old. Since Earth was formed at the same time as the rest of the solar system, Earth must be around 4.6 billion years old, too.

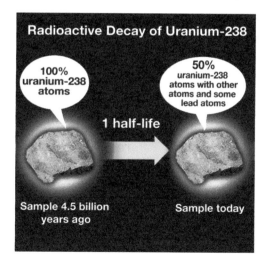

Figure 9.11: *The radioactive decay of uranium to lead. Radioactive decay is measured in half-lives. After one half-life, 50% of the uranium-238 atoms have decayed.*

Trees and absolute dating

What tree rings can tell us
If you look at a log of wood, you will notice circular layers called *tree rings* (Figure 9.12). Counting these rings can tell you how old a tree is. Studying tree rings is a method of absolute dating. The pattern of the rings is a record of the tree's growth over a number of years.

One tree ring equals one year
A tree grows one tree ring for every year that it is alive (Figure 9.12). For pine trees, one tree ring includes two bands—one light and one dark.

Very old trees
The oldest tree that we know about, a bristlecone pine called Methuselah, is 4,838 years old. It is located in the White Mountains of California. A bristlecone pine is pictured in Figure 9.13. Redwood trees, the world's tallest trees at about 300 feet tall, are also found in California and can live as long as 2,000 years.

Tree-ring dating
Andrew Douglass (1867–1962) was an astronomer who discovered the significance of tree rings. In the early 1900s, Douglass hypothesized that trees might record what Earth's climate was like in the past. He began to test his hypothesis by studying and recording the tree ring patterns of various types of trees. By 1911, he had proven that trees within a similar area had matching tree ring patterns. Wide tree rings indicated a very wet year and narrow rings indicated a dry year. Douglass named this new field of science *dendrochronology* (tree-ring dating).

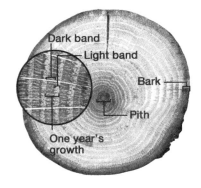

Figure 9.12: *A cross-section of a pine tree shows tree rings. Each ring is composed of two bands—a dark and a light band. One tree ring equals one year's growth.*

Figure 9.13: *A bristlecone pine.*

9.2 Section Review

1. Explain how time is divided in the geologic time scale.

2. Which answer is correct? During the Precambrian:
   a. human beings lived and thrived.
   b. dinosaurs became extinct.
   c. single-celled and soft-bodied organisms appeared.
   d. flowering plants evolved.

3. List two events of the Mesozoic Era.

4. What is the difference between relative dating and absolute dating?

5. How much uranium is left if a solid piece exists for one half-life?

6. How have scientists determined the age of Earth? How old is Earth?

7. The half-life of uranium-238 is 4.5 billion years. The half-life of carbon-14, another radioactive element, is 5,730 years. You want to use absolute dating to determine the age of a rock that was about as old as Earth. Would you measure the radioactive decay of carbon-14 or uranium-238? Explain your answer.

8. If a tree has 25 rings, how old is it?

9. Figure 9.14 shows cross-sections from two trees that grew in different environments.
   a. The trees were the same age when they were cut. How old are these trees?
   b. Write a description that explains the wet and dry conditions for each tree during each year of its lifetime.

Pick one period in Earth's geologic history and do *one* of the following projects.

1. Research it and create a colorful timeline for this period.

2. Write a report about the major events that happened during this period.

3. Write a short story about this period in Earth's geologic history. Your story should include one or more major events that happened during this period.

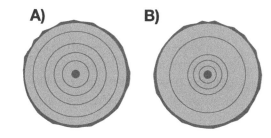

Figure 9.14: *Question 9.* Note: *When counting rings, do not count the very center (called the pith).*

It's All in the Rings

How old are you? Can you think of how you changed between your last two birthdays (other than to add a candle to your cake, that is)? As children grow, they get taller, or more muscular, or acquire other characteristics that indicate they are getting older. Trees get older and taller each year, too, and their years are marked by growth rings. Dendrochronologists are scientists who study tree rings to date past events. By studying the rings, they can tell how old the wood is to the exact year. Imagine finding trees that are 500, 1,000, or even more than 4,000 years old!

Tree rings

Generally, trees growing in mild climates produce one growth ring per year. Tree-ring growth is affected by rainfall, temperature, and nutrients in the soil. Trees that grow under good conditions have wide ring growth. Those growing under poor conditions produce narrow rings. Each tree ring typically represents an annual growth cycle.

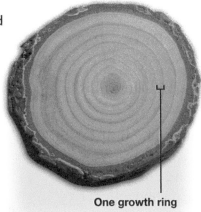

One growth ring

However, counting tree rings to determine a tree's age is not enough. Occasionally, a tree may grow a "false band" that looks like a ring, but is not. Also, extreme drought or injury to the tree can reduce its growth so that a ring is only present in some parts of the trees and may be only visible with a microscope. Dendrochronologists use cross-dating (matching patterns among tree samples) to make sure dates are accurate. This means studying 20 or more trees of the same species growing under similar conditions.

Bristlecone pines—the oldest living trees

Conifers are cone-bearing, needle trees that are often chosen for research. Fir and pine trees are easy to work with because they have clear rings and they grow to be quite old. Some trees, such as maples and oaks, may live to be 250–500 years old. But conifers may live thousands of years.

Bristlecone Pine

Bristlecone pines are the oldest known living trees on Earth. People often think that big trees with big, wide trunks are old. But big does not necessarily mean old. Bristlecone pines grow slowly and are not that large. They are able to ward off insects and disease and that allows them to live a long, long time. A bristlecone pine named Methuselah is growing in the White Mountains of California and is the oldest living tree in the world. Discovered in 1953 by Edmund Schulman, this tree is more than 4,838 years old and still alive!

Clues from the past

We can learn a lot about the past from tree rings. Scientists use tree-ring data to understand past climates, glacier movements, fires, droughts, and insect outbreaks. This information can be used to solve problems in other areas of science such as ecology, climatology, geology, and anthropology. For ecologists studying living things and their environment, tree-ring analysis provides information about insect outbreaks and fires. Climatologists (who study climates) learn about droughts and cold spells. Geologists studying Earth's structure use the data to learn about volcanic eruptions and earthquakes. Anthropologists studying human societies learn how they lived in the past, using tree-ring data to understand historical buildings and ruins. For examples, scientists have used tree rings to date ruins from Ancestral Puebloans in the Southwest United States.

Laboratory of Tree-Ring Research: touchdown!

Who would expect to find scientific research going on under a football stadium? The Laboratory of Tree-Ring Research (LTRR) at the University of Arizona in Tucson has been there for years. In 1937, Andrew Ellicott Douglass founded the lab—the first of its kind in the country—and became the father of dendrochronology. Douglass, an astronomer, hoped tree rings would provide records about past sunspot cycles. He looked for a link among the Sun, climate, and tree-ring growth.

Douglass needed space for his tree-ring samples and a sports stadium seemed to be the answer. Today, the lab occupies two floors under the stadium, and contains over 600,000 tree-ring samples.

At LTRR, researchers, professors, and students are involved in many projects. Rex Adams, senior research specialist (seen in this photo), takes field trips across the western United States for climate, fire, and ecology studies.

Photo - courtesy of Melanie Lenart, Laboratory of Tree Ring Research, University of Arizona

He studies the tree-ring samples he brings back to unlock past events. For Adams, the best part of his job is working in the field collecting samples. He compares his work to doing a crossword puzzle or solving a mystery. And yes, if Adams or others work on a Saturday afternoon in the fall, the lab does rock a bit during a football game!

QUESTIONS

1. What do wide and narrow tree rings mean?
2. Count the tree rings in the cross-section on the previous page. How old was this tree when it was cut down?
3. Why are fir and pine trees commonly used for tree-ring analysis?
4. How are tree-ring data used?
5. Who was Andrew Ellicott Douglass?

Relative and Absolute Dating

Relative dating is a process used to place rocks and events in the order in which they occur. *Absolute dating* is used to determine the more precise age of a rock. Both types of dating help tell Earth's history.

Activity 1—Relative dating practice

1. Look at Diagram A. Place the leaves in the order of when they fell on the ground from first to last. Can you order all of the leaves? Why or why not?

2. Look at Diagram B. Put the rock layers in order of youngest to oldest. Include in the list Fault M. This one is challenging!

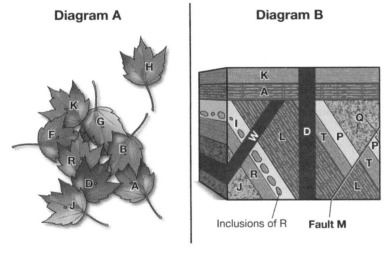

Diagram A   **Diagram B**

Inclusions of R   **Fault M**

Activity 2—Relative and absolute dating

In this activity, you will learn how scientists figure out the age of rocks using relative and absolute dating. This part is challenging so you may work with a partner.

Materials: four small containers (like film canisters)—one has 16 pennies, one has 8 pennies, one has 4 pennies, and one has 2 pennies

1. Look at Diagram C. This is a graph showing the decay of unstable atoms in a rock sample. Unstable atoms are called *radioactive isotopes*. A half-life is the time that it takes for half the amount of radioactive isotope to decay. After one half-life, the amount of isotope in the rock decays by one half, so only half the original is left. After two half-lives, the isotope decays again by half, so only one quarter of the original is left. This trend continues.

2. Each of your four containers is a rock made of radioactive isotopes (pennies). Over time, the isotopes have decayed. Place the containers in order from youngest to oldest.

3. The half-life of the penny isotope is 2 million years. If each rock (container) started with 32 pennies, how many half-lives have gone by for each rock (container)?

4. How old is each rock (container)?

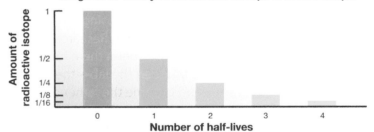

Diagram C: Decay of radioactive isotope in a rock sample

Applying your knowledge

a. What is the relative dating principle that you used to determine the order in which the leaves fell—superposition or cross-cutting relationships?

b. Which of these relative dating principles are used to determine the order of rock layers and the fault? *superposition, original horizontality, inclusions, cross-cutting relationships*

c. How much of a radioactive isotope sample exists after one half-life?

Chapter 9 Assessment

Vocabulary

Select the correct term to complete the sentences.

geology   relative dating   radioactive decay

fossil   paleontologist   absolute dating

geologic time scale   element   half-life

Section 9.1

1. Through their observations of rock formations, Nicholas Steno and James Hutton helped develop the field of _____.

2. _____ is a method that involves putting events in the order in which they happened.

3. An ancient shark tooth is an example of a(n) _____.

4. A scientist who studies fossils is called a (n) _____.

Section 9.2

5. Uranium is a(n) _____ that has a half-life of 4.5 billion years.

6. The _____ is divided into blocks of time called eras and eras are divided into periods.

7. _____ refers to how unstable atoms lose energy and matter over time.

8. The _____ of uranium is 4.5 billion years.

9. _____ is a way of determining the age of something in years.

Concepts

Section 9.1

1. If you had a question about where to find trilobite fossils would you ask a meteorologist or a paleontologist? Explain your answer.

2. Why are superposition and lateral continuity useful ideas in interpreting how the Grand Canyon formed?

3. Use relative dating to identify the order in which each line was drawn. Which line was drawn first? Which line was drawn last?

4. An inclusion is:

   a. younger than surrounding rock.

   b. the same age as surrounding rock.

   c. older than surrounding rock.

5. Due to original horizontality, layers of sediment form in horizontal layers. However, sometimes these layers (once they become rock) are found in other positions. What kinds of events might cause layers of rock to change positions?

6. Put the rock bodies (A, B, C, and D) illustrated at the right in order from oldest to youngest.

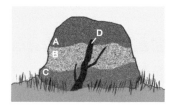

7. How do scientists use the ideas of faunal succession to identify how long ago different animals lived?

Section 9.2

8. Which era lasted the longest time during geologic history?

9. Match the organism or event to the era in which it first appeared.

   a. dinosaurs   e. mass extinction of dinosaurs

   b. therapsids   f. Pangaea

   c. humans   g. giant ferns

   d. single-celled organisms   h. fishes

10. Uranium decays into a more stable element called:

   a. lead.   c. carbon.

   b. nitrogen.   d. phosphorous.

11. How might a tree fossil help a scientist understand the climate of certain places millions of years ago?

12. You notice that a tree cross-section has a very wide tree ring that occurred in 1985 and a very narrow tree ring that occurred in 1992. From this information, what can you infer about the tree's environment in 1985? In 1992?

13. How do scientists know which plants and animals lived at the same time as the dinosaurs?

14. *Lystrosaurus* fossils are found in Antarctica and Africa. How it is possible for fossils of this organism to be found in both places?

15. Is measuring the amount of uranium-238 in a fossil to determine its age relative or absolute dating?

Math and Writing Skills

Section 9.1

1. Nicolas Steno and James Hutton contributed to the development of modern geology. Through research, find a fact about each of these scientists that was not mentioned in the chapter.

2. You want to explain superposition to a group of second graders. Think of a creative model you could use that would help them understand this concept. Describe your model and how you would teach superposition in a paragraph.

3. Explain in a short paragraph how the shell of a ocean creature could become a fossil.

Section 9.2

4. A fossil is estimated to be about 280 million years old.
   a. How do scientists estimate the age, in years, of a fossil?
   b. To which era and period does the fossil belong? What are some organisms that lived during that time?

5. A rock that is 100 percent uranium goes through three half-lives.
   a. How many years is three uranium half-lives?
   b. How much uranium is left after three half-lives: 2 percent, 10 percent, or 12.5 percent?

6. Use this tree core diagram to answer the questions. Do not count the bark or pith when determining the age of the tree. One tree ring equals a white area and one dark line.

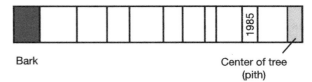

Bark   Center of tree
                                      (pith)

   a. How old is the tree?
   b. What year was this tree cut down?
   c. Give an example of a year that was probably warm with a lot of rainfall.
   d. Name a year that was probably cool and dry.

7. Research bristlecone pines. In what kind of environment do they live? Where do you find bristlecone pines? Are they all over the world or just in certain locations?

Chapter Project—What's Your Time Scale?

Find out about your personal history by talking to your parents, grandparents, and/or guardians. Follow these steps.

1. Write out the important parts of your history.

2. Divide your personal history into eras and periods.

3. Come up with names for the different eras and periods.

4. Describe the important events in each era and period of your life. How long is each era and period in years?

5. Make a poster that presents your personal history. Be creative and colorful.

Inside Earth

People often travel to tropical areas to get warm in the winter time. What would you think if you saw an advertisement that said, "Warm up this winter in the hot center of Earth"? The center of Earth is hot, but could you actually get to the center of Earth and take a vacation there? On the next page, you will read about a science-fiction story that was based on this idea. However, in the chapter, as you learn what Earth looks like inside, you will also learn that traveling to the center of Earth is not possible!

Key Questions:

1. Is it possible to travel to Earth's core through a volcano?

2. What is the composition of Earth's core?

3. How is a continent like a boat?

10.1 Sensing Earth's Interior

No one has ever seen the center of our planet. The distance from Earth's surface to its center is about 6,400 kilometers. The deepest we have drilled into Earth is about 13 kilometers—not even close! For a long time, our knowledge of the center of Earth could be drawn only from studying its surface. In this section, you will learn how we study Earth's interior and what it looks like.

Ideas from the past

Science fiction   Jules Verne wrote popular science-fiction books in the mid-1800s (Figure 10.1). Verne was popular among readers because he researched his topics and wrote stories that could have been true. In 1864, he wrote *Journey to the Center of the Earth*. The main characters were three adventurers who explored a hollow Earth and lived to tell their tale. Along the way, they:

- entered Earth through an opening in a volcano in Iceland;
- climbed down through many strange chambers;
- crossed an ocean at the center of Earth; and
- escaped to the surface by riding a volcanic eruption.

Today scientists know that this adventure story is purely fictional and could never happen. But, how do they know this? What has changed our view of the interior of Earth since the 1800s?

Special vibrations   Scientists began to study special vibrations that travel through Earth shortly after Verne's book was written. These vibrations, called **seismic waves**, have revealed the structure of Earth's interior. Seismic waves are caused by events like earthquakes and human-made blasts. The waves pass along the surface and through Earth. A **seismologist** is a scientist who detects and interprets these vibrations using sensors at different places on Earth's surface.

Figure 10.1: *Jules Verne wrote popular science-fiction books—including* Journey to the Center of the Earth—*in the mid-1800s.*

Wave motion

A push moves along a line

Imagine a line of students waiting for a bus. A student at the end of the line falls forward and bumps into the student in front of him. This causes that student to bump into the next student. The bumped student bumps another student, and so on along the line. Eventually, the student at the head of the line feels the push that began at the end of the line.

A domino example

A line of dominoes also illustrates how a disturbance can travel. The first domino is pushed and soon the last domino falls over, even though it is far from the first one!

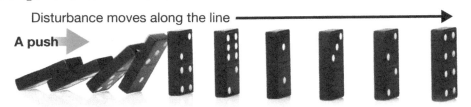

Disturbance moves along the line →

A push →

Eventually, all of the dominoes will fall down.

The disturbance travels

The "push" or disturbance that travels down a line of students or a line of dominoes helps explain how wave motion occurs. The students and dominoes stay in place while the disturbance travels forward. Likewise, wave motion involves a disturbance that begins in one location and sets things in motion farther away.

Up-and-down and side-to-side motion

One way that wave motion is different from a line of students or dominoes is that wave motion is up-and-down or side-to-side (Figure 10.2). You are probably familiar with the up-and-down motion of water waves in a pool. You can demonstrate side-to-side wave motion by wiggling a rope.

disturbance - a movement that begins in one location and sets things in motion farther away.

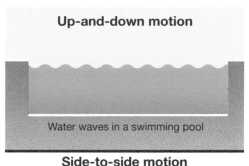

Up-and-down motion

Water waves in a swimming pool

Side-to-side motion

A rope moving sideways

Figure 10.2: *Up-and-down and side-to-side motion.*

What kinds of disturbances can create water waves? Make a list of these disturbances and draw sketches to illustrate your list.

Kinds of seismic waves

P-waves and S-waves

There are several kinds of seismic waves. Two that are important for studying Earth's interior are primary and secondary waves. These waves are usually called by their first letter, P-waves and S-waves. P-waves travel faster than S-waves and move with a forward-and-backward motion. Slower S-waves travel with a side-to-side motion. S-waves do not pass through liquids, unlike P-waves that pass through solids and liquids.

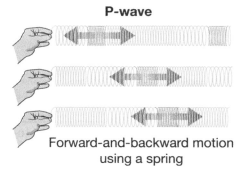

P-wave

Forward-and-backward motion using a spring

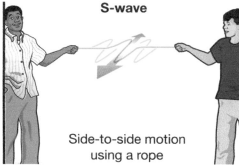

S-wave

Side-to-side motion using a rope

Waves tell us about Earth's interior

As P-waves and S-waves travel through Earth, they might be bent, reflected, sped up, slowed down, or stopped depending on the nature of the material they encounter. By studying what happens to the waves on their paths through Earth, scientists are able to make detailed models of Earth's interior.

A clue from S-waves

Here's an example of how scientists use seismic waves. Scientists observed that when an earthquake produced S-waves on one side of Earth, there was a large area on the other side where the waves couldn't be detected (Figure 10.3). They called this area the *S-wave shadow zone*. Something was blocking the S-waves as they tried to pass through! Scientists knew that secondary waves cannot pass through liquid. With this fact and these observations, they realized that the outer core of Earth must be liquid.

VOCABULARY

P-waves - seismic waves that move with a forward-and-backward motion; these waves are faster than S-waves and travel through solids and liquids.

S-waves - seismic waves that move with a side-to-side motion, are slower than P-waves, and only travel through solids.

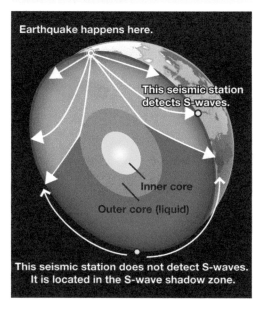

Earthquake happens here.

This seismic station detects S-waves.

Inner core

Outer core (liquid)

This seismic station does not detect S-waves. It is located in the S-wave shadow zone.

Figure 10.3: *In the graphic above, S-waves deflect off the liquid outer core of Earth. Since S-waves cannot pass through the outer core, an S-wave shadow zone is created on the side of Earth opposite the earthquake.*

10.1 **Section Review**

1. What is Earth's radius in kilometers? What is Earth's radius in miles (1 kilometer = 0.62 miles)?

2. Answer these questions about the vibrations that travel through Earth.

   a. What are these vibrations called?

   b. What causes them?

   c. What have these vibrations revealed about Earth's interior?

3. What is a seismologist?

4. During wave motion, what moves from one place to another?

5. What two general types of wave motion were described in this section?

6. List the two most important seismic waves used for studying Earth's interior. Give three facts about each type of wave.

7. After an earthquake, P-waves travel at an average speed of 5 kilometers per second and S-waves travel at an average speed of 3 kilometers per second. A seismic station is located 30 kilometers from where the earthquake occurred (Figure 10.4).

   a. How many seconds would it take for the P-waves to reach the seismic station?

   b. How many seconds would it take for the S-waves to reach the station?

8. What can happen to seismic waves as they travel through Earth?

9. What is the S-wave shadow zone?

10. What does the S-wave shadow zone tell us about the interior of Earth?

MY JOURNAL

Is it possible to travel to Earth's core through a volcano?

Write a paragraph that answers this question based on what you knew about Earth *before* you read Section 10.1.

Then, write a paragraph that answers this question based on what you know about Earth *now that you have finished* reading Section 10.1.

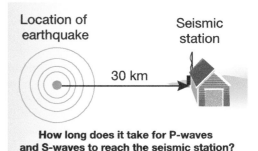

How long does it take for P-waves and S-waves to reach the seismic station?

Figure 10.4: *Question 7.*

10.2 Earth's Interior

Simple diagrams of Earth's interior show it as having three layers—an outer crust, a mantle, and a core. Modern science has revealed much more detail about these layers. The graphic below shows some of this detail.

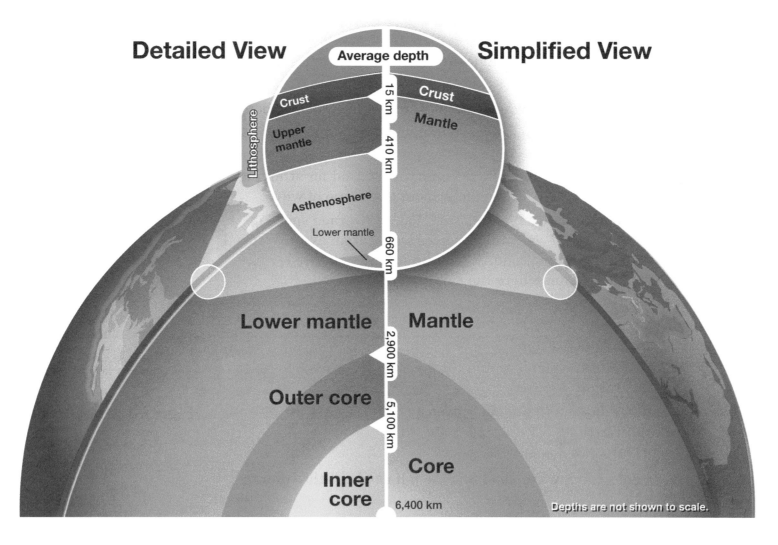

The crust and the mantle

What is Earth's crust? The **crust** is the outermost layer of Earth. *Oceanic crust* lies under the oceans and is thin. The average thickness of oceanic crust is about 5 kilometers. *Continental crust* forms continents and is thicker. Its average thickness is 30 kilometers (Figure 10.5). Because rock in the crust is cool, the crust is brittle (cracks and breaks easily). Shallow earthquakes occur in the crust. The crust floats on the mantle.

What is Earth's mantle? In the simplified view of Earth, the **mantle** is the thick layer between the crust and the core. The mantle is about 2,900 kilometers thick. In the detailed view, the mantle includes the upper mantle, the asthenosphere, and the lower mantle.

Lithosphere The **lithosphere** includes the crust and upper mantle. The plates that move about Earth's surface are pieces of lithosphere.

Asthenosphere The **asthenosphere** lies just under the lithosphere and is the lower part of the upper mantle. It is a soft, weak zone of hot rock where temperature and pressure cause the mantle rock to be more fluid than anywhere else in the mantle. Geologists compare the asthenosphere to jelly between slices of bread. The crust and upper mantle represent the top piece of bread and the lower mantle is the bottom piece.

Lower mantle Below the asthenosphere, at depths of 660 to 2,900 kilometers, lies the rest of the lower mantle. The lower mantle is the largest part of Earth's interior. It is under great pressure and the rock found there gradually becomes more rigid with depth. Despite its rigidity, the rock of the lower mantle is very hot and flows slowly. This slow movement takes hundreds of millions of years.

crust - the outermost layer of Earth.

mantle - the hot, flowing, solid layer of Earth between the crust and the core.

lithosphere - a layer of Earth that includes the crust and upper mantle.

asthenosphere - the lower part of the upper mantle; lithospheric plates slide on this layer.

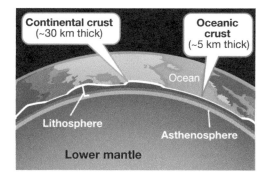

Figure 10.5: *The continental crust is about 30 kilometers thick. The oceanic crust is about 5 kilometers thick.*

The core

What is Earth's core? The core is the name for the center of Earth. The core is divided into two layers, the inner and outer core. The material that makes up the core is denser than the material in the mantle. The core is also an extremely hot place! Earth's temperature increases with depth from the crust to the core.

Outer core Seismic S-waves show that the outer core is liquid. It is made mostly of iron, and is so hot the iron is melted! Powerful electric currents are formed as the liquid outer core moves. These electric currents create Earth's magnetic field. This magnetic field protects the planet from harmful solar radiation (Figure 10.6). It also protects the atmosphere. Life on Earth would be in danger if the outer core cooled and stopped moving.

Inner core The inner core is also made mostly of iron, but it is solid. The inner core is hot enough to melt iron, so why is it solid? Melting depends on pressure as well as temperature. The pressure at the inner core is so enormous that iron, and the rest of the inner core, remains a solid.

Summary Information about the layers of Earth is summarized below.

Layers of Earth		Average depth (km)	Temperature (°C)	Description
Lithosphere {	Crust	15	0	The uppermost layer
	Upper mantle	410	870	The lower part of the lithosphere
	Asthenosphere	660		Zone where mantle rock is most fluid
	Lower mantle	2900	3700	Largest part of Earth's interior
Core {	Outer core	5100	4300	Liquid iron
	Inner core	6400	7200	Solid iron (hotter than the surface of the Sun)

Temperature increases with depth

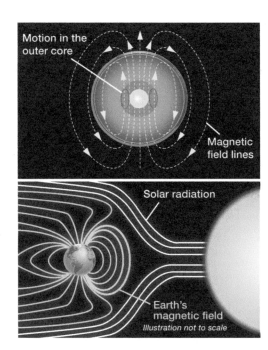

Figure 10.6: *Earth's magnetic field is created by powerful electric currents formed by the motion of liquid iron in Earth's outer core. Earth's magnetic field protects the planet from harmful radiation from the Sun.*

core - the center of Earth; it is divided into the inner core and the outer core.

10.2 **Section Review**

1. Simplified diagrams of Earth's interior show three layers. What are these layers?

2. Use Figure 10.7 to help you answer the following questions.
   a. What is the outermost layer of Earth called?
   b. What layers compose Earth's core?
   c. The upper mantle and crust make up which layer of Earth's interior?
   d. What is the name of the thickest layer of Earth's interior?

3. How thick is the outer core in kilometers?

4. Which is thicker: oceanic crust or continental crust?

5. Is the crust brittle? Why is this? Do earthquakes occur in the crust?

6. The plates that move about Earth's surface are pieces of the _____.

7. What is the asthenosphere and why is it important?

8. Describe the rocky material and conditions of the lower mantle.

9. What material makes up most of the outer core? Is it solid or liquid? Why?

10. What material makes up most of the inner core? Is it solid or liquid? Why?

11. What factor increases as you go deeper toward Earth's core?

12. How is Earth's magnetic field generated?

13. What role does Earth's magnetic field play in protecting the planet?

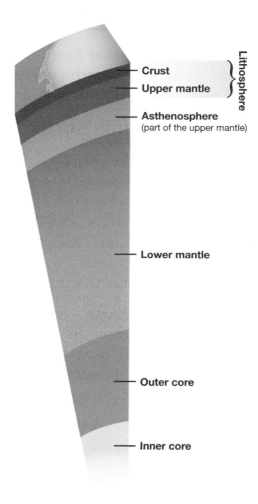

Figure 10.7: *Question 2.*

10.3 Earth's Surface

Scientists conclude that Earth formed from the gas and dust that surrounded our young Sun. At first, Earth's surface was made of the same materials as its center. Later on, these materials melted and began to flow.

Earth's materials sorted by density

Earth's layers You have learned that less-dense objects will float in more-dense fluids. Once the interior of Earth began to flow, the materials sorted out by their densities (Figure 10.8). Less-buoyant, denser materials settled toward the center. More-buoyant and less-dense materials rose toward the surface. Aluminum and silicon are common within Earth's crust. These elements have low densities. Earth's inner and outer cores are composed mostly of dense iron.

Earth's crust floats on the mantle Earth's crust is made of different types of rock that are less dense than the mantle. Oceanic crust is made of basalt and is slightly denser than continental crust. Continental crust is made of andesite and granite (Figure 10.9). Oceanic crust is thinner than continental crust, but both kinds of crust float on the mantle.

Rocks float on rocks It's hard to imagine rocks floating on other rocks, but it happens inside Earth. The cold, brittle rock of the crust floats on the hot, soft, denser rock below.

	Density (g/cm³)
aluminum	2.7
silicon	2.3
iron	7.9
water	1.0

Figure 10.8: *Density values for substances that make up Earth.*

Figure 10.9: *The oceanic crust is made mostly of basalt. The continental crust is made mostly of andesite and granite.*

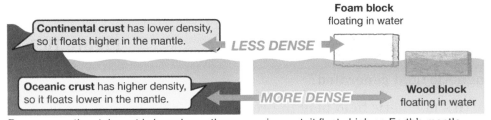

Because continental crust is less dense than oceanic crust, it floats high on Earth's mantle. Blocks of foam and wood floating in water demonstrate this phenomenon.

Floating continents

How is a continent like a boat? Imagine stacking blocks on a toy boat floating in a pool. As you add blocks, the stack gets higher and heavier. The extra weight presses more of the boat into the water to support the stack. The finished stack stands taller than the original boat, but the boat is also deeper in the water.

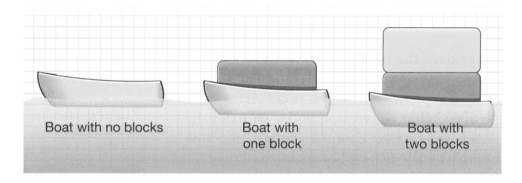

Boat with no blocks   Boat with one block   Boat with two blocks

Mountains on continents Earth's crust floats on the mantle just like the boat. A mountain on land is just like the stack of blocks (Figure 10.10). Like the boat, the part of the crust with a mountain on it sticks down into the mantle. The average thickness of continental crust is 30 kilometers, but the combination of a mountain and its bulge underneath may make the crust as thick as 70 kilometers.

Glaciers on continents During an ice age, the weight of glacial ice presses the crust down just like a mountain. After the ice age ends and the glacier melts, the crust springs back up again (Figure 10.11).

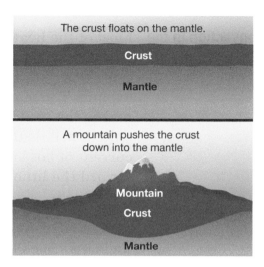

Figure 10.10: *How a mountain affects the crust.*

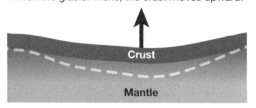

Figure 10.11: *How a glacier affects the crust. The effects have been exaggerated to show the changes.*

Convection

Convection in the lower mantle Most of the heat left over from the formation of our planet lies in the core. The hot core heats the lower mantle where the two layers come together. Heating the lower mantle causes the material to expand. The mass doesn't change, but the volume increases. This makes the heated material less dense. You know that less-dense objects will float in more-dense fluids. The result is a convection current of hot lower mantle material rising up from near the core toward the lithosphere.

Convection cells As the convection current nears the lithosphere, it turns and runs along underneath. Eventually the convection current loses its heat and sinks back toward the core. This is a convection cell (Figure 10.12). You've learned that convection is the transfer of heat as material circulates. In the next chapter you will see how lower-mantle convection drives the lithospheric plates across Earth's surface.

Seismic tomography Seismology tools are much better today than they were in the past. The biggest improvement is the use of computers and the invention of seismic tomography. *Seismic tomography* uses seismic waves collected from all over the world to create a computer-generated, three-dimensional image of Earth's interior (Figure 10.13).

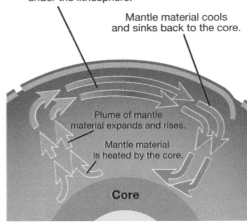

Figure 10.12: *How convection in the mantle occurs.*

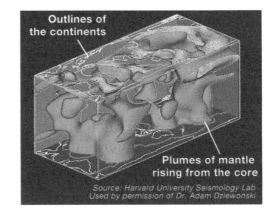

Figure 10.13: *The red blobs in the graphic are warmer, less-dense plumes of mantle rising toward Earth's surface from the core. The yellow blobs show cooler material.*

10.3 **Section Review**

1. Explain how the young Earth separated into layers. Use the term *density* in your answer.
2. Draw a diagram of Earth's interior.
   a. Indicate on the diagram where you would find aluminum and silicon.
   b. Then, indicate on the diagram where you would most likely find iron.
   c. Using the density values in Figure 10.8, explain why water floats on Earth's surface.
   d. How do you think the density of the mantle compares to the densities of the crust and the core? Explain your answer.
3. Name the type of rock that makes up the ocean floor.
4. Name the two kinds of rock that make up the continents.
5. How is a continent like a boat? Explain.
6. What might happen to a mountain that would cause the crust to float higher in the mantle?
7. What might happen to a glacier that would cause the crust to float higher in the mantle?
8. What process drives the lithospheric plates across the surface of Earth? Draw a diagram of this process.
9. Review what you learned about convection in Chapter 3. Describe how convection works in the mantle, in a heated room, and in the atmosphere. What is the source of heat in each situation?
10. What is seismic tomography?
11. Do some research. How is a CAT scan like seismic tomography?

Drilling to Earth's Core

Earth's core is nearly 6,500 kilometers (4,000 miles) beneath your feet. If we could somehow reach Earth's core, from there every direction would be "up."

We may never reach that center core, but scientists are getting a little closer to it. For the first time, people have drilled into the lower section of Earth's crust. Just getting through the planet's outer layer was a huge job: eight weeks of drilling a hole in the ocean floor.

Scientists will not stop there. They hope to break into the upper mantle, the layer just beneath the crust, some time in the coming years. That is one of the goals of the Integrated Ocean Drilling Program (IODP).

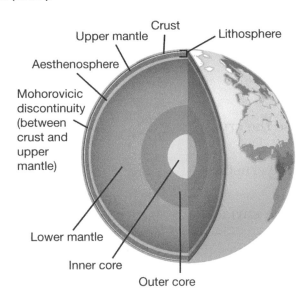

Scientists are looking for a boundary they call the "Moho," short for the Mohorovicic discontinuity. This boundary between Earth's crust and the upper mantle below is named for Andrija Mohorovicic, the Croatian seismologist who first identified it in 1909.

The planet's crust is thin and hard. The mantle lies just below the crust, and it is hot and soft and a more *plastic* layer. Plastic here means that the material flows slowly without breaking. The mantle (the upper mantle, the aesthenosphere, and the lower mantle) makes up nearly 80 percent of Earth's total volume. Beneath the mantle is the liquid outer core and the solid inner core.

Digging for clues

By drilling deep into the crust, scientists hope to learn more about how it forms. They also hope to learn more about the movement of the upper mantle.

Why drill in the oceans? The simple reason is that the oceanic crust is thinner, about 5 kilometers (3 miles) thick in the oceans. The continental crust is about 30 kilometers thick (about 18 or 19 miles).

If the drill can reach the Moho, we may learn how the mantle and the crust interact, or, more importantly, how the crust forms. All of this information will help scientists understand the differences between the mantle and the crust.

Ocean drilling platform

The complex inner Earth

Drilling has allowed scientists to learn more about Earth's complex structure. The IODP scientists have collected data for the first time from the lower crust. Mantle material, however, has yet to be recovered.

Finding the Moho isn't easy because it isn't at the same depth everywhere. The latest IODP hole—that took almost eight weeks to drill—went about 1,415 meters (4,642 feet) below the floor of the Atlantic Ocean.

Even at that depth, the Moho was not reached. Still, the rock from the hole provided information about the complexity of the planet's structure.

Drilling into the rock

Another glimpse deep down

Another way we learn about Earth's interior is from earthquakes. An earthquake's seismic waves travel through the layers of the mantle and through the core.

The study of seismic waves has already convinced scientists that Earth's core is rotating faster than its surface. This was confirmed by comparing the travel times of P-waves passing through the core.

Researchers did this by studying two almost identical earthquakes that happened at the same place near South America. The earthquakes occurred on different dates. Then they compared the time it took each quake's shockwaves to pass through the core. Some parts of the core are denser than others, which can speed up or slow the shock waves as they pass through the core.

If the core was moving at the same speed as the surface, the time it took for the seismic waves to be recorded would be the same for each earthquake. But the times and shapes of the waves were different. This meant that the seismic waves passed through a different part of the core in each earthquake.

Based on this, scientists conclude that Earth's core is spinning faster than the planet's surface. It actually "laps" the surface about every 400 years!

QUESTIONS

1. What is the IODP and what is one of its goals?

2. Has the IODP succeeded in reaching its goal? Why or why not?

3. What is the Moho?

4. Which layer of Earth makes up nearly 80 percent of its total volume?

5. What has convinced researchers that Earth's core is spinning faster than the planet's surface?

Wave Motion Through Different Materials

In this activity, you will be observing wave motion. You will look at the movement of primary and secondary waves. You will also look at the change in behavior of a wave as it passes from one material to another.

As you have learned, seismic waves have given humans a great amount of information about our Earth. You have also learned that there is more than one kind of seismic wave and that even though all of them produce wave motions, the individual disturbances along the wave move very differently through the planet. Let's look and see if we can demonstrate how this energy travels.

Materials

- Large springs (both metal and plastic)
- Electrical tape
- Meter stick
- Water and a shallow rectangular bin for the water
- Small stone

What you will do

1. Modeling wave motion: Fill the bin with an inch or two of water. Drop the stone into the water and watch the waves. Try this several times and then answer questions a-c. You have just modeled wave motion!

2. With a partner, take the metal spring and stretch it about three meters and lay it on a flat surface such as the floor.

3. To demonstrate P-wave motion, one person will hold the spring at one end. The other person will move their hand holding the spring forward and backward. Answer question d.

4. To demonstrate S-wave motion, one person will hold the spring on one end firmly and the other person will move his or hand quickly side-to-side. Answer question e.

5. Now take the plastic spring and tape one end to one end of the metal spring. The two springs represent two different materials. This demonstration will show what happens when wave energy passes through a boundary of two different materials, like different layers in Earth. Generate both P- and S-waves as you did before using the metal spring. Watch as the wave motion travels through to the plastic spring. Answer question f.

What happens when a wave travels from one material to another?

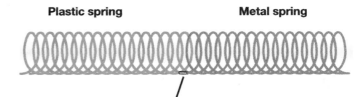

Plastic spring   **Metal spring**

Tape the springs together

Applying your knowledge

a. Draw or describe how the waves looked in the water.

b. Did the waves in the water tend to move over the surface or down through the water to the bottom of the bin?

c. How is the motion of water waves different from the motion of seismic waves?

d. Describe or draw what happens with the P-wave motion.

e. Describe or draw what happens with the S-wave motion.

f. Describe what happens at the boundary of the two springs.

g. A P-wave from an earthquake goes through the mantle and then through the core of Earth. Based on what you have observed in this lab, what would you expect about the path of this wave?

Chapter 10 Assessment

Vocabulary

Select the correct term to complete the sentences.

seismologist	crust	seismic waves
lithosphere	core	P-waves
mantle	S-waves	disturbance

Section 10.1

1. _____ are seismic waves that do not pass through liquids.

2. A scientist that detects and interprets seismic waves at different locations on Earth is called a _____.

3. Vibrations that travel through Earth are called _____.

4. _____ are seismic waves that move in a forward-and-backward motion.

5. During wave motion, a _____ moves from one place to another.

Section 10.2

6. The largest part of Earth's interior that is made of rock, but is flexible, is the _____.

7. The _____ is the inner iron-containing layer of Earth.

8. Made of the crust and upper mantle, the _____ makes up the plates that move about Earth's surface.

9. The outermost surface of Earth is called the _____.

Concepts

Section 10.1

1. Jules Verne described Earth and its interior in his book *A Journey to the Center of the Earth.* Was he a scientist? Why or why not?

2. People cannot travel to the center of Earth in person. How then do scientists study what Earth looks like inside?

3. You can create an up-and-down wave by wiggling a jump rope. What travels from one place to another during the wave motion? What stays in place?

4. For each of these statements write either P-wave or S-wave.
   a. Travels through all material
   b. Does not travel through liquids
   c. Forward-and-backward motion
   d. Side-to-side motion
   e. Slower
   f. Faster

Section 10.2

5. How is Earth's crust different from the mantle? List three ways.

6. The _____ is the slippery surface on which the lithospheric plates move around Earth's surface.

7. What causes Earth's magnetic field? Why is Earth's magnetic field important?

8. The inner core is really hot but solid. Why isn't the inner core a liquid like the outer core?

Section 10.3

9. With all the layers that make up Earth, which layer is the densest and which is the least dense? Why?

10. List the differences between the continental crust and the oceanic crust.

11. What do you think would happen if there was no convection in Earth's mantle?

12. The up-and-down movement of the crust due to the weight of overlying objects, such as mountains or melting of glaciers is a result of _____.

a. convection in the mantle

b. buoyancy of the crust floating on the mantle

c. magnetic fields

d. mantle plumes

13. The main rock of the ocean floor, basalt, is slightly _____ than granite, the rock of the continents.

a. denser

b. less dense

c. more salty

d. more flexible

Math and Writing Skills

Section 10.1

1. In the box below is a list of four events that happen in *A Journey to the Center of the Earth*. Write a paragraph that explains whether each is a realistic event or not.

In *A Journey to the Center of the Earth*, the main characters were three adventurers who explored a hollow Earth and lived to tell their tale. Along the way, they

- entered Earth through an opening in a volcano in Iceland;
- climbed down through many strange chambers;
- crossed an ocean at the center of Earth; and
- escaped to the surface by riding a volcanic eruption.

2. Reading about the way scientists learned about the outer core being liquid, do you have a personal experience where you learned something new in an indirect way? Explain your experience in a paragraph.

3. After an earthquake, P-waves travel at an average speed of 5 kilometers per second and S-waves travel at an average speed of 3 kilometers per second. A seismic station is located 15 kilometers from where the earthquake occurred. How many seconds would it take:

a. the P-waves to reach the station?

b. the S-waves to reach the station?

Section 10.2

4. What is the radius of Earth in kilometers? What is the diameter of Earth in kilometers?

5. Scientists have only been able to drill into the lower part of Earth's crust. What percentage of the radius have scientists drilled into?

a. 100%

b. 50%

c. less than 1%

d. 25%

6. The continental crust averages about 30 kilometers thick. You learned that the continental crust is thickest at mountains. Where would it be thinnest?

7. Where would the oceanic crust (which averages about 5 kilometers thick) be thinnest?

8. How thick is the lower mantle?

Section 10.3

9. Why does water float on Earth's surface? Refer to the table below to help you answer this question.

	Density (g/cm^3)
aluminum	2.7
silicon	2.3
iron	7.9
water	1.0

10. Imagine you are a lithospheric plate on Earth's surface. Describe yourself. Explain how you move around on Earth.

Chapter Projects—Earth Model and Flash Cards

1. Make a three-dimensional model of the detailed view of Earth's interior (see Figure 10.7). Include all the layers and label them. For your materials, you will need to be creative. Some ideas—use modelling clay or place layers of colored sand in a transparent container.

2. In Section 10.3, you learned a good study skill—making flash cards to help you learn concepts and vocabulary. Now, make flash cards of the vocabulary you have learned in Unit 3 (Chapters 8, 9, and 10). Add colorful diagrams to your flash cards!

UNIT 4

THE CHANGING EARTH

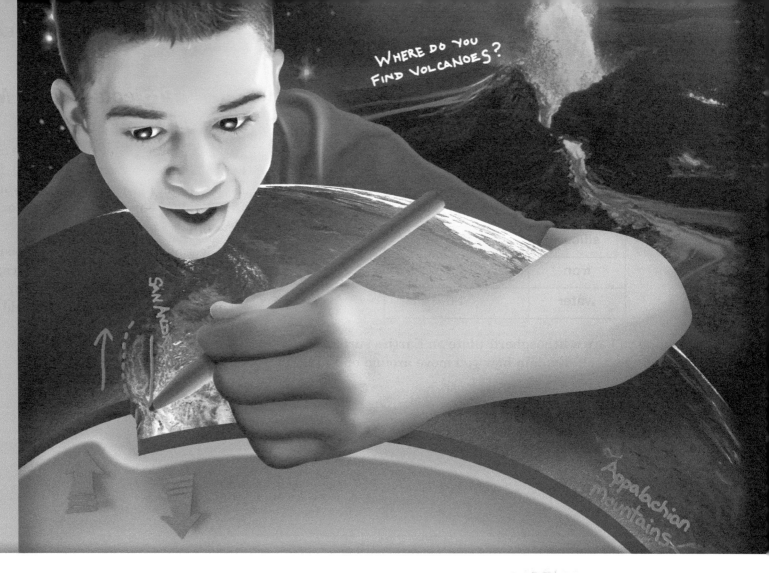

WHERE DO YOU FIND VOLCANOES?

Exploring on Your Own

You are a science journalist, and your assignment is to write an article about the geology of your neighborhood or city. First, investigate on your own. Find rocks near your house. Wash off any soil on the rocks. Study them and take notes. What colors do you see? Do you see layers or crystals? What do the rocks tell you about your area? Next, interview a geology expert. Discuss your results from your own investigation with this expert. Then, write your article.

Chapter 11

Plate Tectonics

In this chapter, you will learn about one of the most important discoveries of the 20th century—plate tectonics. You have already learned that Earth's surface is covered with a lithosphere that is broken into pieces called "plates." Plate tectonics is the study of the movement of these plates. It is a relatively new field of study. Scientists have only arrived at our current understanding of plate tectonics over the past 40 years. This is a very short time in science history!

Key Questions:

1. How is the surface of Earth like a giant jigsaw puzzle?

2. Why are magnetic patterns important?

3. How do Earth's movements affect the locations of mountains?

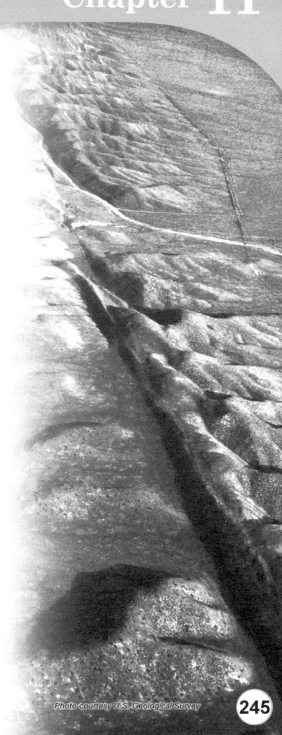

Photo courtesy U.S. Geological Survey

11.1 **Pangaea**

While looking at a map of the world, have you ever noticed that the continents look like pieces of a puzzle? If they were moved closer together across the Atlantic Ocean, they would fit together neatly to form a giant landmass (Figure 11.1). In this section, you will learn about Alfred Wegener and his idea that a "supercontinent" once existed on Earth.

continental drift - the idea that continents move around on Earth's surface.

Pangaea - an ancient, huge landmass composed of earlier forms of today's continents; an ancient supercontinent.

plate tectonics - a theory explaining how the pieces of Earth's surface (the plates) move.

Movement of continents

Continental drift   Alfred Wegener was a German scientist and arctic explorer who suggested the concept of continental drift. **Continental drift** is the idea that the continents move around on Earth's surface.

Wegener's hypothesis   In the early 1900s, Wegener hypothesized that the continents were once connected. Today, after a lot of scientific research and collected evidence, we know that Wegener was right.

Pangaea— a supercontinent   In 1915, Wegener published his ideas in a book, *Origins of the Continents and Oceans*. Wegener thought that the continents we know today had once been part of an earlier *supercontinent*. He called this great landmass **Pangaea** (Greek for "all land"). According to continental drift, Pangaea broke apart and the pieces moved to their present places, becoming today's continents.

What is plate tectonics?   In Chapter 1, you were introduced to plate tectonics, the study of lithospheric plates. You learned that the surface of Earth is broken into many pieces like a giant jigsaw puzzle. **Plate tectonics** describes how these pieces move on Earth's surface. By the time you finish this chapter, you will know more about this theory than any scientist knew only 40 years ago! You will also learn that the development of this theory is an excellent example of how the scientific process works. Now, let's return to Wegener and his idea of continental drift.

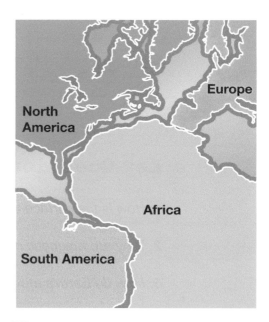

Figure 11.1: *The continents on either side of the Atlantic Ocean fit together like puzzle pieces.*

Evidence for continental drift

Matching coal beds, mountains, and fossils

Wegener was not the only scientist to suggest that continents move. His theory stood out because of the evidence that he gathered to support his idea of continental drift. Wegener's evidence is presented in the graphic below and listed in Figure 11.2.

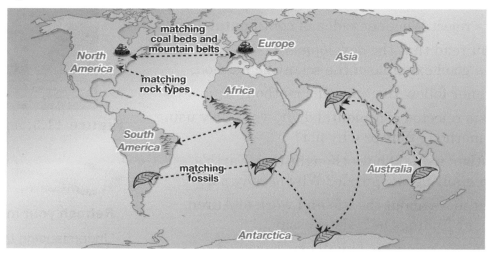

A good hypothesis

Wegener's theory that the continents were connected in the past was a good idea. It was a *scientific hypothesis based on observations.*

Continental drift was rejected

Continental drift was a good hypothesis that was rejected by other scientists. A key part of Wegener's hypothesis was that some unknown force had caused the continents to slide over, or push through, the rocky bottoms of the oceans. Yet, neither he nor anyone else could identify the source of the force needed to move continents. Continental drift helped explain issues in geology—like why South America and Africa seem to fit together. However, continental drift could not be accepted by scientists because there was no evidence to explain how the continents moved.

Wegener's evidence for continental drift

- Coal beds stretch across the eastern United States and continue across southern Europe.
- Matching plant fossils are found in South America, Africa, India, Australia, and Antarctica.
- Matching reptile fossils are found in South America and Africa.
- Matching early mammal fossils are found in South America and Africa.
- Fossils in South America and Africa are found in rocks of identical age and type.
- Matching rock types and mountain belts occur in North America and the British Isles, and Africa and South America.
- Evidence of glaciers is present in regions with warm, dry climates. This indicates that continents that are close to the equator today were once closer to the South Pole in the distant past.

Figure 11.2: *A summary of Wegener's evidence for continental drift.*

11.1 **Section Review**

1. What is plate tectonics? Is it an old or a new field of science?

2. Alfred Wegener (Figure 11.3) is featured in this section. Who was he?

3. Alfred Wegener thought that all continents were once connected. Explain one observation that led to this belief.

4. Why did scientists reject Wegener's idea of continental drift?

5. In this section, you read that the development of the theory of plate tectonics is a good example of the scientific method.

    a. How did Wegener follow the scientific method?

    b. When scientists rejected continental drift, were they using the scientific method? Why or why not?

6. Would most scientists in 1900 have thought that Earth's surface was like a giant jigsaw puzzle? Why or why not?

7. *Research*: Find out more about the life and work of Alfred Wegener. Write your findings as a short essay.

8. Continental drift was a scientific hypothesis based on observations. Pick one question below and make observations. Record your observations. *Extension*: Develop a hypothesis that you could test with an experiment.

    a. Where in my yard do plants grow best?

    b. What is the sediment and soil like in my yard?

    c. What activity does my pet spend the most time doing during one day?

Photograph courtesy of the Alfred Wegener Institute for Polar and Marine Research, Bremerhaven, Germany

Figure 11.3: *Alfred Wegener.*

STUDY SKILLS

Refresh your memory

Understanding the scientific method was helpful while you were reading this chapter. Answer these questions as a way to refresh your memory about the scientific method, which was covered in Chapter 1.

1. What is the difference between an inference and a hypothesis?

2. What is the difference between an opinion and an observation?

3. What are the steps of the scientific method?

11.2 Sea-floor Spreading

In Wegener's time, the world's ocean floors were largely unexplored. Mapping the sea floor provided more important evidence for the theory of plate tectonics.

Undersea mountains discovered

A map of the ocean floor
During World War II, the U.S. Navy needed to locate enemy submarines hiding on the bottom of shallow seas. Because of this, large areas of the ocean floor were mapped for the first time. American geophysicist and naval officer Harry Hess did some of the mapping. His work helped develop the theory of plate tectonics.

Mid-ocean ridges
The naval maps showed huge mountain ranges that formed a continuous chain down the centers of the ocean floors. These mountain ranges are called **mid-ocean ridges**. Hess wondered if it was possible that new ocean floor was created at mid-ocean ridges. If new ocean floor formed at a ridge, then continents on either side would get pushed apart during the process (Figure 11.4).

ⓐ VOCABULARY

mid-ocean ridge - a long chain of undersea mountains.

Harry Hess' idea
As new sea floor is made at mid-ocean ridges, the continents are pushed away.

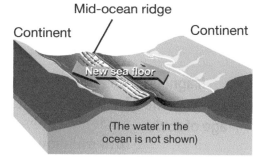

Figure 11.4: *Harry Hess wondered if it was possible that new ocean floor was created at the mid-ocean ridges.*

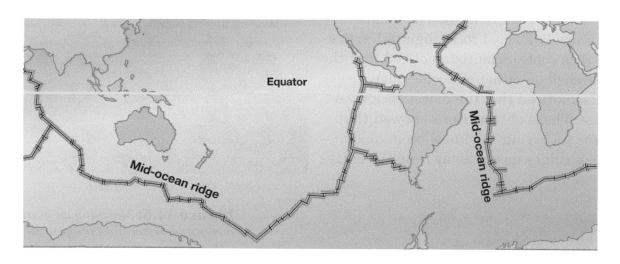

The sea-floor spreading hypothesis

A hypothesis is born
Hess thought that Wegener was partly right. The continents *had* separated from a supercontinent, but not by plowing through the sea floor. Instead, continents moved along as part of the growing sea floor! Hess called his hypothesis sea-floor spreading.

A good idea needs more evidence
Sea-floor spreading was an intriguing hypothesis. But for many years scientists had viewed the continents as permanently fixed in place. Sea-floor spreading would need strong evidence to support it before it would ever be more than just a hypothesis.

Rapid scientific progress
A time of tremendously rapid scientific progress followed Hess's sea-floor spreading hypothesis. Many scientists added to each other's work and found the evidence needed to explain sea-floor spreading.

Magnetic patterns and the age of rocks
The discovery of *magnetic reversal patterns* in the rocks on both sides of the mid-ocean ridges was a key piece of evidence. These striped patterns are formed as magnetic minerals found within newly formed rock align to Earth's magnetic field as the rock cools. Scientists noticed that the magnetic patterns matched on either side of a ridge (Figure 11.5). They also noticed that the oldest rocks were furthest from the ridge. These observations showed that sea-floor spreading was occurring—the new ocean floor that forms at mid-ocean ridges moves away from the ridges as time passes.

VOCABULARY

sea-floor spreading - a hypothesis that new sea floor is created at mid-ocean ridges and that, in the process, the continents are pushed apart from each other.

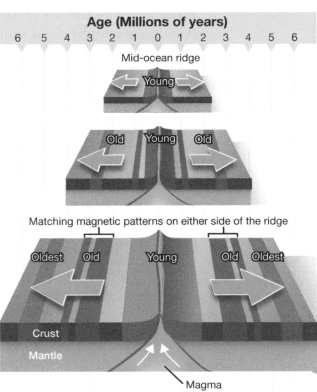

Figure 11.5: *Matching magnetic reversal patterns and the age of rocks on either side of mid-ocean ridges provided strong evidence for sea-floor spreading.*

Moving pieces of the lithosphere

After a breakthrough After the breakthrough discovery of magnetic patterns was understood, there was a lot of interest in the idea of sea-floor spreading. Scientists realized that large pieces of Earth's surface moved about like rafts on a river.

Today we know these "rafts" are pieces of lithosphere called lithospheric plates that move over the asthenosphere. Plate tectonics is the study of these lithospheric plates.

There are two kinds of lithospheric plates: oceanic plates and continental plates. Oceanic plates form the floor of the ocean. They are thin and mostly made of dense basalt. Continental plates are thicker and less dense than oceanic plates. Continental plates are made of andesite and granite.

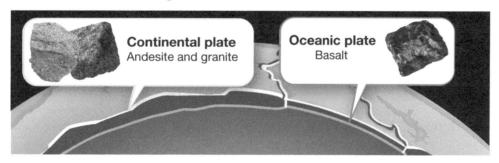

Continental plate
Andesite and granite

Oceanic plate
Basalt

Plate tectonics answers other questions Science is a process that builds on itself. Early discoveries provide a better understanding that leads to more discoveries. The evidence that Alfred Wegener collected to support an ancient supercontinent is valid today. And our understanding of plate tectonics has allowed us to answer other questions such as:

- Why are volcanoes and earthquakes located where they are?
- Where can we find oil, gas, gold, and other important resources?

VOCABULARY

lithospheric plates - large pieces of Earth's lithosphere that move over the asthenosphere.

oceanic plates - thin lithospheric plates that are made of basalt and form the ocean floor; denser than continental plates.

continental plates - thick lithospheric plates that are made of andesite and granite and form the continents; less dense than oceanic plates.

MY JOURNAL

How is plate tectonics related to earthquakes and volcanoes?

Write an answer based on what you know. Then, check your answer by doing research to answer this question. Use research resources in your classroom and school library.

What drives lithospheric plates?

Convection cells
Convection cells in Earth's lower mantle drive the lithospheric plates on the surface. Earth's core heats the rock material of the lower mantle. As it is heated, it expands and becomes less dense.

What happens at mid-ocean ridges?
The lower mantle rock material rises toward Earth's surface. Lithospheric plates move apart over the rising part of a convection cell. Basaltic lava is extruded between the plates along the mid-ocean ridge. The basaltic lava adds to the plates so that they grow in size. Over time, as newly-formed plate material moves away from the mid-ocean ridge, it ages, cools, and becomes denser.

Subduction
The cooler, denser edge of a lithospheric plate eventually sinks below another lithospheric plate and enters the mantle (Figure 11.6). This sinking process is called subduction. As the subducting plate enters the mantle, it cools the adjacent mantle material. Cooling makes the nearby material denser and it sinks deeper into the mantle. This sinking completes the mantle convection cell. Subduction also happens when a denser oceanic plate encounters a continental plate. The oceanic plate subducts under the continental plate.

VOCABULARY

subduction - a process that involves a lithospheric plate sinking into the mantle.

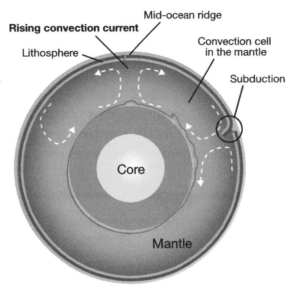

Mid-ocean ridge

Rising convection current

Convection cell in the mantle

Lithosphere

Subduction

Core

Mantle

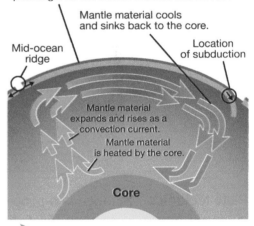

The lithospheric plate rides like a passenger on the mantle material underneath.

Mantle material cools and sinks back to the core.

Mid-ocean ridge

Location of subduction

Mantle material expands and rises as a convection current.

Mantle material is heated by the core.

Core

→ Hot, expanded, less dense, more buoyant
→ Cool, contracted, denser, less buoyant

Figure 11.6: *A convection cell in the lower mantle.*

Hot spots and island chains

Volcanic activity can be found on mid-ocean ridges. Sometimes a single, hot, rising mantle plume causes a volcanic eruption in the plate above it. If the eruption is strong and lasts long enough, the volcanic eruption may form an island on the plate. After the island forms, the movement of the plate carries it away from the mantle plume. Without the heat from the mantle plume underneath, the volcano that formed the island becomes dormant. In the meantime, a new volcano begins to form on the part of the plate that is now over the mantle plume.

This process can repeat over and over, forming a chain of islands. The first island formed in the chain is made of old dormant volcanoes, while the most recent island in the chain generally has active volcanoes. Scientists determine the direction and speed of plate movement by measuring these island chains. The speed of moving plates ranges from 1 to 10 centimeters each year. The Hawaiian Islands are a good example of an island chain formed by a mantle plume hot spot.

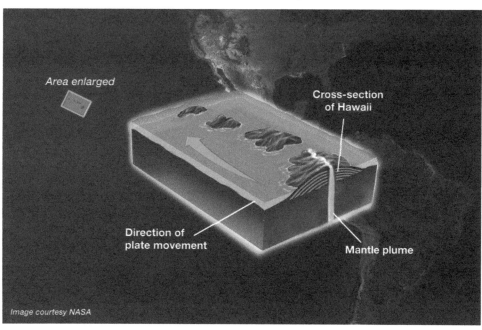

Area enlarged

Cross-section of Hawaii

Direction of plate movement

Mantle plume

Image courtesy NASA

 VOCABULARY

mantle plume - heated lower mantle rock that rises toward the lithosphere because it is less dense than surrounding mantle rock.

 SOLVE IT!

Are you faster than the speed of a moving plate on Earth's surface?

The speed of a moving plate ranges from 1 to 10 centimeters each year. On average, that's about as fast as your fingernails grow! So, even if you are walking slowly, you are moving very quickly compared to a plate moving on Earth's surface. Plates move so slowly that scientists measure their movement in millions of years.

If a lithospheric plate moved 5 centimeters per year for 1,000 years, how far would it have traveled during this time?

11.2 Section Review

1. Explain why magnetic patterns are important evidence for plate tectonics.

2. How were mid-ocean ridges discovered?

3. What was Harry Hess's hypothesis regarding the ocean floor and how it was made?

4. What two discoveries supported Hess's hypothesis?

5. What is the study of lithospheric plates called?

6. Over what surface do lithospheric plates move?

    a. lower mantle   b. outer core

    c. inner core   d. asthenosphere

7. Name the two types of lithospheric plates and describe them.

8. What are some questions that are answered by plate tectonics?

9. What is the source of energy that drives the movement of the lithospheric plates?

10. Do lithospheric plates move quickly or slowly? Explain your answer.

11. Describe the process of subduction in your own words. What causes subduction to happen?

12. Name an example of an island chain formed by a mantle plume hot spot. Describe/draw the process of how it formed.

13. *Research*: The mid-ocean ridge in the Atlantic Ocean goes through the country of Iceland. What effect is it having on this country?

14. *Research*: It is thought that when Pangaea broke apart, it first split into two large landmasses, each of which were given names. What are the names? What do these names mean?

Create a table to compare and contrast continental drift and plate tectonics. Include the answers to the following questions.

1. Which is a hypothesis and which is a theory?

2. What is the difference between these two ideas when explaining why Africa and South America seem to fit together like two puzzle pieces?

Drummond Matthews and Fred Vine, British geologists from Cambridge University, England, are credited with recognizing the significance of magnetic patterns on the sea floor.

Research these magnetic patterns so that you understand what they are and how they are formed. Make a poster to display your findings.

11.3 Plate Boundaries

In this section, you will learn how movement at the boundaries of lithospheric plates affects Earth's surface.

Moving plates

Three types of boundaries
Imagine a single plate, moving in one direction on Earth's surface (Figure 11.7). One edge of the plate—the trailing edge—moves away from other plates. This edge is called a **divergent boundary**. The opposite edge—called the leading edge—bumps into any plates in the way. This edge is called a **convergent boundary**. The sides of our imaginary plate slide by other plates. An edge of a lithospheric plate that slides by another plate is called a **transform fault boundary**.

How plates move relative to each other
Earth's surface is covered with lithospheric plates. Unlike our single imaginary plate, the boundaries of real plates touch each other. Plates move apart at divergent boundaries, collide at convergent boundaries, and slide by each other at transform fault boundaries.

divergent boundary - a lithospheric plate boundary where two plates move apart.

convergent boundary - a lithospheric plate boundary where two plates come together.

transform fault boundary - a lithospheric plate boundary where two plates slide by each other.

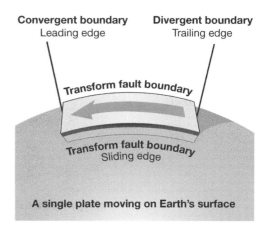

Figure 11.7: *Divergent, convergent, and transform fault boundaries.*

Plate Boundaries

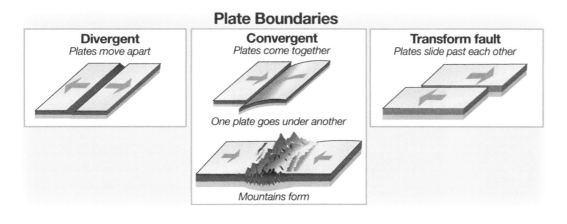

Divergent boundaries

New sea-floor at mid-ocean ridges Mid-ocean ridges in the oceans are divergent boundaries, where two plates are moving apart. This type of boundary is found over the rising part of a mantle convection cell. Convection causes the two plates to move away from each other. As they move, molten rock fills the space created by their motion. The molten rock cools and becomes new ocean floor.

Rift valleys Divergent boundaries can also be found on continents as *rift valleys*. When a rift valley forms on land, it may eventually split the landmass wide enough so that the sea flows into the valley. When this happens, the rift valley becomes a mid-ocean ridge. The East African Rift Valley is an example of rifting in progress. This rift is marked by a series of long lakes that start near the southern end of the Red Sea and move southward toward Mozambique.

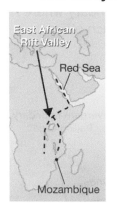

East African Rift Valley

Red Sea

Mozambique

Divergent Plate Boundaries

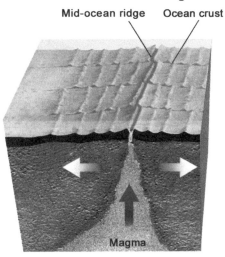

Mid-ocean ridge   Ocean crust

Magma

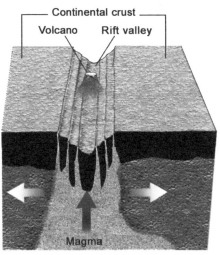

Continental crust

Volcano   Rift valley

Magma

Convergent boundaries

Deep-ocean trenches
A deep-ocean trench is a valley on the ocean floor. These trenches are formed when two oceanic plates collide and one plate subducts under the other.

Why does one plate subduct under another?
A denser plate subducts under a less dense one. Older oceanic plates are cooler, and therefore denser than young oceanic plates. So older plates tend to subduct or slide under younger plates.

 VOCABULARY

deep-ocean trench - a valley in the ocean created when one lithospheric plate subducts under another.

Convergent plate boundary

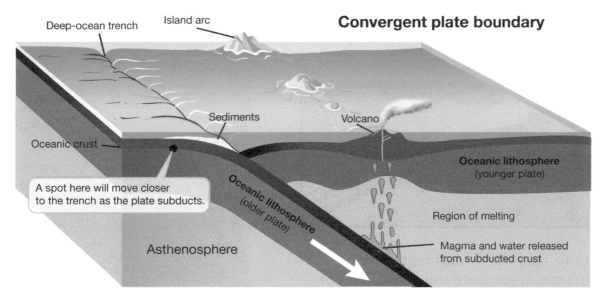

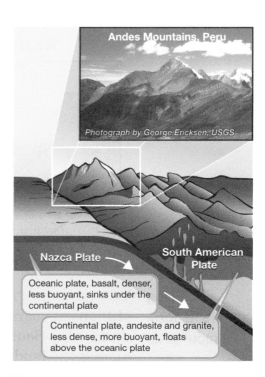

Oceanic and continental plate subduction
What happens if an oceanic plate and a continental plate collide? Continental plates are largely made of andesite and granite. Andesite and granite are much less dense than the basalt of oceanic plates. Which plate would subduct? A continental plate is simply too buoyant and too thick to subduct under an oceanic plate. The oceanic plate must subduct under the continental plate. A good example of this is the Nazca Plate off the coast of South America. The Nazca Plate is subducting under the South American Plate (Figure 11.8).

Figure 11.8: *The collision of the Nazca and South American Plates has deformed and pushed up the land to form the high peaks of the Andes Mountains.*

Mountains and convergent boundaries

What happens when two continents collide? What happens if an oceanic plate with a continental plate attached is subducted under another continental plate? Eventually all of the oceanic crust is subducted and the continental plates collide! The continent on the oceanic plate cannot be sucked down into the trench because its granite rocks are too buoyant to be subducted.

What happens when two continents collide?

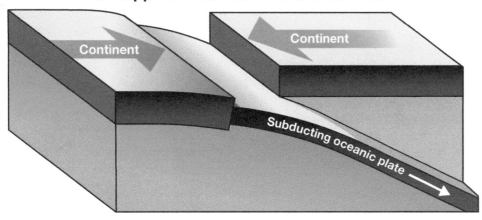

Colliding continents form mountains Vast mountain ranges are formed when continents collide. Millions of years ago, India was a separate continent and not attached to South Asia. The Indo-Australian oceanic plate carried the landmass of India toward China as it subducted under the Eurasian continental plate. The Himalaya Mountains are the result of this collision (Figure 11.9). The impact of the collision still causes earthquakes in China today. The formation of mountains is a slow process. The Himalaya Mountains are still growing, millions of years after the collision!

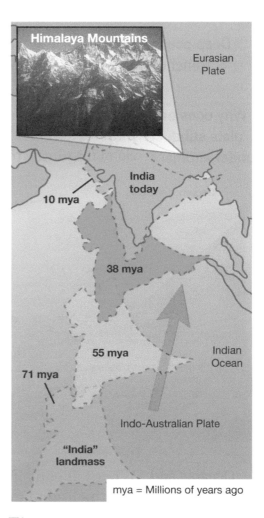

mya = Millions of years ago

Figure 11.9: *The Himalaya Mountains are the result of the slow but powerful collision between India on the Indo-Australian Plate and China on the Eurasian Plate.*

Transform fault boundaries

Finding boundaries
Once scientists began to understand lithospheric plate boundaries, finding divergent and convergent boundaries was easy. Mid-ocean ridges and continental rift valleys are divergent boundaries. Deep-ocean trenches and mountain ranges occur at the locations of convergent boundaries. Finding transform fault boundaries is more difficult. Transform faults leave few clues to indicate their presence.

Zig-zags are clues
Sometimes the action of a transform fault will form a small valley along its line of movement. Often there will be ponds along the line. A good clue for locating transform faults is *offsetting*. If a feature like a creek or a highway crosses a transform fault, the movement of the fault will break, or offset, the feature. When seen from above, the feature will appear to make a zig-zag (Figure 11.10). Also, look at the map of the world's plate boundaries on page 262. Here, you can easily see the zig-zags of the transform fault boundaries that make up the Mid-Atlantic Ridge and the East Pacific Rise.

Earthquakes are another clue
Another good way to detect transform faults is by the earthquakes they cause. The San Andreas Fault is a well-known fault that causes earthquakes in California (Figure 11.11). The San Andreas Fault is the transform fault boundary between two lithospheric plates—the Pacific Plate and the North American Plate.

Using plate tectonics to understand other events
Before plate tectonics was understood, scientists knew where earthquakes commonly occurred, but they didn't know why. This is another example of how understanding plate tectonics led to other new discoveries. Today we know that earthquakes occur at all three types of boundaries. Volcanic activity only occurs at convergent and divergent boundaries. You will learn more about earthquakes and volcanoes in the next chapter.

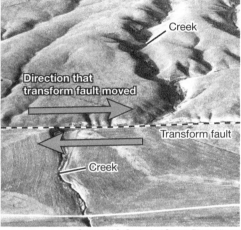

Source: U.S. Geological Survey Photo Library

Figure 11.10: *The creek is offset to the right as viewed from bottom to top in the photo.*

Photo courtesy of Dr. John B. Reid

Figure 11.11: *This line of students stretches across part of the San Andreas Fault in California.*

Slickensides, evidence of plate boundaries

What are slickensides? The photo at the near right shows the effect of rock moving against rock along a fault in the Coronado Heights section of San Francisco. The polished rock surface is called *slickensides*. At one time, the slickensides were below Earth's surface with another mass of rock pressing against it. The other mass has since weathered away.

Photo by Jim Sammons, Sammons' INK.

Figure 11.12: *The edge that is sticking out indicates that the slickensides moved away from you.*

Motion of the slickensides Figure 11.12 is a close-up of the slickensides looking to the right. Look at the edge that is sticking out. This edge indicates that the direction that the slickensides moved in the past was away from you. The rock mass that weathered away would have been to the right of the slickensides. The graphic below at the left gives you a bird's eye view of how these plates moved.

Looking at a transform fault boundary

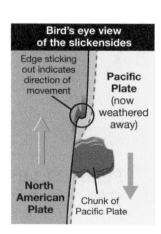

Figure 11.13 is another close-up of the same slickensides, but looking to the left. From this view we can see part of the rock mass that moved against the slickensides rock mass. The blue pen marks the fault that separates the two rock masses. The rock mass to the left of the fault was part of the Pacific Plate. The slickensides rock mass to the right of the fault was part of the North American Plate. This is the location of a transform fault boundary!

Photo by Jim Sammons, Sammons' INK

Figure 11.13: *A transform fault boundary between the Pacific Plate to the left and the North American Plate to the right (marked by the photographer's blue pen).*

Earth's lithospheric plates

This map shows the largest lithospheric plates that cover Earth. There are many small plates, but some of these have been combined with the larger ones to simplify the map.

Study the map below. Can you identify the types of plate boundaries labeled A, B, and C? Use the arrows on the map to help you. Remember that the types of plate boundaries are divergent, convergent, and transform. Then, see if you can answer the questions. A more detailed view of Earth's lithospheric plates is on the next page.

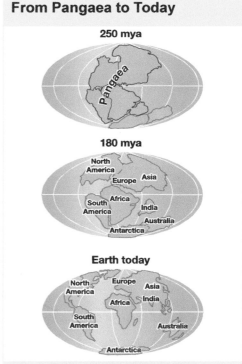

From Pangaea to Today

250 mya

180 mya

Earth today

About 250 million years ago (mya), all land on Earth was part of the supercontinent called Pangaea. About 180 mya, this huge landmass began to split apart into many sections. Seven of the largest sections form our continents. It is important to note that Pangaea was not the original landmass. Before Pangaea, there were other earlier oceans and continents, and, over a very long period of time, forces brought them together to form Pangaea.

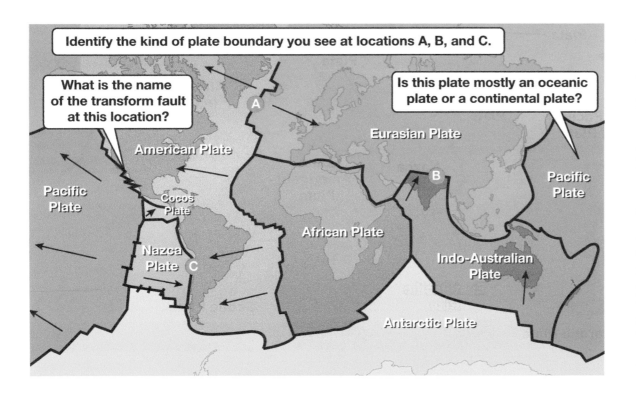

Identify the kind of plate boundary you see at locations A, B, and C.

What is the name of the transform fault at this location?

Is this plate mostly an oceanic plate or a continental plate?

Eurasian Plate

American Plate

Pacific Plate

Pacific Plate

Cocos Plate

Nazca Plate

African Plate

Indo-Australian Plate

Pacific Plate

Antarctic Plate

Earth's lithospheric plates

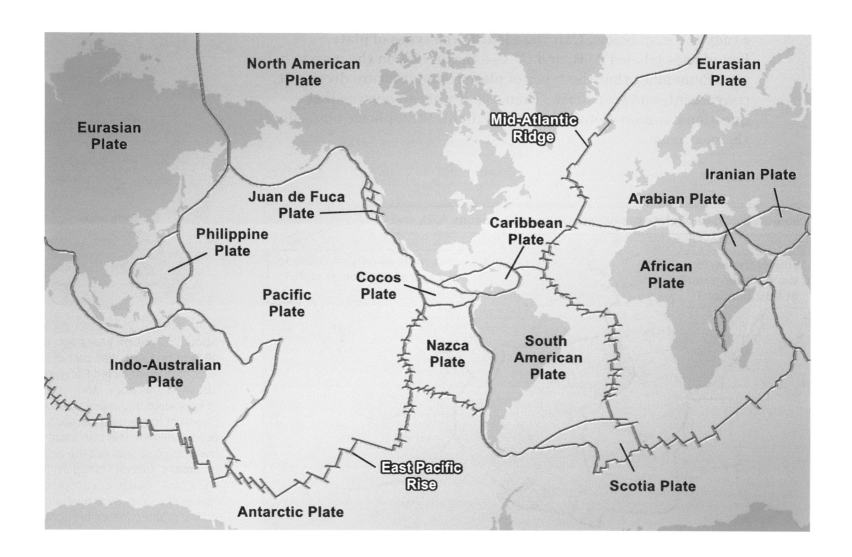

11.3 Section Review

1. What are the three types of plate boundaries and what direction of movement does each have?

2. What kind of plate boundary is a mid-ocean ridge?

3. What is pillow lava and where is it formed?

4. Give an example of a divergent boundary on land.

5. What happens when oceanic plates collide? What surface feature does this plate boundary create?

6. What features of a plate determine whether one plate will subduct under another plate? Pick the three correct features below.

a. the name of the plate

b. the age of the plate

c. whether the plate is oceanic or continental

d. how fast the plate is traveling

e. whether the plate is in the northern or southern hemisphere

f. the density or buoyancy of the plate

7. Which is more buoyant—a continental plate or oceanic plate? Which would subduct if the two were to collide?

8. What happens when two continental plates collide? Give an example of continents colliding today.

9. What are two clues to finding transform faults?

10. The polished surfaces of rock that are a result of rock moving against rock along a fault are known as _____.

11. The previous page shows a detailed map of Earth's larger and smaller lithospheric plates. Pick a plate and find out one fact about this plate.

CHALLENGE

1. The oldest parts of Earth's crust are found on the continents and not in the oceans. Why do you think this is?

2. Earth is 4.6 billion years old, but the oldest sea floor is only about 200 million years old. Why do you think this is?

3. Where might you find the oldest rocks on Earth?

4. How likely are we to find any rocks that are as old as Earth itself?

MY JOURNAL

Careers in Earth science

Have you ever thought about being an Earth scientist?

Find out what kinds of careers are available to people who study Earth science and geology.

For example, a *geodynamacist* studies how lithospheric plates move and change shape.

Write a description of one Earth science career that interests you.

Where to go for Volcanoes

Streams of molten lava, rocks glowing fiery red inside, steam spewing from a mountaintop—does this sound like a volcano you could see in Hawaii? It is true that Hawaii has some picturesque and spectacular volcanoes, but there are many volcanoes on the mainland of the United States too.

Why do some regions of the world have volcanoes while others do not? Volcanoes typically happen along the boundaries of the Earth's massive tectonic plates. The plates move and shift, creating both volcanoes and earthquakes. Volcanoes may also occur in the middle of plates or sometimes over places called "hot spots."

In the recorded history of Earth, more than 500 volcanoes have erupted. In the United States, 50 volcanoes have erupted. The three countries with the most active volcanoes are Indonesia, Japan, and the United States. Around the rim of the Pacific Ocean, also called the Ring of Fire, there are more than 1,000 volcanoes and earthquakes.

The western part of United States is in this Pacific Ring of Fire. Alaska, Washington, Oregon, and California all have volcanoes in the ring. Not including Alaska and Hawaii, there are 40 volcanoes in the United States, and you might recognize some of these famous ones out West.

Washington's big five

There are five major volcanoes, called composite volcanoes, in Washington. These steep-sided conical volcanoes are, from north to south, Mount Baker, Glacier Peak, Mount Rainier, Mount St. Helens, and Mount Adams, and with Mount Hood in Oregon, they are part of the Cascade Range, a volcanic arch that stretches from British Columbia to California.

Mount Rainier, at 14,411 feet (4,392 meters), is Washington's highest mountain. Its most recent eruption was in the early 1800s. Located near Seattle, it is closely monitored for activity. Approximately 30 earthquakes occur under Mount Rainier each year, making it a very earthquake active area. In 1899, Mount Rainier became the country's fifth national park.

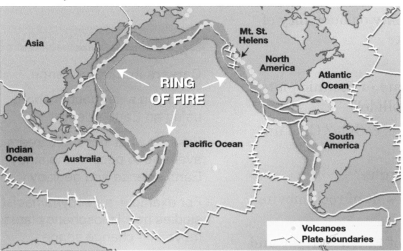

Mount St. Helens erupting in 1980

Nearby stands another famous volcano: Mount St. Helens. It had been quiet for over 100 years until on the morning of May 18, 1980, it erupted violently for nine hours. A magnitude 5.1 earthquake kicked off the huge explosion. In just minutes, the 9,677-foot-high mountain collapsed, reduced 1,200 feet by the explosion and mammoth landslide. So much ash was released that the sky got dark. Recently, Mount St. Helens has erupted again. Scientists view each eruption as a chance to learn more about volcanoes.

Oregon's user-friendly Mount Hood

Moving south along the Cascades, you come to Mount Hood, 11,239 feet high and Oregon's highest peak. The last big eruptions took place 200 and 1,500 years ago. Mount Hood is one of the most climbed peaks in the Pacific Northwest. At 6,000 feet you find the famous Timberline Lodge, built in 1938 and where scenes from *The Shining*, the 1980 movie based on the Stephen King novel, were shot. The slopes of the volcano are used almost year-round for skiing and snowboarding. The nearby ski area is known for having the longest ski season in the United States.

California's hot spots

When you think of California, you typically think of perfect weather, golden beaches, and great surf. But the Golden State is also home to several volcanoes. Active or possibly active volcanoes include Black Butte, Lassen Peak, Long Valley Caldera, Medicine Lake, Mount Shasta, and Crater Lake (formed by the eruption of Mount Mazama).

Potentially Active Volcanoes of Western United States

Volcano active during past 2,000 years

Other potentially active volcanic areas

0   100   200 kilometers
0   100 miles

USGS
Topinka, USGS/CVO, 1999, Modified from: Brantley, 1994, Volcanoes of the United States: USGS General Interest Publication

Still part of the Cascades, and one of the world's largest composite volcanoes (14,161 feet), Mount Shasta is located 265 miles north of San Francisco. The most recent eruption is thought to have occurred in 1786. The mountain is part of the Shasta-Trinity National Forest, the largest national forest in California.

In east-central California, the Long Valley Caldera stands along the east side of the Sierra Nevada. Rocks formed in the past 2 million years from volcanic eruptions cover most of the area.

Our tour comes to an end south of both Shasta and Medicine Lake at Lassen Peak, the baby of the Cascades, one of the youngest of the major volcanoes in those mountains.

Cascades Volcano Observatory

After the eruption of Mount St. Helens, the U.S. Geological Survey created the Cascades Volcano Observatory (CVO). CVO monitors volcanoes and related dangers such as earthquakes and landslides. Thousands of visitors are attracted each year to the spectacular volcanic scenery of the Cascades, but they should not forget the mountains' potential hazards and how they are monitored.

QUESTIONS

1. Why does the Cascade Range have so many volcanoes?

2. Identify and describe two mainland U.S. volcanoes that erupted in the 20th century?

3. What benefits resulted from the eruption of Mount St. Helens?

Make a Plate Tectonics Book

In this chapter, you learned about plate tectonics—about how Earth has large blocks of lithospheric plates moving about, interacting with one another. You learned that some blocks move toward each other and make mountains and others get subducted. In the oceans, plates are moving apart from each other, creating new sea floor. In places like the Pacific Rim, there are many earthquakes which means transform fault boundaries are there. Earth is an amazing place!

Materials

Pieces of paper (copy paper, construction paper, or newsprint), staples and a stapler, glue, colored pencils and markers, pens, scissors, old magazines, and any other material you need to make your book

What you will do

1. Get into a group of three or four people to make the book.

2. With your group, decide on a title for your book. Here are a couple of ideas: *Plate Tectonics* or *How South America and Africa Moved Apart*.

3. Your book will recount part of the plate tectonics story. Use the graphic on this page and others in Chapter 8 to help you outline your story.

If you would like, you can come up with mythical creatures that lived on the ancient continents before they reached their current positions—just as long as you explain in some way how the continents got to where they are today. Use lots of pictures. Maybe someone in your group is an artist.

Your book will need a cover and back, a title, and a list of the authors. You may want to give credit to the artist or maybe there were a few artists in the group. The book size is optional. An oversized book can be very attractive to younger children. Use

whatever resources you can find, but ask your teacher to check your information for accuracy. Maybe the book will be in the form of a poem or a pop-up book. There are many creative ways to tell a story—have fun!

Applying your knowledge

a. What was the title of your group's book?

b. Imagine that your book will be in a library or sold in a book store. Write a short summary of the book so that a reader will know what it is about.

c. What did you like most about making the book with your group?

d. Share your plate tectonics story in class or read it to a group of younger students. Describe your experience at sharing your book with others.

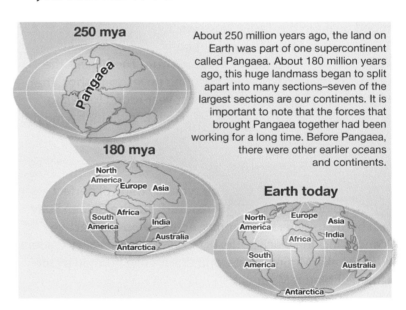

About 250 million years ago, the land on Earth was part of one supercontinent called Pangaea. About 180 million years ago, this huge landmass began to split apart into many sections–seven of the largest sections are our continents. It is important to note that the forces that brought Pangaea together had been working for a long time. Before Pangaea, there were other earlier oceans and continents.

Vocabulary

Select the correct term to complete the sentences.

Pangaea	oceanic plates	mid-ocean ridge
mantle plume	deep-ocean trench	lithospheric plates
subduction	plate tectonics	sea-floor spreading
continental plates	continental drift	transform fault boundary
convergent boundary	divergent boundary	

Section 11.1

1. _____, meaning "all land," is the name for the great landmass that existed millions of years ago.

2. The idea that the continents move around on Earth's surface is called _____.

3. The theory that explains how lithospheric plates move _____.

Section 11.2

4. The _____ are thick and made of andesite and granite.

5. The sinking process that completes the lower mantle convection cell is _____.

6. _____ move over the aesthenosphere.

7. New ocean floor is created at the locations of these undersea features called _____.

8. Hess proposed the idea of _____.

9. _____ are thin and made of basalt.

10. A _____ rises toward the lithosphere and may create a volcanic center.

Section 11.3

11. Mountains form along a _____.

12. Mid-ocean ridges indicate the presence of this type of boundary: _____.

13. The occurrence of earthquakes and offsetting are clues that a location is near a _____.

14. A _____, or valley in the ocean floor, is created when one lithospheric plate subducts under another.

Concepts

Section 11.1

1. According to the hypothesis of continental drift, how would a world map have changed over the last 250 million years?

2. How do fossils support the idea of continental drift?

3. Earth's surface is often described as a giant jigsaw puzzle. What are the pieces of the puzzle?

4. Wegener collected a lot of evidence to support his idea of continental drift. Was his evidence enough to prove continental drift was correct? Why or why not?

Section 11.2

5. Describe how Harry Hess thought the continents moved apart. What did Hess call his set of ideas?

6. The Mid-Atlantic Ridge is a mid-ocean ridge in the Atlantic Ocean. Is the Atlantic ocean getting larger or smaller?

7. The graphic below shows the magnetic pattern on one side of a mid-ocean ridge. Make a sketch of the magnetic pattern that would appear on the other side of the ridge.

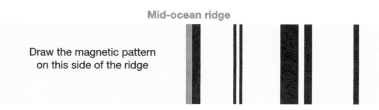

Mid-ocean ridge

Draw the magnetic pattern on this side of the ridge

8. Where would you find the oldest rocks on the sea floor? Where would you find the youngest rocks?

9. In your own words, describe how an island chain forms.

Section 11.3

10. List the three types of plate boundaries. What famous feature in California represents one of these boundaries?

11. What kinds of geologic features form when two continental plates come together?

12. Where is the East African Rift Valley located? What kind of boundary does it represent?

Math and Writing Skills

Section 11.1

1. Imagine that Alfred Wegener and Harry Hess could have a conversation. Write a dialog between these two important figures in the history of plate tectonics.

Section 11.2

2. To calculate the speed of plate motion, divide the distance the plate moves by the time it takes to move that distance (speed = distance ≥ time). Give your answer in kilometers per 1 million years (km/1 million years). (Usually these values are stated in centimeters/year or millimeters/year.)

   a. It takes 10 million years for the Pacific Plate to slide 600 kilometers past the North American Plate. How fast is the Pacific Plate moving?

   b. There are two islands on opposite sides of a mid-ocean ridge. During the last 8 million years, the distance between the islands has increased by 200 kilometers. What is the rate at which the two plates are diverging?

Section 11.3

3. Draw diagrams of the three types of plate boundaries.

Chapter Project—Sea-Floor Spreading Model

Materials: Shoe box lid, piece of copy paper cut lengthwise (in half), red and black markers, scissors.

1. Cut a slit in the shoe box so that the paper can fit in widthwise.

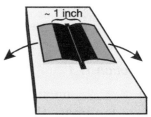

~ 1 inch

Keep creating stripes until you're almost finished with the paper.

2. Put the pieces of paper in the slit from the underside of the shoebox lid. Allow about 2 cm of paper to show through the slit.

3. One piece of paper will be folded back to the left of the slit and one will be folded to the right of the slit.

4. Use your red marker to color the paper that is showing (on both sides of the slit). Optional: Write the year you were born on this stripe.

5. Now pull another inch or so of paper through the slit. The amount pulled through doesn't matter as much as the fact that both sides need to pull through the same amount.

6. Now color this new strip of white paper in black marker. Optional: Write the year after you were born on this stripe.

7. Continue to pull the paper through the slit and coloring the strips (in alternate colors), until you almost run out of paper. You have now created a model for sea-floor spreading. Optional: Keep writing the year on each stripe. This shows that the older stripes end up further away from the ridge and the youngest are closest to the ridge.

8. Questions: (a) Where can you find the landform represented by the box top and paper? (b) How do these magnetic patterns on the sea-floor support plate tectonics? (c) In the chapter, you learned that these patterns are called "magnetic reversal patterns." Why is this a good name?

Chapter 12

Earthquakes and Volcanoes

The interior of Earth has different layers. The outer layer—the lithosphere—is broken up into pieces called lithospheric plates. As you learned in Chapter 11, lithospheric plates move. As a result, a great deal of geologic action takes place at the boundaries between the moving plates. Some of this action includes volcanic eruptions and earthquakes. In fact, by plotting the locations of volcanoes and earthquakes on a map, you can see the shapes and boundaries of lithospheric plates. In this chapter you will see these kinds of maps and learn why plate boundaries are such active places!

Key Questions:

1. *What is stick-slip motion?*

2. *Can one earthquake cause another?*

3. *Why are some volcanic eruptions explosive and some gentle?*

12.1 **Earthquakes**

In a place where earthquakes are common, it is not unusual to feel the ground shake. You might notice tiny ripples in your juice glass at breakfast and then you might feel small vibrations through your chair. Soon it's quiet again. Chances are good it was just a common, small earthquake. However, these vibrations might be a foreshock. A foreshock is a small burst of shaking that occurs before a large earthquake. Read on to find out more about earthquakes.

What is an earthquake like?

A big earthquake   During an earthquake, strong shaking makes the ground move up and down and back and forth. During the strongest earthquakes, it's nearly impossible to stand up. Large cracks may open up in the ground and the ground may heave up or sink. If the ground becomes saturated with water, the shaking soil might act like a liquid in a process called *liquefaction*. This causes the water-logged soil to engulf buildings as they sink into the ground. The largest U.S. earthquake struck Alaska in 1964 and lasted for four minutes (Figure 12.1).

Foreshocks and aftershocks   Foreshocks can occur days before an earthquake hits, or just minutes before. Foreshocks get closer together just before an earthquake. In 1964, people had almost no warning because the foreshocks arrived only a few seconds before the earthquake. A small tremor that follows an earthquake is called an **aftershock**. Aftershocks can occur hours or even days after an earthquake. The time between aftershocks gets longer as time passes after an earthquake.

Most quakes are small   Most earthquakes are not as large as the Alaskan one. Many earthquakes are so small they can only be detected by scientific instruments.

VOCABULARY

foreshock - a small burst of shaking that occurs before a large earthquake.

aftershock - a small tremor that follows an earthquake.

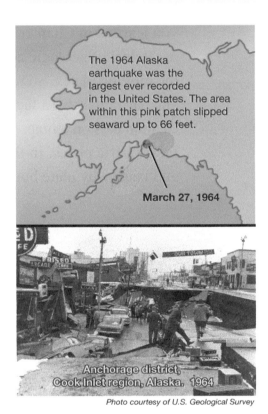

The 1964 Alaska earthquake was the largest ever recorded in the United States. The area within this pink patch slipped seaward up to 66 feet.

March 27, 1964

Anchorage district, Cook Inlet region, Alaska. 1964

Photo courtesy of U.S. Geological Survey

Figure 12.1: *The 1964 Alaska earthquake was the longest ever recorded and the largest ever recorded in the United States.*

What causes earthquakes?

What is a an earthquake?

What exactly is an earthquake? An earthquake is the movement of Earth's crust due to the release of built-up potential energy (stored energy) between two stuck lithospheric plates.

Plates stick together, then break

Lithospheric plates on Earth's surface slide past each other. As this happens, the plates may stick together due to friction. Often the brittle crust will stick near the surface. However, the plastic upper mantle continues to flow underneath. *Plastic* here means "able to change shape without breaking," like modeling clay. With the crust stuck and the upper mantle moving below, the rocks at plate boundaries stretch or compress. As a result, potential energy builds in the plate. When potential energy exceeds the strength of the rock and friction—bang!—the rock breaks and slips. This type of motion is called *stick-slip motion.*

Stick-slip motion
The brittle crust sticks and releases.

Plate

Plate

Lithosphere

The upper mantle is plastic and flows.

Stress relief for plates

The sudden release of potential energy when plates "slip" causes earthquakes. In this sense, an earthquake is a stress reliever for lithospheric plates. However, the relief is only temporary. Potential energy starts building up again as soon as the quake ends.

Parts of an earthquake

The point below the surface where the rock breaks is called the earthquake focus. When the rock breaks, there is movement along the broken surface. The location of this event is called a fault. The energy of the movement is spread by *seismic waves.* The seismic waves from an earthquake are usually strongest at the epicenter, the point on the surface right above the focus (Figure 12.2).

ⓐ VOCABULARY

earthquake - the movement of Earth's crust resulting from the release of built-up potential energy between two stuck lithospheric plates.

focus - the point below Earth's surface where a rock breaks or slips and causes an earthquake.

fault - a region on Earth's surface that is broken and where movement occurs.

epicenter - a point on Earth's surface right above the focus of an earthquake.

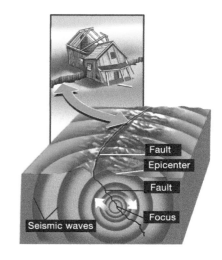

Fault
Epicenter
Fault
Seismic waves
Focus

Figure 12.2: *The focus, epicenter, and seismic waves of an earthquake occurring at an active fault.*

Stick-slip motion

Three conditions   The event of an earthquake is just like what happens when you try to open a stuck door. Both situations involve stick-slip motion. Think about trying to open a stuck door. You pull and pull and then—bang!—the door flies open (Figure 12.3). Three conditions are needed for stick-slip motion.

1. Two objects that are touching each other, where at least one of the objects can move.

2. A force (or forces) that will cause the movement.

3. Friction strong enough to temporarily keep the movement from starting. *Friction* is a force that resists slipping when two objects rub against each other (Figure 12.4).

A stuck door   In the stuck-door example, the two objects are the door and its frame. The force that will cause movement is you pulling on the door. The friction might be caused by moisture making a wooden door swell so that it jams in the door frame. You have to pull hard to overcome the friction. The loud bang you hear when the door opens is some of your pulling energy changed to sound energy as the door vibrates.

Earthquakes   As you've learned, an earthquake is a form of stick-slip motion because lithospheric plates slide past each other and get stuck. Eventually, the stuck plates slip and an earthquake occurs. The movement of lithospheric plates causes earthquakes at all three kinds of plate boundaries (divergent, convergent, and transform fault) and even within plates. Review the different types of plate boundaries in Section 11.3.

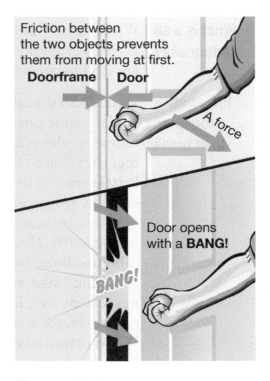

Figure 12.3: *A stuck door is an example of stick-slip motion.*

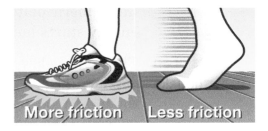

Figure 12.4: *There is more friction between a sneaker and a gym floor than between a sock and the gym floor.*

Lithospheric plates have many sections

Sections of plate boundaries

Although a lithospheric plate moves as a single unit, its boundary acts as though it were made of many sections. A line of grocery carts is a good analogy of lithospheric plate movement (Figure 12.5). A line of grocery carts moves along as a single unit, but there are small movements between each cart. When a person pushes the back end of a line, the carts at the front end remain still for a moment. It takes some time for the first cart to push the second, the second to push the next, and so on, until eventually, the front cart starts to move.

The San Andreas Fault

A lithospheric plate may be thousands of kilometers across. Therefore, it takes a long time for movement on one end of the plate to affect a section further away. Like each cart in a line of carts, each section of a plate can move before or after other sections. For example, parts of the San Andreas Fault can be stuck together and other parts may move at any time. An earthquake happens each time a plate section moves, but only in the section that moved.

A single cart can move independently within the line

A line of carts moves together in one direction

Figure 12.5: *A moving line of grocery carts is like a moving lithospheric plate.*

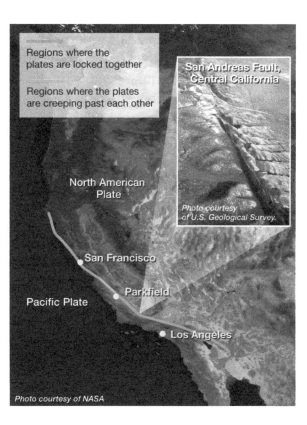

Regions where the plates are locked together

Regions where the plates are creeping past each other

San Andreas Fault, Central California

Photo courtesy of U.S. Geological Survey.

North American Plate

San Francisco

Parkfield

Pacific Plate

Los Angeles

Photo courtesy of NASA

CHALLENGE

What do you know about earthquakes?

Collect a list of 10 interesting facts about earthquakes.

When do earthquakes occur?

Frequency and strength Imagine two sections along the same fault. The first section has earthquakes a few times a year. The earthquakes are mild because relatively little energy is released during each quake. These frequent earthquakes release potential energy before it can build up to a high level. Now, let's say that earthquakes occur only once every 20 years in the second section. The long time period between earthquakes allows a great deal of potential energy to build up. Earthquakes in this section are likely to be devastating.

One earthquake may trigger others It is common for an earthquake in one section of a fault to cause an earthquake in a neighboring section. Imagine two neighboring plate sections. One section is ahead of the other along the fault in the direction of plate movement. Both sections have built up a lot of potential energy. Then, an earthquake occurs in the front section, reducing its potential energy. Now there is an energy difference between the first and second section. This difference may trigger a new earthquake in the second section. It's common for one earthquake to have a ripple effect along a fault.

Earthquakes in the middle of plates Throughout Earth's history, lithospheric plates have been torn apart, added to, and joined with other plates. As a result of this reshaping, there are old plate boundaries inside of the plates we see today. These old boundaries are now faults inside of plates. The New Madrid Fault, for example, is a fault zone within the North American Plate (Figure 12.6). This zone is an "old" plate boundary that can break when the North American crust flexes as a result of plate tectonic activity. This can result in a major earthquake, such as the New Madrid events in 1811 and 1812.

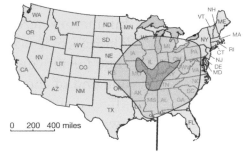

SOLVE IT!

In terms of the release of potential energy, which situation might cause more damage to a city—many small earthquakes, or one big earthquake? Explain your answer.

The New Madrid Seismic Zone

0   200   400 miles

Area affected by an earthquake in 1895

☐ Little damage, but shaking felt

■ Minor to major damage

Figure 12.6: *The New Madrid Fault, a fault zone within the North American Plate.*

Seismic waves

Seismographs An earthquake converts potential energy into kinetic energy (the energy of motion) in the form of seismic waves. The waves start underground at the earthquake focus and radiate in all directions. Seismic waves are usually recorded and measured by a seismograph. The recordings indicate the arrival time, type, and strength of the waves. Seismographs are located around the world at seismic stations on land and in the oceans. Seismographs can look like large drums covered in paper (see above) or the waves can be recorded by computers (Figure 12.7).

Seismograph
Photo courtesy of U.S. Geological Survey.

Body waves Seismic waves inside Earth are called body waves. The two main types of body waves are P-waves and S-waves. P-waves are faster and arrive first at a seismic station (Figure 12.7). They are fast because the rock through which they travel moves in the same direction that the P-waves move. S-waves travel more slowly because they cause the rock to move in a side-to-side motion. The speed at which body waves travel depends on the density and composition of the material they are traveling through. Waves travel faster in cool, dense material and slower in hot, less-dense material. The waves may also bend or be reflected when they contact different materials.

Surface waves When seismic waves reach the surface, they become surface waves. Surface waves are slower than body waves, but they cause more damage. Surface waves can move up and down (like waves on the ocean), or from side to side, often causing buildings to collapse.

VOCABULARY

seismograph - an instrument that measures and records seismic waves.

body waves - seismic waves that travel through the interior of Earth.

surface waves - seismic waves that reach and travel along Earth's surface.

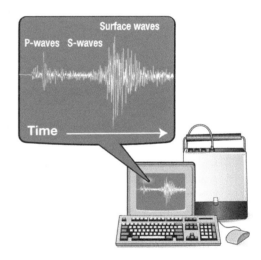

Figure 12.7: *After an earthquake occurs, the first seismic waves recorded will be P-waves. S-waves are recorded next, followed by the surface waves.*

Locating the epicenter of an earthquake

A seismic waves "race" The arrival times of P- and S-waves at a seismic station can be used to locate an earthquake's epicenter (Figure 12.8). This analogy explains how it's done. In a car race, all cars start together. In time, the fastest car gets ahead of the slowest car. The longer the race, the further ahead the faster car gets. Like fast and slow cars, P- and S-waves have different speeds. The difference in the arrival time between P- and S-waves determines the distance to the epicenter from the seismic station. The larger the difference in arrival time, the farther the epicenter is from the station.

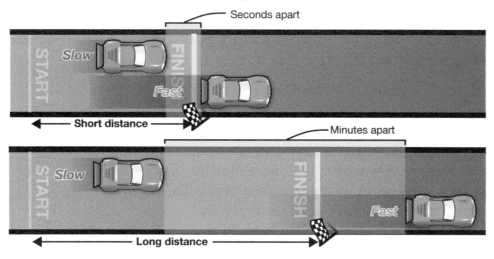

 SOLVE IT!

A time-distance graph is used to determine the distance to an epicenter. If the arrival time between P- and S-waves is 2.5 seconds, what is the approximate distance to the epicenter?

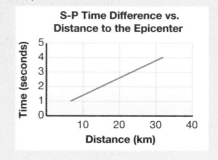

S-P Time Difference vs. Distance to the Epicenter

Three seismic stations are needed At least three stations are needed to locate the epicenter. First, each station determines the distance to the epicenter based on the P- and S-wave arrival times. Then each station draws a circle around its location on a map. The radius of each circle is based on the calculated distance to the epicenter. The edge of each station's circle represents all of the possible locations of the earthquake from that station. When all three circles are drawn on the same map, they will cross at a single point—the epicenter.

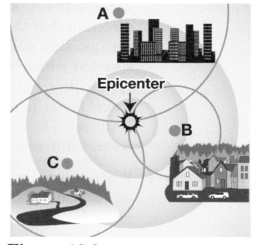

Figure 12.8: *An epicenter is located using data from three seismic stations.*

A seismic mystery solved by soccer

Many signals at one time

Garrett Euler was puzzled. Earthquake-like signals were arriving at all of his 32 seismic stations at the same time. Euler, a graduate student at Washington University, had traveled to the Republic of Cameroon in Africa to set up a network of seismic stations (Figure 12.9). By recording seismic waves, Euler hoped to learn more about Earth's crust and upper mantle.

Usually seismic waves arrive at different times

The strange signals reaching his stations made no sense. When an earthquake occurs, seismic waves reach different stations at different times, depending on the distance from the station to the epicenter. Only if the earthquake was on the opposite side of Earth could you get signals arriving at multiple stations at the same time. But Euler checked and found that no other seismologists had reported earthquakes at the same time. What was going on? What kind of activity could produce a seismic signal like this (Figure 12.9)?

Seismic soccer?

Euler's girlfriend Katy Lofton had a hypothesis. She knew that soccer was popular in Cameroon. A quick check showed that an important soccer tournament, the African Cup of Nations, was played during the time of the strange signals. By checking game records, Euler was able to show that each burst of seismic signals matched the time each Cameroonian goal occurred! The source of the strange signal had been found. But, how did that signal get to all the stations at the same time? The answer to that part of the mystery is radio and television.

Goal!

These games were so popular that they were broadcast all over Cameroon. Radio and television allowed fans to experience the thrill of each goal in villages and cities all over the country at the same instant. Cameroonians cheered and stomped throughout their country, producing signals from countless "mini-epicenters."

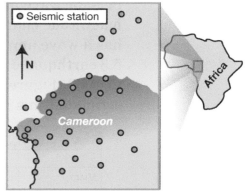

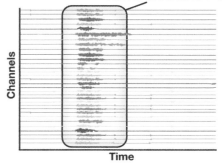

Figure 12.9: *Garrett Euler recorded seismic waves at the same time at all of his 32 seismic stations located in the Republic of Cameroon.*

Measuring earthquakes

The Richter scale   The **Richter scale** ranks earthquakes according to their magnitude of the seismic waves recorded on a seismograph. Seismic wave amplitude increases 10 times for each Richter magnitude change. For example, a magnitude 6.3 earthquake has a wave amplitude that is 10 times greater than a magnitude 5.3 earthquake. The largest recorded earthquake occurred in Chile in 1960 (Figure 12.10). It was off the Richter scale. Seismologists estimated this quake to have been magnitude 9.5.

VOCABULARY

Richter scale - a scale that ranks earthquakes according to the size of the seismic waves.

Moment Magnitude scale - a scale that rates the total energy released by earthquakes.

The Richter scale		
Level	Magnitude	Description of what may occur
Micro	Less than 2.0	Barely felt, but recorded by seismographs
Very minor	2.0–2.9	Recorded but not felt by most people
Minor	3.0–3.9	Little damage but felt by people
Light	4.0–4.9	No serious damage, objects shake
Moderate	5.0–5.9	Major damage to poorly-designed buildings
Strong	6.0–6.9	Serious damage over a 100-km area or less
Major	7.0–7.9	Serious damage over a larger area
Great	8.0–8.9	Serious damage over several hundred km
Rare great	9.0 or greater	Serious damage over several thousand km

Damage Caused by the 1960 Chile Earthquake

Photo courtesy of the National Geophysical Data Center

Figure 12.10: *The 1960 Chile earthquake, which caused devastating damage, was estimated to be a 9.5 magnitude on the Richter scale.*

The Moment Magnitude scale   The **Moment Magnitude scale** rates the total energy released by an earthquake. The numbers on this scale combine energy ratings and descriptions of rock movements. This scale can be used at locations that are close to and far away from an epicenter. The Richter and Moment Magnitude scales are similar up to magnitude 5. However, seismologists tend to use the more descriptive Moment Magnitude scale for larger earthquakes.

Energy and the Richter Scale

Each higher value on the Richter scale represents a 10 times increase in wave amplitude. However, in terms of energy, each higher number represents the release of about 31 times more energy!

Measuring earthquake damage

The **Modified Mercalli scale** has 12 descriptive categories. Each category is a rating of the damage experienced by buildings, the ground, and people. Because earthquake damage can be different from place to place, a single earthquake may have different Mercalli numbers in different locations (Figure 12.11).

VOCABULARY

Modified Mercalli scale - a scale that rates the damage experienced by buildings, the ground, and people during an earthquake.

The Modified Mercalli scale		
Category	**Effects**	**Richter scale (approximate)**
I. Instrumental	Not felt	1–2
II. Just perceptible	Felt by only a few people, especially on upper floors of tall buildings	3
III. Slight	Felt by people lying down, seated on a hard surface, or in the upper stories of tall buildings	3.5
IV. Perceptible	Felt indoors by many, by few outside; dishes and windows rattle.	4
V. Rather strong	Generally felt by everyone; sleeping people may be awakened	4.5
VI. Strong	Trees sway, chandeliers swing, bells ring, some damage from falling objects	5
VII. Very strong	General alarm; walls and plaster crack	5.5
VIII. Destructive	Felt in moving vehicles; chimneys collapse; poorly-constructed buildings seriously damaged	6
IX. Ruinous	Some houses collapse; pipes break	6.5
X. Disastrous	Obvious ground cracks; railroad tracks bent; some landslides on steep hillsides	7
XI. Very disastrous	Few buildings survive; bridges damaged or destroyed; all services interrupted (electrical, water, sewage, railroad); severe landslides	7.5
XII. Catastrophic	Total destruction; objects thrown into the air; river courses and topography altered	8

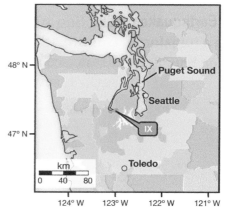
Sample Modified Mercalli map for an earthquake in Washington state

INTENSITY	I	II–III	IV	V	VI	VII	VIII	IX	X+
Shaking	Not felt	Weak	Light	Moderate	Strong	Very strong	Severe	Violent	Extreme
Damage	None	None	None	Very light	Light	Moderate	Moderate/Heavy	Heavy	Very Heavy

Figure 12.11: *From the map, you can see that the earthquake was a category IX on the Modified Mercalli scale in a very small area. Most of the surrounding areas experienced less shaking and damage.*

Earthquakes and plate boundaries

Boundaries of plates
When earthquake locations are plotted for many years, a map like the one below (at the lower left) can be created. Earthquakes commonly occur at the boundaries of lithospheric plates. They occur less commonly at faults that are inside plate boundaries. Note that in Figure 12.12, the earthquakes along the converging plates do not form a neat line. This is because plate boundaries tend to be *zones* of seismic activity. In particular, faults at transform fault boundaries, like the San Andreas Fault in Figure 12.13, have many branches. These fault branches form an *earthquake zone*.

Earthquakes along a transform fault boundary
The San Andreas Fault lies along the California coast (Figure 12.13). This famous fault passes right through San Francisco and part of Los Angeles. San Francisco has experienced several severe earthquakes and many smaller ones. The earthquake of 1906, together with the fires that it caused, destroyed much of the city. The damage caused by the earthquake was probably 8 or 9 on the Mercalli scale. Future earthquakes are expected here because the fault that lies under the city is still active.

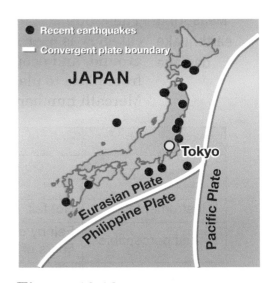

Figure 12.12: *Earthquakes along converging plate boundaries do not occur in neat lines, but occur in zones of seismic activity.*

Earthquakes and plate boundaries

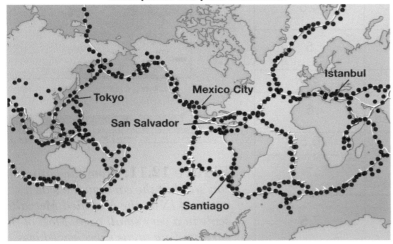

Figure 12.13: *The San Andreas Fault lies along the California coast.*

12.1 Section Review

1. Put these events in order and then describe each: aftershock, foreshock, and earthquake.
2. What is the difference between the focus and the epicenter of an earthquake?
3. What three conditions are needed for stick-slip motion?
4. How is a lithospheric plate like a line of moving grocery carts?
5. How can one earthquake cause another earthquake?
6. What is the difference between body waves and surface waves?
7. List what can happen to a seismic wave as it moves from one material to another.
8. What is measured to determine the location of an epicenter?
9. At least how many seismic stations are needed to find the epicenter of an earthquake?
10. Are earthquakes the only source of seismic waves? Explain your answer.
11. How many times stronger is a 3.0 magnitude earthquake compared to a 2.0 magnitude earthquake on the Richter scale?
12. A friend tells you he witnessed books and other objects falling off his bookcase during an earthquake. What was the magnitude of this earthquake:
    a. on the Modified Mercalli scale?
    b. on the Richter scale?
13. The largest earthquake ever recorded occurred in Chile, which is on the west coast of South America. Why are earthquakes to be expected in Chile? Explain your answer.
14. Why is it possible for a single earthquake to have different Modified Mercalli scale ratings in different locations?

How are seismic waves like race cars?

Write a paragraph that answers this question. Use illustrations to explain your answer.

Earthquakes inside plate boundaries

Here are two descriptions of earthquakes that occurred inside plate boundaries. Pick one and find out more information about the quake. Imagine you are an investigative reporter. Write a paragraph about each quake. Read your paragraph to the class as if you were reporting on the quake after it has happened.

(1) The New Madrid Fault is a 250-mile long fault located in the Midwest. Very strong earthquakes in 1811 and 1812 destroyed most of the town of New Madrid, Missouri.

(2) You probably don't think of New England as an earthquake area. But in 1755, a strong earthquake struck colonial Boston and destroyed many homes. The damage was greatest north of Boston and the earthquake was felt as far north as Montreal, Canada.

12.2 Volcanoes

Early explorers noticed that many volcanoes were located near coastlines, but they didn't know why. One volcano that is near a coastline is Mount St. Helens in Washington state. This famous volcano erupted in 1980 (Figure 12.14). Coastlines, plate tectonics, and volcanoes are all related. In this chapter you'll find out how.

Looking inside a volcano

What is a volcano? A volcano is a site where melted rock, gases, ash, and other materials from Earth's mantle are released or erupted. During an eruption, melted rock called magma leaves the magma chamber and moves up the *conduit*. The magma leaves the conduit at the *vent*. Magma may leave the vent gently, or with violent force. Magma is called lava after it leaves the vent. Magma may leave the conduit by moving sideways along weaknesses between rock layers. This sideways movement of magma forms a *sill*. Magma may also move upward in a sheet to form a *dike*. If a sill or a dike breaks through to the surface, another vent will form.

VOCABULARY

volcano - an erupting vent through which molten rock and other materials reach Earth's surface, or a mountain built from the products of an eruption.

magma - underground melted rock.

magma chamber - a location where magma collects inside Earth.

lava - magma that has reached and cooled on Earth's surface.

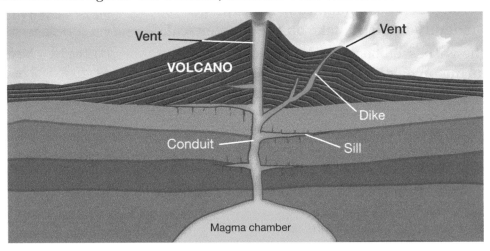

Photo courtesy of USGS

Figure 12.14: *Mount St. Helens in Washington state erupted in 1980.*

Volcano features after an eruption

Formation of a caldera
Eventually, all volcanic eruptions end. The magma chamber is mostly or completely emptied and unable to support the weight of the overlying volcano. As a result, the volcano collapses in on itself forming a bowl-shaped structure known as a **caldera**. Calderas can be very large—up to thousands of square meters.

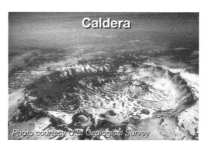

Caldera

Photo courtesy U.S. Geological Survey

Resurgent domes and lava lakes
If more magma returns up the conduit, a mound called a **resurgent dome** may form on the caldera floor. Water may fill the caldera forming a lake. It's also possible that the magma may not drain completely. In that case, the caldera will contain lava and become a **lava lake** (Figure 12.15).

Novarupta Dome
Katmai, Alaska

Resurgent dome

Photo courtesy of U.S. Geological Survey

Lava lake

Photo courtesy U.S. Geological Survey

Figure 12.15: *A lava lake.*

The life of a volcano

Volcanoes have a lifetime
Volcanoes are not permanent features on the surface of Earth. They have a lifetime that occurs in phases. Volcanoes are described according to the phase they are in. The three phases are active, dormant, and extinct.

Active volcanoes
An active volcano is erupting or has erupted recently, and is expected to erupt again in the near future. However, volcanic activity during the life of a volcano doesn't last forever. Eventually, the conditions that make a volcano active change and the volcano becomes dormant.

Dormant volcanoes
A dormant volcano is a quiet volcano. *Dormant* means sleeping. Dormant volcanoes are not active now, but may become active again in the future. Most of the volcanoes along the northern Pacific coast of North America are dormant.

Extinct volcanoes
An extinct volcano is at the end of its life and is no longer able to erupt. The now-solid magma that filled the conduit is exposed due to erosion of the surrounding volcano by wind and water. This solid core is called a volcanic neck. Examples of volcanic necks include Ship Rock in New Mexico and Devil's Tower National Monument in Wyoming (Figure 12.16). Devil's Tower was featured in the 1977 Steven Spielberg movie *Close Encounters of the Third Kind*.

VOCABULARY

active volcano - a volcano that is erupting or that has erupted recently.

dormant volcano - a volcano that is not erupting now, but that may erupt in the future.

extinct volcano - a volcano that no longer erupts and is in the process of eroding.

volcanic neck - solid remains of magma that filled the conduit of an extinct volcano. The neck is exposed as the volcano erodes.

Figure 12.16: *The volcanic necks of Ship Rock and Devil's Tower have been exposed by erosion.*

Where does magma come from?

Solid mantle rock melts
The rock of Earth's mantle is hot but solid. Under the right conditions, this rock melts and becomes magma. Neither the cool lithosphere nor the hot upper mantle is hot enough to melt rock. So what are the conditions for rock to melt?

Pressure
You know that heating solids to their melting temperatures will make them melt. Another way to melt a solid is to lower its melting temperature. One way to lower the melting temperature is to lower the pressure. The hot rock of the mantle is solid because of the great pressure of the material above it. But the pressure decreases as the rock rises toward Earth's surface. Nearer the surface, the pressure is low enough and the temperature high enough for the rising rock to melt. The melted rock, now magma, is less dense than the surrounding solid rock, so it continues to rise and may eventually erupt onto Earth's surface as lava.

Water
Another way to lower the melting temperature of rock is to mix water with the rock. Water comes into the mantle at subduction zones as liquid water. Once mixed with the solid mantle rock, the water occurs as individual molecules that react chemically with the minerals in the rock to promote melting within the mantle.

Pressure and water affect melting temperature
Figure 12.17 shows how pressure and water affect the melting temperature of hot rock. The rock in the bottom right corner of graph A is solid because it isn't hot enough to melt under high pressure. The rock above is melting at the same high pressure because the temperature is higher. The rock in the bottom left corner is melting at a lower temperature because of *lower pressure*. In graph B, the rock in the bottom right corner is solid because it isn't hot enough to melt when dry. The dry rock above is melting because the temperature is higher. The rock in the bottom left corner is melting at a lower temperature because it *contains water*.

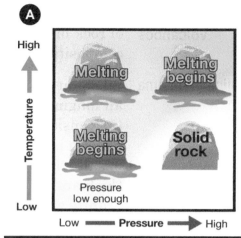

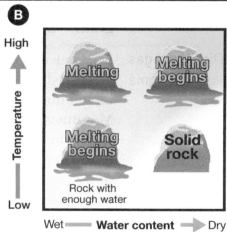

Figure 12.17: *Two graphs of the conditions for making magma.*

Kinds of magma

The shape of volcanoes
Volcanoes can look like tall cones, wide flat mounds, or like a heap of rock bits. Why? The shape of a volcano is related to the composition of the magma that forms it.

Silica in magma
Silica, in one form or another, is present in all magmas. The amount of silica changes the consistency of the magma. Low-silica magma is runny. This magma may form basalt when it cools. High-silica magma is thick and sticky. This magma may form granite when it cools. Magma that can form andesite rocks is more silica-rich than basalt, but not as silica-rich as granite magma.

Quartz
A mineral made of silica

Photo courtesy U.S House Subcommittee on Energy and Natural Resources

Dissolved gas in magma
Another important property of magma is how much gas is dissolved in it. Magma that has only a little dissolved gas doesn't have bubbles. This magma is "flat," like soda that has lost its fizz. Magma with a lot of dissolved gas is like soda before you open it. It can be bubbly or, under the right conditions, it can explode out just like when you open a shaken bottle of soda. The table below shows how silica and gas determine the kind of volcanic eruption that will take place.

	Low gas content	High gas content
Low silica content	• Runny magma, like syrup • Quiet eruption, lava flows easily	• Runny magma, bubbly • Fire fountain, lava flows easily
High silica content	• Thick, sticky magma • Quiet eruption	• Thick, sticky magma • Explosive eruption

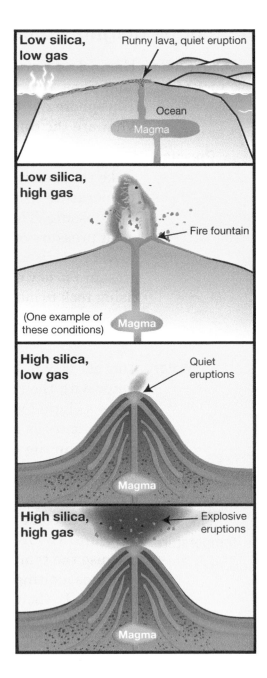

Low silica, low gas — Runny lava, quiet eruption
Ocean
Magma

Low silica, high gas — Fire fountain
(One example of these conditions)
Magma

High silica, low gas — Quiet eruptions
Magma

High silica, high gas — Explosive eruptions
Magma

Volcanoes with low silica magma

Shield volcanoes A shield volcano is a flat, wide volcano that looks like a warrior's shield lying on the ground. The magma and lava associated with a shield volcano has a low amount of silica, and either low or high levels of dissolved gas. Because low-silica lava is runny, it can't build up a tall, cone-shaped volcano. This is why shield volcanoes are flattened. The volcanoes of the Hawaiian Islands are shield volcanoes.

Shield volcano

Photo by D. Little, USGS.

shield volcano - a flat and wide volcano that has low-silica magma and lava with low or high levels of dissolved gas.

cinder cone - a volcano that has low-silica magma and lava with high levels of dissolved gas; these volcanoes produce "fire fountain" eruptions.

Fire fountains When low-silica magma has high levels of dissolved gas, the gas bubbles out as it reaches the volcano vent. The effect is identical to shaking a soda bottle to produce a shower of soda. The high-gas magma produces a spectacular *fire fountain* (Figure 12.18). The resulting spatters of glowing lava cool in the air and hit the ground as solid lava cinders.

Cinder cones The lava cinders form a cone around the vent called a cinder cone. Cinder cones are a common form of volcano. They are often found on the flanks of both shield volcanoes and composite volcanoes (see the next page). Cinder cones may also form in the caldera of dormant volcanoes. Cinder cones are structurally weak because they are simply a pile of rock bits.

Photo by R.T. Holcomb, USGS.

Figure 12.18: *A fire fountain in Hawaii Volcanoes National Park, 1972–1974 eruption of the Kilauea Volcano.*

Volcanoes with high silica magma

Composite volcanoes

Most coastal volcanoes are associated with subduction zones. The magma and lava of these volcanoes is thick and sticky because it is silica-rich. Over time, layers of this thick lava and ash build a tall cone called a **composite volcano** (Figure 12.19).

Dissolved gas in sticky magma

When silica-rich magma is low in dissolved gas, the lava comes out like toothpaste and forms volcanic glass, called obsidian. But if the silica-rich magma contains high levels of dissolved gas, pressure usually builds inside the volcano. The lava of shield volcanoes is so runny that dissolved gas simply bubbles out. But silica-rich magma is too sticky. Before a composite volcano eruption, the magma may be under so much gas pressure that the composite volcano cone bulges (middle image, Figure 12.19).

Pumice and ash

When a composite volcano cone bulges like this, either the eruption will subside and the magma will return down the conduit, or the cone will explode. The cone may explode near the vent, throwing a column of gas and lava bits high into the atmosphere. The lava bits puff up and rip apart as the dissolved gas expands inside each bit. This puffing up action produces two forms of rock: pumice and ash. *Pumice* is a rock with lots of holes. Pumice has a low density because of its holes (which were made by air bubbles) and will float in water. *Ash* is smaller particles of rock, like fine sand. Because ash is so fine, it drifts with the wind and may settle over a very wide area.

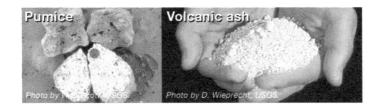

Bulge before eruption – 1980

After the eruption – 1980

composite volcano - a tall, explosive, cone-shaped volcano formed by layers of silica-rich lava and ash.

Figure 12.19: *Mount St. Helens, a composite volcano, before and after an explosive eruption.*

Explosive eruptions

Pyroclastic flows When a column of exploding material collapses, it races down the side of a composite volcano as a pyroclastic flow. The speed (more than a 80 km/h), force, and heat (200–700°C) of the pyroclastic flow make it extremely destructive.

Pyroclastic flow

Photo courtesy USGS

Lava bombs Large pieces of glowing lava may be thrown far from the base of the composite volcano. These pieces, each one called a lava bomb, can be the size of watermelons. Sometimes the composite volcano explodes again, further down its side, adding more material to the expanding lava explosion.

Lahars Mount Saint Helens erupted in Washington State in 1980. This was a classic silica-rich, gas-rich composite volcano eruption. Magma pressure formed a large bulge on the side of the mountain. The eruption was triggered when a portion of the bulge slid off due to earthquakes. This created a weakness in the cone. An enormous explosion blew off a huge part of the side of the mountain. The combination of landslide, explosion, and pyroclastic flow killed 57 people. If water is present as snow and ice on the volcano, a mudflow called a lahar may accompany an eruption like this (Figure 12.20). The mudflows in the Mount Saint Helens's eruption destroyed forests and property and added to the death toll.

 VOCABULARY

pyroclastic flow - a destructive cloud of volcanic material that moves quickly down the side of a volcano after an explosive eruption.

lava bomb - large pieces of glowing lava thrown from an explosive eruption.

lahar - a mudflow that results from a volcanic eruption.

Lahar

Photo by Lyn Topinka, USGS

Figure 12.20: *An example of a lahar, a mudflow that results from pyroclastic flow mixing with water and mud.*

Volcanoes at divergent boundaries

Mid-ocean ridge volcanoes

A mid-ocean ridge forms at divergent boundaries, where two plates are pulling apart (Figure 12.21). As the plates move apart, mantle material below is drawn toward Earth's surface. The rock of the mantle is hot and flexible, but still solid. This rock is solid because of the great pressure of the material above it. But the pressure decreases as the rock rises. What affect will this have on the rising rock material? As you have just learned, the lower pressure also lowers the melting temperature of the rock. The rock melts and becomes magma that erupts underwater at the mid-ocean ridge.

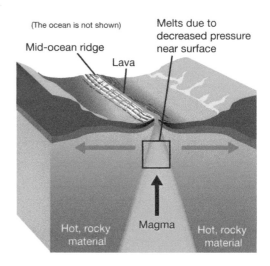

Figure 12.21: *As the plates move apart at a mid-ocean ridge, the mantle material is drawn upward. The pressure decreases as this material rises causing the mantle material to melt.*

Basaltic magma

The magma at a mid-ocean ridge (associated with oceanic plates) is melted basalt. Basalt is a silica-poor, dark-colored rock. Basaltic magma is runny because of its low silica content. When runny basaltic lava oozes out at a mid-ocean ridge, it immediately hits cold seawater. The seawater cools the lava, forming a crust. But soon the crust cracks and another blob of basalt magma oozes out. This cycle repeats over and over, forming lava that looks like a pile of pillows. Geologists occasionally find pillow lava on land. This indicates that there was once a mid-ocean ridge under an ancient ocean at that location.

Basalt and granite are very important rocks. What do you know about these rocks from what you've learned in Chapters 10–12? Write a definition for each type of rock in your own words.

Volcanoes at convergent boundaries

The Ring of Fire Most volcanoes are located along convergent plate boundaries. About half of the active surface volcanoes on Earth occur along the shores of the Pacific Ocean in a region called the Ring of Fire. Mount St. Helens is a volcano within the Ring of Fire. The Ring of Fire lies just above where the Pacific Plate is subducting under other surrounding plates.

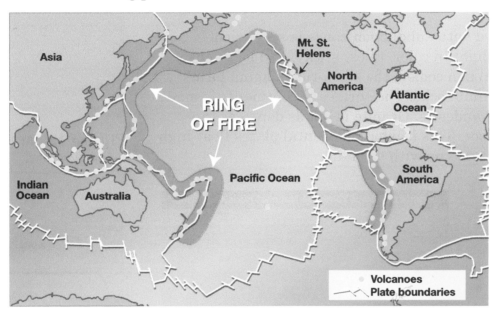

ã VOCABULARY

Ring of Fire - a region of Earth's plate boundaries where oceanic crust is subducting under other plates; active volcanoes and earthquakes are common here.

volcanic island arc - a series of volcanoes formed at a subduction zone.

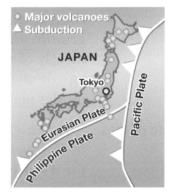

Figure 12.22: *Japan and neighboring islands are a volcanic island arc.*

Volcanic island arcs A volcanic island arc is a string of volcanic islands that forms at a convergent plate boundary. The island of Japan and neighboring islands—all part of the Ring of Fire—are an island arc at the subduction zone where three plates come together (Figure 12.22).

How continents grow In time, plate movements at a subduction zone bring islands and continents together. In this way, continents grow larger! Scientists can detect where island arcs have increased the size of the North American continent on both the west and east coasts.

 CHALLENGE

Island arc volcanoes

The magma associated with island arc volcanoes is silica-rich. This type of magma makes explosive eruptions. Find out about the explosive eruptions of one of these island arc volcanoes: Mount Vesuvius, Etna, or Stromboli.

Volcanoes on continents at convergent boundaries

Water
At subduction zones, water and sediments are carried downward as one plate sinks below the edge of another plate. The water and sediments combine with the hot mantle rock. As you have learned, water lowers the melting point of the mantle rock, so it melts, forming less-dense magma. The magma rises and eventually melts through the overlying plate, forming a volcano near the edge of the overlying plate (Figure 12.23).

Silica-rich magma
The magma associated with subduction zones is silica-rich. Silica-rich magma is light in color, thick, sticky, and less dense than basalt magma. When cooled, the silica-rich magma forms granite and other similar rocks. The surface of continents is made mostly of granite and andesite. Granite is not as dense as the basalt of the ocean floor. This is why continental plates float high on the mantle and provide us with dry land.

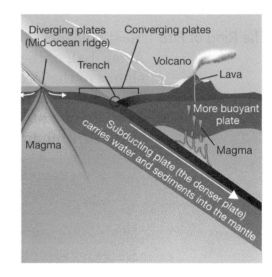

Figure 12.23: *Forming magma at a subduction zone.*

Granite domes
Yosemite National Park in California is famous for its granite domes. These domes formed when silica-rich magma rose to the surface at a subduction zone. When subduction stopped, the flow of magma stopped too (Figure 12.24). The magma below the surface cooled where it was. The surrounding land later eroded away, exposing the granite domes.

Granite domes of Yosemite National Park, California

Photo courtesy of Jim Sammons, Sammons' INK.

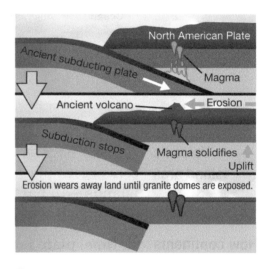

Figure 12.24: *Diagram of how the granite domes of Yosemite formed.*

Volcanic islands away from plate boundaries

Volcanic island chains You have learned that volcanic island arcs form at subduction zones. They also form in the middle of oceanic plates. The magma of these islands begins much deeper in the lower mantle. Deep mantle material flows slowly to the surface in a narrow mantle plume. The plume that feeds a volcanic island doesn't move because it is fixed in the lower mantle. But the plate over the plume does move! The area of the plate that is situated over the mantle plume is called a **hot spot**. Once the area of the plate has moved off the hot spot, the volcano will become extinct. But the mantle plume and hot spot are still active. Soon a new volcano will form beside the old one. In this way, a **volcanic island chain** is formed (Figure 12.25).

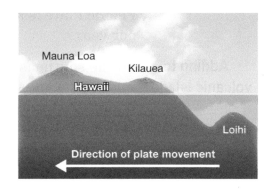

VOCABULARY

hot spot - the top of a mantle plume.

volcanic island chain - a series of volcanoes formed as a lithospheric plate moves over the hot spot.

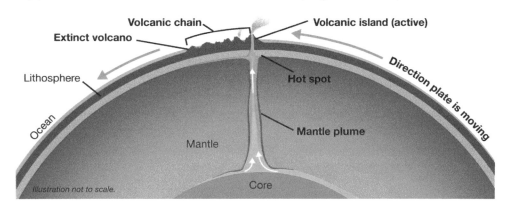

Figure 12.25: *The island of Hawaii sits on top of a hot spot. The hot spot has formed the Mauna Loa and Kilauea volcanoes on the island. Currently, the hot spot is building the undersea volcano Loihi to the southeast of the island. When Loihi gets bigger and reaches the ocean surface, it will increase the size of Hawaii.*

Silica-poor magma The magma that forms a volcanic island chain is runny and silica-poor. These volcanoes have milder eruptions. As both island arcs and island chains are built, the lava that erupts underwater is cooled by the seawater it encounters. In this way, the lava hardens and builds up, eventually creating an island.

Using island chains to measure the motion of a plate

The Hawaiian Islands The Hawaiian Islands are an example of a volcanic island chain. The biggest island, Hawaii, is over the hot spot now and has active volcanoes. Hawaii has been on top of this hot spot for the last 800,000 years. The islands to the northwest of Hawaii are older. Their volcanoes are either dormant or extinct.

Island chains and the speed of plates By studying the direction, age, and length of a volcanic island chain, scientists can determine the direction and speed that a plate is moving. The Hawaiian Island chain shows us that the Pacific Plate is moving to the northwest at nearly nine centimeters per year.

Adding to a volcanic island To the southeast of the Hawaiian Island chain, the mantle plume under Hawaii is building a new volcano—Loihi. Loihi is an undersea volcano. When enough lava builds up so that Loihi is above sea level, it will extend the eastern border of Hawaii!

SOLVE IT!

The Pacific Plate is moving at nine centimeters per year.

1. For starters, draw a line on a piece of paper that is nine centimeters long. What common objects are about this long?

2. How long will it take for this plate to travel 4.5 meters?

3. How far will the plate have traveled in meters after three years?

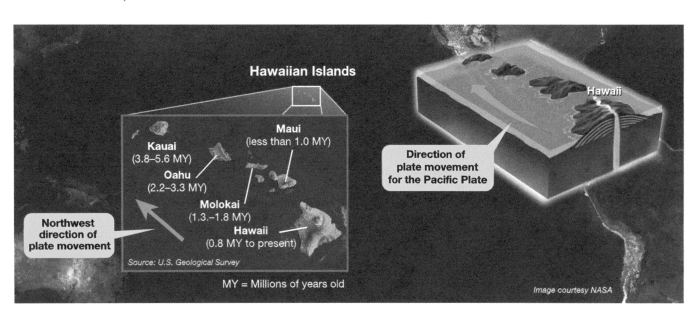

Hawaiian Islands

Kauai (3.8–5.6 MY)

Oahu (2.2–3.3 MY)

Maui (less than 1.0 MY)

Molokai (1.3.–1.8 MY)

Hawaii (0.8 MY to present)

Northwest direction of plate movement

Source: U.S. Geological Survey

MY = Millions of years old

Direction of plate movement for the Pacific Plate

Hawaii

Image courtesy NASA

12.2 **Section Review**

1. What is the difference between magma and lava?

2. What is the difference between a dormant volcano and an active volcano?

3. A solid rock begins to melt:
   a. under what conditions of temperature and pressure?
   b. under what conditions of temperature and water content?

4. If you could increase the silica content of lava, would the lava get more sticky or less sticky?

5. What two ingredients in magma affect the type of explosion and shape of a volcano?

6. Describe what a high-gas, high-silica eruption is like. Then, describe a low-gas, low-silica eruption.

7. Answer *continental plate* or *oceanic plate* in response to these questions.
   a. Where is runny lava found?
   b. Where is thick and sticky lava found?

8. What causes the region called the Ring of Fire?

9. Name a difference between an island chain and an island arc.

10. When volcanic island chains are formed, what moves?

   a. the mantle plume
   b. the plate above the mantle plume
   c. both the plate and the plume
   d. nothing moves

11. What kind of geologic formation is Loihi? Is it a part of the Hawaiian Island Chain? Explain your answer.

12. How have scientists figured out that the Pacific Plate is moving at about nine centimeters per year?

CHALLENGE

About 7,000 years ago, Mount Mazama erupted and the summit (top) of the volcano collapsed, forming a depression that was then filled with rain and melted snow. The depression is now called Crater Lake. Mount Mazama is an extinct volcano. What is the best term to describe the depression that holds Crater Lake?

Do some research to find out about this interesting geologic formation and write a report about your findings.

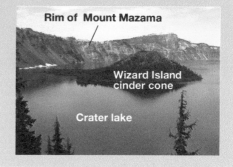

Rim of Mount Mazama

Wizard Island cinder cone

Crater lake

Indian Ocean Earthquake and Tsunami

Tilly Smith probably never imagined that what she learned in geography class would help save lives. When the Indian Ocean tsunami hit on December 26, 2004, Tilly and her family were

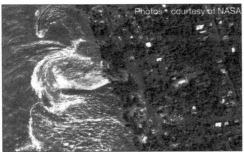

December 26, 2004

January 1, 2004

The top satellite picture of Kalutara, Sri Lanka was taken about an hour after the first tsunami wave hit on December 26, 2004. Water is rushing back out to sea after inundating the land. The lower picture shows what the same area looked like under normal conditions in January 2004.

vacationing at Miakho Beach in Phuket, Thailand. Tilly, 10 years old, noticed something strange happening on the beach. The water at the beach suddenly went away. In the distance, she could see boats bouncing wildly and the water bubbling. The ocean water returned quickly and kept coming onto shore. Tilly screamed for her family to leave the beach right away. Her parents warned others. Due to her knowledge of the early warning signs of tsunamis, the girl from England saved other tourists on the beach that day.

What is a tsunami?

Tilly had just learned that underwater earthquakes could cause tsunamis. *Tsunami* is a Japanese word meaning "harbor wave." Underwater earthquakes, landslides, and volcanoes may cause tsunamis. Not every earthquake leads to a tsunami. Yet, large ocean earthquakes that move the sea floor up and down cause many tsunamis.

The size of a tsunami depends on many factors. How large is the earthquake? Where does the earthquake occur? How much of the sea floor moves up and down? How deep is the ocean water where the earthquake occurs? In the deep ocean, tsunamis may be only several feet high. Often ships at sea never feel a tsunami. This is not the case as the tsunami travels toward shore and shallower water. The amount of water begins to build. Wave height increases as they approach land. Some waves may travel 500–1,000 kilometers per hour and be as high as 35 meters.

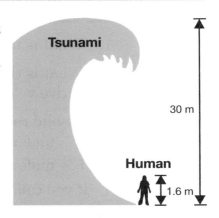

Tsunami

30 m

Human

1.6 m

The Indian Ocean tsunami

The Indian Ocean tsunami may be one of the deadliest natural disasters in modern history. Officials believe more than 275,000 people died. The final number of deaths may never be known. The U.S. Geological Survey originally reported the earthquake at a 9.0 magnitude. This is the strongest in the world since 1964 and the fourth largest since 1900. Scientists used data from around the world to revise the earthquake to a 9.3 magnitude. This would make it the second largest earthquake since the 9.5 magnitude earthquake in Chile in 1960.

Earth's surface is made up of plates that are constantly in motion. Plates meet one another along plate boundaries. Pressure along these boundaries builds over time and sometimes releases abruptly creating earthquakes.

During the Indian Ocean earthquake, 1,200 kilometers (750 miles) of the plate boundary slipped when the Indian Plate (part of the Indo-Australian Plate) slid under the Burma

Plate (part of the Eurasian Plate). That is about 400 kilometers (250 miles) more than the distance between San Diego and San Francisco! The seabed rose more than two meters causing huge tsunami waves.

Imagine a plastic squeeze bottle filled to the top with water. As you squeeze the container the water spills out over the top. The upward motion of the earthquake displaced an enormous amount of water similar to the squeeze bottle. This displacement of water created the tsunami that flooded the coastlines.

The Indian Ocean earthquake occurred off the west coast of Sumatra, an Indonesian island. Waves reached 20 to 30 meters (65 to 100 feet) high. The tsunami destroyed the shores of Indonesia, Sri Lanka, and Thailand. The tsunami even traveled as far as Africa, nearly 8,000 kilometers (5,000 miles) from the center of the earthquake.

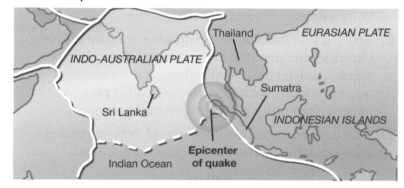

The tsunami waves did not start from one central location, but occurred along the entire 1,207 kilometers of fault line. That is why the waves affected so many areas of the world.

Indian Ocean tsunami warning system

Why did so many people die from the tsunami? Tsunamis are rare in the Indian Ocean and a warning system was not in place. The last major tsunami in the region was caused by the 1883 volcanic eruption of Krakatoa in Indonesia.

People were not aware of the signs of a tsunami—a strong earthquake in the area and a quick rise or fall in water levels by the coast.

Historically, tsunamis usually happen in the Pacific Ocean where many earthquakes occur. In the Pacific, there are two warning centers monitoring the area: the Alaska and the Pacific Tsunami Warning Centers. The Alaska Tsunami Warning Center includes the west coast of the United States and Canada. The Pacific Tsunami Warning Center covers Hawaii and all other Pacific areas. The centers monitor the size and location of earthquakes in the ocean. If a tsunami is possible, the center sends out a warning estimating when the tsunami will reach land. This allows coastal areas to have time to evacuate.

One month after the Indian Ocean tsunami, the United Nations recommended a warning system for the Indian Ocean. Plans are in place to have as many as 27 centers created, one for each Indian Ocean country. In May 2005, Thailand opened a center linked to the Pacific Tsunami Warning Center. There has been discussion about creating a global warning system that would include the Atlantic Ocean and the Caribbean.

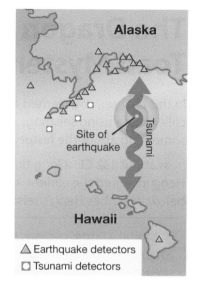

△ Earthquake detectors
▢ Tsunami detectors

QUESTIONS

1. What causes a tsunami?

2. What are signs that a tsunami might be coming?

3. Why was there no tsunami warning system in the Indian Ocean?

The Dragon and Toad Mystery

In this chapter, you learned about earthquakes and how scientists collect data using seismographs. In this activity, you will learn something about the history of using seismographs.

In about 132 CE, a long time ago, Chinese philosopher Chang Heng invented the earliest-known seismograph. The paragraph below describes Heng's seismograph.

> Imagine a large, ceramic vessel or jar about six feet in diameter. On the outside of this vessel were eight dragon heads. These faced the eight main directions that you would find on a compass. Not attached to the vessel, but seated below each of the dragon heads were eight toads, with their mouths open in the direction of the dragon head it was below. In the mouth of each dragon was a ball. The idea was that when an earthquake happened, a dragon would release its ball and it would fall into the appropriate toad's mouth. The direction of the shaking would determine which ball was released. Heng would know if an earthquake happened and from what direction it came.

The mystery is this—what was inside of this early seismograph is unknown.

What you will do

1. Draw your interpretation of the outside of this vessel.

2. Spend some time thinking about mechanisms that might be found inside to make this instrument work. Once you have given it some thought and come up with an idea, draw/sketch your idea.

3. Below your sketch, write a step-by-step procedure of how this instrument works. Be sure to write clearly.

4. Exchange your instrument description and procedure with the instrument and procedure completed by someone else in your class.

5. You will present the description and procedure of one your classmates. This classmate will present your description and procedure to the class.

6. Your procedure on how to use it needs to be clear because that person is going to explain your instrument to the class and you will be explaining theirs based on the sketch and description. Remember, there are no right answers for this activity!

Applying your knowledge

a. Which instrument in the class would work best and why? Write a paragraph to answer this question.

b. How did your description and drawing compare to Chang Heng's seismograph? Learn more about Chang Heng's seismograph on the Internet—http://earthquake.usgs.gov/learn/topics/seismology/history/part03.php. Write a paragraph comparing your seismograph to Heng's.

c. How do modern seismographs work? Research modern seismographs and write a paragraph about them.

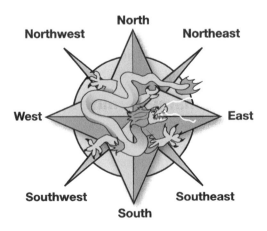

Vocabulary

Select the correct term to complete the sentences.
Note: Not all terms are used.

earthquake	foreshock	aftershock	shield volcano	Ring of Fire
surface waves	lava	focus	active volcano	composite volcano
body waves	magma chamber	magma	caldera	hot spot
fault	dormant volcano	extinct volcano	lava lake	volcanic island chain
seismograph	lahar	volcanic neck	lava bomb	Modified Mercalli scale
epicenter	resurgent dome	pyroclastic flow	volcano	Moment Magnitude scale
Richter scale	cinder cone	volcanic island arc		

Section 12.1

1. A(n) _____ is a place where magma collects underground.

2. A(n) _____ is a small tremor that occurs after an earthquake.

3. The place on Earth's surface above where the rock breaks during an earthquake is the _____.

4. Stick-slip motion between lithospheric plates causes a(n) _____.

5. The point below the epicenter is called the _____.

6. A(n) _____ is a place where rocks break and there is movement.

7. These seismic waves travel at Earth's surface: _____.

8. _____ are seismic waves that travel through the planet.

9. The instrument used to record seismic waves is a(n) _____.

10. Each number change on the _____ means a 10-fold increase in seismic wave amplitude.

11. Eyewitness accounts of earthquake damage are incorporated into this earthquake measurement scale: _____.

12. The _____ rates the total energy of an earthquake.

Section 12.2

13. The products of an eruption can build a mountainous _____.

14. _____ is magma that has reached Earth's surface.

15. A bowl-shaped volcanic feature is a(n) _____.

16. _____ is melted rock from the mantle.

17. A(n) _____ occurs when a mound of magma forms in a caldera.

18. A volcano that is quiet now, but may erupt in the future is a(n) _____.

19. A(n) _____ has erupted recently.

20. A(n) _____ is the solid remains of magma of an extinct volcano.

21. The _____ is a region where about half of the active surface volcanoes on Earth occur.

22. A volcanic island chain forms over a(n) _____.

23. A(n) _____ can form on the sides of either a shield volcano or a composite volcano.

24. After an explosive eruption, a(n) _____ moves quickly down the side of a volcano and can cause a great deal of destruction.

Concepts

Section 12.1

1. When two plates slide past each other, what happens to the crusts of these plates? What happens to the upper mantle?

2. Why is *plastic* a good term to describe the upper mantle?

3. Describe stick-slip motion and give an example.

4. When an earthquake occurs at a transform plate boundary, does it occur at every place along the boundary or in one location? Justify your answer.

5. How can one earthquake cause another earthquake?

6. Describe surface waves and how they affect an area that is experiencing an earthquake.

7. How are S- and P-waves used to find the distance from a seismic station to the epicenter of an earthquake?

8. You need three seismic stations to determine the location of the epicenter of an earthquake. Why wouldn't just two stations provide enough information? *Hint*: You may need to make a diagram to help you answer this question.

9. Why is a seismograph useful for measuring the magnitude of an earthquake on the Richter scale?

10. Is it possible that an earthquake could happen and you would not know it? Explain your answer.

11. Compare and contrast the Moment Magnitude scale and the Richter scale.

12. After an earthquake, one person says that the intensity of the quake was VI on the Modified Mercalli scale. Another person says that the intensity was III. Why might these individuals have had different experiences?

13. Where do most earthquakes occur? Explain your answer.

Section 12.2

14. What is the difference between a conduit and a vent on a volcano?

15. Describe the three phases of the lifetime of a volcano.

16. Is the material that forms a volcanic neck considered to be solidified magma or lava? Explain your answer.

17. What factors affect whether or not solid rock in the mantle will melt?

18. Give two factors that affect the consistency of magma.

19. Fill in the blanks.
    a. High-silica magma forms _____ rocks.
    b. Low-silica magma forms _____ rocks.

20. Describe the magma of fire fountain eruptions in terms of silica and gas content.

21. Explain how a shield volcano differs from a composite volcano.

22. Where do composite volcanoes tend to be found?

    a. a subduction zone

    b. a transform plate boundary

    c. a divergent plate boundary

    c. where two continental plates come together

23. What is the difference between a pyroclastic flow and a lahar?

24. Mount St. Helens formed at what kind of plate boundary?

    a. a subduction zone

    b. a transform plate boundary

    c. a divergent plate boundary

    c. where two continental plates came together

25. What is the Ring of Fire?

26. Volcanoes found near subduction zones have:

    a. magma with high silica content.

    b. an explosive eruption.

    c. large amounts of gas released during the eruption.

    d. All of the above

27. Describe how the granite domes of Yosemite National Park were formed.

28. What volcanic land feature has helped the east and west coasts of North America grow bigger?

29. How does plate tectonics cause volcanic islands to form in chain?

30. The Hawaiian Islands are what type of volcano? What causes these volcanoes to form?

Math and Writing Skills

Section 12.1

1. Since 1964, the longest earthquake ever recorded was the 1964 Alaskan earthquake. It lasted 4 minutes. The 2004 Indonesian earthquake broke the 1964 record. Find out the new record for the longest earthquake ever recorded. Write a short paragraph that describes three interesting facts you learned from your research.

2. How wide was the area affected by the 1895 New Madrid earthquake? Refer to the New Madrid Seismic Zone graphic in Section 12.1. Give your answer in miles. Then, convert this value to kilometers (1.6 km = 1 mile).

3. The distance from the epicenter of a quake to a seismic station is 180 kilometers. If the distance scale on your map is 1 centimeter = 20 kilometers, what would be the radius of the circle that is drawn around this station on the map?

4. P-waves travel faster than S-waves, and both of these seismic waves travel faster than the speed of sound (in air). Given the approximated values in this table, how much faster do P-waves travel than S-waves? How much faster do S-waves travel than sound? (*Hint*: Divide the smaller value into the larger value.)

	Approximate Speed (km/s)
P-wave	7
S-wave	3.6
Sound in air	0.34

5. In the text, you learned that it is unusual for seismic waves to arrive at many different seismic stations at the same time. This is because the waves have to travel from the epicenter to the station. Each station usually is a different distance from the epicenter. Using this information, match the correct seismic wave recording below with the diagram that shows the epicenter of an earthquake and the locations of three seismic stations.

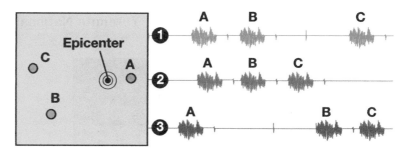

6. If each Richter value represents seismic waves 10-times greater than the one before, then how much larger are the waves of an earthquake with a magnitude 6 versus a magnitude 3?

7. What are the Richter magnitude and Modified Mercalli values for an earthquake that causes enough shaking to wake you up, but not enough to cause damage?

Section 12.2

8. Mount Kilimanjaro in Tanzania is Africa's highest mountain and a controversial volcano. Research this volcano to find out whether experts think it is extinct, dormant, or active. Write your findings in a short paragraph.

9. A volcanologist finds that the silica content of the volcanic rock near an ancient volcano is high. From this information, describe the probable type of volcano and its eruption. Where might the volcano be located?

10. Pumice is used in commercial cleaning products as an abrasive. Research pumice and find out more about its uses.

11. The speed of a pyroclastic flow is 100 km/h. How far would this flow travel in 10 minutes?

12. Hot springs are interesting geologic features that happen to occur on every continent. Find out how hot springs are heated and pick one to research. For example, the image below shows Hot Creek, a stream that is associated with the Long Valley Caldera in eastern California. Other well-known hot spring regions occur in Yosemite National Park and in Warm Springs, Georgia.

Hot Creek, California

Photo courtesy of Jim Sammons, Sammons' INK.

Chapter Projects—Quakes and eruptions

Part 1: Demonstrating liquefaction

First, gather the following items: brick, rubber mallet, water, sand, a plastic bin. Place the bin on a table. Fill the plastic bin 2/3 full with sand. Pour water into the bin to just below the surface of the sand. Hold the brick upright so that it represents a tall building. Wiggle it into the sand so that it stands up on its own. Using your mallet, tap the side of the bin repeatedly and gently. Watch what happens to the sand and brick.

This model demonstrates what can happen when an earthquake shakes an area that has been filled with sediments by humans, such as Boston's Back Bay or the China Basin in the southeast portion of San Francisco. There are several regions in the Bay Area of California that have been filled to create land. They are all susceptible to liquefaction.

Liquefaction occurs when the seismic waves travel through the ground. The sandy soil becomes suspended in the water as the water fills in all the spaces in between the soil particles. Now the soil acts like a liquid and loses the ability to support buildings.

Part 2: Eye-witness account

Choose a famous volcanic eruption and research the eruption. Visit the United States Geological Survey web site to find out about present day and past volcanic eruptions (www.usgs.gov).

Write a letter to a local newspaper from the point of view of an eye-witness who survived the eruption. In your letter include details about what happened before, during, and after the eruption. You should include the type of volcano, the type of lava you witnessed during the eruption. Also, include information about the damage and destruction caused by the volcano. Finally, your letter should include the environmental impact that the eruption had. How far around the world was the impact felt? Include pictures or drawings of the volcano before, during, and after the eruption.

Chapter 13

Formation of Rocks

When you pick up a rock, you hold a lot of history in your hands. This is because any rock is the result of numerous, intense processes that created it over millions of years. The history of a rock begins with minerals, which are the building blocks of all rocks. Processes that create rocks include eruptions of volcanoes, erosion of land by rivers, and mountain-building. These processes are part of the rock cycle—a kind of "rock recycling program." Although a rock may be millions of years old, in time the rock cycle will transform it into a new rock. This chapter is all about how rocks are made and what they might become as part of the rock cycle.

Key Questions:

1. What is a mineral?

2. What kind of rock is made from lava?

3. How can one kind of rock change into another kind of rock?

13.1 The Composition of Rocks

A **rock** is a naturally-formed solid made of one or more minerals. In this section, you will first learn about the minerals that make up a rock, and then about a special set of processes called the *rock cycle*.

Rocks are made of minerals

What is a mineral?
A **mineral** is a solid, inorganic object with a defined chemical composition. Minerals have a crystal structure. This means they have an orderly arrangement of atoms. Minerals can be made of one or more elements. Graphite and diamonds are single-element minerals made of carbon (Figure 13.1).

Minerals in Earth's crust
There are more than 4,000 minerals on Earth. Eight of these minerals make up 98.5 percent of Earth's continental crust by weight! The two most abundant elements in Earth's minerals and therefore, in Earth's crust, are oxygen and silicon (Figure 13.2). Oxygen and silicon combine to make minerals called *silicates*.

How minerals are made

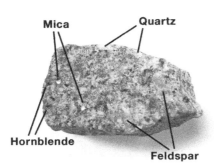

Minerals are made by geologic processes. One process is the cooling of magma. For example, during the underground cooling stage of magma into granite rock, different minerals crystallize. These minerals are easy to see in a piece of granite. Feldspar and quartz crystals make up the majority of a piece of granite. Mica and hornblende crystals are also visible. Minerals also form when water containing dissolved minerals evaporates. Existing minerals change into different minerals due to heat, pressure, or chemical reactions.

VOCABULARY

rock - a naturally-formed solid made of one or more minerals.

mineral - a solid, naturally occurring, crystalline object with a defined chemical composition.

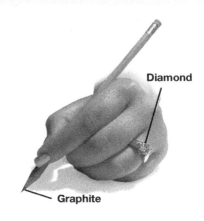

Figure 13.1: *Diamonds and graphite are minerals that are made of carbon.*

Approximate percentage by weight of oxygen and silicon in Earth's crust	
oxygen	46.6%
silicon	27.7%
other minerals	25.7%

Figure 13.2: *Oxygen and silicon are the two most abundant elements in Earth's crust.*

Common minerals and cleavage planes

Mica Mica is composed of a silicon-oxygen compound called *silicon dioxide* or *silica* along with iron, magnesium, and sodium. A piece of mica is like a stack of pages in a book. Both a page and a single layer of mica are described as having a single cleavage plane. A cleavage plane is a surface along which a mineral cleanly splits. The placement of a cleavage plane occurs where there are weak bonds between the molecules in the mineral (Figure 13.3).

Mica (muscovite)
One cleavage plane

cleavage plane - a surface along which a mineral cleanly splits.

There is **one cleavage plane** for the page of a book.

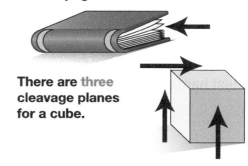

There are **three cleavage planes** for a cube.

Figure 13.3: *Mica has one cleavage plane and breaks into sheets. The mineral halite has three cleavage planes and breaks into cubes.*

Feldspar and hornblende Feldspar is the most abundant mineral in Earth's crust. Feldspar is composed of silica along with sodium, calcium, and potassium. Feldspar has two cleavage planes. Hornblende, also found in granite, is a dark mineral made of a mixture of elements including silicon, oxygen, and calcium along with iron, magnesium, or aluminum. Like feldspar, hornblende has two cleavage planes.

Hornblende   **Feldspar**
Two cleavage planes

Quartz Quartz is the second most abundant mineral in Earth's crust. Quartz crystals can appear to glisten as if they are wet or oily. Unlike feldspar, quartz lacks cleavage planes (Figure 13.4). When quartz breaks, it does not split along planes. Quartz is made of silica and is used in making glass. Gemstones like onyx, agate, and amethyst are made of quartz.

Quartz
No cleavage planes

Figure 13.4: *Quartz is a mineral in granite. It lacks cleavage planes.*

Mohs hardness scale

Identifying minerals Mohs hardness scale was developed in 1812 by Friedrick Mohs (an Austrian mineral expert) as a method to identify minerals (Figure 13.5). This scale uses 10 minerals to represent variations in hardness. Here, "hardness" means resistance to being scratched. You can identify a mineral's place on the scale by whether it can scratch another mineral. For example, gypsum (hardness = 2) scratches talc (hardness = 1). The hardest mineral, diamond, can scratch all other minerals. Minerals of the same hardness (and without impurities) scratch each other.

Common items test hardness You can use common items to test the hardness of a mineral. For example, your fingernail, a penny, a steel nail, or glass can be used. The following scenarios illustrate how to use Mohs hardness scale.

- A fingernail scratches gypsum, but gypsum does not scratch the fingernail. The fingernail is scratched by calcite. What is the hardness of a fingernail? (Answer: More than 2 but less than 3.)
- Fluorite scratches a penny, but the penny cannot scratch fluorite. Describe the penny's hardness. (Answer: Less than 4.)
- A piece of glass has a hardness of 5.5. Name one mineral that it can scratch. (Answer: Any mineral with a hardness 5 or less.)

Streak plate test Sets of minerals often come with a white, unglazed, ceramic streak plate or tile. You can identify certain minerals by scratching them on the streak plate. The color of the streak they leave behind can help you identify the mineral. For example, both pure gold and pyrite (also called Fool's Gold) are gold-colored minerals (Figure 13.6). Gold is rare and valuable. It leaves a golden-yellow streak. Pyrite is shiny, brassy, and a common mineral. It could be mistaken for gold, but it leaves a gray or black streak on a streak plate!

 VOCABULARY

Mohs hardness scale - a scale to identify minerals based on their hardness or resistance to being scratched.

Mineral	Hardness
talc	1
gypsum	2
calcite	3
fluorite	4
apatite	5
orthoclase (feldspar)	6
quartz	7
topaz	8
corundum	9
diamond	10

Figure 13.5: *Mohs hardness scale.*

Gold

Pyrite
"Fool's gold"

Gold photo courtesy David John, USGS.

Figure 13.6: *Gold and pyrite.*

Introducing rocks

Three groups Now, that you have learned about minerals, let's learn about rocks. All rocks on or below Earth's surface belong to one of three groups depending on how the rock formed.

Rock group	Formation
Igneous	These rocks form when molten rock (lava or magma) cools and becomes solid.
Sedimentary	These rocks form from pieces of other rocks, bits of once-living things, or minerals. The pieces are moved by water, wind, or glaciers and eventually settle in layers and are cemented to form new rock.
Metamorphic	These rocks form from other rocks by heat and pressure.

SOLVE IT!

Use the definition of a mineral to answer these questions.

1. Is ice a mineral? Why or why not?

2. Is coal a mineral? Why or why not?

Ice is inorganic and crystalline.

Millions of years

Coal is derived from plants and lacks a crystal structure.

Rocks are made of old material Like the other planets, Earth was formed from the gas and dust that surrounded the Sun when it formed. It took 4.6 billion years for Earth to look like the planet that we know today. The rocks that are currently on our planet's surface are made of material that formed long ago. The oldest rocks found on Earth so far are around 4 billion years old. However, some rocks are "young." A young rock may be a million years old! The presence of young rocks on Earth suggests that old rocks have been recycled. Read on to find out how rocks are recycled on Earth.

Groups of rocks

Original recyclers The rock cycle is the original recycling plan. The rock cycle (or geologic cycle) illustrates the formation and recycling of rocks by geological processes. We will review the rock cycle at the end of the chapter. For now, let's look at the three groups of rocks that are formed by the rock cycle.

Igneous rocks An igneous rock forms from the cooling and crystallizing of magma or lava. How fast the magma or lava cools affects the size of mineral crystals in the rock.

Sedimentary rocks All rocks eventually break down into pieces that can become part of another kind of rock called a sedimentary rock. A sedimentary rock is made of sediments. Sediment includes small rock particles like gravel, sand, silt, and clay. Sediment also includes minerals and bits of once-living things. Pressure and chemical changes cement the particles together to form a rock.

Metamorphic rocks A metamorphic rock is a rock that is formed from another rock because of heat and pressure. The word *metamorphic* means "changed form." For example, limestone is altered by heat and pressure to form marble. The movement of Earth's lithospheric plates create the conditions of heating and squeezing that result in metamorphic rocks.

The rock cycle The rock cycle does not always follow a simple path with igneous rocks forming first followed by sedimentary then metamorphic rocks (Figure 13.7). An igneous rock could become a metamorphic rock or a metamorphic rock could melt and become igneous. All rocks will break down over time and may become part of a sedimentary rock. The important thing to remember is that the rock cycle allows material to keep changing form and moving from place to place on Earth.

VOCABULARY

rock cycle - the formation and recycling of rocks by geologic processes.

igneous rock - a rock formed from the cooling and crystallizing of magma or lava.

sedimentary rock - a rock made of sediments that are cemented together by pressure and chemical changes.

sediment - small rock particles, minerals, and bits of once-living things.

metamorphic rock - a rock formed from another rock because of heat and pressure.

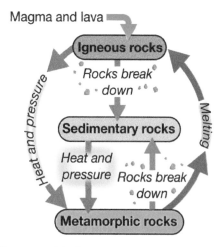

Figure 13.7: *The rock cycle.*

13.1 Section Review

1. What is the difference between a mineral and a rock?

2. Is a diamond a rock or a mineral? Explain your answer.

3. The mineral halite naturally forms cubes. How many cleavage planes does it have?

Photo courtesy U.S House Subcommittee on Energy and Natural Resources

4. What does hardness mean in reference to the Mohs harness scale?

5. Use Mohs hardness scale (Figure 13.5) to answer these questions.

   a. A mineral scratches talc and gypsum. This mineral does not scratch fluorite. What is the Mohs hardness of this mineral?

   b. A mineral scratches topaz and quartz. You find that a diamond would scratch this mineral. What is the Mohs hardness of this mineral?

   c. A steel nail scratches apatite but not quartz. What might be the hardness of a steel nail?

   d. Which mineral scratches all other minerals?

   e. Name a mineral that is so soft that it rubs off on your fingers.

6. How does a streak plate test help identify a mineral?

7. Name the three groups of rocks.

8. A rock is 500,000 years old. Would you classify this rock as young or old? Explain your answer.

9. In what kind of location might you find a rock that has just appeared on Earth's surface? What kind of rock would this be?

More Mineral Tests

You can identify a mineral using cleavage planes, a streak test, and the Mohs hardness scale. Following are some additional tests that geologists use to identify minerals:

Density: The density of the mineral is measured in g/cm^3. Some minerals are dense and heavy for their size. Others less dense and light-weight.

Luster: Luster is how a mineral reflects light. Metallic minerals (like pyrite) are shiny. Nonmetallic minerals can appear dull or reflect light the way glass does.

Magnetism: Some minerals (like magnetite) are magnetic.

Acid test: Some minerals react with hydrochloric acid.

Pyrite has a metallic luster.

13.2 **Igneous Rocks**

Igneous rocks begin to form when rock melts in Earth's mantle. In this section, we will review how rock melts. Then, you will learn that the length of time for magma or lava to cool affects the size of the crystals in the rock. By the end of this section, you will be able to tell a lot about the history of an igneous rock.

Melted rock

Plastic mantle rock A good way to describe hot, solid mantle rock is that it is like stiff putty that takes millions of years to move. As you learned in Chapter 11, material like this is described as being *plastic* or able to change shape without breaking.

Pressure and water Although mantle rock is very hot, it only melts under certain conditions of pressure and water content (Figure 13.8). Mantle rock melts when it is carried toward the surface at mid-ocean ridges. As the mantle rock rises, the pressure drops and the rock melts, becoming a liquid. Mantle rock also melts near a subducting plate where water is carried into the mantle. Both decreased pressure and the addition of water lower the melting temperature of mantle rock so that it melts.

Why is the mantle so hot? As you learned in Chapter 4, Earth is 4.6 billion years old. The interior of Earth is so hot because Earth is still cooling from when it formed so long ago! As materials came together to form Earth, the collisions from these extraterrestrial impacts generated heat. Also, as the denser components of Earth—iron and nickel—sank to Earth's core, there was a conversion of potential energy to heat. In addition, some of the heat inside of Earth is caused by the decay of radioactive elements.

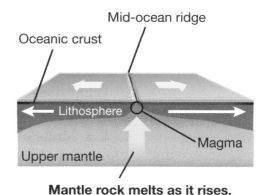

Mantle rock melts as it rises.

Lithosphere is heated and melts
as it goes deeper into
the mantle and as water is added.

Figure 13.8: *Changes in pressure and the addition of water causes the hot rock in the mantle to melt.*

Crystals in igneous rocks

Crystals in igneous rocks Minerals in magma or lava form crystals as the melted rock cools. Crystallization is the process by which crystals form and grow in size. Crystallization begins when atoms in a liquid begin to collect on the surface of a solid particle called the *seed crystal*. If it takes a long time for a liquid to crystallize, the atoms have a long time to attach to and grow on the seed crystal. Large crystals form. If the liquid crystallizes quickly, only small crystals form.

 VOCABULARY

crystallization - the process by which crystals form and grow in size.

How crystals grow

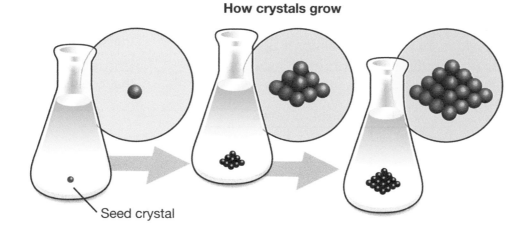

Seed crystal

Large and small crystals The size of crystals in an igneous rock is related to how fast the magma or lava cools. Magma, because it is underground, tends to cool and crystallize slowly. Therefore, igneous rocks formed from magma have larger crystals and a coarse texture. Lava, flowing out of a volcano, tends to cool quickly as it is exposed to the air. Cooling lava forms igneous rocks with small crystals and a fine texture.

Surface area The surface area of a cooling liquid also determines how fast it will cool (Figure 13.9). A thin layer of flowing lava (with a lot of exposed surface area) will cool quickly. Thicker layers of lava or magma have less surface area and will take longer to cool.

A thick rounded piece

Less surface area

A thin flow

More surface area

Figure 13.9: *The surface area of melted rock affects how fast it will cool.*

Comparing igneous rocks

VOCABULARY

basalt - a dark-colored igneous rock with fine crystals. Formed from lava that is not silica-rich. This rock forms oceanic crust.

granite - an igneous rock with large, visible crystals. Formed from silica-rich magma. This rock forms continental crust.

extrusive rock - an igneous rock that cools outside of Earth's crust.

intrusive rock - an igneous rock that cools inside Earth's crust.

Basalt and gabbro
Basalt and gabbro are similar rocks formed from magma or lava. Basalt is made from lava that is not silica-rich (so it tends to be runny lava). Remember that oceanic crust is made of basalt. When you compare the two silica-poor rocks, you see shiny, angular crystals in the gabbro but no crystals are visible in the basalt. This tells you that the basalt cooled much faster than the gabbro.

Granite and obsidian
Granite and obsidian are made of similar materials. Granite is made from silica-rich magma that cooled slowly within Earth. It cooled so slowly that it has large visible crystals. Granite forms much of the continental crust. In contrast, obsidian is so smooth that it is called volcanic glass. Obsidian contains almost no crystals because it cooled very quickly.

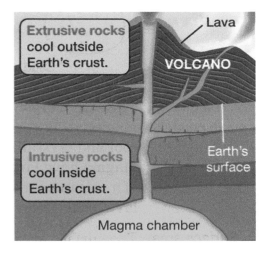

Figure 13.10: *Extrusive and intrusive rocks.*

Extrusive and intrusive rocks
An igneous rock that forms above Earth's surface is called an extrusive rock. Basalt is an extrusive rock. An igneous rock that forms within Earth's crust is called an intrusive rock (Figure 13.10). Granite is an intrusive rock. Based on what you have learned, would extrusive or intrusive rocks be more likely to have large crystals?

13.2 Section Review

1. An igneous rock has very large crystals. Describe a possible history of this rock. Where was it formed? How was it formed?

2. List two factors that cause mantle rock to melt.

3. What is crystallization?

4. If lava on Earth's surface cools quickly, will the crystals in the resulting igneous rock be small or large? Explain your answer.

5. Pick two things below that could happen to a piece of magma that would make it cool quickly.

   a. It could reach Earth's surface as lava.

   b. It could stay underground.

   c. It could increase in thickness.

   d. It could spread out into a thinner layer.

6. Pick the most reliable information you could obtain by only looking at an igneous rock.

   a. how old it is

   b. how fast it cooled

   c. how long it will take to metamorphose

   d. what time of day it formed

7. How is gabbro similar to granite?

8. Make a table that compares and contrasts basalt and granite.

9. What is the difference between an intrusive and an extrusive igneous rock?

10. The Mid-Atlantic Ridge goes through the country of Iceland. Would you expect to find igneous rocks in Iceland? Explain your answer.

CHALLENGE

An igneous rock can be identified according to the size of its crystals. Crystals are a fascinating part of the natural world. In particular, you may know that snowflakes are unique formations of ice crystals.

Research snowflakes and how they are studied and photographed. Find out about the conditions needed to make a snowflake in nature or in a laboratory. Write a report on your findings.

13.3 **How Rocks Change**

Rocks are formed when lava or magma solidifies. These rocks can become other kinds of rocks when they are broken down by weathering, then cemented together with other sediment, or changed by heat and pressure (Figure 13.11). Sedimentary rocks are formed from pieces of weathered rock. Metamorphic rocks are formed when rock is changed by heat and pressure.

Sedimentary rocks

A downhill journey Sunlight, wind, water, ice, and changing temperatures cause all rocks to form cracks, break into smaller pieces, and eventually become sediment. Wind and water carry the rock pieces downhill until they reach a low place like a lake or sea. Larger pieces of rock break into smaller, smoother particles as they bump along on their downhill journey.

Layers of sediment After a while, thick layers (or beds) of sediment build up in low places. Sediment moves downhill due to the force of gravity. Downhill movement is important in forming sediment beds. Sedimentary rocks are the most common rock found on Earth's surface. They cover 75 percent of the land area in many places.

Compaction Water and air are squeezed from between the particles as more rock particles settle on top of previously formed sediment beds. Compaction is the pressing together of layers of sediment. Even though compacted sediment beds might be hard to dig into, the particles are still separate grains and not yet sedimentary rock.

Cementation Cementation is the process by which particles become "glued" together and form a sedimentary rock. This may happen when the corners of two particles are pressed together hard enough to partially dissolve them. Dissolved minerals between the particles cause cementation as the minerals form crystals.

compaction - the process by which sediment is pressed together as more and more layers or beds of sediment form on top of each other.

cementation - the process by which sediment particles are "glued" together to make a sedimentary rock.

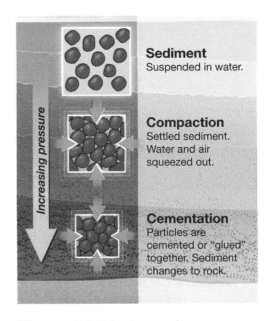

Sediment
Suspended in water.

Increasing pressure

Compaction
Settled sediment. Water and air squeezed out.

Cementation
Particles are cemented or "glued" together. Sediment changes to rock.

Figure 13.11: *Compaction and cementation.*

Types of sedimentary rock

The size of particles

The size of the particles in a sedimentary rock help identify it (Figure 13.12). Clay and silt particles form *mudstone*. Clay is not visible in the mudstones, and feels smooth. Silt is barely visible and feels gritty. Sand particles that you can see and feel form *sandstone*. *Conglomerate*, a lumpy rock, is made of rounded gravel.

Rock type	Particle size (mm)	Sediments
mudstone	0.002–0.05	clay or silt
sandstone	0.05–2	sand
conglomerate	> 2	gravel

Figure 13.12: *Types of sedimentary rocks.*

Sediments from animals and plants

The tiny shells of dead marine plants and animals sink to the ocean floor and form layers of shells and mud. Over millions of years, these layers eventually become sedimentary rock. Most *limestone*, a sedimentary rock, is formed this way. Also, fossil remains form sedimentary rocks. Peat and bituminous coal are sedimentary rocks made from ancient plant remains.

Fossils in sedimentary rocks

Fossils can be found in metamorphic rocks, but most are found in sedimentary rock. This is because many animals live near low areas (that hold water) where sediments accumulate. Also, the process of making a sedimentary rock is good for preserving fossils.

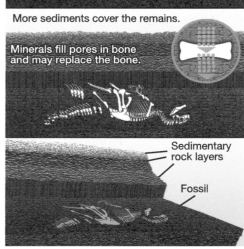

Figure 13.13: *The process that forms sedimentary rocks also preserves fossils.*

Fossil formation

Fossil formation begins when an organism's body is quickly covered in sediments from an event like a mud slide. Body parts that do not decay quickly, like bones and teeth, are buried under sediment layers. After a long time, these harder body parts may be preserved or replaced by other minerals. Fossils are the remains or traces (like footprints) of prehistoric organisms. Eventually, the sediments and fossil are compacted and cemented into sedimentary rock (Figure 13.13).

Crystals in water

Some sedimentary rocks also form by precipitation of minerals from solution. Here, "precipitation" means that the dissolved minerals collect as solid particles as the water evaporates. This group of sedimentary rocks includes halite, gypsum, and chert.

Metamorphic rocks

Heat and pressure
Metamorphic rocks are formed when an existing rock is heated and squeezed under pressure. How much heating and how much pressure is required to make a metamorphic rock? Temperature can be high or low. Pressure can also be high or low (Figure 13.14).

Low-grade metamorphism
Low-grade metamorphism occurs under conditions of low temperature and pressure. It is similar to but stronger than the process of cementation. The result of low-grade metamorphism is that new minerals begin to form.

Contact metamorphism
Rocks formed by *contact metamorphism* are heated, but not squeezed by high pressure. An example is hot magma coming in contact with limestone so that it is changed into marble.

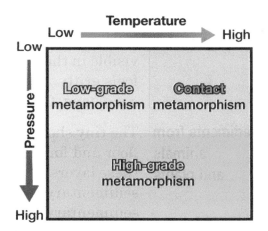

Figure 13.14: *Metamorphism is caused by heat and pressure.*

High-grade metamorphism
High-grade metamorphism involves high pressure and either low or high temperatures. In this process, the minerals in a rock change to form new minerals. For example, minerals in clay are altered to form mica. Pressure causes the new minerals to form in flat layers perpendicular to the direction of pressure. This is called *foliation.* Phyllite and gneiss (pronounced as "nice") are two metamorphic rocks that are formed in this way (Figure 13.15). They have mica flakes that are layered (foliated) across the direction of pressure. Gneiss has light and dark bands of re-formed minerals that lie across the direction of pressure.

Direction of pressure

Layers of minerals across direction of pressure

Direction of pressure

Phyllite

Gneiss

Figure 13.15: *Phyllite and gneiss.*

Metamorphic rocks tell great stories

Rock detectives Geologists work like detectives. They use rocks as clues to understand the history of Earth. The only real difference is that detectives solve crimes in days and weeks, but geologists study events that took place over hundreds of millions of years. Here are two examples of amazing events that are discovered by rock clues.

Finding old subduction zones High-grade metamorphism can occur at low temperature. Where do the conditions of high pressure and low temperature exist? An ocean floor plate encounters great pressure when it subducts into Earth's mantle. But it is cool because it is covered by ocean water. High-pressure metamorphism changes the sediments on the ocean floor to the metamorphic rock called blueschist. It also changes the basalt of the ocean floor to the metamorphic rock eclogite (Figure 13.16). When geologists find these metamorphic rocks they know that they have found the remains of an ancient subduction zone!

Finding mountains Mountains are formed when converging plates cause one continent to collide with another. These continental collisions produce both tremendous heat and pressure. High-grade metamorphic rocks, like gneiss, form at the core of the growing mountains.

Remains of a mountain Plate movements change direction, and after some time, these collisions stop. Then the mountains stop growing and weathering begins to wear them down. Today there are the remains of great mountain ranges that are as flat as a playground! All that is left of these giants are the gneiss rocks that were formed at their core.

Blueschist

Eclogite

Clues that a subduction zone existed

Gneiss
A clue that a mountain range once existed

Figure 13.16: *Blueschist and eclogite are formed by high-pressure metamorphism.*

Summarizing how rocks are formed—the rock cycle

The processes that keep rock material moving through the rock cycle include weathering, erosion, compaction and cementation, melting and crystallizing, and metamorphism. Weathering and erosion are ways in which rock is broken down and the pieces are moved from place to place. You will learn more about weathering and erosion in Chapter 14. Compaction and cementation are processes which cause pieces of rock to become a sedimentary rock. When lava or magma cools, it forms crystals in a process called crystallization. Additionally, plate tectonics plays an important role in the rock cycle. Rocks melt or metamorphose when they are subducted into the mantle. The pressure between two plates that are coming together can create mountains of folded rock. If new mountains weren't always being built, the weathering and erosion of rocks over time would leave the continents smooth and flattened.

MY JOURNAL

Write a story about what happens to a small amount of hot rock in the mantle as it experiences the rock cycle. Write the story from the point of view of this piece of hot rock.

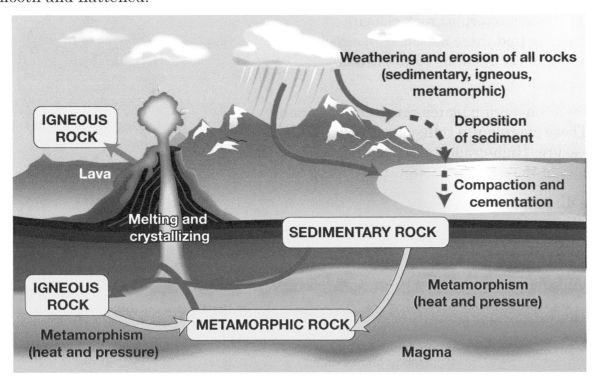

13.3 **Section Review**

1. Why are sedimentary rocks the most common rocks found on Earth's surface?

2. What is the difference between compaction and cementation?

3. Why are fossils usually found in sedimentary rock?

4. List a feature that is used to identify a sedimentary rock.

5. What does the term *metamorphism* mean?

6. What two conditions can cause metamorphic rocks to form?

7. What is contact metamorphism?

8. Look at the rock images in Figure 13.17. Which image is most likely to be a metamorphic rock? Explain your answer.

9. Metamorphic rocks are commonly formed at what kind of plate boundary?

10. Name one event that occurs at a plate boundary that can cause a rock to be metamorphosed into another rock?

11. Challenge question: For the following, state whether the description describes a metamorphic, sedimentary, or igneous rock.

    a. A rock formed from pieces of broken down rock.

    b. A rock formed after a volcano erupts.

    c. This kind of rock is likely to be formed at a subduction zone.

12. List one rock cycle process that is involved in forming each of these rocks.

    a. an igneous rock

    b. a metamorphic rock

    c. a sedimentary rock

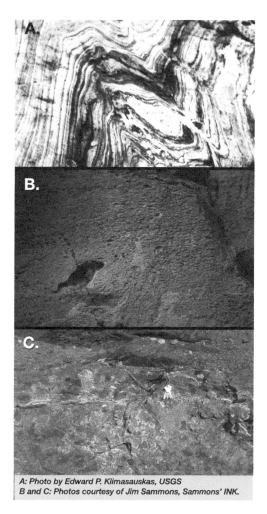

A: Photo by Edward P. Klimasauskas, USGS
B and C: Photos courtesy of Jim Sammons, Sammons' INK.

Figure 13.17: *Question 8.*

How Do You Grow a Diamond?

Diamonds are the world's hardest mineral. They are formed deep under Earth's surface where there is intense heat and pressure. Most diamonds are mined in Africa, but diamond mines exist on all continents.

Graphite and a gem

You may be surprised to learn that the graphite in your pencil and a diamond have the same chemical composition. Both are made entirely of carbon atoms. The difference between graphite and diamond is how the carbon atoms are connected into a crystal structure.

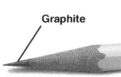

Graphite

The atoms in graphite have strong bonds in two directions and weak bonds in the other directions. This bonding pattern makes graphite dark, soft, and useful for writing. Graphite is easy to find—it's used to make pencil lead!

Diamond is a clear, hard crystal. The carbon atoms in diamond are connected by strong bonds in all directions. The carbon atoms of diamonds are closer together than the atoms in any other substance. The structure and properties of diamonds make it a sparkling gemstone and the hardest of all the minerals.

Sparkling diamonds grown from "seed" diamonds.

Photo courtesy of Apollo Diamond, Inc.

Diamond growing

There are two ways that a diamond can be made. One way squeezes graphite while it is very hot (like what happens under Earth's surface). The other way to make diamonds is like making rock candy.

Rock candy

Crystals of sugar

You may have had experience making rock candy. The main ingredient is a water solution that has a lot of dissolved sugar. Under the right conditions, the dissolved sugar collects as large, hard crystals.

To grow a diamond, you need carbon atoms to collect as a sparkling crystal. Instead of a water solution of carbon atoms, scientists use *plasma*. Plasma a state of matter that is neither a liquid or a gas. It is the phase of matter that makes up the Sun. The plasma to make diamonds is made of carbon and hydrogen atoms.

To get a diamond growing from the plasma, you have to start with a "seed" diamond. A seed diamond is a thin square of diamond. These small squares are placed on a small tray. The tray is placed in a vacuum chamber. It's like placing a cookie sheet full of unbaked cookies into an oven!

"Seed" diamonds on a tray that will be placed in a vacuum chamber.

"Seed" diamonds

Inside the vacuum chamber, a vacuum is created. A vacuum means there is no air in the chamber. The temperature is elevated to 3,000°C, about as hot as the Sun. Under these conditions, the carbon atoms will bond to the "seed" diamond.

Vacuum chamber

Photo courtesy of Apollo Diamond, Inc.

How does a diamond grow?

The plasma used for growing diamonds is only made of carbon and hydrogen atoms. Within the vacuum chamber, the conditions are just right for carbon atoms to settle on the surface of the "seed" diamond. But, the hydrogen atoms also settle. But, because hydrogen atoms are very reactive, a hydrogen partners with another carbon and then they switch positions. This allows the carbons to link together. Eventually, layers of linked carbon atoms form a diamond. The presence of the hydrogen makes the linking of the carbons happen more easily.

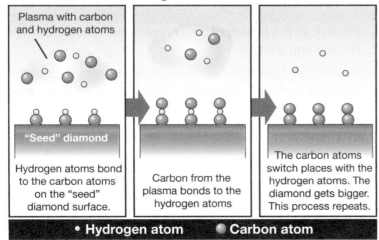

How to grow a diamond

Plasma with carbon and hydrogen atoms

"Seed" diamond

Hydrogen atoms bond to the carbon atoms on the "seed" diamond surface.

Carbon from the plasma bonds to the hydrogen atoms

The carbon atoms switch places with the hydrogen atoms. The diamond gets bigger. This process repeats.

● **Hydrogen atom**   ● **Carbon atom**

Making diamonds

An elaborate technique for growing diamonds has been worked out by scientists at Apollo Diamond, Inc., a Boston-based company. Apollo Diamond can grow diamonds as much as 5 millimeters thick. These diamonds are thick enough to make cut gems for items like earrings, necklaces, and rings. The girl in the picture is wearing grown-diamond earrings and a necklace.

Photo courtesy of Apollo Diamond, Inc.

Another project that Apollo Diamond is working on has to do with computers. The company is working on getting a large enough diamond plate so that it can be used for making semiconductors. Semiconductors "conduct" information from place to place very quickly in a computer. Currently, the most common semiconductor material is silicon. Diamond semiconductors work better and faster than silicon semiconductors.

You may have heard of Silicon Valley in California. It is a region where there are many people and companies working on and developing computers. One day Silicon Valley might become Diamond Valley!

QUESTIONS

1. Compare and contrast graphite and diamonds. Be sure to talk about how carbon atoms are arranged in each.

2. What is plasma?

3. Under what conditions of temperature and pressure are diamonds grown?

4. Name two uses for grown diamonds.

Metamorphism

Contact and regional metamorphism are two processes by which rock can change from one form to another using heat and pressure. Contact metamorphism forms rocks such as marble and quartzite. Banded gneiss and phyllite are examples of regional metamorphism. In this activity, you will simulate contact and regional metamorphism.

Materials

Safety goggles and apron, glass petri dish, 100-mL beaker, water, hot plate, pot holder, heat-proof mat, 1 raw egg white, table salt (sodium chloride), two colors of clay, a piece of wax paper, a plastic knife, and a book to press the clay

Contact metamorphism

1. Put on goggles and apron. Keep them on until the hot water has cooled to a safe handling temperature.

2. Place the petri dish on the heat-proof mat. Add the egg white. Wash your hands after handling the raw egg.

3. Pour about 50 milliliters of water in a beaker, and add one teaspoon salt (to increase the boiling point).

4. Place the beaker on the hot plate. Bring the salt water to a boil. Do not touch the hot beaker or hot plate!

5. Once the water is boiling, ask your teacher to remove the beaker and place it in the petri dish in the center of the egg white. Leave it for 10 minutes and then return to observe what has happened.

Beaker

Petri dish

Raw egg white

Be very careful! The beaker will be hot!

Regional metamorphism

1. Take one color of clay and press it into a flat square. Cut the square into four pieces with a plastic knife.

2. With the other color of clay, make at least 15 small balls. Arrange the clay balls on three of the flat pieces.

3. Stack the flat pieces with the balls on top of each other. Place the last flat piece (without the balls) on top.

4. Wrap the stack in wax paper. Just cover the surfaces. Do not wrap it like a gift. The clay needs room to spread out.

5. Use a book to press the stack, then use the plastic knife to carefully slice through the flattened stack of clay.

Applying your knowledge

Contact metamorphism:

a. What does the beaker of water represent? What does the cooked egg white represent?

b. What type of general metamorphic environment does the egg white activity represent? Where could a geologic event like this have happened?

Regional metamorphism:

a. What do the balls of clay represent? What happened to the balls of clay when the stack was pressed?

b. In what type of general metamorphic environment would this happen? Give an example of where a geologic event like this could actually happen.

Vocabulary

Select the correct term to complete the sentences.

rock	mineral	cleavage plane
Mohs hardness rock	crystallization	extrusive rock
igneous rock	basalt	compaction
sedimentary rock	granite	sediment
metamorphic rock	intrusive rock	rock cycle
cementation		

Section 13.1

1. The resistance to scratching that mineral exhibits is identified using the _____.

2. When rocks are weathered, _____ is created.

3. The _____ represents the formation and recycling of rocks by geologic processes.

4. Heat and pressure are applied to a sedimentary rock, enough so that it begins to melt and recrystallize into a new rock. The new rock is a(n) _____.

5. A surface along which a mineral cleanly splits is a(n) _____.

6. A(n) _____ is a naturally formed solid composed of one or more minerals.

7. Quartz is a(n) _____ found in granite.

8. A shield volcano erupts and the lava pours out of the vent, cooling as it is exposed to the air. When hardened, this rock will be a(n) _____.

9. A rock that is made of layers of sediments is called a(n) _____.

Section 13.2

10. _____ is the process by which crystals form.

11. _____ is the rock of the ocean floor.

12. _____ forms inside the Earth's crust, and is therefore a(n) _____.

13. _____ tends to have smaller grains than those that are able to slowly cool inside the Earth's crust.

Section 13.3

14. _____ is the pressing together of layers of sediment.

15. _____ is the process by which particles become stuck together and form a sedimentary rock.

Concepts

Section 13.1

1. Name one similarity and one difference between graphite and diamond.

2. Describing pyrite (fool's gold) and gold:

    a. name one characteristic that can be used to tell pyrite and real gold apart.

    b. are pyrite and gold rocks or minerals? Explain your answer.

3. What does the term *hardness* mean? What is the hardest mineral on the Mohs hardness scale?

4. What is the rock cycle? List the three groups of rocks that are formed by the rock cycle?

5. Peat and bituminous coal are rocks that are formed from ancient plant remains. What kinds of rocks are peat and bituminous coal?

Section 13.2

6. Why is the mantle so hot? Give specific reasons.

7. What two factors affect the melting temperature of mantle rock?

8. What about the appearance of an igneous rock gives you a clue about whether it cooled slowly or quickly?

9. Give an example each of an intrusive rock and an extrusive rock.

Section 13.3

10. When layers of sediment build up, are compacted, and cemented together, what type of rock is formed?

11. Name one feature of sedimentary rocks that is used to tell one from another.

12. Which of these sedimentary rocks has the smallest particles, conglomerate or mudstone?

13. What two factors affect the metamorphosing of rocks?

14. What type of rocks are clues to ancient mountain building?

15. How does plate tectonics play a role in the rock cycle?

Math and Writing Skills

Section 13.1

1. Make a pie graph based on the information is provided in Figure 13.2 of the text.

2. You are looking for a birdbath for your garden in a catalog. You see a granite birdbath that costs $100. You see another birdbath made of limestone that costs $75. Granite is made of quartz and feldspar. Limestone is mostly made of the mineral calcite. Write a paragraph describing the birdbath you will purchase and why you will purchase it.

Section 13.2

3. Explain how the shape, surface area, and volume of a piece of magma or lava affects how fast it cools.

4. Obsidian is also called volcanic glass because it cools so fast, what could obsidian be exposed to when it cools for this to happen? *Hint*: Obsidian is found in Iceland.

Section 13.3

5. There are different types of sedimentary rocks. Rocks made of fragments of other rock particles are called *clastic sedimentary rocks*. Rocks made of bits of living materials like shells are called *biological sedimentary rocks*. Sedimentary rocks made when minerals crystallize are called *chemical sedimentary rocks*. Identify each as being clastic, biological, or chemical.

    a. Mudstone

    b. Sandstone

    c. Gypsum

    d. Most limestone

6. What type of metamorphism is taking place if there is high temperature and low pressure? Give an example or a rock that is formed in this situation.

Chapter Project—Sedimentary Rock Hunt

Go on a geological "dig" to find five sedimentary rocks. First, research sedimentary rocks to find out where they might be found in nature and what they look like. Then, go on your "dig" to find the rocks. It may take a while to find this many rocks in your area so be patient. Keep in mind that rocks are not only outdoors. Your house, the mall, local stores, benches, playgrounds and other areas may also have many sedimentary rocks for you to find. As you find a sample, bring it or a photograph of it to class. Write a description that explains where you found each rock and why you think it is a sedimentary rock.

Chapter 14

Weathering and Erosion

You know from experience that rocks are hard objects. Sitting on a stone bench is not as comfortable as sitting on a sofa! And it takes a lot of work to break a rock into pieces. Over time though, rock does break down. This chapter describes how that happens and how rock is moved from place to place. Weathering is a term that describes how rock is broken down to form sediment. Erosion describes the transportation of sediment by water, wind, ice, or even gravity. In time, even the hardest rock will become small pieces and particles of sediment.

Key Questions:

1. How do rocks and minerals break down?

2. What is the difference between weathering and erosion?

3. How do rivers shape the land?

14.1 **Weathering**

Weathering is the process of breaking down rock and minerals. Weathering is caused by many different factors, including the Sun's energy, wind, running water, moving ice, chemical reactions, and the actions of plants or animals.

Mountains and weathering

Mountains   Mountains—because they are so big and impressive—seem to be unchanging features in a landscape. However, mountains wear down over time due to weathering. What does a weathered mountain look like?

Old versus young mountains   A good example of old, weathered mountains are the Great Smoky Mountains, which are part of the Appalachian mountain range. In contrast, the Rocky Mountains in the western United States and Canada are younger mountains (Figure 14.1).

What happens as mountains age?   At one time, the Great Smoky Mountains (or Smokies) were as tall as the Rockies and also had sharp peaks. But, since the Smokies are hundreds of millions of years older than the Rockies, the peaks have been worn down by weathering. Eventually, the Smokies will be no more than rolling hills, and the Rockies will look like the Smokies do now.

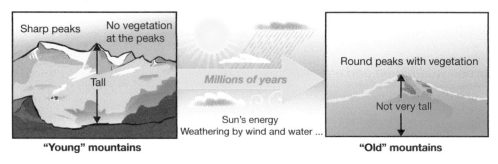

Photos courtesy of Jim Sammons, Sammons' INK.

Figure 14.1: *The sharp peaks of the Canadian Rocky Mountains, and the rounded peaks of the Great Smoky Mountains.*

weathering - the process of breaking down rock and minerals. Weathering is caused by the Sun's energy, wind, running water, ice, chemical reactions, and the actions of organisms.

Ways that weathering occurs

Energy sources for weathering
The two main sources of energy that cause weathering are the Sun and Earth's internal energy. The Sun drives our weather and the water cycle. Earth's internal energy results in the movement of lithospheric plates on Earth's surface. Earth's internal energy also plays a role in the rock cycle. A rock may be changed by mechanical weathering, chemical weathering, or both (Figure 14.2).

Mechanical weathering
Mechanical weathering occurs when forces break or chip rocks and minerals into smaller pieces without changing their composition. Mechanical weathering may break large blocks loose or chip away tiny grains, one at a time.

Chemical weathering
Chemical weathering is the process of breaking down rocks and minerals by chemical reactions between water and the rock or mineral particles. Other agents of chemical weathering include oxygen and acids (from plants or acid rain). Rock material is chemically changed by this kind of weathering. Some kinds of rock are more easily chemically weathered than others. For example, marble is chemically weathered faster than granite. Chemical weathering has worn away the surfaces of many old marble statues (Figure 14.2).

Gravity and surface area
The force of gravity is important in the weathering process because gravity causes water and pieces of rock to move downhill. In this way, rock and mineral pieces from a mountain top move to low areas like beaches. As a rock breaks down, more and more surface area is exposed. The more surface area that is exposed, the faster weathering occurs.

 VOCABULARY

mechanical weathering - the process of breaking down rocks and minerals into smaller pieces by physical force. Also called physical weathering.

chemical weathering - the process of breaking down rocks and minerals by chemical reactions.

Mechanical Weathering

Photo courtesy of Jim Sammons, Sammons' INK.

Chemical Weathering

Figure 14.2: *Mechanical and chemical weathering.*

Agents of mechanical weathering

Running water   Weathering often involves water. Changing conditions of wetness and dryness cause rocks and minerals to break down. Also, weathering occurs quickly when running water knocks rocks against each other. Sediment carried by running water also wears away rock by abrasion, making it smooth and round. You can see this by looking at the rocks in any river or at the base of a waterfall.

Frost wedging   **Frost wedging** is a form of mechanical weathering that occurs when a small amount of water enters a tiny crack in a rock. When the water freezes, it expands, making the crack a little wider. More water enters the crack, freezes, and widens the crack even more. Eventually frost wedging splits the rock into separate pieces (Figure 14.3).

Where frost wedging occurs   Frost wedging tends to occur in areas with available water and temperatures that fluctuate around the freezing point. Rocks that have many pores or cracks are susceptible to frost wedging. The photo in Figure 14.3 shows an example of frost wedging near the crest of Mount Hoffman in the Sierra Nevada Mountains. Many hand-sized rocks have been split away by frost wedging.

frost wedging - mechanical weathering that results from freezing water.

Mount Hoffman, Sierra Nevada Mountains

Rocks that have been split away by frost wedging

Photo courtesy of Jim Sammons, Sammons' INK.

Water   Ice

Freezing

Figure 14.3: *An example of frost wedging.*

Biological weathering by plants

Weathering by plants or animals is called *biological weathering*. Mechanical weathering by plants occurs when roots grow into cracks in a rock. In this process called *root wedging*, roots exert force on the rock as they grow and may cause the rock to split (Figure 14.6). Chemical weathering occurs when plants release chemicals that break down the rock on which they are growing.

Biological weathering by animals

Animals cause mechanical weathering when they dig into soil or burrow underground. When they do this, they create pockets for water to move deeper underground. Ultimately, this means that the weathering process of rocks that are underground speeds up.

Figure 14.4: *Over time, the tree's roots will split the rocks on this cliff by root wedging.*

Exfoliation

Exfoliation is a weathering process that results in rock layers peeling away. Weathering causes an outer layer to peel away first. The layers of rock underneath experience a decrease in pressure and expand. As they expand, they crack and more weathering occurs. Eventually, the resulting rock structure can look rounded with cracked layers.

Half Dome in Yosemite National Park

An example of exfoliation

Photo courtesy of U.S. Geological Survey

Sedona, Arizona

hoodoos (tall pillars)

Photo courtesy of Jim Sammons, Sammons' INK.

Figure 14.5: *Wind-blown sand has mechanically weathered this sandstone into tall pillars called hoodoos.*

Wind

Wind is also a mechanical weathering agent. Wind-blown sand chips away tiny bits of rock from the surface of exposed rock. During this process, the remaining rock can take on unusual shapes and the removed bits eventually become sand (Figure 14.5).

Chemical weathering

Water and minerals

When water washes over a rock, it can react with minerals in that rock and cause chemical changes. A result is that the mineral dissolves or a new mineral is made. For example, the mineral feldspar reacts with water to make clay.

Acid rain

Chemical reactions can occur on the surface of a rock or mineral when water is present. For example, acid rain occurs when pollutants or volcanic ash in the atmosphere mixes with water (rain) and form an acidic solution. Acid rain can weather rocks, including statues. If the statues are made of marble, they will weather more quickly (see the statue in Figure 14.2). Marble is made of calcite (calcium carbonate) which dissolves in acidic water. Granite statues do not dissolve when exposed to acid rain.

Oxygen in the atmosphere

Oxygen in the atmosphere also participates in weathering. Oxygen combines with metals in minerals and changes them. This process is called *oxidation*. For example, oxygen combines with iron in the minerals biotite and hornblende to make rust.

Weathering by plants

Moss, lichens, and other plants can cause chemical weathering. Chemicals released by the plants eventually cause the rock on which they are growing to break down (Figure 14.6).

Chemical and mechanical weathering

Both chemical and mechanical weathering can affect rock at the same time. Look at Figure 14.7. Originally there were a few tiny cracks in the rock. Frost wedging probably opened up these cracks. Now chemical weathering is changing the rock so that the sides of the crack are filled with loose grains. You can see the tufts of plants growing in the loose grains of rock.

Figure 14.6: *Moss growing on rocks causes chemical weathering.*

Photo courtesy of Jim Sammons, Sammons' INK.

Figure 14.7: *Both mechanical and chemical weathering often occur at the same time.*

Factors that affect the rate of weathering

Water and climate
If an area has a humid, warm climate, then rocks and minerals will tend to weather faster. Chemical weathering is more likely to happen in humid conditions. Weathering is slowest in dry, cold climates. Frost wedging will occur more often in an area with abundant water and freezing temperatures. Running water—like the water from a river or a waterfall—speeds up mechanical weathering by wearing down and breaking up rocks. This water can also cause chemical weathering to occur.

Plants and animals
Weathering is also faster when there are plants and animals in the area. Plants growing on or near rocks can speed up weathering. Animals can dig or burrow and alter how much exposure a rock has to weathering.

Minerals
The kind of minerals found in a rock also affects how fast it is weathered. Marble, which has calcite, weathers faster than granite. Calcite dissolves in acidic solutions (like acid rain). The minerals in granite are more resistant to weathering.

Surface area
The greater the surface area of a rock or mineral compared to its volume, the faster it will weather. For example, a flat, jagged rock will weather more quickly than a rounded rock of the same volume.

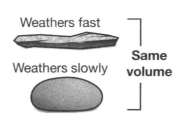

Weathers fast

Weathers slowly

Same volume

Sediments are the products of weathering
The result of the weathering of rocks and minerals is *sediment* which is small pieces and particles of rock. Eventually, sediment becomes part of soil, which you will learn about in the next chapter.

MY JOURNAL

Find an outdoor place near your house that will not get disturbed. Make a pile of sediment and rocks. You may want to put a sign near your pile that says "Do Not Disturb!"

Make a prediction about what you think will happen to the pile over the next two weeks. Keep in mind that weathering events usually take longer than two weeks to happen. However, what events might occur that would affect the pile during this time period?

Make regular observations in a journal. Then, write up your finding in a short report.

DO NOT DISTURB!
Scientific observations in progress

14.1 Section Review

1. Are mountains permanent structures? Justify your answer.

2. Name two differences between old and young mountains.

3. How long does it take for a mountaind's sharp peaks to wear down? Choose an answer below and explain your reasoning.

   a. millions of years   b. hundreds of years
   c. about 10 years   d. one year

4. How does the Sun play a role in weathering?

5. Compare and contrast mechanical and chemical weathering.

6. Why is gravity important in weathering?

7. How is frost wedging similar to root wedging?

8. How can animals speed up the process of weathering?

9. For the following examples, state whether mechanical or chemical weathering is occurring.
   a. A bicycle left in the rain becomes rusty.
   b. A chunk of rock breaks off of a mountain.

10. Over time, how might the grass growing up through a crack in a sidewalk affect the sidewalk? Use the terms *mechanical weathering* and *chemical weathering* in your answer.

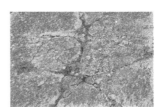

11. List three factors that affect how fast a rock might weather.

CHALLENGE

Limestone (calcium carbonate) weathers when it is exposed to acidic water or acid rain. A number of famous caves have been formed by chemical weathering of underground limestone. Research Mammoth Cave in Kentucky to find out more about how this cave formed.

SOLVE IT!

In which situation will weathering happen faster? Pick the correct situation for each.

a. a tropical rainforest or a dry desert

b. a rock with lots of jagged edges or a smooth, round rock

c. a warm environment or a really cold environment

d. a rock with a lot of surface area compared to its volume or a rock with a small amount of surface area compared to its volume

14.2 **Erosion**

Weathering eventually breaks rock into bits and pieces called sediment (Figure 14.8). When you sit on a sandy beach, you are sitting on sediment that might have once been a rocky mountain top. How does sediment get from a mountain peak to a beach? The answer is erosion. Erosion is the process of moving pieces of rock and sediment by wind, water, ice, and gravity.

Moving sediment

What moves sediment? Running water, wind, and ice are all involved in moving sediment. Sediment generally moves downhill because of the force of gravity.

Running water Running water—like that found in rivers, streams, and waterfalls—carries sediment. A river is a large, flowing body of water. A stream is a small river. The path that a river or stream follows is called a channel. Due to gravity, sediment carried by running water eventually arrives at the lowest place that it can reach, such as a beach. Then the sediment is carried into the ocean water by waves.

Athabasca Glacier, Canada

Flowing water carries off sediment of all sizes.
The water is cloudy because it is filled with many tiny rock particles.

Photo courtesy of Jim Sammons, Sammons' INK.

VOCABULARY

erosion - the process of moving sediment by wind, water, ice, or gravity.

river - a large body of water that flows into an ocean or lake.

stream - a small river.

channel - the path that a river or stream follows.

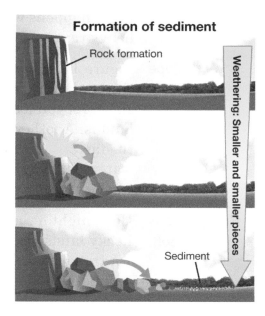

Formation of sediment

Rock formation

Weathering: Smaller and smaller pieces

Sediment

Figure 14.8: *Weathering causes rock to break down into sediment.*

Running water moves sediment

Deposition The process of depositing sediment after it has been moved by water, wind, or ice is called **deposition**. The amount of sediment that can be carried and deposited by running water depends on many factors such as the volume of water, the slope of the land, and how rocky or smooth the land is.

Volume The volume of running water affects how much sediment can be carried. You probably know this from experience. Think about a gentle rainfall. When the volume of flowing rainwater is small, some sediment is moved. However, after a heavy rainfall, the greater volume of water can move a lot of soil or sediment from yards and then deposit it in driveways and on streets. The same thing happens with rivers. When the water volume increases after heavy rains or when snow melts, more sediment can be carried.

Slope Figure 14.9 shows a stream table modeling how water flows over the land. In this graphic, a steep slope is compared to a less-steep slope. As you learned in Chapter 8, *slope* refers to how steep the land is. Another word for slope is *gradient*. The steeper the slope, the faster the water and sediment will move over land. Faster water means that larger particles can be moved and more particles can be moved at one time.

Rocky versus smooth How might a rocky landscape affect how sediment is carried? Rocky landscapes can trap sediment. Therefore, the sediment will not travel as far. A smooth landscape or river bed might mean that sediment can be carried a long way. Barriers or rocks can be used by people to stop the transport of sediment and reduce the effects of erosion.

deposition - the process of depositing sediment after it has been moved by water, wind, ice, or gravity.

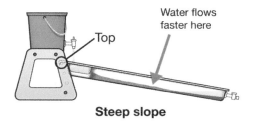

Water flows faster here

Top

Steep slope

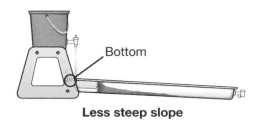

Bottom

Less steep slope

Figure 14.9: *A stream table can be used to model the effects of the slope on how fast water flows.*

Sorting sediment

Fast versus slow water How fast water moves is directly related to how much energy it has. Both the speed of water and its energy are directly related to how big a piece of rock can be moved. Fast, high-energy water can move big pieces of rock. Slow-moving water can only move fine sediment.

Sediment is sorted by water When running water slows down, the pieces of rock and sediment that are being carried settle out. This situation can happen when a flowing river enters a lake or a pond. The flow stops and the water drops its sediment. First, the largest particles settle to the bottom. Next, the medium-sized particles settle. Finally, the smallest particles settle out. The particles settle in order, making a pattern called graded bedding. It's common to find graded bedding in repeating layers, one on top of the other. For example, a stream that flows into a lake may run fast only during thunderstorms. The stream lays down a graded bed of sediments after each storm.

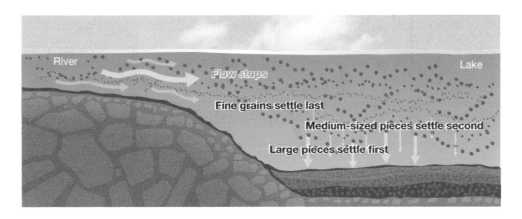

 VOCABULARY

graded bedding - a layer of sediment with the largest particles at the bottom and smallest particles on top; the particles are deposited as flowing water slows down.

 SOLVE IT!

The speed of a river is measured in meters per second. You can use a stopwatch to record how many seconds it takes for a twig floating on the river's surface to move 5 meters. If it takes the twig 10 seconds to travel that distance, what is the speed of the running water at the river's surface?

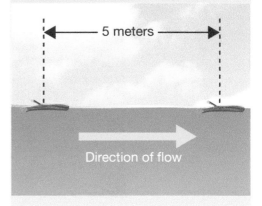

Interpreting layers of sediment

Direction of younging Sedimentary rocks hold clues to their past. One of these clues is "the up direction." You learned that large particles settle before small particles, forming graded bedding. Figure 14.10 shows two graded beds. A layer of the finest particles is on the top of each bed. This layer of fine particles helps you know which direction is "up." If you know the up direction, you know the direction of younging—this is the direction of younger layers. Graded bedding is preserved when sediments become sedimentary rock.

Cross bedding When sediment is carried by the wind or running water, it often forms a pattern of alternating beds where it is deposited. This pattern, called cross bedding, is easy to recognize in sedimentary rocks where one layer ends abruptly as another layer passed over it.

Direction of younging

Youngest layer

Cross bedding

Oldest layer

Stream channel outline where layers first formed

Photo courtesy of Jim Sammons, Sammons INK.

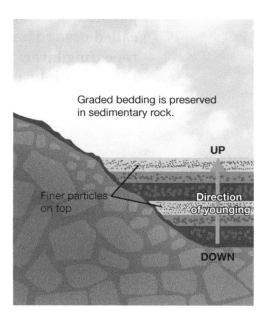

Graded bedding is preserved in sedimentary rock.

UP

Finer particles on top

Direction of younging

DOWN

Figure 14.10: *Direction of younging. This graphic shows two graded beds.*

Moving sediment by ice

Abrasion Particles that are trapped in ice or suspended in water can cause weathering by abrasion. The particles rub the surface of a rock as the water or ice moves over it. You might not think that ice moves, but it can! A glacier is a huge mass of ice that is *plastic* (similar to the way the hot rock in the mantle is plastic). *Plastic* means "able to change shape without breaking." As the ice of a glacier flows down a valley, it grinds the valley floor with pieces of rock caught up in the ice (Figure 14.11). This grinding changes the shape of the valley.

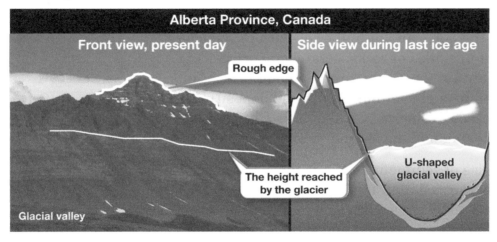

Figure 14.11: *A glacier passed over this rock moving from left to right. The scratches were made by rocks caught in the moving ice*

A *U*-shaped glacial valley The image above is of a large valley that held a glacier during the last ice age. From the side, this glacial valley is *U*-shaped. Notice that the highest part of the ridge is rough. This is because abrasion by the glacier didn't occur that high up before it melted. The change from smooth to rough rock is the "bathtub ring" left by the glacier that shows the highest point the glacier abraded the mountain.

Rock flour The fine rock powder that results from abrasion by glaciers is called "rock flour." Rock flour can be washed into lakes and make them a milky blue color (Figure 14.12).

Figure 14.12: *Rock flour makes this water look cloudy.*

More on moving sediment

Glaciers A glacier can be many kilometers thick and thousands of kilometers wide. Glaciers are formed from the accumulation of snow over hundreds or thousands of years. Each year more snow may pile up and not entirely melt during the warmer summer months. As the snow piles up and pressure increases, it changes into ice. With the buildup of ice, a glacier becomes so thick and heavy that it flows (Figure 14.13). The force of gravity drives this movement.

The effect of glaciers on land About 30 percent of Earth's surface was covered by glaciers 10,000 years ago. As Earth's climate warmed, glaciers melted, except for those near the poles and at higher elevations. Glaciers moved and deposited huge piles of rocks, scratched surfaces of rocks, and eroded mountain tops. For example, Long Island, in New York, was created by a glacier bulldozing and depositing rocks as the glacier receded. The rocky soil of New England is evidence of glaciers moving and depositing rocks.

Wind erosion Wind can move particles of sediment from one place to another. Small particles may be carried aloft by the wind. Larger particles and rocks are too heavy to be moved by the wind. In this case, the particles are rolled along on the ground and the rocks stay put. The result might be a *desert pavement* left behind after the removal of soil over time (Figure 14.14). Eroded sediment is eventually deposited when the wind dies down. Beach dunes are one example of large amounts of deposited sand. *Loess* is another wind-blown deposit of fine sediment. Loess is an important resource because the deposit is rich with nutrients and good for growing plants.

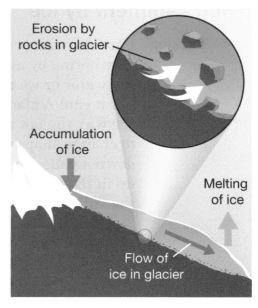

Figure 14.13: *Erosion by a glacier.*

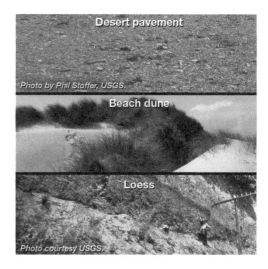

Figure 14.14: *Results of wind erosion.*

Moving sediment by gravity

Mass wasting Mass wasting is the downhill movement of large amounts of rock and sediment due to the force of gravity. There are different ways that mass wasting occurs. For example, mass wasting might occur as a landslide, a rockfall, a mudflow, or a slump.

Landslides A landslide occurs when a large mass of soil or rock slides down a steep slope. Landslides are common on composite volcanoes. The slope is steep and the material is loose. Landslides may be triggered as magma rises and falls inside the volcano. This rising and falling often causes the side of the volcano to move. The Mount St. Helens eruption began when an earthquake occurred and one side of the volcano collapsed resulting in the largest landslide ever recorded. The landslide left a weak place in the side of the volcano that could no longer hold in the magma that had been building up inside. The landslide and the subsequent eruption killed 57 people and destroyed about 600 square kilometers of forest.

Landslide

Saint Bernard, Philippines, 2006

Photo courtesy Department of Defense

Rockfalls A rockfall can occur when a big chunk of rock is split off of a large landform due to weathering (like frost or root wedging) or another event (Figure 14.15). Rockfalls speed up the weathering process by quickly breaking up large pieces of a rock formation.

<table>
<tr><td>

VOCABULARY

mass wasting - the downhill movement of large amounts of rock and sediment due to the force of gravity.

landslide - a large mass of soil or rock that slides down a volcano or mountain. Landslides can be caused by volcanic events, earthquakes, or other factors.

rockfall - an event that results in a large amount of rock splitting off of a landform.

</td></tr>
</table>

Rockfall

Photo courtesy Colorado Department of Transportation

Figure 14.15: *Huge boulders fell on a roadway during this rockfall in Glenwood Canyon, Colorado, in 2003.*

Mudflow
A **mudflow** occurs when a large amount of rock, sediment, and plant material flows down a mountain. As the name implies, a mudflow also involves water. Water weakens the side of a mountain and eventually the mountain cannot hold on to all this material. Mudflows can be dramatic and fast events. They flow down a mountain very quickly, engulfing everything in their paths. The eruption of Mount St. Helens involved mudflows. Mudflows on and around a volcano are called *lahars*. Mud on a volcano is made from volcanic ash.

The difference between dry and wet soil
When soil is dry, friction between the grains of soil keeps it firm enough that you can build a house on it. However, if the soil is wet, the spaces between the grains are full of water. The water makes the grains slippery and friction is a lot lower.

What is slumping?
Slumping describes what happens when loose soil becomes wet and slides or "slumps" (Figure 14.16). Slumping can happen after a period of very heavy rainfall. Houses are at risk of being destroyed by slumping when they are built on steep, loose soil or below hills that are made of loose soil. A house could be destroyed if it slides down with the soil or if the soil on a hill above falls on the house!

VOCABULARY

mudflow - an event that occurs when a large amount of rock, sediment, plant material, and water flows down a mountain.

slumping - an event that occurs when soil particles become surrounded by water so that the ground slides or "slumps."

Photo by Robert L. Schuster, USGS.

Figure 14.16: *A slump occurred in La Conchita, California, in 1995.*

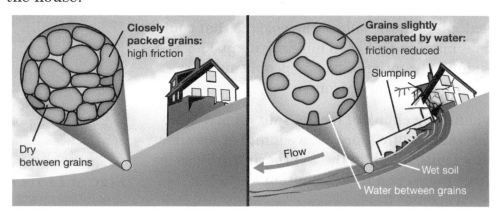

Erosion by people

The Dust Bowl Water, ice, wind, and gravity are powerful forces for causing erosion. People also cause erosion by how they use the land and build on it. For example, in the 1930s, the Great Plains of North America experienced the Dust Bowl, a series of serious wind erosion events (Figure 14.17). The catastrophic damage was due to natural and human causes. A drought made the sediment and soil so dry that it could be easily carried by the wind. In addition, this area suffered from removal of topsoil and grasses by farmers. Topsoil (which you will learn about in the next chapter) helps protect deeper soil and sediment from erosion. The roots of plants like grasses help hold the soil in place so that it doesn't blow away.

What people can do to prevent erosion The Dust Bowl was caused in part by poor farming practices. Farming practices that protect sediment and soil from erosion include installing windbreaks, planting ground cover, and using contour plowing for farming. A windbreak is usually a line of trees that serves to reduce the speed of wind so that less topsoil is removed from an area. Ground cover refers to low-growing plants that protect soil from erosion. Contour plowing is a way to till the soil and plant crops that follows the natural topography of the land (Figure 14.18). More erosion occurs when farmers try to till the soil in ways that do not follow the natural topography of the soil.

Photo courtesy NOAA (George E. Marsh Album)

Figure 14.17: *The Dust Bowl was a series of severe dust storms during the 1930s. The storms resulted in land and property damage, and thousands of people were displaced.*

Photo courtesy of USDA NRCS

Figure 14.18: *An example of contour plowing.*

Photo by Lynn Betts, USDA NRCS

The windbreak and ground cover in this photograph reduce erosion on this farm.

14.2 Section Review

1. What is the difference between weathering and erosion?

2. List four ways that sediment is moved from place to place.

3. What is deposition?

4. What effect does a steep slope have on the erosion of a hillside?

5. What causes a glacial valley to be *U*-shaped? Write your answer as a short, detailed paragraph.

6. List two factors that affect how running water erodes the land.

7. A lake has one graded bed. Then, a rain storm causes a stream to flow faster and deposit more sediment into the lake. A week later, another rain storm occurs. Draw what this would look like. *Hint*: Your drawing should have three patterns.

8. In a graded bed, what clue do you use to figure out which way is "up."

9. Name one piece of evidence that might indicate that an area had been eroded by a glacier. Then, name a piece of evidence that might indicate that an area had been eroded by wind.

10. You have learned that gravity is an important force involved in mass wasting. How is water involved? Give one example from the reading.

11. Describe at least one experience you have had where you observed erosion by water, ice, or wind.

12. How might the Dust Bowl of the 1930s have been lessened or prevented?

13. Look at the photograph of a beach area in Figure 14.19. The fence and beach grass slow the wind so that sand is deposited. Would you say the fence and beach grass are preventing erosion? Why or why not?

Figure 14.19: *Question 11.*

Imagine you are small piece of sediment that gets eroded off of a rock. Describe your erosion journey using terms from this section. Be sure to describe which force or forces—wind, water, ice, or gravity—help you begin your journey. What is your starting place? Where do you get deposited?

14.3 Rivers Shape the Land

This section describes how rivers shape and change the land by moving sediment. As you will see, erosion by rivers is an important part of why land looks the way it does at any given time.

Rivers of running water

River valleys A river valley is created when rivers carve into mountains. *Valleys are low-lying land features that are surrounded by higher land features such as hills and mountains.* River valleys are changing environments because the amount of water that flows through them changes. The amount of water increases or decreases based on rain or snow melt.

V-shaped valleys Earlier in the chapter you learned that glaciers scrape *U*-shaped valleys through land areas. In contrast, rivers tend to cut *V*-shaped valleys (Figure 14.20). A strong *V*-shaped valley indicates that the river is fairly young or near its source (called the headwaters). Along the length of the river and toward the mouth, the river widens and forms a floodplain.

Floodplains A floodplain is flat land alongside a river that tends to flood. A floodplain also forms over time as the river erodes the land at each of its sides. A floodplain is very good land for growing plants because seasonal flooding of the river deposits nutrients in the soil. However, because flooding occurs regularly, these areas are not ideal for buildings or homes.

Rain or snow melt cause flooding Flooding commonly occurs when heavy rain or snow melt add more water to a river than it can carry. The extra water overwhelms normally dry land areas. Fortunately, this type of flooding is usually predictable several days in advance.

VOCABULARY

floodplain - flat land alongside a river that tends to flood. A floodplain is usually located at a distance from the headwaters of the river.

Figure 14.20: *A* V-*shaped valley cut by a river.*

Meanders

What are meanders? Some rivers form *S*-shaped curves called meanders (Figure 14.21). Water flows at different speeds in different parts of the meanders. The fastest flow is on the outside of each curve while the slowest flow is on the inside. Fast-moving water picks up particles. Slow-moving water drops particles so that they settle to the bottom of the river. The fast-moving water erodes the outside river bank and at the same time, slower water deposits sediment on the inside bank. The sediment that settles near the inside bank forms a *point bar*. The point bar adds to the inside of the meander curve and extends it. A *channel bar* is formed by sediment that is eroded from the river bank. The extra sediment is too much for the stream to transport, so it settles near the bank.

Moving meanders The combination of cutting on the outside bank and extending the inside bank causes the river to make side-to-side looping motions as it moves through a river valley. Sometimes this process causes a meander to become cut off from the river and form a curved lake called an *oxbow lake*.

VOCABULARY

meanders - *S*-shaped curves in a river.

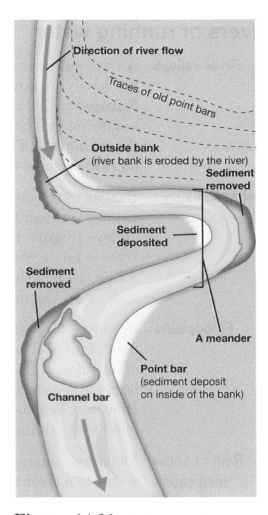

Figure 14.21: *A diagram of a meandering river.*

Tuolumne River, Yosemite National Park

Water flowing right to left

Point bar

Channel bar

Outside bank (bank being eroded by river)

Water is flowing toward you

Photo courtesy Jim Sammons, Sammons' INK.

Meandering scars

This is a picture of the Tuolumne River Valley. Tuolumne is pronounced "two-all-oh-me." The dark traces of old meanders in the field to the right of the river are called *meandering scars*. They indicate that the river has moved over time.

Tuolumne River Valley, Yosemite National Park

Meandering scars

Photo courtesy of Jim Sammons, Sammons' INK.

What is a braided stream?

The channel of a meandering stream moves downhill with time, but it remains a single channel. In contrast, a braided stream has many channels that crisscross each other. A braided stream gets its name from the braided appearance of its many channels. The channels of a braided stream are constantly changing. New channels are cut and old ones are abandoned in a matter of days or weeks.

Sediment that is being moved by the braided stream

Photo courtesy U.S. Geological Survey

 VOCABULARY

braided stream - a stream that has many channels that crisscross each other.

SOLVE IT!

Here is a map of the Tuolumne River. Use the scale at the bottom of the map to answer the following questions. First measure the scale bar using a ruler and then use your ruler to carefully measure the distances on the map.

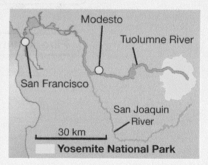

Modesto

Tuolumne River

San Francisco

San Joaquin River

30 km

Yosemite National Park

1. How many kilometers of the river are located in Yosemite National Park?

2. How far would sediment have to travel to go from Modesto to San Francisco?

A river valley

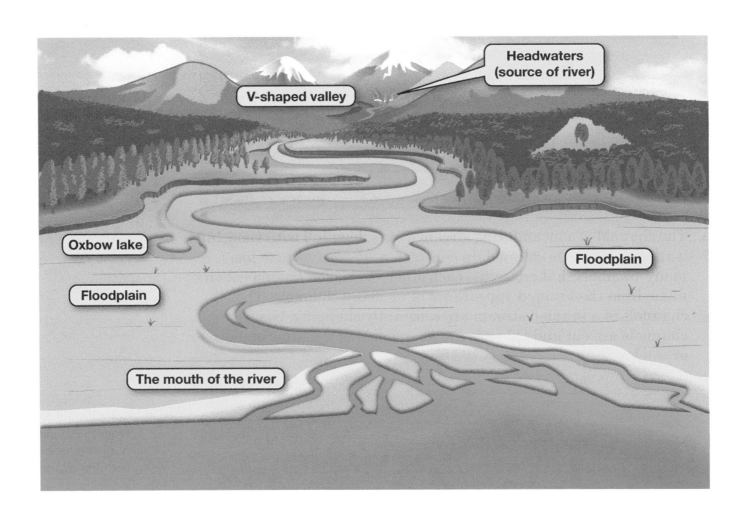

14.3 **Section Review**

1. What is the difference between a river valley and a valley shaped by a moving glacier?

2. What two events might cause a river to flood?

3. List two ways that a floodplain forms.

4. What is the soil like near a floodplain?

5. What causes a river to begin to meander?

   a. The amount of sediment in the river.

   b. The water in the river flows at different speeds in different places in the river.

   c. The age of the river.

   d. How long the river is.

Photo courtesy of NASA

Figure 14.22: *Question 9.*

6. In a meandering river, where does the water flow fastest? What happens at this location?

7. In a meandering river, where does the water flow slowest? What happens at this location?

8. What features indicate that a river has moved over time?

9. Look at Figure 14.22. Name the feature that the arrow is pointing to in this photograph.

10. Scientists can use a wading rod, a spinning propeller device, and a velocity sensor to measure the speed of flowing water at any point in the river. Refer to Figure 14.23 and answer the questions below.

    a. Where is the river flowing the fastest?

    b. Where is the river flowing the slowest?

    c. Come up with a hypothesis for why the river is flowing the slowest at this location.

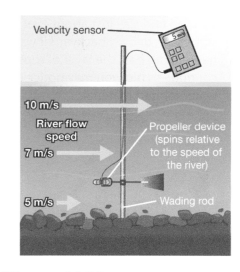

Figure 14.23: *Question 10.*

Creative Expression with Clay

Did you ever play with play-dough or cookie dough? You probably enjoyed how the dough felt in your hands while you molded it. Potters have been molding clay into pots and other items since the Stone Age. Some of the earliest archaeological digs have uncovered clay pottery from thousands of years ago. Clay has been used to create some of the most ancient things on Earth. Today, it is used to produce ceramic tiles, porcelain, cement, and more.

Molding and sculpting clay is an art form. Turning clay into pottery or a sculpture is a creative activity that people of any age can do.

Where can you find clay?

You can find clay just about everywhere. In fact, you might find some in your own backyard if you dig deep enough. First you'll need to dig past the layer of topsoil and other sediment. If you continue to dig, you may notice a very shiny, wet, and often water-logged material.

Photos courtesy Catherine Reed

If you gather a clump of the material in your hands, it will feel wet, cold, and sticky. If the material can be molded into a ball and stays together, then most likely you've reached clay.

Wet clay has the properties of a plastic and can be easily shaped. When it is dry, it becomes very hard and sometimes brittle. It has the unique characteristic of being able to withstand high temperatures. This is why it is used to create ceramic items such as bowls, pots, dishes, and cups.

Photos courtesy Catherine Reed

Wet clay can be shaped   **Dry clay is hard and breaks easily**

What is clay made of?

Clay is made up of weathered rocks and minerals. When rock is exposed to the action of wind and water, it begins to break down. Eventually the rock breaks down into smaller and smaller pieces of sediment that gets mixed into soil. The soil will contain the original minerals from the weathered rock in that area. The most common rock-forming mineral is feldspar. Feldspar is found in many different rock types and makes up about 60 percent of Earth's crust. As a result of weathering, feldspar breaks down to form clay. Clay is an aluminum-bearing silicate mineral. One type of clay is kaolin, and another is illite.

Chapter 14 Connection

It's all about senses

Today, many students have the opportunity to experience clay in pottery classes at their schools. Teaching students to express themselves creatively is a passion for Ms. Laurie Clugh, a middle school art teacher. Ms. Clugh has been teaching art for over 20 years. She enjoys witnessing students' creative expression in her classroom art studio.

Photo courtesy Catherine Reed
Ms. Clugh, middle school art teacher

Ms. Clugh's middle school students really enjoy working with the clay medium. A medium is the material an artist uses to express their creativity. Clay is considered a tactile medium. Tactile comes from the Latin word *tactilis* and means "to touch." Touch is only one of the senses used by students when working with clay. Basically, one or more senses can be used when working with clay.

Here are a few examples of senses at work in Ms. Clugh's art studio.

- Tactile experiences of molding and shaping the clay
- Sound of students slapping, pounding, kneading, and cutting clay
- The earthy smell of the wet clay
- Visualization of the clay taking shape

Working with clay

Clay must be kept moist or you will not be able to change its shape. As clay dries, it becomes brittle and shrinks slightly in size. Students keep their hands and clay wet with a spray bottle to prevent drying. When the clay is not being worked it is kept in a moist plastic bag or air tight container. After students complete molding and shaping their project, the clay is allowed to air dry. This process is called *leather-hard*. At this point, the clay is somewhat damp and can still be carved in detail, but the shape can not be changed. It can be painted and glazed to add color. Finally, the clay projects must be fired in an open fire or in a clay oven known as a kiln. When the clay is exposed to high temperatures, it becomes very hard and strong and is considered to be a ceramic object. It is also a "one of a kind" expression of creativity by the artist.

Photo courtesy Catherine Reed

QUESTIONS

1. Where can you find clay?
2. Describe the characteristics of clay.
3. Explain the role of weathering in the formation of clay.
4. List the steps of making a clay project from start to finish.

Wearing Away

In this activity, you will examine your school and the surrounding property to find evidence of mechanical and chemical weathering. Recall that mechanical weathering breaks down material into smaller pieces but does not change the composition of the material. Mechanical weathering can be caused by a variety of forces such as temperature changes, release of pressure, growth of plants, actions of animals, and so on. Chemical weathering breaks material down by changing the composition of material through a chemical reaction. Chemical weathering can be caused by water, oxygen, carbon dioxide, acid rain, living organisms, and so on. Chemical and mechanical weathering often work together to slowly break down materials.

Materials

Pencil, notebook or sketch book, digital camera (optional)

What you will do

1. With your whole class, a small group, or a partner, examine your school and the surrounding grounds for evidence of mechanical and chemical weathering.

2. In your notebook or sketch book, create a table similar to the one below. Record your observations.

3. Make sketches and/or take digital photographs of what you find.

Applying your knowledge

a. Write a description of your school. What types of building materials were used to build the school and to develop the school grounds, such as paved paths, driveways, and signs? *Note:* You may need to interview the school building manager to find out the answer to this question.

b. List the examples of mechanical weathering that you observed.

c. List the examples of chemical weathering that you observed.

d. Which type of material eroded the most? Explain how you know.

e. Which type of material eroded the least? Explain how you know.

f. Which type of weathering was more destructive in your opinion, mechanical or chemical? Explain your viewpoint.

g. Could any of the weathering you found have been prevented? Explain why or why not.

h. If repairs to your school building stopped being done, predict how your school would look in 100 years.

Type of material	Location	Approximate age	Describe the evidence of weathering	Type of weathering: mechanical, chemical, or both	How do you think the weathering occurred?
Ex. asphalt	driveway	15 years (found out by asking the school building manager)	cracks	mechanical	frost wedging: water seeped in, froze, expanded, and caused cracks

Chapter 14 Assessment

Vocabulary

Select the correct term to complete the sentences.

river	weathering	floodplain
stream	mechanical weathering	meanders
channel	chemical weathering	braided stream
deposition	frost wedging	rockfall
graded bedding	direction of younging	mudflow
cross bedding	mass wasting	slumping
landslide	erosion	

Section 14.1

1. The breaking down of rock into sediment is the result of _____.

2. Breaking a rock into two pieces is an example of _____.

3. _____ is a type of mechanical weathering where the agent is ice.

4. The way a limestone statue wears down over time is an example of _____.

Section 14.2

5. A(n) _____ is a small river.

6. A(n) _____ is a large body of water that flows into an ocean or lake.

7. Sediment particles, when deposited in an aquatic environment, settle in order from largest to smallest. This is _____.

8. When a large amount of rock splits off of a landform, the event is called a(n) _____.

9. Agents of erosion drop sediment after moving it a distance in a process called _____.

10. The path that a river or stream follows is called a(n) _____.

11. The _____ is the order in which sedimentary rock layers are formed—from larger to finer particles.

12. A(n) _____ is a form of mass wasting that can be caused by earthquakes, volcanic events, or other factors.

13. The two types of mass wasting described in the text that involve water are _____ and _____.

14. _____ is a pattern of tilted beds that often form as wind or water deposit sediments.

15. The downhill movement of large amounts of rock and sediment due to the force of gravity is _____.

16. Moving water is one of the most important agents of _____.

Section 14.3

17. Flat land alongside a river is called a(n) _____.

18. Channels of the same river that crisscross each other form a(n) _____.

19. The outside edges of _____ in a river are points of erosion.

Concepts

Section 14.1

1. What happens as mountains age?

2. Can both mechanical and chemical weathering affect a rock at the same time? Why or why not?

3. What role does gravity play in weathering?

4. What type of weathering causes a bicycle to rust?

5. Would you see evidence of frost wedging in locations near Earth's equator? Why or why not?

6. Is there any similarity to the way hoodoos are created and the use of sandblasters by humans?

7.   Why are rocks at the base of a waterfall smooth?

8.   Tree roots, burrowing organisms, mosses, and lichens all can cause rocks to weather. What is the name for this kind of weathering?

9.   Exfoliation is associated with the formation of mountains. Why might this type of weathering be associated with mountain-building?

10. Describe how a tree can cause chemical weathering and mechanical weathering.

11. In what type of climate is weathering the slowest?

Section 14.2

12. Over time, a sand castle you build on a beach completely disappears! What happened? Is this an example of weathering or erosion?

13. Name one channel characteristic that affects how sediment is carried in a river?

14. The size of a rock that can be moved by running water is determined by what two main factors?

15. You find a sedimentary rock that has one graded bed. Describe how you know the which layer of the graded bed was formed last?

16. Is rock flour evidence of weathering or erosion?

17. In a hilly area after heavy rains, what kinds of erosion events might occur? Explain why they might occur.

18. Why is topsoil an important resource on farmlands and on other lands?

Section 14.3

19. Give one pro and one con about life in a floodplain.

20. Describe the difference between a valley shaped by a river and a valley shaped by a glacier. Draw a side-view of each type of valley.

21. List features of river valley to indicate that a meandering river has moved over time?

Math and Writing Skills

Section 14.1

1.   Stonehenge in England is about 5,000 years old and attracts many visitors each year. People are only allowed to look at this landmark from a distance. They cannot touch the stones. Why do you think this is so?

Stonehenge

Section 14.2

2.   Can it be assumed that sediment in the soil found in a location was weathered from the rock in that same location? Write a paragraph to explain your answer.

3.   A type of mass wasting called *creep* occurs very slowly over time so it is not always easily seen as it is happening. Soil on a mountainside moves downhill so slowly it is hard to see. What might be a way to measure that it is happening?

4. Find another peninsula, besides Long Island, New York, that was deposited at its location after the retreat of glaciers. Is the rock deposited there considered consolidated (tightly compacted, not easily separated) or unconsolidated (loose sediment of different sizes)?

5. What might you do in your own yard or in a park nearby to decrease the amount of soil erosion?

Section 14.3

6. How do you tell if a river is young? What happens as it gets older?

7. Find out how an oxbow lake is formed. Describe the process.

Chapter Project—Modelling Weathering

Materials: 2 medium-sized plastic containers with lids, pre-moistened limestone chips, a filter, a balance, water, household vinegar, permanent marker, stopwatch, a notebook to record your data, and graph paper

1. Copy the data table into your notebook. Using the permanent marker, label one container "water" and the other container "vinegar."

2. Measure the mass of each container plus its lid. Record these measurements.

3. Put some limestone chips in each container. Find the mass of each container with the chips. Record these measurements.

4. Fill the container marked "water" half-full with water. For no less than about 4 or 5 minutes, vigorously shake the container.

5. Drain all the water using the filter (having placed it over the mouth of the container). Do not let any limestone pieces escape!

6. Now, find the mass of the container, chips, and lid. Record this value.

7. Repeat the procedure (steps 1 to 5) three more times with water.

8. Then, repeat the whole procedure (steps 1 to 6) using vinegar in place of water. Use the container marked "vinegar."

9. Graph your results of the experiment.

10. Questions: (a) What type of weathering does each container represent? (b) What does the graph tell you about the weathering over time?

	Water				Vinegar			
Trial number	1	2	3	Ave	1	2	3	Ave
Mass of container plus lid before experiment (grams)								
Mass of container plus limestone and water during experiment (grams)								
Mass of container plus limestone after experiment, no water (grams)								

EARTH'S RESOURCES

CHAPTER 15
Soil and Freshwater Resources

CHAPTER 16
Natural Resources and Conservation

RENEWABLE

NON RENEWABLE

SOLAR

GEOTHERMAL

Wind

HYDRO

Recycle

Exploring on Your Own

Have you ever thought about the resources that were used to make a car, a whole pizza, or your favorite shirt? Select any object and make a list of all the materials it contains. Then, make a list of the energy sources that were used to make the item and transport it to a place where you could buy it. Finally, come up with ways in which this object could be made or transported so that fewer resources are used. Present your work as a colorful poster. Research the strategy and make a poster that lists the pros and cons of using it.

Soil and Freshwater Resources

Weathering breaks down rock into small pieces called sediment. When sediment is mixed with organic matter (living and decaying parts of plants and animals), minerals, and nutrients, soil is formed. Soil is an important natural resource. Most of our food is grown in soil. Grains, fruits, and vegetables require sunlight, good soil, and water to grow. Soil and water, both important natural resources, are the subjects of this chapter. You will learn about soil and fresh water, and how we can best conserve these natural resources.

Key Questions:

1. What is soil?

2. Why is it important to conserve soil?

3. How do we measure water quality?

15.1 **Soil**

Angela had been helping her grandfather in the garden. Now it was time to eat lunch. "Wash your hands!" said Angela's mother. "But if I do that, I'll waste soil and water—two important natural resources!" You probably know that water is an important resource, but what does Angela mean by saying that soil is important? Read on to find out!

What is soil?

A garden of resources Look at the garden in Figure 15.1. Note that near the garden there is a compost bin. Compost is plant material that is decaying. When it is all decayed, it will become a dark, organic material called humus. In nature, humus refers to the material that is produced by the bacterial decay of plant and animal matter, also known as organic matter.

Soil What is soil? Chances are, you ate something today that was grown in soil. Soil is the portion of Earth's surface that consists of organic matter mixed with sediment (weathered pieces of rock and minerals), air, and water. Most of the fruits, vegetables, and grains that you eat are grown in soil.

An end and a beginning As a result of weathering, rocks and minerals are broken down into sediment that becomes incorporated into soil. Soil may be seen as the last step of the weathering process. But, rather than an "end" of a story, soil is a beginning! Go into any garden and you will find new growth of plants. Soil is full of nutrients and is a suitable medium in which plants can anchor their roots and grow. Important compounds and elements would remain trapped in rocks and unavailable to plants if it was not for weathering. And these nutrients are passed on to people and animals when the fruits and vegetables are eaten.

humus - the dark, organic material in soil produced by the decay of plant and animal matter.

soil - the portion of Earth's surface that consists of organic matter, sediment, air, and water.

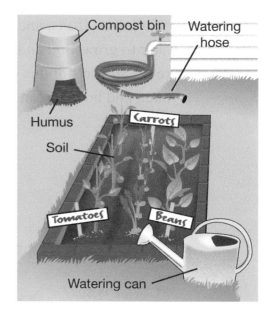

Figure 15.1: *Angela's garden.*

Components of soil

Soil is not dirt Angela knew that it was important to wash her hands after working in the garden (Figure 15.2). However, Angela protested washing her hands to make a point—that there is a big difference between "dirt" and "soil." We use the word "dirt" to mean particles and dust that we don't want around. Soil, however, is a natural resource that is needed to support life on Earth. You know that soil contains humus. What else is in there?

The main components Soil also contains particles of weathered rock including sand, silt, and clay (Figure 15.3). Sand grains are weathered particles of quartz and some feldspar. Sand particles measure from 0.05 to 2 mm in diameter. Silt particles measure from 0.002 to 0.05 mm in diameter, and clay particles are less than 0.002 mm in diameter. Clay is formed when water is involved in the weathering of minerals such a feldspar. The best soil for plants is a mixture of sand, silt, and a small amount of clay. This type of soil is called *loam*. Loam is rich in nutrients and retains water.

Additional components Water, air, and living organisms are important components of soil. Plants obtain water through their roots, which are anchored in soil. Soil that is *aerated* (has air) provides plants with carbon dioxide and oxygen, which are used for photosynthesis and respiration (the process of breaking down sugars for energy). Plants also get these gases from the atmosphere through their leaves. Organisms like earthworms are important to soil because they help loosen particles so that more air and water gets into the soil. These organisms also enrich the soil with their waste products. Organisms in the soil benefit plants in other ways too. Certain bacteria help plants obtain nitrogen from the atmosphere. Nitrogen helps plants make proteins. The nitrogen then becomes available to animals that eat the plants. In this way, soil plays a crucial role in sustaining life.

Soil safety note

Working in a garden is a fun and healthy activity. However, it is always important to wash your hands to prevent any exposure to harmful bacteria that sometimes live in soil.

Figure 15.2: *Soil safety note.*

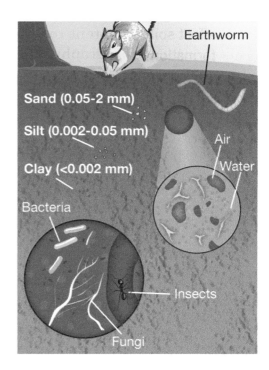

Figure 15.3: *Components of soil.*

How soil forms

Soil is part of the rock cycle
Weathering and soil formation play different parts in the rock cycle (Figure 15.4). For example, over time, sediment and soil may become sedimentary rocks. Also, when water weathers rocks, dissolved minerals enter rivers, lakes, or seas. These dissolved minerals can eventually crystallize and become rocks (like gypsum rock) when the water evaporates (Figure 15.5).

Factors that affect soil formation
The factors that affect soil formation include the climate, the type of parent rock or mineral, the presence of living organisms, topography, and time.

Climate: Climate is one of the most important factors that affects soil formation. Soil forms more quickly in wet, warm environments than in cold, dry ones.

Parent rocks and minerals: Some types of rocks weather and become soil faster than others. Parent rocks or minerals influence the color, texture, and chemistry of soil.

Organisms: Soil formation happens more quickly when plants, animals, fungi, and bacteria are present. They loosen and aerate the soil and add nutrients. Also, decaying plants and animals increase the amount of humus in the soil.

Topography: The steeper the slope of an area, the more rocks are exposed to weathering and the faster rocks and minerals break down. Soil also forms more quickly on top of other soil than on top of solid rock. Finally, the more surface area that is exposed, the faster a rock weathers.

Time: Soil formation can take thousands or even millions of years. The speed of the process depends on the factors listed above.

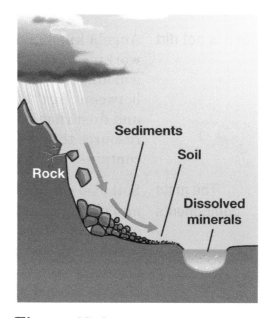

Figure 15.4: *Rocks weathering to soil.*

Photo courtesy Pamela J.W. Gore

Figure 15.5: *These gypsum crystals (called selenite) formed when water evaporated from a lake.*

Layers of soil

A soil profile A **soil profile** is a cross-section that shows the different layers (or horizons) of soil in the ground. It takes a long time and a lot of weathering for soil to have all the layers you see in Figure 15.6. Mature soil has all these layers. Young (or immature) soil does not have as many layers (see diagram below).

Horizon O: A dark layer composed of decaying plant matter (like leaves) and humus that is only a few centimeters thick.

Horizon A: A dark layer called *topsoil* that is composed of more humus and small pieces of rock. It is home to many animals. For example, around 1 billion small and microscopic animals live in one cubic meter of topsoil. Minerals dissolve from this layer in a process called **leaching**.

Horizon B: A layer of clay and small rocks called *subsoil* where dissolved minerals from Horizon A collect. The color of this layer depends on the rock and mineral types in the soil.

Horizon C: A layer of weathered rock pieces and minerals.

Horizon D: Solid rock, called *bedrock,* which formed over time. This layer cannot support plant life.

VOCABULARY

soil profile - cross-section that shows the different layers (or horizons) of soil in the ground.

leaching - a process by which water dissolves substances and causes them to be removed from one location to another.

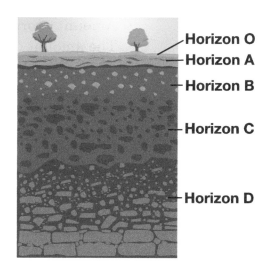

Figure 15.6: *Layers of soil.*

General timeline for soil formation

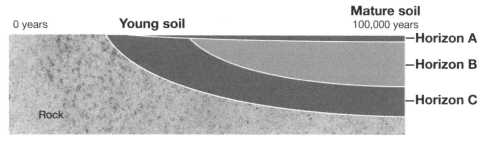

Types of soil

Soil texture　Since soil is a product of weathering, it can contain bits and pieces of rock and humus of different sizes. The amount of water or air in soil is related to its texture—how smooth, gritty, or rocky it feels in your hands. Usually there are more rock and mineral particles than organic material (humus) in soil. Soil that contains humus has a greater tendency to retain water. This means it is better suited for growing plants.

Classifying soil　There are 12 soil types, or *orders* (Figure 15.7). Soil classification is based on the following properties:

- How much the soil horizons are developed
- Amount of organic material versus rock and mineral sediments
- The amount of weathering and leaching of minerals that has occurred
- Presence of a subsurface horizon of calcium carbonate
- Location below grasslands or forests
- Presence of a particular kind of clay that shrinks and swells when mixed with water
- The composition of the different soil horizons
- Presence of permafrost within 2 meters of the surface of the ground. **Permafrost** is permanently frozen soil found about 25 to 100 centimeters below the surface.
- Presence of volcanic ash from erupting volcanoes

VOCABULARY

permafrost - permanently frozen soil located from 25 to about 100 centimeters below Earth's surface.

Type	Uses
entisol	young soil
ultisol	**pedalfer, laterite**
inceptisol	young soil
oxisol	**laterite**, only in tropics
mollisol	grasslands
aridosol	**pedocal**, arid climates
alfisol	forested areas
histosol	peat
spodosol	forested areas
vertisol	clays
gelisol	permafrost
andisol	volcanic soil

Figure 15.7: *Twelve types of soil.* Note: *The soil names in the right-hand column that are in bold will be discussed on the next page.*

Permafrost

This individual is standing in a deep hole cut into permafrost

Photo by H.C. Stone, NOAA

General terms for soil types

Simplifying soils On the previous page, you read about a number of soil types. Let's focus on three of these: pedocal, pedalfer, and laterite. These soil types are illustrated in the sidebar.

Pedocal Pedocal forms in dry or semi-dry climates like those found in the southwestern United States. This type of soil is rich in calcium. As a result, the soil commonly has a calcium carbonate deposit called *caliche* or *hardpan*.

Pedalfer Pedalfer forms in humid climates like those found in the southeastern United States. This type of soil is high in aluminum and iron, but also contains other elements and nutrients.

Laterite Laterite forms in tropical climates that have a lot of rain. Due to the heavy rain, this type of soil is leached of most of its elements except aluminum and iron. Although some agriculture can be done on this type of soil, it is quickly depleted of its nutrients. Then, the soil becomes so hard that it cannot be used for farming. The parent material for this soil is weathered basalt.

Soil Types				
	Pedocal	**Pedalfer**	**Laterite**	**No soil**
Climate	Temperate dry and semi dry (<76 cm rainfall)	Temperate humid (>76 cm rainfall)	Tropical (heavy rainfall)	Extreme arctic or desert
Vegetation	Grass and brush	Forest	Grass and trees	Almost none, so no humus develops
Typical Area	Southwestern U.S.	Southeastern U.S.		
Topsoil (Horizon A)	Thin	Thick	Little or no	No real soil forms because there is no organic material. Chemical weathering is slow.
Subsoil (Horizon B)	Calcium carbonate particles	Clays, rock fragments, iron and aluminum	Elements removed by leaching	

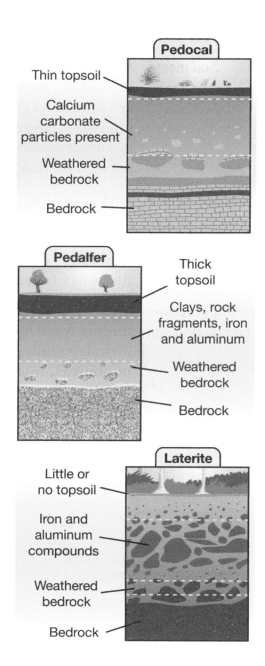

Pedocal
- Thin topsoil
- Calcium carbonate particles present
- Weathered bedrock
- Bedrock

Pedalfer
- Thick topsoil
- Clays, rock fragments, iron and aluminum
- Weathered bedrock
- Bedrock

Laterite
- Little or no topsoil
- Iron and aluminum compounds
- Weathered bedrock
- Bedrock

Erosion and agriculture

Soil meets our needs Soil that contains a mixture of sediments, humus, air, and water is ideal for growing crops (Figure 15.8). Unfortunately, more soil is lost each year through erosion than is formed by natural processes. And once some soil is lost, even more soil is exposed to loss from erosion. On the other hand, the presence of soil helps prevent further erosion.

Causes of loss of soil Just about any human activity can potentially cause a loss of soil. Some major causes are construction, deforestation, grazing by livestock (like cows), and farming (Figure 15.9). Since these activities—especially farming—are necessary, it is important to find ways to reduce their effects on soil erosion.

Gaining ground— conserving soil The Natural Resources Conservation Service is in charge of finding ways to reduce soil erosion. Their recommendations include managing construction projects so that erosion is minimized, intercepting surface runoff so that less soil is lost, planting ground cover, and improving farming techniques.

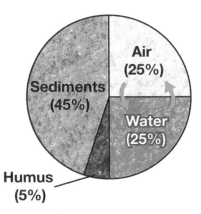

Figure 15.8: *A pie chart that shows the percentages of sediments, humus, air, and water in soil that is suitable for growing plants. Percentages of air and water may change more frequently due to the season and other conditions.*

These farming practices conserve soil by reducing use of water and preventing erosion by water.

Drip irrigation

Terraces

Photos courtesy of USDA NRCS

Corn plant

Horizon A
Topsoil

Photo courtesy of USDA NRCS

Figure 15.9: *This soil profile shows the layer of topsoil on a farm in Iowa. Due to farming, Iowa's average topsoil depth has decreased from 14 to 18 inches to only 6 to 8 inches.*

15.1 Section Review

1. How is soil part of the rock cycle?

2. Compare and contrast humus and loam. How are these soil components different? How does each improve the quality of the soil?

3. True or False: True soil is only found on Earth. Explain your answer.

4. List at least two factors that would improve conditions for soil to form.

5. Describe each of the soil layers—O, A, B, C, and D—in your own words.

6. What does *leaching* mean?

7. Name one way to tell the difference between young soil and mature soil.

8. Why do you think there are many different types of soil on Earth's surface? List two reasons and justify your answer.

9. You have learned where you can find pedalfer and pedocal on Earth's surface. Where might you find laterite soil?

10. Resources can be classified as "renewable" and "nonrenewable." A renewable resource can be replaced, like wind or Sun energy. A nonrenewable resource is like gasoline—once we use it, it is gone. How would you describe soil? Is it a renewable or a non-renewable resource?

11. Could human life exist on Earth if soil didn't exist? Why or why not?

CHALLENGE

Testing soil

Collect a sample of soil from your yard. Record observations of your sample. What color is it? What is the texture? Does it have a lot of humus or just a small amount?

After you have handled the soil and recorded your observations, remember to wash your hands!

Send the sample to your local cooperative extension office so that it can be tested. This office will test your soil for pH (whether it is acidic or basic), nutrient composition, organic matter, the types of salts present, and texture.

Evaluating soil color

Testing soil pH

Photos courtesy of USDA NRCS

15.2 **Water Resources**

Water is one substance that makes our planet unique. All life on Earth depends on water. In our solar system, only Earth has water in such great abundance. Because we seem to have so much water it is easy to take it for granted. Think about what you did yesterday. How often did you use water? Now think about how yesterday would have been different if you had no access to water!

From rocks to water

The water and rock cycles   As water erodes rock, some minerals are dissolved from the rock. This means that our water resources and the water cycle are connected with the rock cycle.

Water in nature   Pure water is water that does not contain any dissolved minerals. A dissolved mineral exists as a charged element or molecule called an **ion**. To get pure water that lacks ions, you would need to buy "deionized" water from a grocery store. Pure water is rare in nature because water is very good at dissolving substances. Substances that dissolve easily are described as *soluble*, and those that do not dissolve easily are called *insoluble* (Figure 15.10).

What is in water?   Typically, water contains a range of dissolved substances. These substances include both minerals—which are useful to organisms that live in water—and pollutants. Pollutants are harmful substances or excess amounts of substances that enter our water supply from human activities.

The salty ocean   Most of the water on Earth is in the oceans. The oceans are salty because water has weathered salt from rocks on Earth's surface then transported the salt to the oceans as part of the rock cycle. Salt also gets into the oceans from underwater volcanoes and from the oceanic crust.

VOCABULARY

ion - a charged element or molecule; substances dissolved in water occur as ions.

Most of Earth's crust is made up of silicate minerals. These minerals are composed of eight elements.

Soluble minerals

Mineral compounds with sodium, calcium, potassium, iron, and magnesium are soluble and can be leached from soil.

Insoluble minerals

Clay minerals are insoluble. They contain the elements aluminum, silicon, and oxygen.

Figure 15.10: *Soluble and insoluble minerals. Water that has dissolved soluble minerals contains sodium, calcium, potassium, iron, and/or magnesium ions.*

Water quality at home

Standards for water quality
Because water is important to our health and way of living, the Environmental Protection Agency (EPA) and the Food and Drug Administration (FDA) regulate water quality (Figure 15.11). The EPA sets standards for tap water. The FDA regulates bottled water. Water that meets their standards is safe for drinking, cooking, and other household activities.

Natural components
Calcium, magnesium, and carbon dioxide occur naturally in the water that's available for human consumption. Water with a lot of dissolved calcium and magnesium is called *hard water*. Dissolved calcium and magnesium interfere with how soap works. *Soft water* has few dissolved elements. Soapsuds form well in soft water. Use the "soap test" in Figure 15.12 to see if your water is hard or soft.

What else is in tap water?
Tap water may also contain iron, zinc, and copper depending on where you live. Iron (rust), lead, and copper can dissolve into your water supply from plumbing pipes. Additionally, tap water may be treated with sodium fluoride (to prevent tooth decay) and with chlorine (to kill bacteria). The graphic below illustrates the source of ions that are in tap water. The variety and amount of ions in your tap water give it a certain taste.

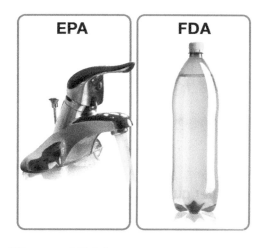

Figure 15.11: *The EPA and FDA set standards for water quality.*

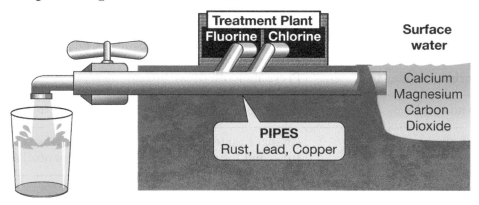

Figure 15.12: *Soap foams up in soft water but not as well in hard water.*

Analyzing water quality

Analyzing water quality is important The quality of your tap water is important. You rely on this water for drinking, cooking, and washing. Table 15.1 summarizes the components typically found in tap water. The quality of the water found in rivers, streams, lakes, and ponds is also important because all the water on Earth is connected via the water cycle. The water that we use at home was once in a river, lake, pond, or groundwater. Before that, the water was precipitation (such as rain or snow) that reached the ground from the atmosphere.

Water quality tests Water quality from a faucet in your house or from a location in nature is evaluated using a series of tests. Common tests and the procedures for testing water quality are explained in the next few pages of this section.

The Clean Water Act

In the past, our rivers, lakes, and oceans were used as dumping grounds for consumer and industry waste. Citizen interest in preventing further pollution of our water supply caused the United States government to pass the Federal Water Pollution Control Act Amendments of 1972.

The Clean Water Act of 1977 is the amended version of the 1972 laws. This act, which is still in use today, entitles the EPA to regulate what can be added to our water. Only within certain guidelines and with a permit can pollutants be discharged into waterways.

Table 15.1: What is in your tap water?

Possible component	Source	Description
acid	Dissolved carbon dioxide from soils	Corrodes pipes; leaches lead and copper into water supply; causes deposits in pipes
base	Calcium and magnesium salts dissolved from rocks occurring naturally in the water supply	Components of hard water; essential minerals for human health
chlorine	An additive in water treatment	Changes taste; smells; kills bacteria
fluorine	Added as sodium fluoride in water treatment	Prevents tooth decay by making teeth stronger
iron	Dissolved from pipes and rocks	Causes orange stains in sinks, tubs, and toilets.
copper	Dissolved from copper pipes	Changes taste in high concentrations; causes blue stains in sinks, tubs, and toilets; trace amounts are essential to human health
lead	Dissolved from pipes or the solder for pipes	Toxic even in very low concentrations

Water quality

Freshwater resources
Perhaps you live in a coastal region, where the ocean is part of your everyday life. But whether you are near an ocean or inland, you depend on freshwater resources. We depend on fresh water for drinking, for staying clean, and for farming and industries.

Water quality testing
Clean, high-quality water is important to our daily lives and to plants and wildlife. Therefore, we must protect the quality of our freshwater resources. Governments and civic groups test the quality of surface water regularly (Figure 15.13).

Observing a body of water
To learn about the water quality of a pond, river, or lake, you would first make careful observations. What does the pond water look like or smell like? What animals and plants are living in the pond? Where is the pond located? Are there houses or farms nearby? Is the pond near a factory?

Temperature
The water temperature is an indicator of the quality of the water. The higher the water temperature, the less dissolved oxygen there may be in the water. Dissolved oxygen is needed by most organisms living in ponds, rivers, and lakes.

Turbidity test
A *turbidity test* measures the cloudiness of water. If the water is cloudy due to suspended sediment, sunlight will be blocked and pond plants will not grow well. This can be harmful because pond plants are needed as food for other living things in the pond. A *secchi disk* provides an easy way to measure turbidity (Figure 15.14). The disk is lowered into the water until the black and white panels are no longer visible to a person looking into the water from above. The rope holding the disk is marked at half-meter intervals to measure the depth of the disk when it disappears from view underwater.

Photo courtesy of U.S. Department of Agriculture - NRCS

Figure 15.13: *Testing water quality in a pond ecosystem.*

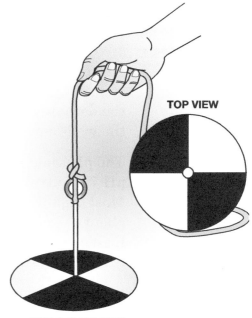
TOP VIEW

THE SECCHI DISK

Figure 15.14: *A Secchi disk.*

More water quality tests

Dissolved oxygen test   Oxygen enters fresh water from the air and by the photosynthesis of aquatic plants and microscopic organisms called phytoplankton. Water quality is higher when dissolved oxygen levels are high. Water samples for a dissolved oxygen test should be taken away from the water's edge and below the water's surface.

Biological oxygen demand test   The biological oxygen demand test is a two-part test. Two water samples are taken at the same time. Dissolved oxygen is measured in the first sample right away. The second sample is shielded from light and measured at a later time. The amount of oxygen in the first and second samples is compared to find out how much oxygen was used by bacteria as they decompose organic material.

Nitrate and phosphate tests   Nitrates and phosphates are chemicals that can enter ponds that are near farms, fertilized lawns, or septic tanks. Excess nitrates or phosphates can cause large growths of algae, a type of rootless, stemless plant (Figure 15.16). Decomposers (like bacteria) feed on the decaying algae and use up valuable oxygen. This endangers the well-being and interactions of other organisms in the pond.

pH test   The pH scale ranges from 0 to 14 (Figure 15.15). Pure water is pH 7 (neutral). Most surface water ranges from about 6.5 to 8.5. Most organisms that live in water function best when the pH is about 7. Many life processes do not function well when pH is too high or low. For example, fish have trouble reproducing when the pH of their water environment is too low (acidic).

Working together for fresh water   Water quality tests help scientists and concerned citizens monitor the water quality of our freshwater resources. Government, agricultural, industry, and civic groups use the test results to collaborate on protecting, preserving, and conserving freshwater resources.

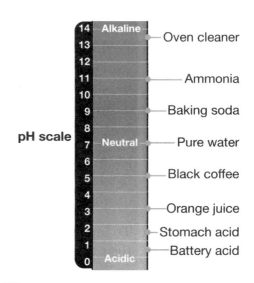

Figure 15.15: *The pH values of some common solutions.*

Photos courtesy of USDA NRCS

Figure 15.16: *A healthy pond and one with too much algae.*

15.2 **Section Review**

1. Is the water in a pond "pure water"? Why or why not?
2. The element calcium (Ca) dissolves in water and becomes a positively charged particle called a(n) _____.
3. Most of Earth's crust is made of what kind of minerals?
4. List four elements that are soluble and four that are insoluble.
5. Is water that is safe to drink "pure water"? Why or why not?
6. What is the difference between hard and soft water?
7. Why do water treatment plants add fluorine and chlorine to water supplies?
8. Water quality is very important to the health of a pond. Copy and complete the water quality test chart on your own paper. It has been started for you.

Water Quality Test	What it tests for	Results for a healthy pond
Temperature	How warm or cold the water is	Cold water has more oxygen available for living things than warm water.
Turbidity		
Dissolved oxygen		
Nitrates and phosphates		
pH		

9. An ecosystem is a group of living things and their physical surroundings. In this chapter, you have learned how soil and freshwater resources support living things including people, animals, and plants. Look at Figure 15.17. List the living things that are part of this ecosystem (including ones that you might not see in this picture). Then list the parts of the physical surroundings that are part of this ecosystem.

CHALLENGE

The ocean is salty, in part, from weathering and erosion of land. Although weathering and erosion are continuous processes, the saltiness of the oceans is stable at about 3.5 percent. Why doesn't the ocean get saltier and saltier over time? Research the answer to this question and record your findings in a short essay.

A pond ecosystem

Photo courtesy of USDA NRCS

Figure 15.17: *Question 9.*

Bogged Down in Resources

What exactly is a bog? In the simplest of words, a bog is a type of wetland. Even more simply put, a wetland is an area of land that is wet. Bogs will often look like a field or meadow with what appears to be solid ground. However, if you take a closer step, you'll find that it feels wet and soggy, kind of like a sponge. Wetlands are important wildlife habitats and help maintain the quality of our water resources.

The presence of sphagnum moss is responsible for the soggy spongy bogs in North America. The word sphagnum is from the Greek word *sphagnos* meaning "a kind of moss."

Photos courtesy P. F. Stetkiewicz, Jr.

Close-up of sphagnum moss.   Sphagnum moss grows in bogs.

Sphagnum moss is also known as peat moss, and has hundreds of species. You may know that peat moss can be purchased and used in gardens! Peat moss grows naturally in areas that are wet and acidic like bogs. Sphagnum has the unique ability to hold large quantities of water. In fact, some varieties can absorb almost 20 times their dry weight in water. This is just like a dry sponge growing larger as it soaks up water.

Characteristics of a common bog

It can be mind-boggling to try to keep up with the different types of bogs from one area to another. For example, in Canada and Alaska, bogs are called *muskeg*.

Along the Atlantic coast in Virginia and the Carolinas they are known as *pocosins*. Additional names include *peatlands*, *fens*, *moors*, *mires*, and *heaths*. Regardless of their name bogs share some similar characteristics.

A peatland

Photo courtesy P. F. Stetkiewicz, Jr.

Characteristics of bogs

- It contains acidic water that only allows acid-loving vegetation to grow.
- Over time sphagnum moss and other plant matter will decay forming "peat" deposits. Under certain conditions, peat is the earliest stage of the formation of coal.
- The water is nutrient poor due to the decay and rot of plant matter.
- Decayed plant matter, known as peat, is deposited in layers and forms the spongy, soggy bottom of the bog.
- The water is still or slow moving with little oxygen.
- Most bog water comes from precipitation such as rain and snow.

Life in a bog

Bog water is unique because of the lack of oxygen, and because it has a low pH and lacks nutrients. Oxygen levels are low because of a lack of water movement. The lack of oxygen slows down the process of decay. But what causes the lack of nutrients and acidic water? Sphagnum moss grows on the surface of the water in a typical bog. The moss soaks up and absorbs available nutrients found in the water. As the moss begins to die and decay, the water becomes more acidic.

A cranberry plant

Photo courtesy P. F. Stetkiewicz, Jr.

Few plants are able to thrive in the harsh bog environment. However, you maybe very familiar with one that grows wild in bogs. Chances are you may have eaten the berries of this popular plant on Thanksgiving—cranberries. These colorful red berries were first harvested by Native Americans and used as a source of food.

Photo courtesy Catherine Reed

Cranberries are a cold-weather crop that thrives in the acidic peat environment of the bog. In the fall, the cranberry bogs are flooded with water. The ripe cranberries float to the top and are harvested. Cranberries are sold fresh, dried, canned, or used for juice. In the United States, farmers harvest more than 100,000 tons of cranberries a year!

An unsettling place

You should never try walking in a bog because the spongy area may not be able to support the weight of your body. Bogs are really fragile ecosystems and are sensitive to human intrusion. In fact, it can take several years for your footprint impression to fill and not be noticeable. And, you never know what you might step on or find buried in a bog.

Sketch of the Tollund Man, a bog body found in 1950 in a bog in Denmark.

This sketch is of a famous "bog body"—the Tollund Man found in 1950 in a bog in Denmark. The Tollund Man was a young man who lived 2,400 years ago and died from hanging (apparent from the rope around his neck).

In 1982, a machine operator was digging at a construction site at Windover Pond in Florida when he noticed some skeletal parts. The skeletal parts turned out to be ancient human remains. This muck pond, which is considered a bog, became a well-known archaeological site. Archeologists unearthed more than 160 bog bodies at the site. Scientists have left more than half of the site unexplored so that future techniques can be discovered and used at a later time. Over the years, the Florida site, along with locations in northern Europe have yielded more than 1,000 bog bodies.

Bog bodies are similar to mummies in that entire bodies have been preserved over time. Scientists think that bogs lack the bacterial growth needed to decay flesh. They also think that the acidic water and peat act as a natural embalming fluid that preserves the bodies so that they eventually appear tan and leather-like. Bog bodies, also known as bog mummies, are so well preserved that many of the bodies still contained brain matter and the stomach's last meal. You might just consider bogs to be a place where the past rests in peat!

QUESTIONS

1. Describe the conditions of a typical bog.

2. Make a list of the ways in which bogs are a natural resource

3. What causes bodies in a bog to become mummified?

Mineral Extraction

Minerals are valuable to humans. For example, they are used in cosmetics, in health care products, as supplements in foods, for commercial and industrial uses, and for jewelry. Since minerals are formed in Earth, they need to be extracted in order to be used. The mineral ore is separated from its host rock in a variety of ways. In this activity, two methods of extraction (magnetic separation and flotation) will be examined to better understand the methods in use today to remove mineral resources from the ground.

Materials

Iron-fortified cereal (cold cereal), beaker, magnetic stir bar (preferably white) and a stir plate, hot tap water, a foam cup, quartz pebbles (larger than sand), popcorn kernels (unpopped), clear 2-liter plastic bottle with the top cut off, vinegar, baking soda, small sieve.

Part 1: Magnetic separation

1. Add the stir bar to the beaker. Place the beaker on the stir plate.

2. Use a foam cup to transfer about two cups of hot tap water to the beaker. Then, add about 1 cup of the cereal to the water.

3. Turn on the stir plate. The stir bar will mix the ingredients and create a slurry.

4. Mix for 20 minutes (or longer to improve results).

5. Remove the stir bar and observe it. Answer questions a and b.

1 cup of iron-fortified cereal

2 cups of hot water

White stir bar

Beaker

Stir plate

Part 2: Flotation

1. Have an adult help you cut the top off of the 2-liter plastic bottle.

2. Make up one cup of a mixture of quartz pebbles and raw popcorn kernels.

3. Put the mixture into the 2-liter bottle half filled with water. Pour off about one half cup of water.

4. Add one third cup of vinegar. Mix the solution well. Note if anything happens.

5. Now add one tablespoon of baking soda. Observe what happens. On a piece of paper, illustrate the process you observe taking place in the bottle.

6. Use the sieve to skim the kernels off the top before they drop back down again.

7. Now, answer questions c through g.

Add baking soda

Add vinegar

Water

Unpopped kernels and pebbles

Applying your knowledge

a. What do you notice about the stir bar after the slurry has been created? Describe and explain what you observe.

b. What other products (in addition to fortified cereal) could you use in this procedure to produce the same results?

c. If both the quartz pebbles and the popcorn kernels settled to the bottom of the 2-liter bottle, how do you think flotation works, given the name?

d. Did anything happen when the vinegar was added?

e. What happened when the baking soda was added?

f. You drew a sketch of what you observed. Now can you explain why what you observed happened?

g. What were you demonstrating by using the sieve to remove the kernels floating at the top before they sank back down again?

Chapter 15 Activity

Chapter 15 Assessment

Vocabulary

Select the correct term to complete the sentences.

humus	permafrost	soil profile
soil	ion	leaching

Section 15.1 and Section 15.2

1. Permanently frozen soil is called _____.

2. The three main components of _____ are sand, silt, and clay.

3. A(n) _____ is a cross-section that shows the different layers of soil in the ground.

4. Produced by the bacterial decay of plant and animal matter, _____ is found above and within the topsoil.

5. Minerals can be lost in the process of _____ from Horizon A.

6. A charged particle is called a(n) _____.

Concepts

Section 15.1

1. Why is soil beneficial to plants?

2. Is soil the same thing as dirt? Why or why not?

3. Which component of soil would you expect to more easily allow water to flow through—sand or clay? Why?

4. Describe two ways that earthworms benefit the soil.

5. A factor that affects soil formation is the parent rock.
   a. Define the term "parent rock" in your own words.
   b. Do you think the color of a soil would be different if the parent rock were granite versus basalt?

6. Describe the best condition for soil formation for each of the listed factors that affect soil formation.

7. How can a rock form from dissolved minerals in a lake?

8. In what climate is the O horizon of a soil profile very thick?

9. How does a high percentage of humus affect a soil?

10. In what kind of environment might there be no soil?

11. How does deforestation cause a loss of soil?

Section 15.2

12. When the element sodium dissolves in water, what is the particle of dissolved sodium called?

13. Why is water mostly found in an impure state?

14. How can you tell if your water is hard or soft?

15. What is used to kill bacteria in drinking water?

16. Why is it less likely today, compared to before 1986, to find lead water pipes used in residential settings?

17. What are two ways that oxygen enters freshwater?

Math and Writing Skills

Section 15.1

1. Below are the soil profiles for pedalfer. Sketch this profile and identify Horizons A, B, C, and D.

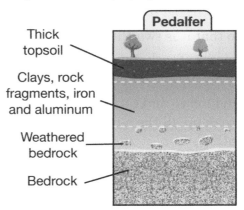

Pedalfer

Thick topsoil

Clays, rock fragments, iron and aluminum

Weathered bedrock

Bedrock

2. Write a short story that describes the formation of soil from a rock. Include the factors that affect soil formation

3. What can you do personally to help conserve soil?

Section 15.2

4. Find an article in a local newspaper or on the Internet that mentions or discusses the Clean Water Act. Write a short report about what you learned about this important environmental law.

5. Study the table below. Name the lake that has poor water quality and explain the reason for your answer.

Table 15.1: *Water quality test results*

Lake	pH	Nitrate level	Dissolved oxygen
Citizen Lake	7.5	low	high
Lake Armstrong	4.5	high	low

Chapter Project—Soil Texture

Materials: clear plastic cup, soil sample from backyard or local public space, water, stirring rod, ruler

1. Fill the cup so that it is two-thirds full of water.

2. Remove any pieces of rock, twigs, or other matter from your soil sample. Now fill the cup half-full with the soil sample.

3. Use the stirring rod to make a soil slurry—a "soup" of soil and water. Break up all the clumped soil pieces so that the slurry is smooth.

4. Let the slurry sit for a few days until the soil has settled into layers at the bottom of the cup. Most, but not all soil, will have three distinct layers—sand (the bottom layer), silt (the the next layer), and clay (the top layer).

5. Measure the height of each layer as a percentage of the total height of the settled layers. Remember, the three should add up to 100 percent.

6. Now, use the textural triangle below, figure out what type of soil you have. Where the percentages of each type of particle meets in the triangle is the type of soil you have. The most preferred type of soil for plant growth is loam.

7. Questions: Why is it important to understand soil structure? How might you improve your soil structure?

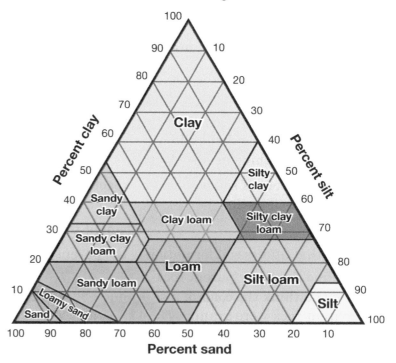

Textural triangle

Chapter 16

Natural Resources and Conservation

Hoover Dam, near Las Vegas, Nevada, towers more than 200 meters above the raging Colorado River. This gigantic concrete structure is known as one of the greatest engineering projects in the world. Hoover Dam is called a hydroelectric plant because it turns the energy of falling water into electricity. The dam is important to the American southwest, because it brings water and electricity to millions of people. Using a natural resource like water to make electricity is one way to meet our growing demand for energy. What other natural resources do we use in our daily lives? Read this chapter to find out!

Key Questions:

1. *What are some of Earth's resources?*

2. *Where do we get the energy for making electricity and for running automobiles?*

3. *What does it mean to conserve Earth's resources?*

16.1 Natural Resources and Energy

For tens of thousands of years, people have depended on Earth's resources for food, clothing, shelter, energy, medicine, and even entertainment, arts, and riches. What are the basic resources that Earth has to offer?

Natural resources

Material resources A natural resource is a feature of Earth that benefits people. Earth's natural *material* resources are things like air, fresh water, and soil. What would happen if any of these resources were missing? Study the scenes below and find the material resources. How does each of these benefit people?

Energy resources Some natural resources are used to supply energy to our busy world. Important *energy* resources include:

Energy Resources	
the Sun	tides
wind	coal, oil, natural gas
moving water	nuclear (radioactivity from uranium)
Earth's internal heat	biomass fuel (such as wood)

VOCABULARY

natural resource - a feature of Earth that benefits people.

MY JOURNAL

A forest can be considered a natural resource. Why do you think this is so?

Write an essay that answers this question.

Energy and daily life

Energy use   Your alarm clock rings and you wake up for school. You shower, brush your teeth, dress, and grab a quick breakfast before catching a bus. This is how the day starts for hundreds of thousands of students all across the country. What part of that simple morning routine requires electricity and transportation energy? Almost all of it!

Electricity   The first electric light company in the United States was started in 1878. Since then, our use of electricity has grown each year. What do you need to make electricity? You need an energy source. Earth's natural energy sources are used to make electricity. Think of all the ways you use electricity each day. The average American household uses about 10,000 kilowatt-hours of electricity each year. How much energy is that? If your body were able to utilize electricity as an energy source (rather than food) that much energy could keep you running for almost five months!

Transportation   Electricity is not the only modern use of natural energy sources. Transportation uses a lot of energy too. In the United States alone, about *130 billion gallons* of gasoline are consumed each year. Where does gasoline come from? Gasoline is made from crude oil, which is pumped out of the ground, either on land or from the ocean floor.

Heating and consumer products   In addition to being used for gasoline, oil can be used to heat homes. **Petroleum** is another name for oil, which is often used to heat homes. *Petrochemicals* are compounds made from oil. Petrochemicals are used to make plastics, medicines, cosmetics, and paints. Look around you and see how many items are made of plastic. It takes petroleum to make all of those things.

petroleum - another name for the natural resource called *oil*.

Why do we need petroleum?

Petroleum is not just used to make gasoline—it is used to make many products we use daily. Here are some examples:

- plastic
- asphalt for paving roads
- synthetic rubber
- paraffin wax
- fertilizer
- detergents
- photographic film
- packaging materials
- paint
- carpet backing
- synthetic clothing fibers such as kevlar, nylon, polyester, acrylic, and spandex
- cosmetics

Make a sketch of one room in your home, and label all of the things made from petroleum.

16.1 Section Review

1. Define the term *natural resource*, and list all of the natural resources that exist in the area directly around your school.

Transportation energy use in the United States

Data from the U.S. Department of Energy, Transportation Energy Data Book, Edition 24

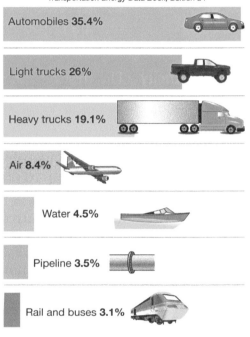

Automobiles **35.4%**

Light trucks **26%**

Heavy trucks **19.1%**

Air **8.4%**

Water **4.5%**

Pipeline **3.5%**

Rail and buses **3.1%**

2. List at least four major natural resources that you see in *each* scene above.

3. What two things in our modern lives require a lot of Earth's natural energy sources?

4. What is gasoline made from?

5. What is a petrochemical? What types of products can be made from petrochemicals?

6. What natural resource is plastic made from?

7. Study the bar graph in Figure 16.1 and answer the following questions.

    a. What type of information does this graph give you?

    b. How would the graph look if many more people in the United States used public transportation?

    c. "Americans love their cars." Does this graph support that statement? Why or why not?

Figure 16.1: *Question 7.*

16.2 Supplying Our Energy Needs

Think of how much you need electricity and how much you rely on motor vehicles every day. Making electricity and driving motor vehicles cause us to use Earth's energy resources.

Making and transporting electricity

Starting at the power plant   To find out how electricity is made and transported, let's trace the energy pathway. Look at the diagram below. Electricity is made in a power plant. Most power plants burn fossil fuels (natural resources like coal, oil, or natural gas) to produce heat. Next, this heat is used to boil water. The steam from the boiling water turns a turbine. The turbine turns a generator which produces electricity.

Electricity is carried by wires   Electricity leaves the power plant and is carried to your house by wires. The fuel energy from the coal, oil, or natural gas changes its form several times on the way to your home. With each change, some energy is converted to heat. In fact, most of the energy that is transferred from fuels like coal, oil, and natural gas will eventually become heat energy. Some will be used, but most will be unusable.

MY JOURNAL

Do some research and find out how far the nearest power plant is from your house. What is the name of the power plant? What energy source is used to make electricity at this power plant? How is the power transported to your house?

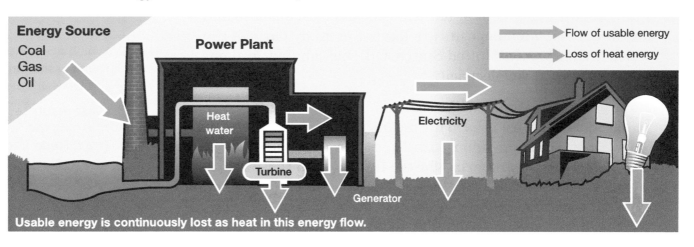

Energy Source
Coal
Gas
Oil

Power Plant

Flow of usable energy

Loss of heat energy

Heat water

Turbine

Generator

Electricity

Usable energy is continuously lost as heat in this energy flow.

Electricity from fossil fuels

What is a nonrenewable resource? A **nonrenewable resource** is not replaced as it is used. **Fossil fuels** are good examples of nonrenewable resources. Fossil fuels are found within the rocks of Earth's surface. They are called fossil fuels because they were formed hundreds of millions of years ago by processes acting on dead plants and animals. The three major fossil fuels are coal, oil, and natural gas.

Fossil fuels

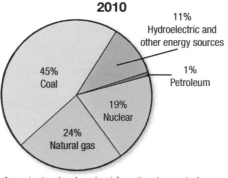

Energy sources for generating electricity in the U.S. 2010

11% Hydroelectric and other energy sources
1% Petroleum
45% Coal
19% Nuclear
24% Natural gas

Approximate values based on information at www.eia.doe.gov.

Earth's coal, oil, and natural gas deposits took hundreds of millions of years to form. Because it took so long for these resources to form, they are considered nonrenewable resources. Natural gas is pumped out of gas pockets both onshore and offshore. Coal is a solid fossil fuel that is mined from the ground in many places across the United States.

Petroleum is drilled out of natural deposits both onshore and offshore. Petroleum deposits are located in many parts of the world, including the United States. Oil, coal, and natural gas can all be used to make electricity.

The future of nonrenewable resources Nonrenewable resources like coal, oil, and natural gas are not replaced as they are used. This means that someday we will not have enough coal, oil, and natural gas to produce the electricity we need. How are we preparing for the future when these resources are no longer available? Perhaps we can use the energy of atoms, wind, or sunlight. Did you notice the "other" category in the pie chart above? Read on to find out about this category.

 VOCABULARY

nonrenewable resource - a natural resource that is not replaced as it is used.

fossil fuels - substances found in Earth's crust that were formed over millions of years from the remains of dead organisms.

 SOLVE IT!

Study the pie chart (also known as a circle graph) and answer these questions.

1. Which fossil fuel is used the most to make electricity?

2. Which fossil fuel do you think is found in the largest amount in the United States?

3. What resources do you think make up the "other" category? (*Hint*: Read ahead to learn about renewable resources that can be used to make electricity.)

Electricity from nuclear energy

What is nuclear energy?

The United States gets about 20 percent of its electricity production from nuclear power plants. The fuel used in nuclear power plants is *uranium*. Uranium is an extremely high-energy source of heat. Uranium atoms split apart in the nuclear reactor and the energy released is used to heat water and make steam. The steam drives a turbine, which spins a generator to produce electricity.

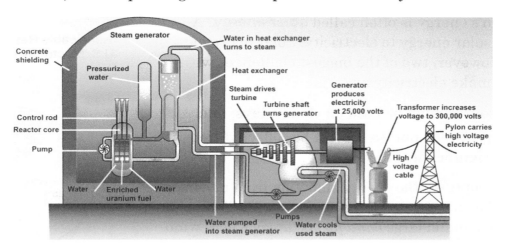

U
92
uranium

Uranium is an element, and you can find it listed on the periodic table of elements. Elements are the most basic substances. Uranium has characteristics that make it very useful as a fuel for nuclear reactors. Uranium is naturally radioactive, and it releases particles from its atoms that have a lot of energy.

Do some research on uranium.

1. How is uranium used to produce electricity? (*Hint*: If you can describe the process shown in the picture to the left, you will have your answer!)

2. Nuclear power plants do not pollute the air like fossil fuel plants do. However, there is a big drawback to nuclear power plants. What is it?

Advantages and disadvantages of nuclear energy

The main advantage of using nuclear energy to produce electricity is that it doesn't pollute the air like fossil fuel power plants do. We will discuss the problems of pollution in the next section. There are no new nuclear power plants being built in the United States. In fact, all plants that have been scheduled to be built since 1973 have been canceled. Why is this happening? One reason is that used uranium fuel from a reactor stays dangerously radioactive for a long time. Storage of nuclear waste has always been a major disadvantage of nuclear power plants. When scientists find a way to dispose of spent nuclear fuel safely, nuclear energy will be more widely used to produce electricity.

Electricity from renewable resources

Renewable resources   A **renewable resource** can be replaced naturally in a relatively short period of time. The Sun and wind are renewable resources that can be used as energy sources. Figure 16.2 shows the types of renewable resources used for electricity production in 2009.

Solar energy   The Sun is our biggest source of light and heat. In fact, 99 percent of the energy used to heat Earth and all of our buildings comes from the Sun. The Sun's energy is often called **solar energy**. A solar cell can convert solar energy to electricity. Solar energy is plentiful and clean. However, two of the biggest challenges with using solar energy to make electricity are:

1.   a backup energy source must be used on cloudy days; and
2.   solar energy is very spread out, so it must be collected from a huge area to be a significant source of energy.

Wind energy   A wind energy system captures the energy of motion from moving air (wind) and turns the energy into electrical energy. California was the first U.S. state to build large *wind farms* (areas where wind turbines are located). Today, California produces more electricity from wind energy than any other state in the United States. In fact, wind is the world's fastest-growing energy source used to make electricity. Wind is a clean, plentiful fuel source. What disadvantages are there to using wind as an energy source? Well, the wind does not always blow when electricity is needed, and right now the cost of building a wind farm is greater than the cost of building a power plant that uses fossil fuel to make electricity.

Other renewable energy sources   It is also possible to use moving water (hydroelectric), hot spots near Earth's surface (geothermal), fuels made from once-living things like wood or corn (biomass), and tides to produce electricity.

renewable resource - a natural resource that can be replaced.

solar energy - energy from the Sun.

Renewable Resources Used for U.S. Electricity Production, 2009

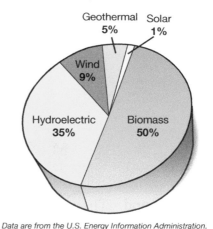

Data are from the U.S. Energy Information Administration.

Figure 16.2: *Types of renewable resources used for electricity production in 2009.*

Evaluating resources used to produce electricity in the U.S.

For discussion This evaluation chart compares different resources that can be used to make electricity in the United States. An evaluation chart is a powerful tool used to organize large amounts of information. According to the chart, which resources will the United States be using less and less of in the future? Which resources will be used more as time goes by? Can you explain why?

Using the evaluation chart

This evaluation chart was adapted from several similar charts, and some of the high, medium, and low ratings are open to debate. The information is not meant to represent specific scientific research data—it is meant to stimulate discussion.

Resource	What is the chance that this source can be used 50 years from now?	What level of *cost* is involved with using this system?	What level of impact does using this resource have on the environment?
Nonrenewable resources			
Petroleum	Low	High	Medium
Natural gas	Medium	High	Low
Coal	High	Medium	Very high
Nuclear	Medium	Very high	Very high
Renewable resources			
Hydroelectric (dams)	Low	Medium	Low
Solar	High	High	Low
Wind	High	Medium	Low
Geothermal (using Earth's energy)	Medium	Medium	Medium
Biomass (burning wood and agricultural waste)	Medium	Medium	Medium

Transportation and energy sources

Gasoline use If you were asked to estimate how many automobiles there are in the United States, what number would you guess? According to the U.S. Department of Transportation, there were *over 132 million automobiles* in the United States in 1997. What is the main energy source used for operating automobiles? If you guessed petroleum, you are correct. Gasoline is made from petroleum. Americans use about 375 million gallons of gasoline *every day*. It is important to know that the United States does not produce enough crude oil to make all of the gasoline used by American motorists. The United States produces only about 40 percent of the crude oil it uses. Where does the rest come from? It is imported from other countries.

Efficiency What does it mean to say that a machine or a process is efficient? If a machine is *efficient,* the machine is able to use most of its energy source to do a job. For efficient machines, very little of the energy source is converted to unusable energy like heat. Efficiency is a very important concept to understand when you are learning about how we use different energy sources. A bicycle is a very efficient machine (Figure 16.3). When you ride a bicycle, almost 80 percent of the energy you put into pedaling the bike is converted to motion. Automobiles, however, have a low efficiency. Only about 20 percent of the gasoline energy is converted to motion. Most of the energy is lost as unusable heat.

Usefulness and trade-offs If bicycles are so efficient, why don't we use them more, instead of automobiles, when we travel? You know the answer to that question! Cars can take us where we want to go much faster and more conveniently than bicycles can. Bicycles aren't as useful to us as cars are. Useful energy sources are sources that meet our needs *and* have the right balance of cost and efficiency.

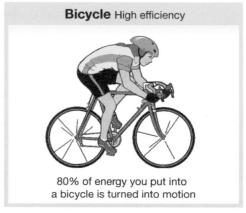

Bicycle High efficiency

80% of energy you put into a bicycle is turned into motion

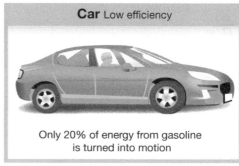

Car Low efficiency

Only 20% of energy from gasoline is turned into motion

Figure 16.3: *Bicycles are efficient but they are not useful for most transportation needs!*

Comparing notes

For discussion Compare gasoline-powered cars to cars of the future. What will cars of the future use for energy sources? What type of car will you drive some day?

16.2 Section Review

1. Some of the energy that comes from burning a fossil fuel can be turned into electricity, but most of the energy is lost. Explain why this is a true statement and identify the unusable or lost energy.

2. Define *nonrenewable resources* and list three that are used for making electricity.

3. Define *renewable resources* and list three that can be used for making electricity.

4. List one major advantage and one disadvantage of making electricity in a nuclear power plant.

5. List two advantages and two disadvantages of using solar energy to make electricity.

6. List two advantages and two disadvantages of using wind energy to make electricity.

7. Study the pie chart at right. Redraw your own version of this pie chart as it will most likely look *50 years from now*. Use the evaluation table in this section that compares energy resources to help you decide how to draw your graph.

Energy sources for generating electricity in the U.S. 2010

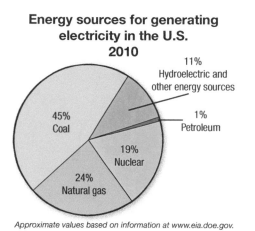

- 45% Coal
- 11% Hydroelectric and other energy sources
- 1% Petroleum
- 19% Nuclear
- 24% Natural gas

Approximate values based on information at www.eia.doe.gov.

MY JOURNAL

Hybrid car

Hybrid Cars

The entire world, not just the United States, depends on oil—mostly for transportation energy. What are scientists doing to prepare for the time when there is not enough oil to meet the world's needs? One new type of car that will help reduce our need for oil is a hybrid car. Do some research and find out how hybrid cars might help reduce our need for oil. Write an essay on what you learn.

16.3 **Resources and Conservation**

 VOCABULARY

In this chapter you have been learning about Earth's material and energy resources. Natural resources benefit people, and it is important to think about how we can take care of Earth's resources. Resource conservation happens when people protect, preserve, and manage Earth's natural resources.

resource conservation - protecting, preserving, and managing Earth's natural resources.

Air—an important resource

pollution - a change to the environment that is harmful to humans or other living things.

Air is everywhere   Air is a very important natural resource, even though you may forget that it is all around you. Air is a mixture of nitrogen, oxygen, carbon dioxide, water vapor, and other gases. We do not need to worry that the air will get "used up," because there are natural cycles that keep the supply steady. However, these natural cycles can't always keep the air clean.

emissions - tiny particles and gases released into the air.

Air pollution   Pollution is a change to the environment (air, water, or soil) that is harmful to humans or other living things. Some changes to the air can have harmful effects on humans and other living organisms. Air pollution (Figure 16.4) is caused by tiny particles and gases called emissions that are released into the air. Some things that produce emissions and pollute the air include:

- power plants that use fossil fuels to make electricity
- motor vehicles (trucks, cars, airplanes, etc.)
- factories
- erupting volcanoes

Reducing pollution   The U.S. government has passed laws to control the levels of emissions from power plants, factories, and motor vehicles. If you use less electricity, you can help keep the air clean too.

Figure 16.4: *Air pollution is caused by emissions from some factories, power plants, and motor vehicles.*

Conserving the water supply

Earth is a watery planet   The amount of water on Earth today is about the same as it was during the age of dinosaurs, 65 to 220 million years ago. About 70 percent of Earth's surface is covered by water. That's a lot of water! However, only a small amount of this water is useful to humans. Why? About 97 percent of Earth's water is salt water. That leaves only 3 percent as fresh water. About 70 percent of this fresh water is frozen, and the rest is found in rivers, streams, lakes, ponds, and even below the ground in layers of soil and rock (Figure 16.5). If this is true, and Earth has been around for such a long time, why haven't we run out of water? The answer is that Earth's water is recycled by natural processes.

Water pollution   Earth's water supply will stay steady, but the amount of water that we can actually use is a precious resource which must be conserved. Water is often polluted by human activities and human-made chemicals. Some of these are listed below:

- Gasoline or chemical spills from cars may be washed off roads or driveways into water supplies.
- Chemicals and other wastes from households may be washed down sinks.
- Factories and power plants produce polluting substances.
- Pesticides and fertilizers can end up in the water supply.
- Oil spills from large ships that transport oil across the oceans can cause serious pollution problems.

What can you do?   Using less water at home and at school can certainly help by putting less demand on the water supply. Also, never pour things like paint, paint thinner, motor oil, or garden chemicals on the ground or down the drain. Your town or city probably has a special collection area for these hazardous substances.

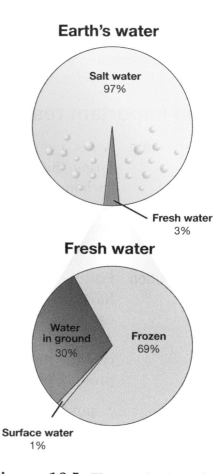

Figure 16.5: *The top pie chart shows how much of Earth's total water is salt water, and how much is fresh. The bottom pie chart shows how much of the fresh water is frozen, and how much is in the ground and on the surface.*

Land, forests, and wildlife resources

Land and soil
Earth's land and soil are used to benefit people in many ways, and everyone must share these nonrenewable resources. How is land used to benefit people?

- Mining minerals: A *mineral* is a solid, naturally occurring substance with a defined chemical composition that is found in Earth's crust. A rock is made of one or more minerals. Gold, silver, diamond, aluminum, iron, and tin are important minerals that you have heard of.
- Development: People use land to build houses, schools, and industries.
- Agriculture: Growing crops and raising animals for food are important land uses.

Forests and fisheries
Think of all the products we use that come from forests. Maple syrup, rubber, fruits, and nuts come from living trees. Lumber for constructing buildings and furniture comes from trees that have been cut down. Paper is another important forest product. Don't forget that trees and other plants produce oxygen that humans and other organisms need to survive. Fish are also valuable resources. Both trees and fish are renewable resources, but we cannot use them up faster than they are replenished, or the supply will decrease quickly.

What can you do?
Do you recycle paper, metal, and plastic in your home and school? Recycling programs all over the country have been put in place to help reduce the solid waste that takes up so much of our landfills by finding ways to reuse products instead of producing new ones (Figure 16.6).

What minerals are mined from Earth in the United States? Do some research and make a list of these minerals. Which ones are mined in your state?

Trash takes up space in landfills: recycle and re-use!

Figure 16.6: *Recycling programs help reduce the solid waste that takes up so much of our landfills.*

A resource conservation issue: global climate change

Global climate change
Have you ever heard the phrase "global climate change"? This is an important concern that has received a lot of attention in recent years. *Global climate change* refers to an increase in the temperature of Earth's climate due to increasing amounts of certain gases in the atmosphere—mostly carbon dioxide.

Carbon dioxide and global climate change
There is very little carbon dioxide in the atmosphere, compared to the amounts of nitrogen and oxygen (Figure 16.7). Does this surprise you? The amount of carbon dioxide in Earth's atmosphere is just enough to trap heat from the Sun to make Earth warm and comfortable. Earth would be too warm with too much carbon dioxide, and too cold if the carbon dioxide level was too low. When we use fossil fuels, we add more carbon dioxide to the atmosphere. Increased levels of carbon dioxide can contribute to global climate change. Using public transportation, using less electricity (turn out the lights), and driving hybrid vehicles can all help reduce carbon dioxide levels.

Consequences
The amount of carbon dioxide in the atmosphere has increased by about 30 percent since the 1800s. Also, Earth's average surface temperature has increased 0.6 to 1.2 degrees Fahrenheit over that same time period. These increases are not huge, but they are enough to have warmed the North Pole and caused the sea level to rise 4 to 10 inches. Have you heard about any other consequences of global climate change?

Trees and air quality
One acre of trees can provide oxygen for about 20 people each day. This same acre of trees can also absorb emissions, including carbon dioxide (Figure 16.8). Trees are not the solution to the problem of increased carbon dioxide levels, but they can certainly help!

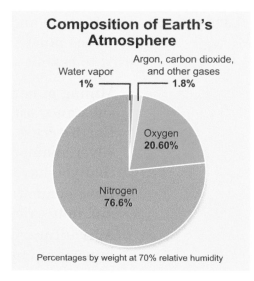

Figure 16.7: *The amount of carbon dioxide in Earth's atmosphere, compared to the amounts of nitrogen and oxygen.*

Figure 16.8: *Trees can improve Earth's air quality.*

16.3 Section Review

1. What does it mean to conserve Earth's natural resources?

2. Why is air an important natural resource?

3. List four possible causes of air pollution.

4. Why can humans only use a small part of Earth's water supply for drinking, cleaning, and other daily needs?

5. Why is water an important natural resource?

6. List four possible causes of water pollution.

7. Describe two things you can do to help conserve Earth's water resources.

8. Study the fresh-water pie chart in Figure 16.5. What percentage of fresh water can readily be used for drinking water and other needs? Why?

9. Make your own illustration of natural resources provided by trees. Draw a living tree and show on your diagram all of the different products that can come from different kinds of living trees. Draw a tree that has been cut down and show on your diagram all the different products that can come from trees that have been harvested. Be creative!

10. Why are fish considered a natural resource? Is this a nonrenewable or a renewable resource? Explain your answer.

11. Land is a natural resource. List at least three ways that land and soil are used to benefit humans.

12. How can global climate change cause the ocean levels to rise? What problems could increased ocean levels cause?

13. Do some research to find at least two consequences of global climate change, in addition to rising ocean levels.

What percent of *your* state do you think is covered by water? What state do you think has the greatest area covered by water? Write down your predictions, then do some research to find the answers to these questions. (*Hint*: http://ga.water.usgs.gov/edu/wetstates.html is a website maintained by the United States Geological Survey that will give you information on this topic.)

Earth's Energy

Remember the last time you dipped your foot into a bathtub of hot water? Or how good it feels to take a hot shower on a cold rainy day? The hot water we use every day has to be heated by a system. Your home probably has a hot water heater to heat water. However, there are places on Earth, like Iceland, that use Earth's plumbing and heating system to get hot water. Parts of this system are geysers and hot springs. The source of heat is geothermal energy—heat that comes from inside our planet.

At Earth's core, temperatures can reach 4,982°C (9,000°F). Heat from the core travels to the next layer of rock, the mantle. Mantle rock that melts becomes magma. Magma, lighter than the surrounding rock, travels upward carrying heat. This upward movement and transfer of heat through a fluid is called convection. Convection moves heat away from its source at a lower, hotter area to a higher, cooler area.

Magma that reaches Earth's surface is lava, but most magma stays below the surface. That underground magma heats nearby water and rocks.

Hot springs and geysers are created by surface water that seeps into the ground and finally reaches those hot rocks. When that heated water rises by convection back to the surface, hot springs and geysers are created.

Hot water from Earth

Rocks are hotter the deeper they are inside Earth. In areas where there is no volcanic activity, those hot rocks heat the hot springs. In areas with volcanic activity, the hot springs are heated by magma. Extremely hot magma can cause the water in a hot spring to boil.

Water temperatures in hot springs vary. Usually the water is warmer than body temperature—37°C (98.6°F)—which makes it feel hot to the skin. In hot springs with high temperatures, the water is usually clear because the water is too hot for algae or bacteria grow. However, this water is not safe to drink because of the minerals dissolved in it.

Hot spring

Photo courtesy of Geoff Tierney

Things come to a boil

Geyser is an Icelandic word meaning "roarer." A geyser is a type of hot spring that shoots water and steam into the air. The roaring sound comes from the eruption of the water and steam. As it does with a hot spring, water seeps into the ground until it reaches hot rocks. Most geysers are located in areas of volcanic activity. One big difference between a hot spring and a geyser is constriction, which is a narrowed area of plumbing that causes pressure to build.

Far below Earth's surface, geysers fill with water. Near the top of the geyser, a constricted area forms a seal and pressure is created. Pressure also differentiates a hot spring from a geyser. Cooler water sitting in the area pushes down on the hot reservoir of water. Under increased pressure, the reservoir below heats up even more. As the temperature rises, the reservoir starts to boil.

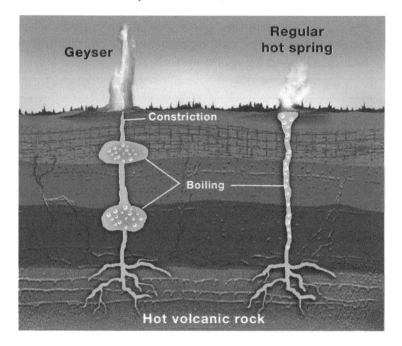

The building pressure of the boiling water causes an eruption. Water and steam are forced out of the geyser to the surface through an opening called a vent. Pressure is released—and, naturally, the process begins again.

Old Faithful

There are four big locations for geysers on the planet: Iceland (where they got their name), Yellowstone National Park in Wyoming, North Island in New Zealand, and Kamchatka Peninsula in Russia. Old Faithful in Yellowstone is one of the world's famous geysers. Just about every 35 to 120 minutes, it shoots water 30 to

60 meters (about 100 to 200 feet) into the air. Yellowstone is located over a hot spot in the planet's mantle and this makes it one of the richest locations for geysers—nearly 500 of them in all.

Importance of geothermal energy

Hot springs and geysers are more than rare natural attractions. They also can be sources of energy. In the 1970s, Iceland started to use its hot springs and geysers to provide energy for power, heat, and hot water. Today, Iceland uses geothermal energy to provide heat to nearly 87 percent of its homes. In Northern California, geothermal geyser fields have been used for nearly 40 years and produce electricity for San Francisco.

Old Faithful

Photo: Geoff Tierney

QUESTIONS

1. What is geothermal energy?

2. What is the difference between a hot spring and a geyser?

3. Why is "geyser" a good term for Old Faithful?

Keep the Heat

Heating homes can require great amounts of energy. In this activity, you will test different materials to see how well they keep heat in.

Materials

three thermometers, stopwatch, masking tape, colored pencils, scissors, a metric ruler, three soda cans, hot water, aluminum foil, three rubber bands, ice, three large zipper-lock plastic bags, two materials to test as an insulator (examples: foam, paper, wool, felt, aluminum foil)

What you will do

1. Fill a soda can about 5 cm from the top with the hottest water from the tap.

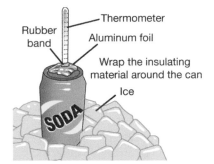
Thermometer
Rubber band
Aluminum foil
Wrap the insulating material around the can
Ice

2. Place a rubber band around the middle of the thermometer. Take the aluminum foil and wrap it around the thermometer just below the rubber band. Place the aluminum foil and thermometer in the soda can opening. Use enough aluminum foil to cover the hole completely and make sure the thermometer is about halfway into the can and isn't touching the can at all.

3. Select a material and completely wrap the soda can with the material, including the top. Tape the material in place and list the material in the table.

4. Using a different material, repeat steps 1–3 for another can.

5. The third can is a control. The control has no insulting material. Repeat steps 1–3.

6. Fill the zipper-lock bags halfway with ice. Lay the bags of ice flat. Place each can in the center of a bag of ice.

7. Record the initial water temperature in degrees Celsius for each can in the table. Continue to observe and record the temperatures every five minutes for the next 20 minutes.

8. Graph your data. Include a title. Label the x-axis "Time" and the y-axis "Temperature." Use a separate color to draw a line for each type of insulating material and for your control. Include a legend for your graph.

Material	Temperature (°C)				
	Initial	After 5 min	After 10 min	After 15 min	After 20 min
Control					

Applying your knowledge

a. Calculate the change in temperature for each of the cans.

b. Did the materials help to insulate the can? How do you know?

c. Which, if any, of the insulating materials was the most effective at holding the heat in?

d. Selecting a material to use as insulation in a home can be a difficult decision. What other factors, besides the material's ability to hold in heat, might a builder need to consider when choosing a material?

e. Why is it so important to select the best insulating material when designing a home?

f. In addition to insulation, what other ways could designers make their home as energy efficient as possible?

Vocabulary

Select the correct term to complete the sentences.

solar energy	nonrenewable resource	resource conservation
emissions	renewable resource	fossil fuels
natural resources	pollution	petroleum

Section 16.1

1. Another name for the natural resource called oil is _____.

2. Earth's _____ are features that benefit people—like air, fresh water, soil, minerals, trees, and petroleum.

Section 16.2

3. _____ are substances made from things that were once alive.

4. A _____ is a natural resource like uranium or coal that is not replaced as it is used.

5. The Sun's energy is often called _____.

6. A _____ is a natural resource like the Sun, wind, or trees that can be replaced in a relatively short period of time.

Section 16.3

7. Tiny particles and gases released into the air are called _____.

8. If you practice _____, you are protecting, preserving, and managing Earth's natural resources.

9. _____ is a change to the environment that is harmful to humans or other living things.

Concepts

Section 16.1

1. Generate a list of anything that can be considered a natural resource.

2. Look around you right now and name five objects that would not exist if there was no petroleum.

Section 16.2

3. Describe the three fossil fuels and where they can be found.

4. Sort the list of energy resources into *renewable* and *nonrenewable* resources.

    nuclear, natural gas, hydroelectric, solar, biomass, wind, oil, coal, geothermal

5. Refer to the chart "Evaluating resources used to produce electricity in the U.S." to answer the following questions:

    a. Name a resource that has a high chance of being used 50 years from now, has a medium level of cost, and a low impact on the environment.

    b. Is this source of energy being used to produce electricity in your state? Write down where you got your information from to answer this question.

    c. Study the chart and choose the resource that you think will be used to make the most electricity 50 years from now. Justify your answer with information from the chart.

6. Look at the "Comparing notes" illustration that shows a notebook comparison between current cars and future cars. Choose one of the following future cars. Research and find information on your chosen future car to write a notebook list like the one in the illustration.
    Future cars to choose from: electric car, solar car, fuel cell car, biofuel car, and hybrid car.

Section 16.3

7. Why is air an important natural resource?

8. Describe two things *you* can do to help reduce air pollution.

9. Describe one way that water can become polluted.

Math and Writing Skills

Section 16.1

1. Study the bar graph below. Write a paragraph that tells in words what information this bar graph gives about daily life in the United States.

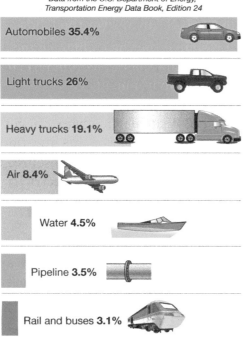

Transportation energy use in the United States

Data from the U.S. Department of Energy, Transportation Energy Data Book, Edition 24

Automobiles **35.4%**

Light trucks **26%**

Heavy trucks **19.1%**

Air **8.4%**

Water **4.5%**

Pipeline **3.5%**

Rail and buses **3.1%**

Section 16.2

2. Use the graph to answer the questions.

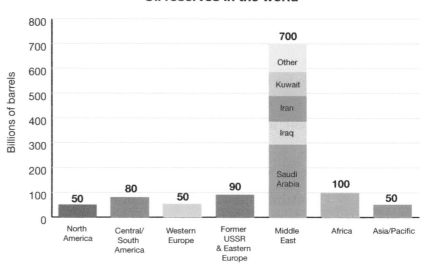

Oil reserves in the world

a. Which area of the world has the most oil in reserves? How many billions of barrels does this area have?

b. Which specific country has the most oil in reserves? How many billions of barrels does this country have?

c. Which area of the world has the least oil in reserves? How many billions of barrels does this area have?

d. What percentage of total world oil does North America have in reserves?

e. *Extension*: Research the following question—what percentage of total world oil does North America use?

3. Use the graph to answer the questions.

    a. What percent of total energy used in California is from oil and gas?

    b. What type of energy is used least in California?

    c. What is the total percent of nonrenewable energy used in California?

    d. What is the total percent of renewable energy used in California?

    e. Based on your analysis of the graph above, how successfully do you think California is conserving natural resources for energy use?

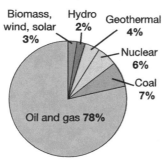

Percent of total energy used in California

Biomass, wind, solar 3%
Hydro 2%
Geothermal 4%
Nuclear 6%
Coal 7%
Oil and gas 78%

Section 16.3

4. Find out about recycling plastics in your community. Prepare a brochure that provides information on how to recycle plastics.

Chapter Project—Can You Conserve?

Keep a journal for one week of the different ways you use natural resources. Don't forget to include electricity use! Keep track of heat used, lights turned on, oven use, shower use, paper used, plastic bottles, etc. Give as much detail as you can about the amount of resources used and the time of day they are used.

After you have kept detailed notes for one week of how you use natural resources, identify two areas that you can practice better resource conservation. Create a poster of an action plan that shows how you will conserve these resources. Be creative and practical!

UNIT 6

ASTRONOMY

CHAPTER 17
The Solar System

CHAPTER 18
Earth, the Moon,
and the Sun

CHAPTER 19
Galaxies and
the Universe

WHY DO PLANETS ORBIT THE SUN?

WHAT IS A COMET?

WHY DOES ONLY ONE SIDE OF THE MOON FACE EARTH?

WHEN ARE STARS MOST VISIBLE?

Exploring on Your Own

Major meteor showers happen each year. In an August nighttime sky, you can see the Perseids meteor shower. The Leonids occur in November, and the Lyrids occur in April. At this NASA website, you can calculate how many meteors you might see for a given date at your location: http://leonid.arc.nasa.gov/estimator.html. If you are able to view a shower, record your observations and compare them with the calculations. Find out why these meteor showers visible at the same time each year. Have fun meteor gazing!

Chapter 17

The Solar System

Earth is a planet that is just right for living things—and among these living things are people who have long wondered if other planets have life. Mars and Europa (a moon of Jupiter) are good candidates for life—but so far they are only just candidates. Space probes have explored only a tiny fraction of the surfaces of Mars and Venus looking for signs of life, and the small amount of evidence collected gives no definite answers. If you were asked to describe a creature that could live on each of the planets (or moons) in the solar system, what characteristics would it have? What would it eat? How would it move? A creature on Venus might have to live at a surface temperature of 500°C. Neptune's environment is frozen; what type of creature could live there? In this chapter, you will learn about the vast, unexplored territories that are the planets and moons of the solar system.

Key Questions:

1. What holds the solar system together?

2. How do the planets compare to each other?

3. What are comets, asteroids, dwarf plants, and meteors?

Images courtesy NASA/JPL-Caltech

17.1 About the Solar System

Ancient observers noticed that five bright objects seemed to wander among the stars at night. They called these objects *planets*, from the Greek word meaning "wandering star," and named them Mercury, Venus, Mars, Jupiter, and Saturn. In 140 CE, the Greek astronomer Ptolemy "explained" that planets and the Moon orbited Earth. For the next 1,400 years, people believed this idea. Eventually, scientific evidence proved Ptolemy wrong.

Evidence that the planets orbit the Sun

Planets shine by reflecting sunlight Today we know that planets are not stars. Stars give off their own light. We see the planets *because they reflect light from the Sun*. A **planet** is a massive object orbiting a star, like the Sun. For example, Venus is a planet. It appears as a crescent like the Moon, becoming dark at times. This is because Venus does not give off its own light. When Earth is on the same side of the Sun as Venus, we see Venus's shadowed side (Figure 17.1 top). The phases of Venus were discovered by the Italian astronomer Galileo Galilei (1564–1642) in the 1600s. This discovery was part of the scientific evidence that eventually overturned Ptolemy's model of the Earth-centered solar system.

Changing ideas about the solar system Almost 100 years before Galileo, Polish astronomer Nicolaus Copernicus (1473–1543) had proposed that the planets orbited the Sun, but few believed him. Then, Galileo, using a telescope he built himself, made two discoveries that supported Copernicus's ideas. First, he argued that the phases of Venus could not be explained if Earth were at the center of the planets. Second, he observed that there were four moons orbiting Jupiter (Figure 17.1 bottom). This showed that not everything in the sky orbited around Earth.

VOCABULARY

planet - a massive object orbiting a star like the Sun.

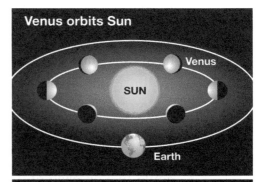

Figure 17.1: *Two of Galileo's discoveries that helped prove that Earth and the other planets orbit the Sun. The top diagram shows how the phases of Venus occur due to its orbit around the Sun. The bottom diagram depicts moons orbiting Jupiter. This observation proved that not all objects revolve around Earth.*

What is the solar system?

The Sun, planets, and other objects

Today, we define the solar system as the Sun and all objects that are bound by gravitational force to the Sun. The gravitational force (also called *gravity*) of the Sun keeps the solar system together just as gravity keeps the Moon in orbit around Earth.

The solar system includes eight major planets and their moons, and a large number of smaller objects (dwarf planets, asteroids, comets, and meteors).

 **VOCABULARY**

solar system - the Sun and all objects that are bound by gravitational force to the Sun.

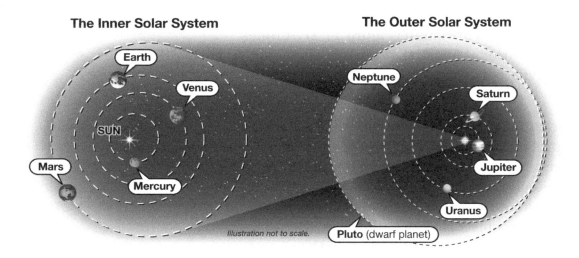

The Inner Solar System

The Outer Solar System

Earth
Venus
SUN
Mars
Mercury
Illustration not to scale.

Neptune
Saturn
Jupiter
Uranus
Pluto (dwarf planet)

The orbits of the planets are not true circles, but *ellipses*. An ellipse is shaped like an oval. While the actual paths are close to circles, the Sun is not at the center, but is off to one side. For example, Mercury's orbit is shifted 21 percent to one side of the Sun.

Inner and outer planets

The solar system is roughly divided into the *inner planets* (Mercury, Venus, Earth, and Mars) and the *outer planets* (Jupiter, Saturn, Uranus, and Neptune). The dwarf planet Pluto is the oldest known member of a smaller group of frozen worlds orbiting beyond Neptune. The diagram above shows the orbits of the planets (the planets are not shown to scale). Notice that Neptune is farther from the Sun than the dwarf planet Pluto over part of its orbit.

Gravitational force

All objects attract
Gravitational force is the force of attraction between all objects. The gravitational force that you are most familiar with is the one between you and Earth. We call this force your *weight*. But gravitational force is also acting between the Sun, Earth, and the planets. All objects that have mass attract each other through gravitational forces.

Gravitational force is relatively weak
You don't notice the attractive force between ordinary objects because gravity is a relatively weak force. For example, a gravitational force exists between you and this book, but you cannot feel it because both masses are small (Figure 17.2). It takes a huge mass to create gravitational forces that are strong enough to feel. You notice the gravity between you and Earth because Earth's mass is huge.

The law of universal gravitation
The law of universal gravitation explains how the strength of the force depends on the mass of the objects and the distance between them. Gravitational force is directly related to the objects' mass. This means the gravitational force increases as the mass of the objects increases. The distance between objects also affects gravitational force. The closer objects are to each other, the stronger the gravitational force between them. The farther apart, the weaker the gravitational force.

Gravity on Earth and the Moon
The strength of gravity on the surface of Earth is 9.8 N/kg. Like pounds, newtons are a measure of force. There are 4.448 newtons in one pound. Earth and a 1-kilogram object attract each other with 9.8 newtons of force. In comparison, the strength of gravity on the Moon is only 1.6 N/kg. Your weight on the Moon would be one-sixth what it is now. The Moon's mass is much less than Earth's, so it creates less gravitational force.

VOCABULARY

gravitational force - the force of attraction between all objects.

law of universal gravitation - states that the strength of the gravitational force depends on the mass of the objects and the distance between them.

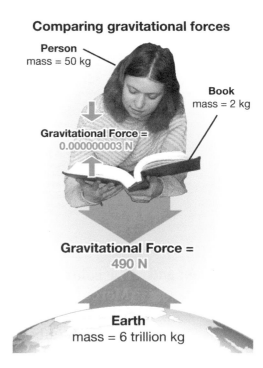

Comparing gravitational forces

Person
mass = 50 kg

Book
mass = 2 kg

Gravitational Force =
0.000000003 N

Gravitational Force =
490 N

Earth
mass = 6 trillion kg

Figure 17.2: *The gravitational force between you and Earth is stronger than the force between you and your book because of Earth's large mass.*

Orbits

What is an orbit? An **orbit** is a regular, repeating path that an object in space follows around another object. An object in orbit is called a **satellite**. A satellite can be natural—like the Moon, or artificial—like the International Space Station.

Why the Moon does not fall to Earth Earth and the other planets orbit the Sun. The Moon orbits Earth. Why doesn't the force of gravity pull Earth into the Sun (or the Moon into Earth)? To answer the question, imagine kicking a ball off the ground at an angle. If you kick it at a slow speed, it curves and falls back to the ground. The faster you kick the ball, the farther it goes before hitting the ground. If you could kick it fast enough, the curve of the ball's path would match the curvature of Earth. The ball would go into orbit instead of falling back to Earth. An object launched at 8,000 m/s will orbit Earth.

Inertia and gravitational force An orbit results from the balance between *inertia* (the forward motion of an object in space), and gravitational force. Because of inertia, the planets are moving in a direction at a right angle to the pulling force of gravity. A scientific law states that an object in motion will remain in motion unless something pushes or pulls on it. This means that without the pull of gravity, a planet would travel off into space in a straight line. The balance between the planet's inertia and the gravitational force between the planet and the Sun results in the planet's orbit (Figure 17.3).

VOCABULARY

orbit - regular, repeating path that an object in space follows around another object.

satellite - an object in orbit around another object.

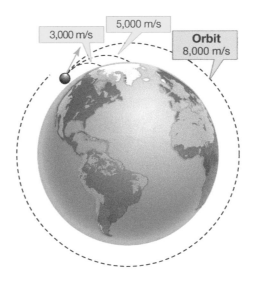

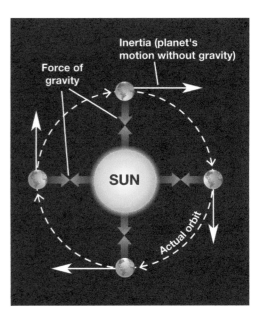

Figure 17.3: *An orbit results from the balance between inertia and gravitational force.*

Motion of the planets

The shape of orbits   The orbits of the planets are slightly elliptical but almost circular. What's more significant is that the Sun is at a point called the *focus* that is offset from the center of the orbit. This causes the distance from the Sun to vary as a planet orbits (Figure 17.4).

Rotation   In addition to orbiting the Sun, the planets also rotate. An **axis** is the imaginary line that passes through the center of a planet from pole to pole. The spinning of a planet on its axis is called its *rotation*. Earth, like most of the other planets, spins from west to east. One complete rotation is called a *day*. One Earth day is 24 hours long. This means it takes Earth 24 hours to complete one rotation on its axis. A day on Jupiter, the fastest rotator of the planets, is only about 10 hours long.

Revolution and years   All of the planets orbit, or revolve, around the Sun in the same direction (counter-clockwise). A *year* is the time it takes a planet to complete one *revolution* around the Sun. A year on Earth takes approximately 365.25 days. A year on Mars takes 686.98 Earth days. The farther a planet is from the Sun, the longer it takes it to complete one revolution. One year on Neptune, the outermost planet, is 164.81 Earth years long! Table 17.1 on page 412 shows the rotation and revolution period for each planet.

VOCABULARY

axis - the imaginary line that passes through the center of a planet from pole to pole.

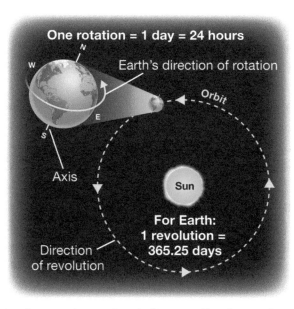

One rotation = 1 day = 24 hours

Earth's direction of rotation

Orbit

Axis

Sun

Direction of revolution

For Earth:
1 revolution =
365.25 days

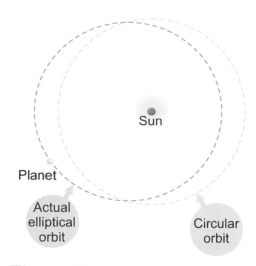

Sun

Planet

Actual elliptical orbit

Circular orbit

Figure 17.4: *Orbits are almost circular (ellipses). The Sun is at a point called the* focus *that is offset from the center.*

Comparing size and distance in the solar system

Relative sizes The Sun is by far the largest object in the solar system. The next largest objects are the planets Jupiter, Saturn, Uranus, and Neptune. As you can see from the scale diagram below, the planets Mercury, Venus, Earth, and Mars appear as small dots compared with the size of the Sun.

The sizes of planets relative to the Sun

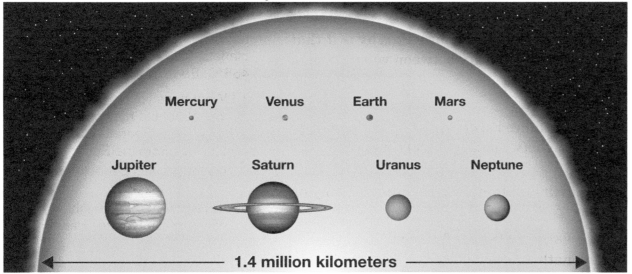

Planet photos courtesy of NASA/JPL.

Distance Astronomers often use the distance of Earth from the Sun as a measurement of distance in the solar system. One **astronomical unit** (AU) is equal to 150 million kilometers, or the distance from Earth to the Sun. Mercury is 58 million kilometers from the Sun. To convert this distance to astronomical units, divide it by 150 million kilometers (or divide 58 by 150). Mercury is 0.39 AU from the Sun (Figure 17.5). Figure 17.6 lists the planets and the distance of each of them from the Sun in AU.

VOCABULARY

astronomical unit - equal to 150 million km, or the distance from Earth to the Sun.

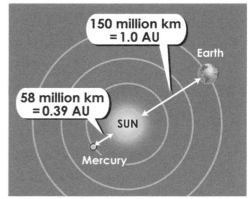

Figure 17.5: *One AU is equal to 150 million kilometers. If Earth is 1.0 AU from the Sun, then Mercury, with a distance of 58 million kilometers, is 0.39 AU from the Sun.*

Planet	Average distance from the Sun (AU)
Mercury	0.39
Venus	0.72
Earth	1.0
Mars	1.5
Jupiter	5.2
Saturn	9.5
Uranus	19.2
Neptune	30.0

Figure 17.6: *Distances of the planets from the Sun in AU.*

17.1 Section Review

1. What makes planets visible in the night sky?
2. Name the planets in order, starting nearest to the Sun.
3. The force that holds the solar system together is called _____.
4. What is an astronomical unit?
5. Gravitational force gets weaker as _____ increases and gets stronger as the _____ of the objects increases.
6. Gravity exists between all objects with mass. So why is it that you don't you notice the force of gravity between you and all of the objects around you?
7. What is inertia?
8. The orbit of a planet is a balance between the planet's _____ and the gravitational force between the planet and the _____.
9. Is a satellite orbiting Earth free from Earth's gravity? Why or why not?
10. What determines the length of a day on a planet?
11. What determines the length of a year on a planet?
12. How long does it take Earth to make one revolution around the Sun?
13. How long, in hours, does it take for Earth to make one rotation on its axis?
14. *Challenge*: Jupiter is 5.2 AU from the Sun. How far is it from the Sun in kilometers? (*Hint*: 1 AU = 150,000,000 km)

Use the data from Table 17.1 on page 412 to make a graph of surface temperature vs. distance from the Sun for the eight planets. Graph the distance on the *x*-axis and the temperature on the *y*-axis. Use these values for the surface temperature of the four inner planets: Mercury 167°C, Venus 465°C, Earth 15°C, Mars –65°C.

1. What does your graph show you about the relationship between temperature and distance from the Sun?
2. Do the planets perfectly follow this relationship?
3. What other factors might affect the surface temperature of the planets?

17.2 **The Planets**

There are eight major planets in our solar system. Some have environments baked by heat and radiation (Mercury) and some are far colder than ice (Neptune). Venus, the most Earth-like planet in size, has a surface atmosphere of hot, dense sulfuric acid! Our own planet (Figure 17.7) is unique in having the right balance of temperature and environment to sustain life—or is it? Might there be unusual forms of life unknown to us on the other planets? Scientists have recently discovered living organisms on Earth that feed off hot sulfur emissions from volcanoes on the ocean floor. Could these organisms survive on Venus? The planets are an unexplored frontier full of discoveries waiting to be made!

An overview of the planets

Classifying the planets — The planets are commonly classified in two groups. The **terrestrial planets** include Mercury, Venus, Earth, and Mars. The terrestrial planets are mostly made of rock and metal. They have relatively high densities, slow rotations, solid surfaces, and few moons. The other group, the **gas giants**, include Jupiter, Saturn, Uranus, and Neptune. They are made mostly of hydrogen and helium. These planets have relatively low densities, rapid rotations, thick atmospheres, and many moons. Table 17.1 on page 412 compares the planets.

Changing ideas — On August 24, 2006, the International Astronomical Union (IAU) passed a new definition of a planet. The new definition excludes Pluto as a planet. According to the new definition, Pluto is classified as a "dwarf planet." Recently, astronomers have begun to find dozens of objects similar to Pluto—all small, icy, rocky, and with similar orbits. The change in Pluto's status as a planet is a good example of the scientific method in progress. New discoveries sometimes cause scientists to revise scientific knowledge.

VOCABULARY

terrestrial planets - made mostly from rock and metal; include Mercury, Venus, Earth, and Mars.

gas giants - made mostly of hydrogen and helium; include Jupiter, Saturn, Uranus, and Neptune.

Photo courtesy of NASA

Figure 17.7: *Crystal-blue Earth is unique in its ability to sustain life—or is it?*

Mercury and Venus

Mercury

Photo courtesy of NASA/USGS

Mercury, the closest planet to the Sun, is the smallest in both size and mass. Mercury appears to move quickly across the night sky because its period of revolution is the shortest of all of the planets. Mercury rotates on its axis very slowly—only one and a half times for every revolution around the Sun. This makes one day on Mercury about 59 Earth days, although its year is not much longer—about 88 Earth days! Only 40 percent larger than Earth's moon, Mercury is a rocky, cratered world, more like the Moon than like Earth. Like the Moon, Mercury has almost no atmosphere (except for traces of sodium). Mercury has no moons. The side of Mercury that faces the Sun is very hot, about 400°C, while the other side is very cold, about –170°C.

Mercury   Earth

Moon

Mercury facts

Type: terrestrial
Moons: 0
Distance from Sun: 0.39 AU
Diameter: 0.38 × Earth
Surface gravity: 38% of Earth
Surface temp.: –170 to 400°C
Atmosphere: none
Length of day: 59 Earth days
Length of year: 88 Earth days
Mercury was named for the messenger of the Roman gods because of its quick motion in the sky.

Venus

Photo courtesy of NASA

Venus appears as the brightest planet and the third brightest object in the sky (after the Sun and the Moon). It has a very thick atmosphere and an atmospheric pressure at its surface that is 90 times that at Earth's surface. Because the atmosphere on Venus is 96 percent carbon dioxide, the greenhouse effect makes it the hottest planet in the solar system with a surface temperature of more than 500°C. Venus rotates "backward," that is, east to west. Its rotation is the slowest of all of the planets; Venus makes a little less than one rotation for each revolution around the Sun. This means that 1 day on Venus is 243 Earth days, while 1 year is shorter: 225 Earth days! Like Mercury, Venus has no moons.

Venus   Earth

Venus facts

Type: terrestrial
Moons: 0
Distance from Sun: 0.72 AU
Diameter: 0.95 × Earth
Surface gravity: 91% of Earth
Avg. surface temp.: 460°C
Atmosphere: dense, 96% CO_2
Length of day: 243 Earth days
Length of year: 225 Earth days
Venus was named after the Roman goddess of love because of its beautiful, shiny appearance.

Earth and Mars

Earth

Photo courtesy NASA/JPL-Caltech

Earth is a small, rocky planet with an atmosphere that is made of mostly nitrogen (78 percent) and oxygen (21 percent). Earth is one of only two bodies in the solar system known to have liquid water (the other is Europa, a moon of Jupiter). Earth has an active geology, including volcanoes and crustal movement. Earth's atmosphere, along with its vast oceans and moderate temperature range, supports an incredible variety of life. *As far as we know,* Earth is the only planet in the solar system to support life. Although space probes have begun searching, the ultimate answer to the question of life on other planets may have to wait until humans can look in person. Earth's single rocky moon is about one-quarter the diameter of Earth. At a distance of 384,400 kilometers, the Moon is about 30 Earth-diameters away from the planet, completing one orbit every 27.3 days.

Mars

Photo courtesy of ESA

Mars appears as a reddish point of light in the night sky. It has a widely varied surface that includes deserts, huge valleys and craters, and volcanic mountains that dwarf those on Earth. The atmosphere of Mars is very thin (about 0.7 percent as thick as that of Earth) and composed mostly of carbon dioxide, while the rest is nitrogen and argon. The temperatures are below freezing most of the time. Like Earth, Mars has polar ice caps, but they are composed of a combination of water and frozen carbon dioxide. Because it has an axial tilt, Mars experiences seasons like Earth. A day on Mars (24.6 hours) is similar in length to Earth, while a year (687 days) is not. Mars has two small moons named Phobos and Deimos.

Earth facts

Type: terrestrial
Moons: 1
Distance from Sun: 1 AU
Diameter: 12,800 km
Surface gravity: 9.8 N/kg
Avg. surface temp.: 10°C
Atmosphere: dense, N_2, O_2
Length of day: 24 hours
Length of year: 365.25 days
Earth is the only planet not named after a Roman god. Its name comes from Old English oerthe, *meaning "land" or "country."*

Mars   Earth

Mars facts

Type: terrestrial
Moons: 2
Distance from Sun: 1.5 AU
Diameter: 0.53 × Earth
Surface gravity: 38% of Earth
Avg. surface temp.: −50°C
Atmosphere: thin, CO_2
Length of day: 24.6 hours
Length of year: 687 Earth days
Mars' red color reminded ancient observers of blood so they named it after the Roman god of war.

Jupiter and Saturn

Jupiter

Photo courtesy of NASA

Jupiter is the largest of the planets, and the fastest rotator, spinning on its axis about once every 10 hours. A year on Jupiter is about 12 Earth years. Jupiter is more liquid than gaseous or solid—more than half of its volume is an ocean of liquid hydrogen. Its atmosphere is about 88 percent hydrogen and 11 percent helium. The atmospheric pressure below Jupiter's thick clouds is more than a million times that of Earth! It has a very stormy atmosphere and one storm known as the Great Red Spot has been observed for more than 300 years. Jupiter's mass is greater than the combined masses of all of the other planets, but its density is very low—about one-quarter that of Earth. With 63 moons, Jupiter is like a mini solar system.

Earth

Jupiter

Jupiter facts

Type: gas giant
Moons: 63, plus faint rings
Distance from Sun: 5.2 AU
Diameter: 11.2 × Earth
Surface gravity: 253% of Earth
Avg. atmos. temp.: −108°C
Atmosphere: 88% H, 10% He
Length of day: 10 Earth hours
Length of year: 11.9 Earth years
Jupiter was king of the Roman gods. The planet's great brightness inspired its name.

Saturn

Photo courtesy NASA.

Saturn, at almost 10 times the size of Earth, is the second largest planet. Like Jupiter, Saturn's atmosphere is made mostly of hydrogen and helium. Saturn is a fast rotator, though slightly slower than Jupiter, with a day on Saturn lasting just longer than 10 Earth hours. A year on Saturn is about 29 Earth years. The most striking feature of Saturn is its system of rings (above, right), which are visible from Earth with a telescope. Saturn's rings are made up of billions of particles of rock and ice ranging from microscopic to the size of a house. Although they are hundreds of thousands of kilometers wide, the rings are less than 100 meters thick. With 47 moons, Saturn is also like a mini solar system.

Earth

Saturn

Saturn facts

Type: gas giant
Moons: 47, plus rings
Distance from Sun: 9.5 AU
Diameter: 9.4 × Earth
Surface gravity: 1.06% of Earth
Avg. atmos. temp.: −139°C
Atmosphere: 96% H, 3% He
Length of day: 10.7 Earth hours
Length of year: 29.5 Earth years
Because of its slow orbit around the Sun, Saturn was named after the Roman god of agriculture and time.

Uranus and Neptune

Uranus

Photo courtesy of NASA

The seventh planet from the Sun, Uranus can barely be seen without a good telescope and was not discovered until 1781. It rotates "backward" and has an axis that is tilted 98 degrees to the plane of its orbit. A day on Uranus is only 18 Earth hours, but a year takes 84 Earth years. Uranus has at least 27 moons, all of them relatively small. Titania, the largest, has only 4 percent the mass of Earth's moon.

Neptune

Photo courtesy of NASA

Neptune, the eighth planet from the Sun, is the outermost of the gas planets. It was discovered in 1846 and its discovery almost doubled the diameter of the known solar system because of its great distance from the Sun. Neptune's orbit is nearly a perfect circle; only Venus has a more circular orbit. A day on Neptune is only 16 hours long but a year takes 165 Earth years! Neptune has a series of faint rings invisible from Earth but that have been seen in photographs taken by space probes such as Voyager. Neptune has 13 known moons, 6 of which were found in photographs taken by *Voyager 2* in 1989. Of the eight moons, only Triton is bigger than a few hundred kilometers.

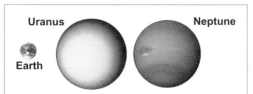

Uranus facts

Type: gas giant
Moons: 27, plus rings
Distance from Sun: 19.1 AU
Diameter: 4 × Earth
Surface gravity: 90% of Earth
Avg. atmos. temp.: −197°C
Atmosphere: 82% H, 15% He
Length of day: 18 Earth hours
Length of year: 84 Earth years
Uranus is the first planet discovered in modern times and is named after the first Roman god.

Neptune facts

Type: gas giant
Moons: 13, plus rings
Distance from Sun: 30 AU
Diameter: 3.9 × Earth
Surface gravity: 114% of Earth
Avg. atmos. temp.: −201°C
Atmosphere: 96% H, 3% He
Length of day: 16 Earth hours
Length of year: 165 Earth years
Because it is so far in the depths of space, Neptune was named after the Roman god of the deep sea.

Comparing the planets

Table 17.1: Comparing the properties of the planets

Property	Mercury	Venus	Earth	Mars	Jupiter	Saturn	Uranus	Neptune
Diameter (km)	4,878	12,102	12,756	6,794	142,796	120,660	51,200	49,500
Mass (kg)	3.3×10^{23}	4.9×10^{24}	6.0×10^{24}	6.4×10^{23}	1.9×10^{27}	5.7×10^{26}	8.7×10^{25}	1.0×10^{26}
Density (g/cm³)	5.44	5.25	5.52	3.91	1.31	0.69	1.21	1.67
Average distance from the Sun (km)	58 million	108 million	150 million	228 million	778 million	1.43 billion	2.87 billion	4.50 billion
Moons (number of)	0	0	1	2	63	47	27	13
Gravitational force (N/kg)	3.7	8.9	9.8	3.7	23.1	9.0	8.7	11.0
Surface temperature (°C)	−170 to +400	+450 to +480	−88 to +48	−89 to −31	−108	−139	−197	−201
Rotation period (Earth days)	59	243	1	1.03	0.41	0.43	0.72	0.67
Revolution period (Earth years)	0.24	0.62	1	1.9	12	29	84	165
Major gases in atmosphere	Na	CO_2	N_2, O_2	CO_2	H_2, He, CH_4, NH_3	H_2, He, CH_4, NH_3	H_2, He, CH_4, NH_3	H_2, He, CH_4, NH_3

17.2 Section Review

1. Which planet has the most extreme temperature variations?
2. Which planet looks brightest in the sky?
3. Mercury is most similar to:
   a. Earth's moon.
   b. Saturn.
   c. Venus.
   d. Mars.
4. Which planet is most similar to Earth in diameter, gravitational strength, and composition?
5. Which planet has the longest year? Which planet has the shortest?
6. Which planet has the longest day? Which planet has the shortest?
7. After Earth, which planet would be the best candidate to support life? Explain your reasoning.
8. What makes up Saturn's rings?
9. Is Saturn the only planet with rings?
10. Which planets rotate backward?
11. Why is Jupiter sometimes called a "mini solar system"?
12. Order the following planets from largest to smallest: Uranus, Mars, Venus, Earth, Neptune, Jupiter, Mercury, Saturn.
13. Compared with Earth's diameter, Saturn's diameter is roughly:
    a. the same.   b. five times larger.
    c. 10 times larger.   d. 50 times larger.

MY JOURNAL

Suppose you were given the opportunity to travel to another planet or to a moon of another planet. Would you go? Why or why not? Would you go to Neptune, knowing the trip would last 20 years? What if you could bring along anything and anyone you wanted? Write an essay exploring your answers to these questions.

17.3 Other Solar System Objects

Triton is Neptune's largest moon (Figure 17.8). Pluto is a dwarf planet, and most of the time it is the farthest object from the Sun. Triton and Pluto are similar objects in both composition and size. In fact, Pluto is slightly smaller than Triton and only a fraction larger than Earth's moon. Some astronomers believe Pluto may actually be an "escaped" moon of Neptune. In this section, you will learn about dwarf planets like Pluto and other solar system objects like asteroids and comets.

Figure 17.8: *Triton is Neptune's largest moon. Some astronomers believe that Pluto may be an "escaped" moon of Neptune. (Photo courtesy of NASA.)*

Pluto and the Kuiper Belt

Pluto

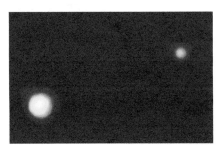

Photo courtesy of NASA

Discovered in 1930, Pluto was named for the Roman god of the underworld. The first dwarf planet discovered, Pluto rotates slowly—one turn every six days—and backward. Its orbit is strongly elliptical and Pluto crosses the path of Neptune for about 20 years out of the 249 years it takes to revolve around the Sun. Their orbits are not in the Same plane, so Neptune and Pluto will never collide. Because it is so far away, little is known about Pluto. The image above, from the Hubble Space Telescope, shows Pluto and its single "moon," Charon.

Are there 8, 9, or 11+ planets?

Outside the orbit of Pluto is a region called the Kuiper (rhymes with "viper") Belt (Figure 17.9). The Kuiper Belt stretches to 1,000 AU and is believed to contain a few Pluto-size objects and many smaller ones. At least three Pluto-size bodies have been found—Sedna, Xena, and Quaoar. To avoid confusion, astronomers no longer count Pluto as a planet. Instead, Pluto is grouped along with similar distant objects in the Kuiper Belt, known as Kuiper Belt Objects (or KBOs).

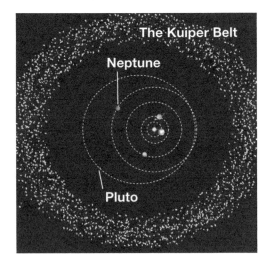

Figure 17.9: *The Kuiper Belt lies beyond Neptune.*

Asteroids and comets

Asteroids Between Mars and Jupiter, at a distance of 320 million to 495 million kilometers, there is a huge gap that cuts the solar system in two. This gap is called the *asteroid belt* because it is filled with thousands of small, rocky bodies called asteroids. An **asteroid** is an object that orbits the Sun but is too small to be considered a planet. So far, more than 10,000 asteroids have been discovered and more are found each year.

The size of asteroids Most asteroids are small—less than a kilometer in diameter—but many have been found that are over 250 kilometers in diameter. The largest asteroid, named Ceres, is 933 kilometers (580 miles) across. While the majority of asteroids are found in the asteroid belt, many have highly-elliptical orbits that allow them to come close to Mercury, Venus, and even Earth. About 65 million years ago, a large asteroid hit Earth near Mexico, leaving a huge crater. Many scientists hypothesize that this event led to the extinction of the dinosaurs.

Comets

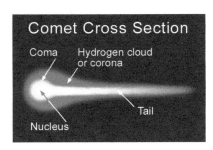

We believe **comets** are made mostly of ice and dust. The ones we can detect are about the size of an Earth mountain. Comets revolve around the Sun in highly elliptical orbits. As a comet approaches the Sun, some of its ice turns into gas and dust and forms an outer layer called a *coma*. The inner core of the comet is the *nucleus*. As a comet gets closer to the Sun, it forms a *tail*. A comet's tail can stretch for millions of kilometers into space. It points away from the Sun due to the "solar wind" as the comet continues its orbit (Figure 17.11). Each time a comet passes the Sun, it loses some of its mass.

 VOCABULARY

asteroid - an object that orbits the Sun but is too small to be considered a planet.

comet - an object in space made mostly of ice and dust.

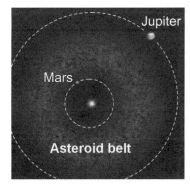

Figure 17.10: *The asteroid belt.*

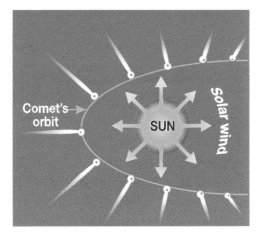

Figure 17.11: *A comet's tail points away from the Sun due to solar wind.*

Meteors and meteorites

Meteors   Occasionally, chunks of rock or dust break off from a comet or asteroid and form a **meteor**. Imagine a tennis ball traveling at about 30,000 miles per hour. That's about the size and speed of most meteors. These chunks of dust or rock travel through space and some of them end up hitting Earth's atmosphere. When this happens, meteors rub against air particles and create friction, heating them to more than 2,000°C. The intense heat vaporizes most meteors, creating a streak of light known as a "shooting star." Occasionally, larger meteors cause a brighter flash called a *fireball*. These sometimes cause an explosion that can be heard up to 30 miles away. On average, a meteor can be seen in the night sky about every 10 minutes—so keep your eyes to the skies!

Meteor showers   When a comet nears the Sun, a trail of dust and other debris burns off and remains in orbit around the Sun. As Earth orbits the Sun, it passes through this debris, creating a *meteor shower* as the small bits of dust burn up in the atmosphere. During a meteor shower, you can see tens and even hundreds of meteors per hour. Because Earth passes the same dust clouds from comets each year, meteor showers can be predicted with accuracy.

Meteorites   If a meteor is large enough to survive the passage through Earth's atmosphere and strike its surface, it becomes a **meteorite**. Meteorites are thought to be fragments from collisions involving asteroids. Most meteorites weigh only a few pounds or less and cause little damage when they hit. Most fall into the oceans that cover almost three-quarters of our planet's surface. Meteor Crater, in Winslow, Arizona, is believed to have been caused by a giant, 50-meter-diameter meteorite about 50,000 years ago (Figure 17.12).

VOCABULARY

meteor - a chunk of burning rock traveling through Earth's atmosphere.

meteorite - a meteor that passes through Earth's atmosphere and strikes the surface.

Meteor Crater
Winslow, Arizona

Photo by by David J. Roddy, USGS.

Figure 17.12: *Meteor Crater in Arizona was formed by a meteor strike about 50,000 years ago. The meteor that formed it is calculated to have been no more than 50 meters in diameter.*

17.3 **Section Review**

1. Why is Neptune sometimes farther from the Sun than dwarf planet Pluto?

2. Why will Pluto and Neptune never collide?

3. How many moons does dwarf planet Pluto have?

4. What is the Kuiper Belt? Where is it located?

5. What is an asteroid?

6. Where is the asteroid belt located?

7. What event do scientists believe caused mass extinctions about 65 million years ago?

8. What is the difference between an asteroid and a comet?

9. Name three parts of a comet.

10. What feature forms on a comet as it approaches the Sun?

11. What is the difference between a meteor and a meteorite?

12. What is a "shooting star"?

13. Why can the dates for meteor showers be predicted with accuracy?

14. Where do scientists think meteorites come from?

Kuiper Belt Research

The Kuiper Belt was discovered in 1992, yet its existence was predicted in 1952. Conduct research on the Kuiper Belt to answer the following questions.

1. What technology led to the discovery of the Kuiper Belt?

2. What evidence was used to predict its existence?

3. What is the largest Kuiper Belt Object found to date?

4. How do astronomers look for objects in the Kuiper Belt?

Dwarf Planets

The International Astronomical Union (IAU) is an organization that promotes and safeguards the science of astronomy. It is considered an authority in the astronomical field. The organization brings together distinguished astronomers from all over the world every three years.

Goodbye, Pluto!

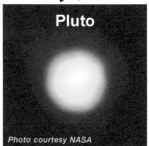

Pluto

Photo courtesy NASA

On August 24, 2006, in Prague, Czech Republic, there was big news at the IAU meeting. Pluto (shown left) was dropped as the ninth planet in the solar system. In order for this to happen, astronomers had to vote on the definition of the term *planet*. In the process, they classified Pluto and some other objects as something other than a planet. They agreed on the term *dwarf planet*. As of this writing, there are three dwarf planets in the solar system, Pluto being one of them. Ceres (upper right), and Eris (below) are the other two. There is a list of dwarf planet candidates being studied to see if they also fit the definition. As of this writing, the eight planets in the solar system are now Mercury, Venus, Earth, Mars, Jupiter, Saturn, Uranus, and Neptune.

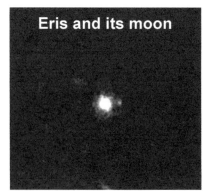

Eris and its moon

Photo courtesy W.M. Keck Observatory

Planet redefined

By a majority vote, the new definition of a planet in the solar system is a celestial body that (1) is in orbit around the Sun, (2) is nearly round in shape, and (3) has cleared its orbit of other objects. What this last part means is that a planet is large enough that as it revolves around the Sun, the other objects in its orbit have either become part of the planet by fusing with it or have collided with the planet and moved out of the planet's orbit.

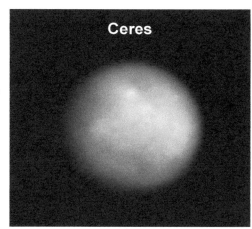

Ceres

Photo courtesy of NASA, ESA, STScI, J. Parker, P. Thomas, L. McFadden

What's a dwarf planet?

By a majority vote, the definition of a dwarf planet in the solar system is a celestial body that (1) is in orbit around the Sun, (2) is nearly round in shape, (3) has *not* cleared its orbit of other objects, and (4) is *not* a satellite (body in orbit around a planet or other body larger than itself). A dwarf planet cannot clear objects out of its orbit because it is too small in mass to significantly alter its environment. For example, Pluto overlaps the orbit of Neptune, which disqualifies it as a planet.

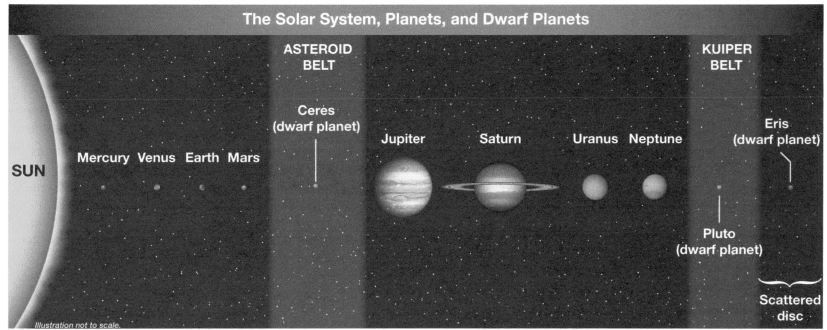

The Solar System, Planets, and Dwarf Planets

Illustration not to scale.

Planet photos courtesy of NASA.

The dwarf planets

Some dwarf planets include

- *Pluto*, which is located among the Kuiper (rhymes with "viper") Belt Objects (KBOs);
- *Ceres*, which is located in the asteroid belt between Mars and Jupiter and;
- *Eris*, which is a Scattered Disc Object (SDO).

Both Scattered Disc Objects and Kuiper Belt Objects are Trans-Neptunian objects (TNOs). This means they are found in a region past Neptune with many comet-like objects. Ceres is the smallest dwarf planet with a diameter of approximately 950 kilometers. Pluto has a diameter of approximately 2,300 kilometers. Eris is the largest with a diameter of approximately 2,400 kilometers.

QUESTIONS

1. What is the difference between a planet and dwarf planet?
2. What is similar about the definition of a planet and dwarf planet?
3. What planet does Pluto's orbit overlap?
4. Name the three dwarf planets in order of size.
5. Two dwarf planets are located in a region of space beyond Neptune and so are called TNOs. Which dwarf planets are these?

Extraterrestrial Design

The plants and animals that live on Earth are uniquely suited to Earth's environment. As humans, our bodies are able to withstand the Earth's temperate climate. We survive by breathing the air in Earth's atmosphere, and by drinking the fresh water in Earth's rivers and lakes. Although no life has yet been found on other planets, it may be possible for some form of life to live on another planet in our solar system, and scientists are continually brainstorming what life might be like on a different planet than Earth. In this activity, you will create an organism that could live on another planet. Follow the guidelines to develop your organism, and be creative!

What you will do

1. Choose any of the planets in our solar system, except Earth.

2. Develop an organism or animal that can survive on this planet. Make sure you explain how your organism overcomes the harsh climate present on its planet. For example, if an animal lived on Mercury, it would need special protection to survive extreme hot and cold temperatures.

3. Explain how your organism exchanges elements with its atmosphere or soil, and how it moves around the planet. For instance, how does it "breathe" if there is no atmosphere? How would an organism move around a planet such as Jupiter, which does not have a solid surface? How would your organism deal with the extra gravity on a planet such as Neptune?

Planet	Temperature range	Weight of a 100-lb Earthling	Length of day	Length of year	Interesting fact
Mercury	−300°F to 870°F	38 lbs	59 days	88 days	No atmosphere; many craters
Venus	850°F	91 lbs	243 days	225 days	Dense atmosphere mostly CO_2 and N_2
Mars	−190°F to 98°F	38 lbs	24 hours	687 days	Water trapped in frozen poles
Jupiter	−244°F	254 lbs	10 hours	11.8 years	No solid surface; H_2O and H_2 oceans
Saturn	−300°F	108 lbs	10 hours	29.5 years	No solid surface, icy rings
Uranus	−300°F	91 lbs	17.2 hours	84 years	Atmosphere mostly H_2, He, methane; possible water
Neptune	−370°F	119 lbs	16 hours	165 years	Atmosphere mostly H_2, He, methane

Chapter 17 Assessment

Vocabulary

Select the correct term to complete the sentences.

gravitational force	planet	comet
satellite	orbit	solar system
gas planets	asteroid	meteorite
astronomical unit	axis	law of universal
meteor	terrestrial planets	gravitation

Section 17.1

1. A(n) _____ is a massive object orbiting a star like the Sun.

2. The _____ includes the Sun and all objects that are gravitationally bound to it.

3. The _____ states that the strength of gravity depends on the mass of the objects and the distance between them.

4. The force of attraction between all objects is known as _____.

5. An object that is in orbit around another object is called a(n) _____.

6. Planets follow a regular, repeating path around the Sun called a(n) _____.

7. The _____ of a planet is an imaginary line through its center from pole to pole.

8. The distance from Earth to the Sun, or 1.0 _____, is equal to 150 million kilometers.

Section 17.2

9. _____ are made mostly of rock and metal.

10. _____ are made mostly of hydrogen and helium gases.

Section 17.3

11. A(n) _____'s tail faces away from the Sun and can stretch for millions of kilometers into space.

12. Most _____s are less than a kilometer in diameter.

13. A chunk of burning rock traveling through Earth's atmosphere is called a(n) _____.

14. Unlike a meteor, a(n) _____ passes through Earth's atmosphere and strikes the surface.

Concepts

Section 17.1

1. According to the law of universal gravitation, the force of gravity acting between two objects involves two variables. Name these two variables.

2. Describe the factors that keep a satellite in orbit.

3. Name one difference between a planet and a star.

4. List the planets in order, from closest to farthest, from the Sun.

5. How is a year defined on a planet? How is a day defined?

6. What are astronomical units and how are they used?

Section 17.2

7. What are the differences between terrestrial planets and gas planets? Which type is Neptune?

8. What is the largest planet in the solar system? What is the smallest planet?

9. Earth has a day that is 24 hours long. Which planet has a day of about the same length as Earth's?

10. Mercury is closer to the Sun than Venus, but Venus has higher surface temperatures. Explain why.

11. Which planets, beside Earth, have an atmosphere?

12. What is the Great Red Spot observed on Jupiter?

Section 17.3

13. What is the difference between a meteor and a meteorite?

14. Compare asteroids to comets by filling in the blanks of the table below.

Object	Size	Material	Orbit shape	Location
Asteroid				
Comet				

Math and Writing Skills

Section 17.1

1. A large truck weighs 6,990 pounds on Earth. Would you expect the truck to weigh more or less on Jupiter? Explain your answer.

2. The moon is approximately 385,000 km from Earth. What is this distance in astronomical units? (*Hint*: 1 AU = 150,000,000 km)

3. Write a short story about a day in the life of an extra-terrestrial creature that lives on Jupiter.

4. Why is the Sun the dominant object in the solar system in terms of gravitational force?

Section 17.2

5. Using the density data from Table 17.1 on page 412, make a bar graph comparing the densities of the planets. Explain the density differences among the planets.

6. Use the data in Table 17.1 on page 412 to answer the following questions.
   a. Which planet would float in a giant bathtub of water?
   b. Which planet has the most moons? What data from the table explains why?
   c. Which planets have similar atmospheres? Why do you think their atmospheres are similar?
   d. Make a graph of mass versus gravitational force. Does the graph show a strong, medium, or weak relationship? Explain the reason behind your answer.

Section 17.3

7. You have just discovered a new solar system object (shown at right)! Write a letter to another astronomer about your object. Classify it as one of the objects you learned about in this chapter and explain your choice. Give it a name!

Chapter Project—Solar System Mobile

Make a mobile of the solar system. You will need: cardboard, string, scissors, tape, many colors of construction paper, colored pencils, and a compass (for making circles). Follow these steps:

   a. Make circles to represent the planets using different colors of construction paper. Write the name of the planet on one side, and some interesting facts on the other side.
   b. Cut out a large circle (about 40 cm in diameter) of the cardboard. Draw the Sun in the center of the circle. Then, draw orbits around the Sun for each planet.
   c. Tape string to each planet and hang them from their orbits below the cardboard circle. You may add comets, asteroids, and dwarf planets, too!
   d. Tape a string to the top of the cardboard circle so you can hang your mobile.

Earth, the Moon, and the Sun

Even though you are sitting reading this book, you are moving really fast! The planet on which you are sitting spins at a speed of 1,000 miles per hour. Earth also revolves around the Sun. Since the Sun is 93 million miles away, the total distance Earth must travel through one complete trip around the Sun is close to 600 million miles. Since Earth travels this distance in only 365.25 days, its average speed is 66,000 miles per hour! The Moon is also a fast-mover. To make a complete revolution around Earth in 27.3 days, it speeds along at over 2,000 miles per hour! The Moon also rotates on its axis, although slowly. It takes the Moon 27.3 days to complete one rotation—the exact amount of time it takes it to revolve around Earth! This is why we always see the same side of the Moon from Earth. Did you know that the Sun also rotates? But since it's made of a gas, different parts of it rotate at different speeds. Near the Sun's equator, it completes one rotation every 27 Earth days. But near the poles, it takes about 31 Earth days. Read on to learn more!

Key Questions:

1. Where did the Moon come from?

2. Why are there cycles on Earth?

3. What is the Sun?

Image courtesy of NASA

18.1 Earth and Its Moon

Revolving around Earth at a distance of 384,400 kilometers is our only moon. Since the invention of spacecraft, our knowledge of Earth and the Moon has grown tremendously. In fact, humans have only walked on Earth and—thanks to spacecraft—the Moon. In this section, you will learn important information about the Moon and how it compares to Earth.

Earth's shape and orbit

Earth's shape Earth's shape is almost spherical except for a slight bulge at the equator. If you were to travel exactly once around along the equator, you would travel 40,076 kilometers. This distance is the *circumference* of Earth. The *diameter*, or the distance from one side to the other through the center, is 12,756 kilometers and its radius at the equator is equal to half of this value, or 6,378 kilometers (Figure 18.1). Because of its slight bulge at the equator, if you were to measure the radius from one of the poles it would be slightly less (6,357 kilometers).

Earth's orbit around the Sun In Chapter 17, you read that the orbits of the planets are slightly elliptical but almost circular. Also, the Sun is not at the center of Earth's orbit. Because of this, the distance from Earth to the Sun changes as Earth revolves. Earth's minimum distance from the Sun is 146 million kilometers. Its maximum distance is 152 million kilometers. At any two points during its orbit, Earth is at a slightly different distance from the Sun. Figure 18.2 shows the distance of Earth from the Sun at the beginning of each season in the northern hemisphere.

Diameter
Distance through the center
(12,756 km)

Radius
Half the diameter
(6,378 km)

Circumference
Distance around the Equator
(40,076 km)

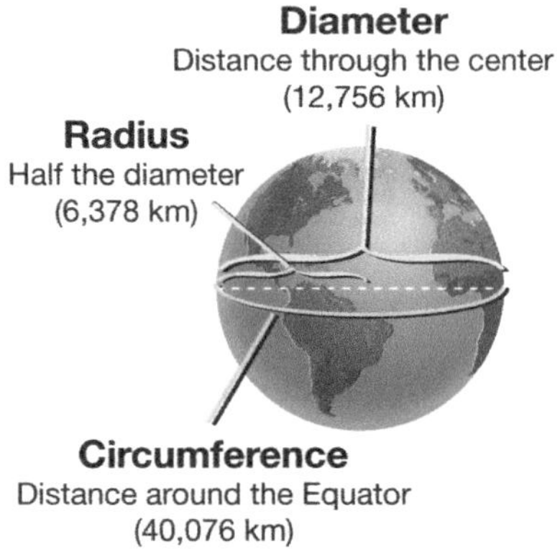

Figure 18.1: *Earth's dimensions.*

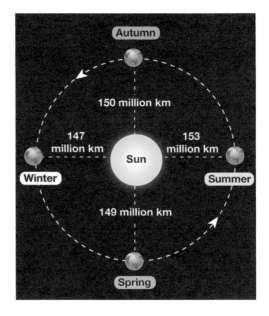

Figure 18.2: *Earth's distance from the Sun at the start of each season in the northern hemisphere.*

Comparing Earth and the Moon

How far away is the Moon? Earth's only moon revolves around us at a distance of 384,400 kilometers. While this may seem like a great distance, it is only a fraction of the distance between Earth and the Sun (an average of 150 million kilometers).

Diameter, mass, and density If you travel in a relatively straight line from Boston, Massachusetts, to Salt Lake City, Utah, you will have covered a distance that is about equal to the Moon's diameter of 3,476 kilometers. The Moon is about one quarter the size of Earth and its mass is 7.3×10^{22} kilograms, which is about one one-hundredth of Earth's mass. Because of the Moon's small mass, its gravity does not attract an atmosphere. Its density is 3.34 g/cm^3, which is much lower than Earth's. Figure 18.3 compares Earth and the Moon.

Gravitational force Because the Moon has much less mass, its gravitational force is about one sixth as strong as the gravity on Earth. Earth exerts a gravitational force of 9.8 newtons on a 1-kilogram object. The Moon exerts a gravitational force of only 1.6 newtons on the same object. This means that a 1-kilogram object weighs 9.8 newtons (2.2 pounds) on Earth and the same object weighs only 1.6 newtons (0.36 pounds) on the Moon. A 2,500 pound car would weigh only 408 pounds on the Moon!

The Moon's rotation If you have ever observed the Moon, you may have noticed that the same side of it faces Earth at all times. This does not mean that the Moon does not rotate. The Moon rotates much more slowly than Earth. Over millions of years, Earth's gravity has *locked* the Moon's rotation to its orbit around Earth. One lunar "day" takes 27.3 Earth days, exactly the same time it takes the Moon to complete one orbit around Earth (Figure 18.4).

Property	Earth	Moon
Diameter	12,756 km	3,476 km
Gravity	9.8 N/kg	1.6 N/kg
Mass	6.0×10^{24} kg	7.3×10^{22} kg
Density	5.52 g/cm^3	3.34 g/cm^3
Rotation period	1 day	27.3 days

Figure 18.3: *Comparing Earth and the Moon.*

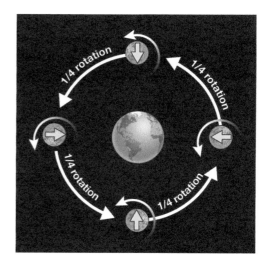

Figure 18.4: *The amount of time it takes the Moon to complete a rotation is the same amount of time it takes it to revolve around Earth. Can you see why only one side of the Moon faces Earth at all times?*

How the Moon was formed

Where did the Moon come from? Throughout history, there have been many different theories about the origin of the Moon. Before the Apollo landings that began in 1969, there were three main theories.

1.   Some scientists hypothesized that the Moon split off Earth during a period of very fast rotation.

2.   Others thought that the Moon formed somewhere else and was "captured" by Earth's gravity.

3.   Still others proposed that the Moon and Earth were formed together from a group of smaller chunks of matter when the solar system formed.

Analyzing lunar rocks

Photo courtesy NASA

When scientists analyzed lunar rocks, they found that they were composed of much less iron and nickel than Earth. Recall that Earth's *core* is composed mostly of iron and nickel. The composition of lunar rocks closely resembled that of Earth's *mantle*. They also found that the Moon's density was the same as Earth's mantle and crust combined.

The giant impact theory These discoveries gave rise to the giant impact theory that is widely accepted today. This theory proposes that about 4.5 billion years ago, an object about the size of Mars collided with Earth, causing material from Earth's mantle and crust to break off. This material, combined with material from the colliding object, was thrown into orbit around Earth and became the Moon. The Moon's spherical shape was a result of gravity and the remaining particles impacted the Moon to form craters. Figure 18.5 shows how the Moon was formed based on this theory.

 VOCABULARY

giant impact theory - a scientific theory that explains how the Moon was formed.

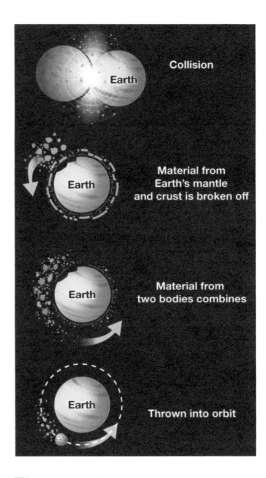

Figure 18.5: *The giant impact theory of the Moon's formation.*

Surface features of the Moon

Craters

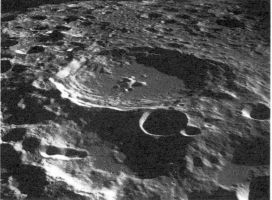

Photo courtesy NASA

If you look at the Moon through a telescope, you can see the three main features of its surface: craters, highlands, and maria (Figure 18.6). **Craters** are large, round pits that cover much of the Moon's surface. For many years astronomers believed they were caused by volcanoes. It was only about 50 years ago that scientists concluded that the craters were caused by the impact of meteoroids—large rocks from space. One of the Moon's largest craters, named Copernicus, is hundreds of kilometers across.

Highlands and marias

When you look at the Moon, some areas appear bright, while others appear dark. The brighter areas are called *highlands* because they are higher in elevation. The darker areas are called *maria* (Latin for "seas") because early observers believed they were oceans. Maria are actually low, dry areas that were flooded with molten lava billions of years ago when the Moon was formed. Among the maria you can see through a telescope is a large one named the Sea of Rains.

Image courtesy of the Image Science & Analysis Laboratory, NASA Johnson Space Center

 VOCABULARY

craters - large, round pits formed by impacts from large space objects.

Sea of Rains (maria)

Copernicus (crater)

Highlands

Photo courtesy NASA/JPL-Caltech

Figure 18.6: *The three main features of the surface of the Moon.*

Tides

Tides are caused by the Moon's gravity

As Earth rotates beneath the Moon, its mass feels a small, "Moonward" force of 0.00003 N from the Moon's gravity. Earth is made of rock that resists this small force, but because water flows, the Moon causes water to slide toward the place directly under the Moon on Earth's surface (Figure 18.7). In most places, ocean levels rise and fall twice each day as the Moon revolves around Earth and Earth rotates. The daily cycle of rising and falling ocean levels is called a **tide**. The Moon passes overhead once every 24 hours. So, you would expect the tide to rise only once every 24 hours. But the oceans on the side of Earth directly *opposite* the Moon also rise. What causes this "second" tide?

The center of mass

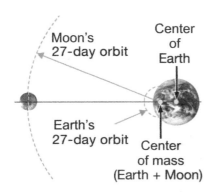

The answer is that the Moon does not really orbit Earth as if Earth were fixed in place. Instead, Earth and the Moon orbit around a common *center of mass*. Imagine balancing Earth and the Moon on a giant see-saw. There is a point at which the see-saw balances even though Earth is much heavier than the Moon. That point is the center of mass of the Earth–Moon system.

Explaining the "second" tide

When you turn a corner sharply in a car, your body slides to the outside of the curve, away from the center. This happens because your body wants to move in a straight line in the direction it was going *before* the turn. This is the explanation for the tide on the side of Earth that does not face the Moon. As Earth revolves around the center of mass, the ocean on the opposite side from the Moon is "flung outward" a little by its own inertia (Figure 18.8).

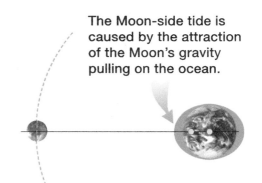

tide - a cycle of rising and falling ocean levels.

The Moon-side tide is caused by the attraction of the Moon's gravity pulling on the ocean.

Figure 18.7: *The cause of the Moon-side tide.*

The far-side tide is caused by the ocean being "flung" outwards due to it's own inertia and Earth's 27-day orbit around the center of mass.

Figure 18.8: *The cause of the far-side tide. Note: The tides shown in the diagram are much larger than actual tides.*

18.1 **Section Review**

1. Label the diagram below using these terms: radius, circumference, diameter.

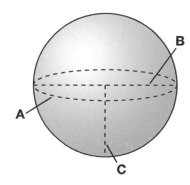

2. For a planet, which is the greatest distance, its diameter or its circumference?

3. Is Earth a perfect sphere? Explain your answer.

4. Why doesn't the Moon have an atmosphere?

5. Why would an elephant weigh much less on the Moon than it weighs on Earth?

6. Arrange the events below in order of occurrence.

    a. Material from Earth's mantle and crust is broken off.

    b. A collision with a large body occurs.

    c. An object is thrown into orbit around Earth.

    d. Material from Earth and an object are combined.

7. Name and describe three features of the Moon that you can see through a telescope.

8. What are tides? What causes the "second" tide on the opposite side of Earth from the Moon?

MY JOURNAL

Photo courtesy NASA

In 1969, Neil Armstrong and Buzz Aldrin were the first people to land a lunar module on the Moon, 384,400 kilometers from Earth. You may have heard of Armstrong's famous phrase, spoken when he stepped out of the module onto the Moon's surface: "That's one small step for man, one giant leap for mankind."

Imagine you are an astronaut on the Moon. Describe everything you see and feel. Use terms that you have learned in this unit so far in your writing.

18.2 Earth Cycles

Do you ever wonder where our calendar comes from? Or why the Moon appears to gradually change its shape? Or why we have seasons? The answers have to do with the relative positions of Earth, the Sun, and the Moon. Earth rotates on its axis as it revolves around the Sun. The Moon rotates on its axis as it revolves around Earth. These movements cause the *astronomical cycles* you experience like days, years, seasons, and the lunar cycle (the Moon's changing shape).

Days and years

Calendars   A *calendar* is a means of keeping track of all the days in a year. Ancient civilizations developed calendars based on their observations of the Sun, Moon, and stars. Many such civilizations independently invented almost identical calendars. Figure 18.9 shows a timeline of various calendars from around the world.

Years and days   As Earth rotates on its axis, it also travels around the Sun. You have learned that one year is the amount of time it takes Earth to complete one revolution around the Sun. This is equal to 365.25 days. Each day is one rotation of Earth on its axis. Since Earth spins from west to east, the Sun appears to travel across the sky from east to west. Ancient observers thought that the Sun really did move across the sky. Can you see why?

Leap years   The ancient Egyptian calendar described in Figure 18.9 added up to 365 days and eventually evolved into the calendar we use today. However, because we know that one year is approximately 365.25 days long, our calendar adjusts for this. It has 11 months with 30 or 31 days each, and one month—February—with 28 days. In a *leap year*, February has 29 days. The extra day every four years makes up for the extra 0.25 days that occur each year.

Calendars throughout human history

20,000 YEARS AGO. Ice-age hunters in Europe scratched lines in bones to mark the passage of days.

7,000 BCE. Babylonians kept a calendar with 29- and 30-day months. They needed to add an extra month every eight years.

4,000 BCE. The Egyptians adopted a solar calendar with 365 days in a year. This was divided into 12 months, each with 30 days, and an extra five days at the end.

2,000 BCE. Mayans of Central America calculated that there were 365.25 days in a year.

700 BCE. The Roman calendar consisted of 10 months in a year of 304 days. It ignored the remaining 61 days, which fell in the middle of winter.

46 BCE. Romans adopted the Julian calendar, named after Julius Caesar. It is very close to the modern calendar we use today.

Figure 18.9: *Calendars throughout human history.*

Keeping track of time

The time of day A *clock* tells you the exact time of day and is used to mark the division of the day into equal parts. It may be hard to imagine, but there once was a time when humans did not need to keep track of the exact time of day. The rise and fall of the Sun was the only "clock" that prehistoric humans needed to regulate their daily activities. Then, around 5,000 years ago, some civilizations found the need to keep track of time.

Obelisks and sundials The ancient Egyptians divided the day into parts that were similar to hours. As early as 3500 BCE, monuments called *obelisks* were built to separate the day into parts. These monuments cast a shadow that moved during the day as the Sun appeared to move across the sky. Markers were placed around the base of the monument to mark the subdivisions of time during the day (Figure 18.10). Obelisks evolved into *sundials* and these became more and more accurate (Figure 18.11).

Water clocks *Water clocks* were an early way to keep track of time at night (Figure 18.11). Early water clocks were stone containers with sloping sides that allowed water to drip at a constant rate through a small hole in the bottom. Markings on the inside surface of the container measured the passage of "hours."

Modern clocks Today we divide each rotation of Earth into 24 equal parts called *hours*. Each hour is divided up into 60 parts called *minutes* and each minute into 60 parts called *seconds*. Like the water clock, modern clocks use a constant, repetitive action or process to keep track of equal increments of time. Where the water clock used the constant dripping of water, modern clocks use a pendulum, vibrating crystal, balance wheel, electromagnetic waves, or even atoms to mark time.

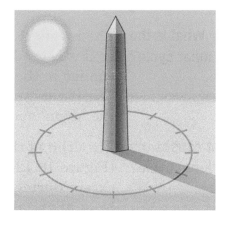

Figure 18.10: *An obelisk allowed ancient Egyptians to divide up the day into parts.*

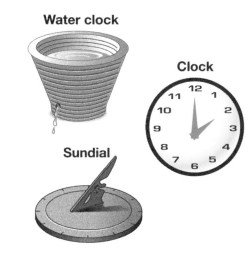

Figure 18.11: *Sundials and water clocks were early ways to keep track of time.*

The lunar cycle

What is the lunar cycle?
The revolution of the Moon around Earth makes the Moon appear as if it is gradually changing shape each night. The gradual change in the appearance of the Moon is called the **lunar cycle**. The lunar cycle occurs because of the relative positions of Earth, the Moon, and the Sun.

What causes the lunar cycle?
The orbit of the Moon is tilted about 5 degrees from Earth's orbit (Figure 18.12). This means the Moon is not in Earth's shadow except during rare *eclipses*. The Sun-facing side of the Moon is lit by sunlight almost all the time. The lunar cycle is caused by the *angle* the Moon makes with Earth and the Sun as it orbits Earth, not by Earth's shadow falling on the Moon.

Moon phases
What you see when you look at the Moon depends on its location in relationship to the Sun and Earth. As the Moon revolves, we see a different fraction of sunlight being reflected from the Moon to Earth. Remember, the Moon doesn't give off light; it reflects the light of the Sun. Although the lunar cycle is a continuous process, there are eight recognized *phases* (see the diagram above)

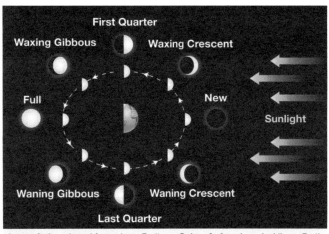

Inner circle - viewed from above Earth **Outer circle** - viewed while on Earth

 VOCABULARY

lunar cycle - the gradual change in the appearance of the Moon due to the positions of Earth, the Moon, and the Sun.

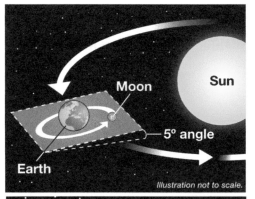

Illustration not to scale.

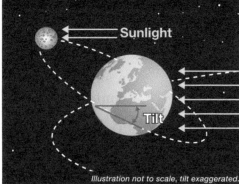

Illustration not to scale, tilt exaggerated.

Figure 18.12: *The orbit of the Moon is tilted at a 5 degree angle compared with Earth's orbit around the Sun (upper diagram). This means that the Moon is not in Earth's shadow (lower diagram).*

New moon — The Moon is not visible (except during a solar eclipse). The lighted side of the Moon faces away from Earth. This means that the Sun, Earth, and the Moon are almost in a straight line, with the Moon in between the Sun and Earth.

Waxing crescent — The lighted fraction of the Moon is increasing. The crescent grows larger and larger each day.

First quarter — The right half of the Moon appears lighted and the left side of the Moon appears dark. The part of the Moon that appears lighted gets larger and larger every day.

Waxing gibbous — *Waxing* means increasing, or growing larger. The Moon appears to be more than half, but not fully, lit by sunlight.

Full moon — The Moon appears to be completely lit by sunlight. The lighted side of the Moon faces Earth. Earth, the Sun, and the Moon are nearly in a straight line, with Earth in the middle.

Waning gibbous — *Waning* means decreasing, or growing smaller. The lighted fraction of the Moon is decreasing. The amount of the Moon that we can see will grow smaller and smaller every day.

Last quarter — The left half of the Moon appears lighted, and the right side of the Moon appears dark. The part of the Moon that appears lighted gets smaller and smaller every day.

Waning crescent — The Moon appears to be less than half lit by sunlight. The fraction of the Moon that is lit is decreasing. The crescent will grow smaller and smaller each day, until the Moon becomes the New Moon.

The length of the lunar cycle — The lunar cycle—from New Moon to New Moon—takes 29.5 days to complete (Figure 18.13). This roughly corresponds to one month. However, if we based our calendar on the lunar cycle, we would soon get ahead of an Earth year. Why? Because a year of lunar cycles adds up to only 354 days, not 365.25, leaving a balance of 11.25 days each year!

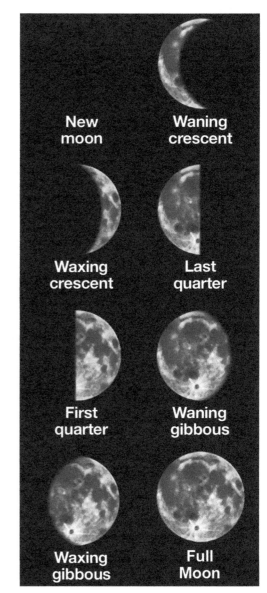

Figure 18.13: *Eight phases of the Moon in the lunar cycle. It takes 29.5 days from New Moon to New Moon.*

Lunar eclipses

The Moon's orbit is tilted
A **lunar eclipse** occurs when Earth's shadow falls on the Moon. If you look at the lunar cycle diagram on page 432, you may wonder why Earth's shadow doesn't cover the Moon when it is between the Moon and the Sun. Instead, you get a Full Moon (Figure 18.14)! The reason a lunar eclipse doesn't occur very often is because of the 5 degree tilt of the Moon's orbit.

Lunar eclipses
Because of its tilted orbit, in most months, Earth's shadow does not block the sunlight from hitting the Moon. However, sometimes the Moon's orbit is perfectly aligned with Earth's orbit during a Full Moon. Because of this alignment, Earth's shadow temporarily blocks the sunlight from hitting the Moon, causing a *lunar eclipse*. As the Moon continues to move in its orbit, it gradually moves into a position where the sunlight hits it again. During a lunar eclipse, the Moon is still visible and appears reddish.

lunar eclipse - an event that occurs when Earth's shadow falls on the Moon.

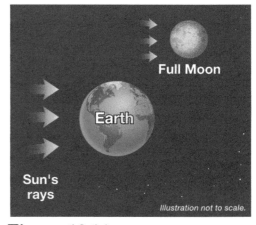

Figure 18.14: *This alignment results in a Full Moon.*

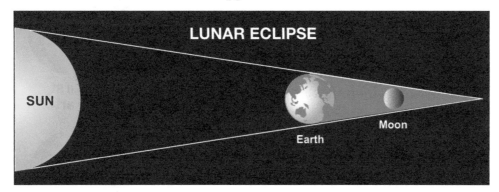

Total and partial lunar eclipses
A lunar eclipse can be total or partial and all observers on the dark side of Earth can see it at the same time. A partial eclipse occurs when only part of the Moon falls in Earth's shadow. Figure 18.15 shows an alignment for a partial eclipse.

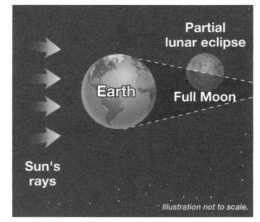

Figure 18.15: *This alignment results in a partial lunar eclipse.*

Solar eclipses

Solar eclipses A **solar eclipse** occurs when the Moon's shadow falls on Earth. During a New Moon, the Moon is almost exactly between Earth and the Sun. Most of the time, however, the Moon travels just above or below the Sun in the sky because of the 5 degree tilt of its orbit. During a *solar eclipse*, the New Moon is directly between Earth and the Sun and the Moon's shadow hits part of Earth as shown below.

solar eclipse - an event that occurs when the Moon's shadow falls on Earth.

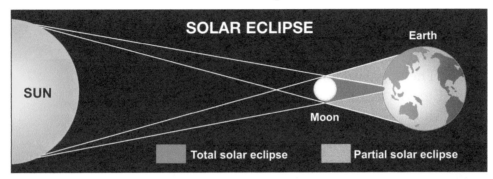

Total solar eclipse The darkest part of the Moon's shadow is cone-shaped and falls on only a small part of Earth's surface. Viewers in this region experience a total eclipse of the Sun because the light is completely blocked by the Moon. During a total eclipse, the Sun gradually disappears behind the Moon and then gradually reappears (Figure 18.16). This is because the Moon revolves around Earth, so it gradually moves into the path of the sunlight, and then gradually moves out again. The Sun is completely blocked by the Moon's shadow for about two or three minutes.

Partial solar eclipse In the diagram above, you can see that the Moon casts a larger, lighter shadow on Earth's surface. Viewers in this region of the Moon's shadow experience a partial eclipse. During this time, only part of the Sun is blocked. You should *never* look directly at the Sun—even during a total or partial eclipse!

Figure 18.16: *A total eclipse is caused by the Moon's shadow blocking out the Sun.*

The seasons

Seasons   As Earth revolves around the Sun, we experience different seasons. The seasons are caused by the 23.5° tilt of Earth's axis with respect to the plane of its orbit around the Sun. As Earth rotates around the Sun, its axial tilt remains fixed.

The axial tilt causes the seasons   During summer in the Northern Hemisphere, the north end of the axial tilt is facing *toward* the Sun. This results in more direct sunlight and higher temperatures. Six months later, the north end of the axial tilt is facing *away* from the Sun. The sunlight is more spread out and is less intense. This brings winter to the Northern Hemisphere (Figure 18.17). The opposite happens in the Southern Hemisphere. The fact that Earth's axial tilt is fixed also explains why the position of the Sun in the sky changes over the course of a year (Figure 18.18).

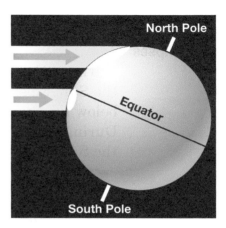

Figure 18.17: *During winter in the Northern Hemisphere, Earth's axial tilt is facing away from the Sun. This means the sunlight in the Northern Hemisphere is more spread out and less intense. Therefore, temperatures are lower in winter.*

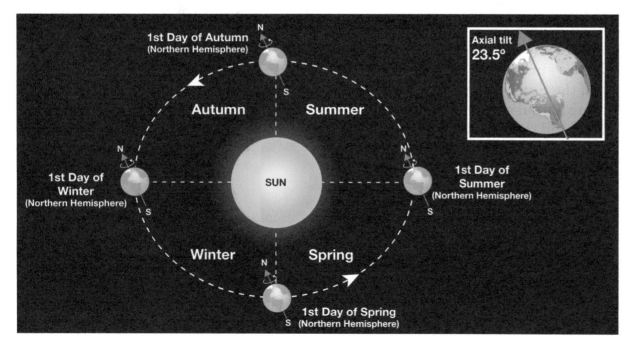

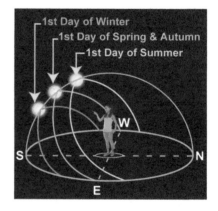

Figure 18.18: *The diagram shows the path of the Sun across the sky in the Northern Hemisphere during the year.*

18.2 **Section Review**

1. Name two examples of astronomical cycles. For each, describe an event that is directly related to it. Example: Moon revolves around Earth, resulting in the phases of the Moon.

2. What is a leap year? Why does a leap year occur every four years?

3. Since the Moon does not produce its own light, how can you see it?

4. The lunar cycle is closely related to which part of our calendar—a year, a month, or a day?

5. True or False: The phases of the Moon are caused by Earth's shadow falling on the Moon.

6. Explain how you could use the shadow of a streetlight pole to track the time of day on a sunny day.

7. Explain the difference between solar and lunar eclipses.

8. Match the letters on the diagram with the correct terms. You may use a letter more than once.

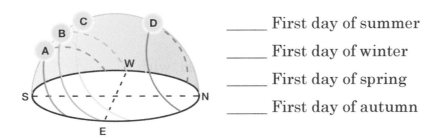

_____ First day of summer

_____ First day of winter

_____ First day of spring

_____ First day of autumn

CHALLENGE

The Sun is 400 times larger in diameter than the Moon. It is also 400 times farther away from Earth than the Moon. Because of this coincidence, the Sun and Moon appear to be the same size in the sky.

Corona

Courtesy NASA/JPL-Caltech

The photo above shows a total eclipse of the Sun. Explain how the paragraph above explains why a solar eclipse occurs.

18.3 **The Sun**

Can you imagine life without the Sun? The Sun is the source of energy that sustains all life on Earth. What is the Sun? Why does it produce so much energy? Read on to find the answers to these questions, and many more.

The Sun is a star

The Sun is a star　The Sun is a star (Figure 18.19). A **star** is a giant, hot ball of gas held together by gravity. Gravity squeezes the atoms in the core of a star so tightly that they fuse together in a reaction called *nuclear fusion* (Figure 18.20). In the process, huge amounts of energy are given off. That's why stars like the Sun give off light and heat. The Sun is one of at least 200 billion stars in our galaxy.

A medium-sized star　The Sun is medium-sized compared with other stars in the universe. Its diameter is about 1.4 million kilometers, or about 109 times the diameter of Earth. Approximately 1 million planet Earths could fit inside the Sun! By contrast, one of the star "supergiants" called Betelgeuse sometimes reaches a diameter that is almost 600 times that of the Sun. If the Sun grew to the size of Betelgeuse, it would swallow up Mercury, Venus, Earth, and Mars!

What is the Sun made of?　The Sun is about 75 percent hydrogen and 25 percent helium, with very small traces of other elements. Unlike Earth, the Sun does not have a solid surface—instead, it is made completely of gas. Because of its size, the Sun contains 99.8 percent of the mass of the solar system. Because of its mass, the Sun's gravitational force is strong enough to hold the entire solar system—including the planets, dwarf planets, asteroids, and comets—in orbit.

star - a giant, hot ball of gas held together by gravity.

Figure 18.19: *Did you know that the Sun is a star?*

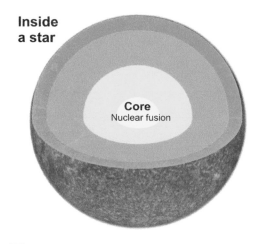

Figure 18.20: *A cross section of a star like the Sun.*

Anatomy of the Sun

The Sun has three regions The apparent surface of the Sun that we can see from a distance is called the *photosphere,* which means "sphere of light." Just above it is the *chromosphere.* This is a very hot layer of plasma, a high-energy state of matter. The *corona* is the outermost layer of the Sun's atmosphere, extending millions of kilometers outward.

Anatomy of the Sun

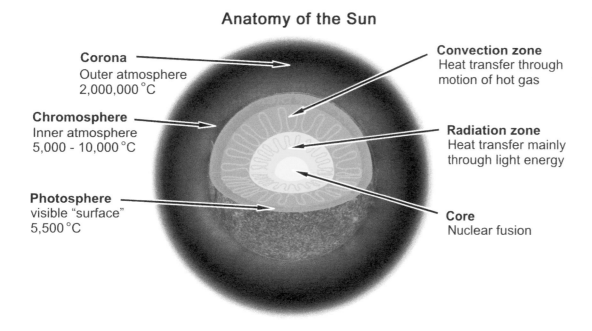

Corona
Outer atmosphere
2,000,000 °C

Chromosphere
Inner atmosphere
5,000 - 10,000 °C

Photosphere
visible "surface"
5,500 °C

Convection zone
Heat transfer through motion of hot gas

Radiation zone
Heat transfer mainly through light energy

Core
Nuclear fusion

Sunspots

Close-up of a sunspot

National Solar Observatory

Figure 18.21: *Sunspots appear as dark spots on the photosphere.*

Sunspots A safe method for viewing the Sun is to use a telescope to project the Sun's image onto a white surface (Remember, you should *never* look directly at the Sun). When the Sun is observed in this way, small, dark areas can be seen on its surface. These areas, called *sunspots,* may look small, but they can be as large as Earth. A sunspot is an area of gas that is cooler than the gases around it. Because they don't give off as much light as the hotter areas, sunspots appear as dark spots on the photosphere (Figure 18.21).

Features of the Sun

Prominences and solar flares
Sunspots are linked to other features of the Sun. Occasionally, large "loops" of gas called *prominences* can be seen jumping up from groups of sunspots. These can be observed during eclipses and appear as loops that extend beyond the chromosphere. Sometimes prominences from different sunspot regions suddenly connect, releasing very large amounts of heat and light known as *solar flares* (Figure 18.22).

Solar wind
The Sun gives off more than just heat and light. It also gives off something called solar wind. *Solar wind* is an electrically-charged mixture of protons and electrons. Evidence of solar wind comes from the tails of comets, which always face away from the Sun. A comet's tail acts like a "wind sock" and shows that there is a continuous flow of particles coming from the Sun.

Magnetic storms
Solar flares can greatly increase the amount of solar wind given off by the Sun. These solar wind particles can affect Earth's upper atmosphere, causing *magnetic storms*. Magnetic storms can disrupt radio and television signals, interfere with telephone and cell phone signals, and even cause electrical power problems for homes and businesses.

Auroras
Solar winds sometimes cause a mysterious phenomenon known as an **aurora** to occur. Auroras (known in the Northern Hemisphere as the northern lights) occur when the protective layers of our atmosphere are energized by solar winds. This energy causes atoms and molecules in the upper atmosphere to give off light. The most common color produced is a yellow-green caused by oxygen atoms at an altitude of about 60 miles. The aurora appears as curtains of light above the horizon (Figure 18.23).

VOCABULARY

aurora - a phenomenon that occurs when Earth's atmosphere is energized by solar winds.

NASA/Goddard

Figure 18.22: *Solar flares release large amounts of heat and light.*

Figure 18.23: *Solar winds can cause auroras to occur.*

18.3 Section Review

1. What is a star? How is a star different from a planet or a moon?
2. Why does the Sun give off heat and light?
3. The Sun is made mostly from which of the following elements?
   a. gold
   b. lead
   c. hydrogen
   d. nitrogen
4. On the diagram below, label the following: photosphere, chromosphere, core, corona.

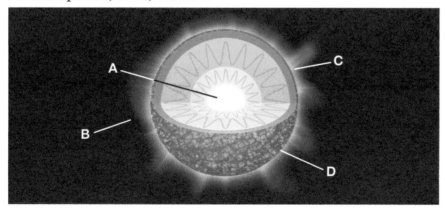

5. Explain the meaning of the following terms.
   a. sunspot
   b. magnetic storm
   c. solar flare
   d. solar wind
   e. aurora

MY JOURNAL

Solar energy research

There are many ways to collect sunlight and use it to produce energy for our everyday needs. When we use energy from the Sun it is called solar energy.

Photovoltaic (or PV) cells, also called solar cells, are devices that convert sunlight directly into electricity. You may have seen solar cells on calculators, watches, or some outdoor light fixtures. Research solar cells and find the answers to the following questions.

1. How do solar cells work?
2. How efficient are solar cells at converting sunlight into energy?
3. What are the drawbacks to using solar energy?
4. How are scientists trying to make solar cells more efficient?

A Solar Observatory

Bring your sunglasses—you are about to visit a location with more than 300 sunny days a year. Big Bear Lake in California has proven an ideal location for a solar observatory. It is located high in the San Bernadino mountains, in the middle of a lake. Its location provides a great opportunity for studying the Sun year round.

Big Bear Solar Observatory/ New Jersey Institute of Technology

A premier site, an improbable location

Big Bear Solar Observatory (BBSO) was built in 1969 by the California Institute of Technology. Since 1997, it has been operated by the New Jersey Institute of Technology. The National Aeronautics and Space Administration NASA), the National Science Foundation (NSF), the U.S. Air Force, the U.S. Navy, and other agencies finance the observatory.

Big Bear Solar Observatory
New Jersey Institute of Technology

The observatory is located on an island in the center of Big Bear Lake. It might seem obvious that high altitude and clear skies would benefit an observatory—but in the middle of a lake? In water, however, scientists have clearer images of the Sun than on land.

The science behind this starts, of course, with the Sun. When the Sun heats the ground, convection occurs, the warm air rising and the cold air sinking in vertical circulation. Water absorbs more heat than does the ground. With less heat rising, the convection currents over the water are smaller than those on land. A natural light wind blowing across the lake also helps to keep images clear—which keeps the observatory one of the best in the world.

The importance of our nearest star

For Earth, the Sun is not merely important, it is essential. It is the planet's source of heat, energy, light, weather, and climate. The Sun's natural furnace is what makes life possible for each and every creature on Earth.

The Sun is the star closest to Earth. Because of that "nearness," scientists are able to see and study the surface of the Sun. Other stars are just too far away to view their surface features. From the Sun, scientists learn about stars in general.

Big Bear Solar Observatory staff study the Sun, solar phenomena, and the solar atmosphere, made up of:

- Photosphere: the visible surface of the Sun.
- Chromosphere: the irregular layer above the photosphere.
- Corona: the outer atmosphere.

Scientists observe solar flares—explosions from the Sun that importantly can disrupt communications, satellites, and other systems on Earth. They also observe sunspots, which are dark, cool areas on the photosphere, and prominences, which are arched clouds of gas extending from the Sun.

Mighty telescopes

BBSO houses several powerful telescopes. As you know, viewing the Sun directly is dangerous and safety measures are always required. But these solar telescopes have cameras and filters specifically crafted for viewing the Sun. They magnify the Sun and provide detailed images of surface events.

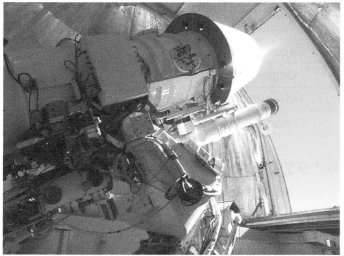

Big Bear Solar Observatory/ New Jersey Institute of Technology

At the top of the observatory are four main telescopes. Two are used to observe sunspots, flares, and prominences. The observatory monitors and predicts solar flares and provides reports to interested groups. A third, smaller telescope examines the entire Sun. On clear days, this telescope works from dawn to dusk, taking images every 30 seconds. The fourth telescope measures earthshine, which is sunlight that reflects onto the darkened portion of the Moon and then back again to Earth. Earthshine can provide scientists with information about our planet's temperature, atmosphere, and global warming.

In November 2005, BBSO replaced its dome with a larger one to accommodate a new solar telescope that will be the largest in the world. It will help scientists to better study solar flares, space weather, and sunspots.

Big Bear Solar Observatory/ New Jersey Institute of Technology

One thing solar observers know for sure is that the Sun is always changing. It is important for us to understand that solar activity so that we can predict its impact on our lives and Earth's future.

QUESTIONS

1. Why is the Sun important to people on Earth?

2. What exactly does Big Bear Solar Observatory observe and how does it do it?

3. What is ideal about the observatory's location?

Distance from Earth to the Sun

The Sun is our closest star. It provides energy for Earth. It influences our seasons. It heats our atmosphere. Because of its importance, scientists have been studying its behavior and its relationship to Earth. One of the things they have learned is what you will find below by completing this activity.

Month	Distance (AU)
January	0.9840
February	0.9888
March	0.9962
April	1.0050
May	1.0122
June	1.0163
July	1.0161
August	1.0116
September	1.0039
October	0.9954
November	0.9878
December	0.9837

Materials

Spreadsheet program or graph paper, pencil, ruler

What you will do

Use the table to the right to construct a graph of the month of the year versus the distance of Earth to the Sun using your spreadsheet program. If one is unavailable, then use graph paper, a pencil, and a ruler. The units are in AU (astronomical units). One AU is the average distance of the Earth from the Sun, approximately 150,000,000 km. These values are from the 1996 U.S. Ephemeris (http://image.gsfc.nasa.gov/poetry/venus/q638.html). An ephemeris is a table of astrological data showing positions of celestial bodies over periods of time.

Applying your knowledge

a. During what season of the year is the Sun farthest from Earth?

b. During what season of the year is the Sun closest to the Earth?

c. Were your answers to questions a and b what you expected? Why or why not?

d. What does this mean about the reason for the seasons?

e. What does this data show about the relative size of the Sun as seen from Earth over the year?

Chapter 18 Activity

Chapter 18 Assessment

Vocabulary

Select the correct term to complete the sentences.

solar eclipse	star	sunspots
tide	craters	giant impact theory
lunar cycle	aurora	lunar eclipse

Section 18.1

1. The _____ explains how the Moon was formed.

2. A feature of the Moon called _____ are large, round pits formed by impacts from large space objects.

3. The cycle of rising and falling ocean levels is called a(n) _____.

Section 18.2

4. The gradual change in the appearance of the Moon due to positions of Earth, the Moon and the Sun is called the _____.

5. A(n) _____ is caused by Earth's shadow falling on the Moon.

6. A(n) _____ occurs when the Moon's shadow falls on Earth.

Section 18.3

7. A giant ball of hot gas held together by gravity is called a(n) _____.

8. Areas of gas on the Sun that are cooler than the gases around them are called _____.

9. A(n) _____ occurs when Earth's atmosphere is energized by solar winds.

Concepts

Section 18.1

1. Explain why objects weigh less on the Moon's surface than on Earth's surface.

2. Explain why the Moon does not have an atmosphere.

3. How did scientific analysis of lunar rocks lead to a theory of the Moon's formation called the giant impact theory?

4. When you look at the Moon through a telescope, what are the three features that you can see?

5. Why do tides occur twice each day?

Section 18.2

6. Name two astronomical cycles. For each, describe an event that is directly related to it. *Example: the Moon revolves around Earth, resulting in the phases of the Moon.*

7. What is a leap year? Why does a leap year occur every four years?

8. Explain how you could use a lamppost to track the time of day on a sunny day.

9. What causes the lunar cycle?

10. Explain the difference between a lunar eclipse and a solar eclipse. Draw a diagram that shows the placement of Earth, the Moon, and the Sun for each kind of eclipse.

Section 18.3

11. What is the Sun made from?

12. What happens in the core of the Sun?

13. What are the characteristics of a star?

14. What are sunspots?

15. In addition to heat and light, what else does the Sun give off?

16. What causes auroras to occur?

Math and Writing Skills

Section 18.1

1. Match each term with its corresponding letter on the diagram below. Terms: revolution, orbit, axis, rotation.

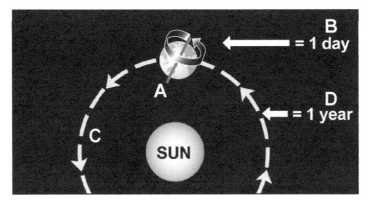

Section 18.2

2. During one revolution around the Sun, how many rotations of Earth occur?

3. How long does it take Earth to revolve around the Sun in *seconds*? Show all of your math.

4. How would the moon appear from Earth if it were in the position shown in the diagram below?

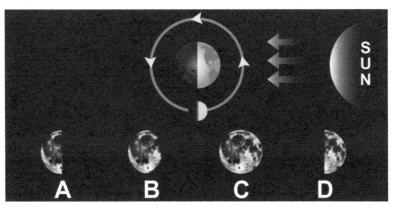

Section 18.3

5. The Sun's diameter is 1.4 million km. What is its radius?

Chapter Project—Ancient Cultures

Our ancestors used their observations of the sky to explain many aspects of their lives including religion, philosophy, science, and architecture. For example, many different Native American tribes planned and arranged buildings to correlate directly with the alignment of Earth, the Moon, and the Sun. Choose an ancient culture, and prepare a short paper that describes how astronomy influenced the lives of its people. Some cultures include: Mayan, Aztec, and the Navajo tribe.

Galaxies and the Universe

How big is everything? How long is forever? In science, everything means the universe, including all matter and energy. In science, forever means the amount of time the universe exists or will exist. As a start to answering these deep questions, think about the night sky. It's dark. But why is the night sky dark? Imagine the universe was infinite, stretching off to infinity in all directions. That means in any direction you looked, you would eventually see a star. If there were stars in every possible direction, the night sky should be light, not dark. This puzzled people for a long time and became known as Olber's Paradox. The solution to Olber's Paradox is that the universe is not infinite in all directions, but has a finite size. Nor is the universe forever. Time had a beginning between 10 billion and 20 billion years ago and it may or may not have an end. Of course, we are not sure all our answers are correct. Read ahead about galaxies and the universe. What do you think?

Key Questions:

1. How do astronomers measure distances in space?

2. How is a star born?

3. How did the universe begin?

Image courtesy of NASA/ESA/STScI/HUDF Team.

19.1 Tools of Astronomers

Frequently in the news we hear about discoveries that involve space. Since the 1970s, space probes have been sent to all of the planets in the solar system and we have seen them "up close" for the very first time. An *astronomer* is a scientist who studies objects in space. In this section, you will learn about some of the tools of astronomers.

Writing very large numbers

Scientific notation   When you look up at the night sky, do you ever think about how far away the stars are? The closest star to the Sun, Alpha Centauri, is 41,000,000,000,000 kilometers away. As you can see, trying to write out such huge distance as 41 trillion requires a lot of zeros. Scientific notation is a mathematical abbreviation for writing very large (or very small) numbers. Numbers are written as a value between 1 and 10, multiplied times a power of 10. For example, the distance in the example above can be written as 4.1×10^{13} km.

How to use scientific notation   Earth is approximately 150,000,000 kilometers from the Sun. How do you write this value using scientific notation (Figure 19.1)?

1. Move the decimal until you get a value that is between 1 and 10. Count the number of times you move the decimal.

2. Write down the new number without all of the zeros.

3. Write × 10 after the number.

4. Write the number of times you moved the decimal as the power of 10 (the *exponent*). If you moved the decimal to the left, the exponent will be positive. If you moved the decimal to the right, the exponent will be negative. The answer is 1.5×10^8 km.

scientific notation - a mathematical abbreviation, using powers of 10, for writing very large or very small numbers.

1. Move the decimal until the number is between 1 and 10.

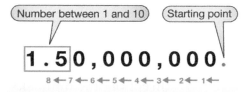

2. Write the number without the zeros.   **1.5**

3. Write "× 10" after the number.
   1.5 × 10

4. Write the number of times you moved the decimal as an exponent after the 10.
   1.5 × 10^8

Figure 19.1: *How to solve the problem on the left.*

Units of distance in space

What is a light year? Astronomers have developed units other than kilometers or meters to measure the vast distances in space. You may have heard of *light years* (ly), an astronomical term. Even though the name may sound like it, this unit does not measure time. One light year is equal to the *distance* that light travels through space in one year.

Calculating a light year In space, light travels at the amazing speed of about 300,000 km/s. How far will light travel in one year? We can calculate the distance light travels in one year by multiplying the speed of light (300,000 km/s) by time (1 year). To get the correct answer, we must convert years into seconds since the value for the speed of light contains seconds. There are 31,536,000 seconds in one year! Here's how to find the distance of one light year, in kilometers:

$$1 \text{ light year} = \text{speed of light} \times \text{time}$$
$$= 300,000 \text{ km/s} \times 31,536,000 \text{ s}$$
$$= 9,460,000,000,000 \text{ km}$$
$$= 9.46 \times 10^{12} \text{ km}$$

Unit conversion How many light years away is Alpha Centauri, the closest star to the Sun? We already know that it is 4.1×10^{13} km away. We also know that one light year is equal to 9.46×10^{12} km. Using unit conversion, we get:

$$4.1 \times 10^{13} \text{ km} \times \frac{1.0 \text{ ly}}{9.46 \times 10^{12} \text{ km}} = 4.3 \text{ ly}$$

Can you see why astronomers like to use light years instead of kilometers when measuring distances to stars? Figure 19.2 shows the distances, in light years, from Earth of some objects outside of our solar system.

VOCABULARY

light year - the distance that light travels through space in one year. One light year is equal to 9.46×10^{12} km.

Object	Distance from Earth (ly)
Sirius (brightest star in the sky)	8.8
Betelgeuse (appears as a red star in the sky)	700
Crab Nebula (remnant of an exploded star)	4,000
Andromeda galaxy (a huge group of billions of stars)	2.5 million

Figure 19.2: *Distance of some space objects from Earth in light years.*

Studying the universe

What is the universe? When you look up at the sky, you can see the Moon and many stars. If you watch the sky each night over a few months, you will notice that some of those "stars" change position over time and appear to wander in the sky. These are the planets of our solar system—our own small corner of the universe. The **universe** is defined as everything that exists, including all matter and energy.

Galaxies A **galaxy** is a huge collection of gas, dust, and billions of stars. These stars are attracted to each other by gravitational force and are constantly in motion. If you look at the sky on a clear night, you can see a milky-white trail across the stars. You are looking at part of the Milky Way—the galaxy to which we belong. Our galaxy contains billions of stars! The location of the Sun in the Milky Way galaxy is shown in Figure 19.3.

Light years and time

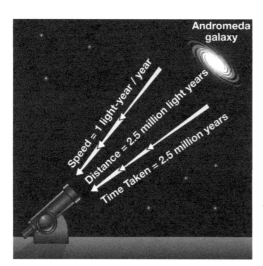

The light we see from an object in space is as old as the number of light years the object is from Earth. For an object that is 4.3 light years away, we see light that was produced 4.3 years ago. When astronomers use a powerful telescope to view the Andromeda galaxy, they are looking back in time 2.5 million years! The farther away the object they are viewing, the further back in time they are looking. This fact has become an important tool that astronomers use to piece together how the universe began, and how it has changed over time.

universe - everything that exists, including all matter and energy.

galaxy - a huge collection of gas, dust, and billions of stars.

Photo courtesy NASA, ESA, S. Beckwith and the Hubble Heritage Team (STScI/AURA)

Photo courtesy NASA, ESA and the Hubble Heritage Team (STScI/AURA) Other galaxies shown to represent the Milky Way Galaxy (M51-top, NGC 5866-bottom).

Figure 19.3: *The location of the Sun in the Milky Way Galaxy.*

Telescopes

History of the telescope

A **telescope** is a device that makes objects that are far away appear closer. In the 1600s, Galileo was the first to use a telescope for astronomical observations. He observed craters on the Moon, tiny moons around Jupiter, and the rings of Saturn. Since then, astronomers have developed powerful telescopes that continue to add to our knowledge of the universe.

How does a telescope work?

Have you ever tried to read the writing on a penny from 100 feet away? The reason you cannot read it with your naked eye is that the image of a penny from 100 feet away does not take up much space on your retina (the screen of your eye). Telescopes work by collecting the light from a distant object with a lens or mirror and bringing that light into a concentrated point, called the *focal point*. The bright light from the focal point is then magnified by another lens so that it takes up more space on your retina. This makes the object appear much larger and closer.

VOCABULARY

telescope - a device that makes faraway objects appear closer.

Telescope milestones

3500 BCE Phoenicians discover glass while cooking on sand.

CE 1350 Craftsmen in Venice begin making lenses for spectacles.

1608 Hans Lippershey applies for a patent for the refracting telescope.

1609 Galileo is the first to use a telescope to view craters on the Moon.

1704 Newton invents the reflecting telescope.

1897 World's largest refracting telescope built and housed in Yerkes Observatory, Wisconsin.

1990 The Hubble Space Telescope is launched from the space shuttle *Discovery*.

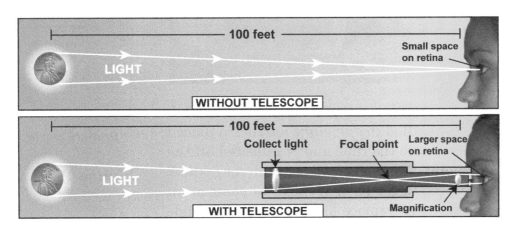

100 feet

LIGHT

Small space on retina

WITHOUT TELESCOPE

100 feet

Collect light Focal point Larger space on retina

LIGHT

WITH TELESCOPE Magnification

Refracting and reflecting telescopes

Refracting telescopes

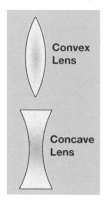

A *refracting telescope* uses lenses to bend, or refract, light, making objects look bigger. Refracting telescopes are made from a long *tube*, a glass *objective lens* that you point toward the sky, and an *eyepiece lens*—another glass lens that magnifies the object. The tube holds the two lenses the correct distance from one another. The objective lens gathers light from an object, and bends it to a focal point near the back of the tube. The objective lens is *convex*, that is, wider in the middle than at the edges.

The eyepiece lens magnifies the image. The eyepiece lens can be either convex or *concave* (thinner in the middle and wider at the edges). The picture below shows how light travels through a refracting telescope to your eye.

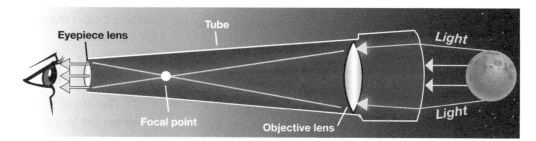

Reflecting telescopes

A *reflecting telescope* uses mirrors instead of lenses to gather and focus light. A concave mirror (called the *primary mirror*) is placed at the back of a tube. Light enters the tube and is reflected off the primary mirror to a focal point. Another small, flat mirror (called the *secondary mirror*) is placed in the path of the focal point at an angle that deflects the light to an eyepiece lens, located at the side of the tube. The eyepiece magnifies the image, just like in a refracting telescope (Figure 19.4).

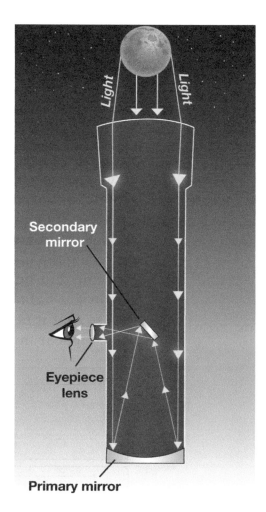

Figure 19.4: *How a reflecting telescope works.*

Other types of telescopes

Electromagnetic waves

Visible light is a type of *electromagnetic wave*. Objects in the universe give off many other types of electromagnetic waves that we cannot detect with our eyes. These include radio waves, infrared waves, and X-rays. Astronomers use different types of telescopes to view the different types of waves emitted by objects in space.

Radio telescopes

A *radio telescope* works like an extremely powerful receiver that picks up radio waves from space. The radio waves are analyzed by a computer, which draws an image of the source of waves. Astronomers use radio telescopes to produce images of stars and galaxies, analyze the chemical composition of objects, and map the surfaces of planets. Figure 19.5 shows an image of the Crab Nebula (the remnants of an exploded star) taken by a radio telescope.

Infrared telescopes

Another type of telescope looks at infrared waves. Since this type of wave is mostly absorbed by Earth's atmosphere, *infrared telescopes* are often placed on satellites that orbit Earth. In 1983, the Infrared Astronomical Satellite (IRAS) was launched to map the entire sky at infrared wavelengths. It discovered a new comet, found evidence of another solar system, and discovered a new type of galaxy. Figure 19.6 shows an image of the Crab Nebula captured by IRAS.

X-ray telescopes

X-ray telescopes are designed to detect high-energy radiation (X-rays) from space. Since these waves cannot penetrate our atmosphere, X-ray telescopes are always placed on satellites. One of the most powerful, NASA's Chandra X-ray Observatory, was launched on the space shuttle *Columbia* in 1999. Its mission is to observe X-rays that are emitted by high-energy objects in the universe such as stars that have exploded. Figure 19.7 shows an image of the Crab Nebula captured by Chandra.

Figure 19.5: *An image of the Crab Nebula taken by a radio telescope. (Photo courtesy Very Large Array / National Radio Astronomy Observatory.)*

Figure 19.6: *An image of the Crab Nebula taken by an infrared telescope. (Photo courtesy NASA / IRAS.)*

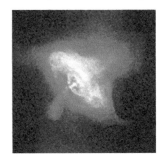

Figure 19.7: *An image of the Crab Nebula captured by an X-ray telescope. (Photo courtesy NASA / Chandra.)*

19.1 **Section Review**

1. Convert the following values to scientific notation.
    a. The distance around Earth's equator is 40,076 km.
    b. The Moon is 384,400 km from Earth.
    c. Earth is 4,600,000,000 years old.

2. Why do scientists use scientific notation?

3. Convert the following values into regular numbers.
    a. 1.5×10^{13} km
    b. 4.8×10^{4} km
    c. 9.46×10^{12} kilometers in a light year

4. What is a light year? Why do astronomers use light years instead of kilometers to describe distances outside of the solar system?

5. List the following terms in order from smallest to largest: galaxy, solar system, universe.

6. What is the universe?

7. What is a telescope? How does a telescope work?

8. Explain the major difference between a refracting telescope and a reflecting telescope.

9. Regulus, the brightest star in the constellation Leo, is approximately 77 light years from Earth. Which year did Regulus give off the light you see when you look at the star today?

10. Name three types of electromagnetic waves.

11. List three types of telescopes that do not view objects using visible light.

A light year is the distance light travels in one year. Other units can be defined according to the distance light travels in a certain amount of time. For example, a light second is the distance light travels in one second.

Calculate the number of meters each of the following units represents:

1. Light second
2. Light minute
3. Light nanosecond (a nanosecond is one-billionth of a second)

Sirius, the brightest star in the sky, is 8.8 light years from Earth. When you look at Sirius, how old is the light you are seeing? Write a short story about the journey of that light from Sirius, to your eyes. What do you think the light would encounter along the way? What discoveries might the light make? Use your imagination!

19.2 Stars

On a clear night, about 6,000 stars can be seen without a telescope. Some of those stars form familiar constellations (Figure 19.8). A **constellation** is a group of stars that, when seen from Earth, form a pattern. Ancient astronomers thought that the Sun and the stars were different from each other. Today we know that the Sun is just one star like all the others in the night sky. The others appear to be so dim because they are incredibly far away. What are stars and where do they come from?

Stars and fusion

How do stars generate light and heat?
You have learned that a star is an enormous, hot ball of gas held together by gravity. Stars generate light and heat through nuclear fusion. Specifically, they are powered by the fusion of hydrogen under conditions of enormous temperature, mass, and density. When hydrogen atoms fuse, helium is created.

The conditions for fusion
The conditions required for the continuous fusion of hydrogen are extremely high temperature, density, and pressure. These conditions are found when the mass of hydrogen is very large. Hydrogen fusion does not take place throughout the star, but only deep in its core, where the temperature is hot enough. The minimum temperature required for fusion to occur is 7 million°C. The Sun's core reaches a temperature of 15 million°C!

Density and mass
Even though stars are made of gas, they have extremely high values for density and mass. For example, the density of the Sun's core is about 158.0 g/cm^3. This is about 18 times the density of copper. The Sun has a total mass that is equal to 330,000 Earths. Stars can range in mass from about 100 times that of the Sun to less than one-twelfth its mass. At masses lower than this, the internal temperature does not get hot enough to sustain the nuclear fusion of hydrogen.

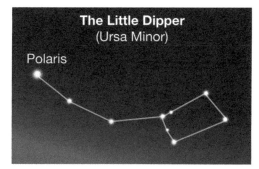

Figure 19.8: *The star at the tip of the Little Dipper's handle is called Polaris. If you look toward Polaris, you are facing the North Pole.*

Constellations

The stars in the sky are divided into 88 constellations. The largest, Centaurus, contains 101 stars. The most familiar star formation, the Big Dipper, is actually part of a larger constellation called Ursa Major (the Great Bear). The Little Dipper, part of Ursa Minor, contains Polaris, the North Star, which is located at the tip of the handle (Figure 19.8). Anybody in the Northern Hemisphere who is looking toward Polaris is facing the North Pole.

The size of stars

The size range of stars

Stars come in a range of sizes. The largest stars have a mass of about 100 times the mass of the Sun. The smallest stars are about one-twelfth the mass of the Sun. This is about the minimum required to create enough gravitational pressure to ignite hydrogen fusion in the core. The Sun is a medium-sized star (Figure 19.9), as is Alpha Centauri, the nearest star to the Sun.

Giant stars

NASA - Hubble Space Telescope

There are two types of giant stars. Blue giant stars are hot and much more massive than the Sun. Rigel, in the constellation Orion, is a blue giant star. Red giants are of similar mass to the Sun and much cooler. The red giants are huge because they began as Sun-like stars but have expanded to become much larger. As they expanded, they cooled down. Betelgeuse, also in the constellation of Orion, is an example of a red giant star. It is easy to find this constellation because of the three stars that form its belt.

Dwarf stars

Stars that are smaller than the Sun come in two main categories, *dwarfs* and *neutron stars*. Dwarf stars are about the size of the smaller planets. Sirius B, the largest known dwarf star, is slightly smaller than Earth. Neutron stars are even smaller. Their diameter is only 20 to 30 kilometers, about the size of a big city.

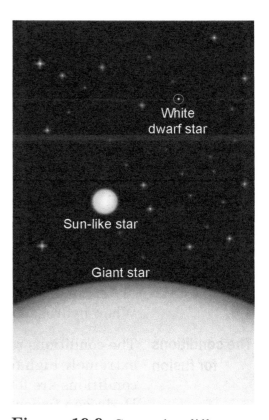

Figure 19.9: *Comparing different sizes of stars.*

Temperature and color of stars

Temperatures of stars

If you look closely at the stars on a clear night, you might see a slight reddish or bluish tints to some stars. This is because stars' surface temperatures are different. Red stars are cooler than white stars, and blue stars are the hottest. The table below lists some stars, their colors, and their surface temperatures.

Star	Color	Temperature range (°C)
Betelgeuse	red	2,000 to 3,500
Arcturus	orange	3,500 to 5,000
Sun	yellow	5,000 to 6,000
Polaris	yellow-white	6,000 to 7,500
Sirius (Figure 19.10)	white	7,500 to 11,000
Rigel	blue-white	11,000 to 25,000
Zeta Orionis	blue	25,000 to 50,000

The color of light is related to its energy. Red light has the lowest energy of the colors we can see. Blue and violet light have the most energy. Yellow, green, and orange are in between. White light is a mixture of all colors at equal brightness (Figure 19.10).

Low energy
Low temperature

High energy
High temperature

Color and temperature

When matter is heated, it first glows red at about 600°C. As the temperature increases, the color changes to orange, yellow, and finally white. The graph in Figure 19.11 shows the colors of light given off at different temperatures. The curve for 2,000°C crosses red and yellow, but drops off before getting to blue. That means a surface at 2,000°C gives off mostly red and some yellow light. At 10,000°C a star gives off an even mix of red to blue so it appears white. At 20,000°C the emitted light is white with a bluish color.

Figure 19.10: *Sirius, the Dog Star in the constellation of Canis Majoris, is a good example of a white star.*

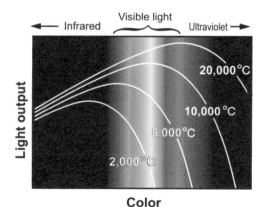

Figure 19.11: *The range of light given off by a star depends on its temperature. Stars at 2,000°C give off mostly red and some yellow light. At 10,000°C a star gives off an even mix from red to blue, so the light appears white.*

Brightness and luminosity of stars

ă VOCABULARY

Light radiates in all directions   You can see a bare light bulb from anywhere in a room because the bulb emits light in all directions. When the rays of light are represented by arrows, the light coming from a bulb looks like Figure 19.12. A star also emits light equally in all directions.

brightness - measures the amount of light reaching Earth from a star.

luminosity - the total amount of light given off by a star in all directions.

Brightness   From experience, you know that as you move away from a source of light, the brightness decreases. Brightness describes the amount of light per second falling on a surface. The brightness of a star is described as the *light reaching Earth*.

Brightness and distance   For a distant source of light like a star, the brightness decreases mathematically with distance. For example, a star that is twice as far away will appear only one-quarter as bright. A star that is three times as far away will appear one-ninth as bright.

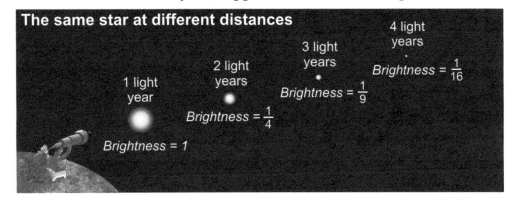

The same star at different distances

4 light years

3 light years

2 light years

$Brightness = \frac{1}{16}$

1 light year

$Brightness = \frac{1}{9}$

$Brightness = \frac{1}{4}$

$Brightness = 1$

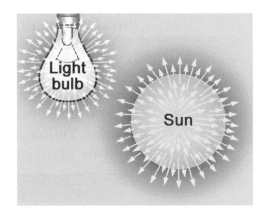

Figure 19.12: *Light emitted from the Sun or from a light bulb.*

Luminosity   The brightness of a star also depends on how much light the star actually gives off. This is called a star's luminosity. Luminosity is the total amount of light given off by a star in all directions. Luminosity is a property of a star whereas brightness depends on both luminosity and distance. Therefore, to find the luminosity of a star we need to know both its brightness and its distance from Earth.

Analyzing the light from stars

What is spectroscopy? Astronomers analyze the light given off by stars to determine the chemical elements from which they are made. Spectroscopy is a tool of astronomy in which the light produced by a star or other object (called its *spectrum*) is analyzed. A *spectrometer* splits light into a spectrum of colors and displays lines of different colors along a scale. The scale measures the wavelength of each of the lines of color in nanometers (nm).

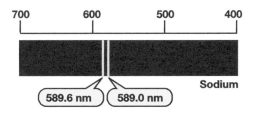

spectroscopy - a process by which the light from a star or other object is analyzed.

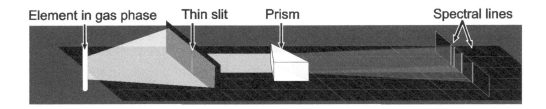

Figure 19.13: *When the element sodium is burned, two yellow lines are observed at 589.0 and 589.6 nanometers on the scale of a spectrometer.*

Scientists have discovered that each element has its own unique pattern of lines—like a fingerprint. For example, when the element sodium is burned, two yellow lines at 589.0 and 589.6 nm are observed when the light is passed through a spectrometer (Figure 19.13).

The composition of the Sun In 1861, Sir William Huggins (1824–1910), an English astronomer, used spectroscopy to determine that the Sun and the stars are made mostly of hydrogen. A few years later, Sir Joseph Norman Lockyer (1836–1920) observed a line at the precise wavelength of 587.6 nm. Since no known element on Earth had a line at this wavelength, he concluded that this must be an undiscovered element and named it helium, after the Greek name for the Sun, *Helios*. Today, we know that hydrogen is the most abundant element in the universe, with helium second. Figure 19.14 shows the spectral lines of some elements.

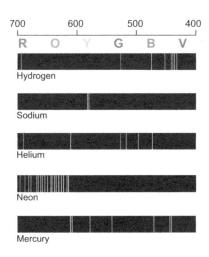

Figure 19.14: *Spectral lines for some of the elements.*

The life cycle of a Sun-like star

The birth of a star Stars begin life inside a huge cloud of gas and dust called a **nebula**. Gravitational forces cause denser regions of the nebula to collapse, forming a protostar. A *protostar* is the earliest stage in the life cycle of a star. The gases at the center of the protostar continue to collapse, causing pressure and temperature to rise. A protostar becomes a star when the temperature and pressure at its center become great enough to start nuclear fusion of hydrogen. Figure 19.15 shows a portion of the Orion Nebula with protostars visible in the center of the nebula.

Main sequence stars Once nuclear fusion begins, a star is in the *main sequence* stage of its life cycle. This is the longest and most stable part of a star's life. The length of the main sequence stage depends on a star's mass. Stars with large masses burn brighter and hotter than smaller stars. So, they use up their hydrogen fuel quicker. The main sequence stage of Sun-like stars lasts for about 10 billion years.

Old age As a star grows old, its core begins to run out of hydrogen fuel. Gravity causes the core to contract, raising its temperature and igniting the helium inside the core, along with any hydrogen in the outer layers. The star expands, and the outer layers begin to cool. At this stage in its life cycle, a Sun-like star becomes a *red giant*.

Death of a star When hydrogen fusion stops, the core glows brightly and is called a *white dwarf*. It is about the size of Earth, and has about the same mass as the Sun. During the white-dwarf stage, the outer layers of the star expand and drift away from the core, forming what is called a *planetary nebula* (Figure 19.16). This is different from a nebula where stars are born. When a white dwarf stops glowing, it is called a *brown dwarf*, the final stage in the life cycle of Sun-like stars.

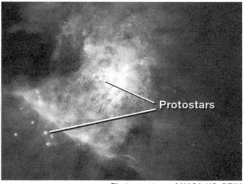

Photo courtesy of NASA-HQ-GRIN

Figure 19.15: *A group of protostars is visible in the center of the Orion Nebula.*

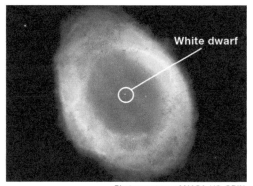

Photo courtesy of NASA-HQ-GRIN

Figure 19.16: *The Ring Nebula, showing the death of a Sun-like star. The outer rings are called the planetary nebula. The glowing, white dwarf is in the center.*

How the solar system formed

How was our solar system formed? Scientists think that the solar system was formed out of the same nebula that created the Sun (Figure 19.17). As the Sun was being formed, it was surrounded by a cloud of dust and gas. This cloud was made mostly of hydrogen and helium, but contained smaller amounts of "heavier" elements such as carbon, nickel, iron, aluminum, and silicon. As this cloud rotated, it flattened, with the help of gravity, into a disk-shape along the axis of its rotation.

Planet formation Most of the mass concentrated at the center of the disc under the influence of gravity. At the center, pressures became high enough for fusion to begin, igniting the Sun. Farther away from the center, the heaviest molecules began to condense into solid and liquid droplets. These droplets began to collide, forming small clumps—the seeds of the planets. Through further collisions, these clumps of material grew larger and eventually formed spherical planets.

The terrestrial planets Terrestrial planets, like Earth, were formed in the warmer, inner regions of the disk. Because the heat drove off the lighter elements such as hydrogen and helium, these planets were made mostly of metals and rock. These materials made up less than one percent of the disk, so these planets could not grow very large. Because of their small masses, their gravity could not attract hydrogen and helium and their atmospheres were thin and contained little of these elements.

The gas planets The outer regions of the disk were rich in icy materials made of lighter elements and the planets there grew larger than the terrestrial planets. Because of their large masses, they were able to capture hydrogen and helium through their gravitational force and form thick atmospheres. These became *gas planets*, rich in hydrogen and helium with dense cores.

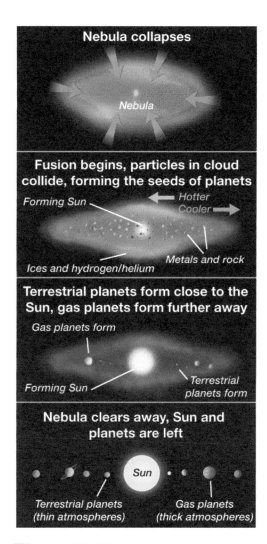

Figure 19.17: *The formation of our solar system. Scientists now believe that this is a common process in the universe.*

19.2 Section Review

1. What is the basic process through which a star releases energy?
2. To which category below does the Sun belong?
   a. main sequence star
   b. white dwarf
   c. red giant
   d. neutron star
3. List the stars below from coolest to hottest.
   a. Sirius (white)
   b. Betelgeuse (red)
   c. Rigel (blue-white)
   d. Sun (yellow)
   e. Arcturus (orange)
4. Explain the difference between a star's brightness and its luminosity.
5. Suppose Star A is three times further away than Star B. If both stars have the same luminosity, how will their brightness compare?
6. What is spectroscopy? How do astronomers use spectroscopy?
7. A star begins its life inside of a huge cloud of gas and dust called a _____.
8. List the following objects from youngest to oldest: red giant, protostar, main sequence star, brown dwarf, white dwarf.
9. In the formation of the solar system, why were the gas planets able to grow larger than the terrestrial planets?

CHALLENGE

A supernova is the explosion of a star that produces an extremely luminous object. A supernova is brighter than 10 billion stars combined and can outshine an entire galaxy for a few seconds. The last supernova to be observed in our galaxy occurred in 1604. It was named Kepler's supernova after the German astronomer Johannes Kepler (1571–1630). The supernova was visible to the naked eye as the brightest object in the night sky.

Use the Internet to research Kepler's supernova to find the answers to the following questions.

1. Was the supernova named after Kepler because he was the first person to see it?
2. How many light years from Earth was the supernova?
3. How did the occurrence of the supernova help support Galileo's view that Earth was not the center of the universe?

19.3 Galaxies and the Universe

Early civilizations thought that Earth was the center of the universe. In the 16th century, we became aware that Earth is a small planet orbiting a medium-sized star. It was only in the 20th century that we became aware that the Sun is one of billions of stars in the Milky Way galaxy, and that there are billions of other galaxies in the universe. In the past 50 years, astronomers have found evidence that the universe is expanding and that it originated 10 billion to 20 billion years ago. In this section, you will learn about galaxies and about a theory on how the universe began.

The discovery of galaxies

The discovery of other galaxies

In Section 19.1, you learned that a galaxy is a huge group of stars, dust, gas, and other objects bound together by gravitational forces. The Sun, along with an estimated 200 billion other stars, belongs to the Milky Way galaxy, a spiral-shaped galaxy (Figure 19.18). At the turn of the 20th century, astronomers thought that the Milky Way galaxy was the entire universe. As telescopes got better, though, some "smudges" that were thought to be nebulae in the Milky Way were found to be whole galaxies far outside our own.

Edwin Hubble discovers a galaxy

This discovery was made in the 1920s by Edwin Hubble (1889–1953), an American astronomer. When he focused a huge telescope on an object thought to be a nebula in the constellation Andromeda, Hubble could see that the "nebula" actually consisted of faint, distant stars. He named the object the Andromeda galaxy. Since Hubble's time, astronomers have discovered a large number of galaxies. In fact, many galaxies are detected each year using the famous telescope launched into orbit in 1990: the Hubble Space Telescope, or HST. Figure 19.19 shows a famous HST photo called Hubble Deep Field. The photo shows many galaxies and stars in a tiny speck of sky. There is a larger version of this photo on the first page of this chapter. Can you find the galaxies in the photo?

NASA - Hubble Space Telescope

Figure 19.18: *The Whirlpool galaxy is spiral-shaped, like the Milky Way.*

Image courtesy of NASA/ESA/STScI/HUDF Team.

Figure 19.19: *HST photo called Hubble Deep Field.*

Types of galaxies

Galaxy shapes Astronomers classify galaxies according to their shape. *Spiral galaxies* like the Milky Way consist of a central, dense area surrounded by spiraling arms. The Milky Way is a typical spiral galaxy. From above, it would look like a giant pinwheel (see Figure 19.20, top). Although some stars are in *globular clusters* above and below the main disk, the majority are arranged in a disk that is more than 100,000 light years across and only 3,000 light years thick.

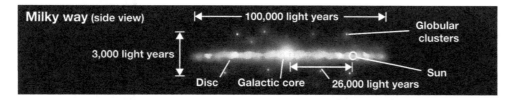

Barred spiral galaxies have a bar-shaped structure in the center. *Elliptical galaxies* look like the central portion of a spiral galaxy without the arms. *Lenticular galaxies* are lens-shaped with a smooth, even distribution of stars and no central, denser area. *Irregular galaxies* exhibit peculiar shapes and do not appear to rotate like those galaxies of other shapes. Figure 19.20 shows examples of some galaxy shapes.

Galaxies change shape over time The shapes of galaxies change over time. It is impossible to actually see the changes in a single galaxy, since the changes take hundreds of millions of years. However, by looking at many galaxies, astronomers can see similar galaxies at different times in their histories. This observational data has allowed astronomers to develop computer-based models that calculate how a galaxy changes over hundreds of millions of years. It is now thought that the barred spiral form is just one phase of a regular spiral galaxy.

Figure 19.20: *Some representative galaxy shapes.*

The distance between galaxies

Galaxies are a million times farther away than stars

Distances between stars are 10,000 times greater than distances between planets. *Distances between galaxies are a million times greater than distances between stars.* For example, the distance from Earth to the nearest star is 4.3 light years (ly). The distance from Earth to the Whirlpool galaxy is over 30 million ly.

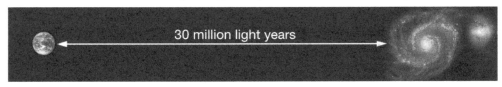

The local group of galaxies

The Milky Way belongs to a group of about 30 galaxies called the local group. This group includes the Large Magellanic Cloud (179,000 ly from Earth) and the Small Magellanic Cloud (210,000 ly from Earth). These Magellanic Clouds are small, irregular galaxies of less than 100,000 stars. The local group also includes Andromeda, an elliptical galaxy 2.5 million light years away (Figure 19.21).

Galactic collisions

Galaxies move through space singly and in groups. Galaxies even collide with each other in slow dances of stars that take millions of years to complete (Figure 19.22).

Estimating the distance between galaxies

Estimating the distance between galaxies is one of the more difficult tasks in astronomy. A faint (low brightness) object in the night sky could be a dim object that is relatively nearby or a bright object that is farther away. The most reliable method for estimating the distance to a galaxy is to find a star whose luminosity is known. If the luminosity is known, then a mathematical relationship can be used to find the distance from the observed brightness. That distance is used to estimate the distance to the galaxy to which the star belongs.

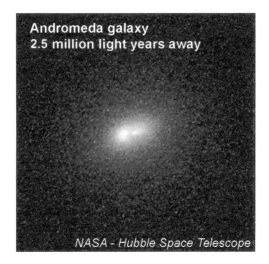

Figure 19.21: *The Andromeda galaxy is an elliptical galaxy in our local group.*

Figure 19.22: *Two galaxies that are near to colliding.*

The expanding universe

Sirius is moving away from Earth

In the 1860s, astronomers began to use spectroscopy to study the stars and other objects in space. One of the first stars they studied, Sirius, had spectral lines in the same pattern as the spectrum for hydrogen. However, these lines did not have the exact same measurements as those for hydrogen. Instead, they were shifted toward the red end of the visible spectrum. This was a puzzle at first, until scientists realized that a red-shifted spectrum meant Sirius was moving away from Earth (Figure 19.23).

Redshift

Redshift is caused by relative motion that increases the distance between the source and the observer. The faster the source of light is moving away from the observer, the greater the redshift. The opposite (blueshift) happens when an object is moving *toward* the observer. A star moving toward Earth would show a spectrum for hydrogen that was shifted toward the blue end of the scale.

Discovery of the expanding universe

In the late 1920s, Edwin Hubble began to measure the distance and redshift of galaxies. Much to his surprise, he discovered that the farther away a galaxy was, the faster it was moving away from Earth. By the early 1930s, he had enough evidence to prove that galaxies were moving away from each other. This concept came to be known as the *expanding universe*.

The Big Bang theory

Before Hubble's discovery, people believed the universe had existed in its same form for all time. The fact that the universe is expanding is evidence that the universe must have been smaller in the past than it is today. In fact, it implies that the universe must have had a *beginning*. Astronomers today believe the universe exploded outward from a single point smaller than an atom into the vast expanse of galaxies and space we know today. This idea is known as the **Big Bang theory**.

VOCABULARY

Big Bang theory - a theory that the universe began as a huge explosion 10 billion to 20 billion years ago.

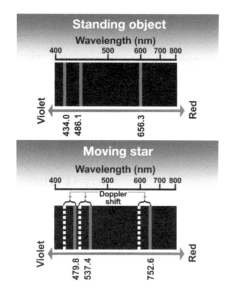

Figure 19.23: *The top diagram shows the hydrogen spectrum for an object on Earth. The bottom diagram shows the hydrogen spectral lines for a moving star. While the lines are in the exact same pattern, they have shifted toward the red end of the spectrum.*

The Big Bang theory

What does the Big Bang theory say? The Big Bang theory says the universe began as a huge explosion between 10 billion and 20 billion years ago (Figure 19.24). According to this theory, all matter and energy started in a space smaller than the nucleus of an atom. Suddenly, a huge explosion occurred (no one knows why) that sent everything that makes up the universe out in all directions. For an instant, the universe was a hot ball of fire that began to expand rapidly. Extreme heat from the explosion (10 billion°C) caused the formation of subatomic particles.

Protons and neutrons form 4 minutes after the explosion Immediately after the explosion, the universe began to expand, cool, and slow down. After a few minutes, hydrogen nuclei began forming. Next, hydrogen nuclei began fusing to form helium nuclei. Because atoms were still flying around with high energy, heavy nuclei were smashed apart. Only one helium atom survived for every 12 hydrogen atoms. Almost no elements heavier than helium survived. When we look at the matter in the universe today, we see this ratio of hydrogen to helium left by the Big Bang, with the exception of elements formed later in stars.

Matter and light decouple in 700,000 years For the next 700,000 years, the universe was like the inside of a star: hot hydrogen and helium. The universe had expanded enough to become transparent to light. At this point, the light from the fireball was freed from constant interaction with hot matter. The light continued to expand separately from matter and became the *cosmic background radiation* we see today.

Stars and galaxies form When the universe was about 1 billion years old, it had expanded and cooled enough that galaxies and stars could form. At this point, the universe probably began to look similar to how it looks today. The Sun and solar system formed about 4.6 billion years ago, by which time the universe was about 12 billion years old.

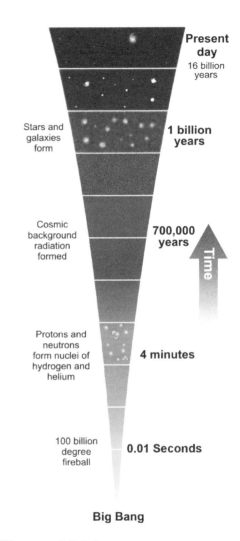

Figure 19.24: *A timeline for the Big Bang. Dates are for the amount of time passed.*

Evidence for the Big Bang theory

Evidence for the Big Bang — When it was first introduced, not everyone believed the Big Bang theory. In fact, the name "Big Bang" was made up by scientists to mock the theory. As with any new theory, the Big Bang became more accepted as new scientific tools and discoveries established more evidence. The fact that galaxies are expanding away from each other is a strong argument for the Big Bang. As far as we can look into the universe, we find galaxies are expanding away from each other (Figure 19.25).

Microwave background radiation — When you light a match, the flame bursts rapidly from the first spark and then cools as it expands. When the Big Bang exploded, it also created hot radiation. This radiation has been expanding and cooling for 16 billion years. The radiation is now at a temperature only 2.7°C above absolute zero and it fills the universe. The *cosmic background radiation* is the "smoke" from the Big Bang that fills the room (that is, the universe), even 16 billion years later. It was discovered by Arno Penzias and Robert Wilson, two American astrophysicists in the 1960s (Figure 19.26).

Ratios of the elements — We have other evidence that supports the Big Bang theory. The proportion of hydrogen to helium is consistent with the physics of the Big Bang (Figure 19.27). Elements heavier than hydrogen and helium are formed in stars. When stars reach the end of their life cycles, they spread heavy elements such as carbon, oxygen, and iron out into the universe. If the universe were significantly older, there would be more heavy elements present compared with hydrogen and helium.

NASA - Hubble Space Telescope

Figure 19.25: *The observed expansion of the universe is strong evidence for the Big Bang theory.*

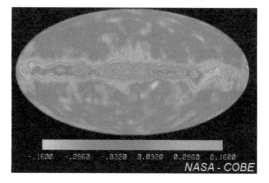

NASA - COBE

Figure 19.26: *The COBE satellite measured this image of the cosmic background radiation. (NASA)*

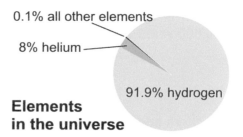

0.1% all other elements

8% helium

91.9% hydrogen

Elements in the universe

Figure 19.27: *The universe is mostly hydrogen with a small amount of helium and tiny amounts of other elements.*

19.3 Section Review

1. In which galaxy do we live?
2. The number of stars in our home galaxy is closest to:
   a. 200.
   b. 200,000.
   c. 200,000,000.
   d. 200 billion.
3. Name an important discovery about the universe that is credited to astronomer Edwin Hubble.
4. List four galaxy shapes.
5. What is the shape of our galaxy?
6. How do astronomers estimate the distance between galaxies?
7. How did astronomers discover that the star Sirius was moving away from Earth?
8. What did Hubble discover about the relationship between a galaxy's location and speed?
9. According to the Big Bang theory, how large was the universe before it exploded and expanded in all directions?
10. How many years did it take for stars to begin to form after the Big Bang?
11. Describe the scientific evidence that supports the Big Bang theory.

 STUDY SKILLS

Summarizing

The chapter contains a lot of scientific information about the universe. It is often helpful to summarize the content found on each page in your own words. Choose any page in this chapter and write a summary paragraph about that page on a note card. Follow these steps to write your summary.

1. Read each paragraph on the page carefully.
2. Identify the summarizing sentence in each paragraph.
3. Rewrite that sentence in your own words.
4. Put the sentences together into a paragraph on the note card.
5. On the other side of the note card, write the general topic of the paragraph.

New Pathways in Space: Dr. Katherine Johnson

April 1970: Two days after launch of the Apollo 13 lunar mission, an oxygen tank explosion crippled the spacecraft. Many systems on board had to be shut down, including the computers. The three astronauts on board were in great danger.

Damaged module

Apollo 13 at liftoff

Photos courtesy of NASA

Among the experts called on alert was an African American woman named Katherine Johnson. An outstanding mathematician, Johnson was part of a guidance and control team at NASA in Langley, Virginia. Her team had published reports containing detailed back-up procedures to guide the spacecraft in emergencies such as on-board computer failure. NASA's advance planning paid off—Apollo 13 returned home safely.

Earlier in her career at NASA, Johnson had worked out the complicated math that charted the path for the first manned space flight in 1961 by astronaut Alan Shepard, the first manned orbit of Earth in 1962 by astronaut John Glenn, and the mission that put Neil Armstrong on the moon in 1969.

Out of a segregated office

Katherine Johnson began her career at the National Advisory Committee on Aeronautics (which later became NASA) in 1953. At that time African American mathematicians did not share work space with white mathematicians; they had a separate office and were loaned out to work with individual engineers.

Soon after her arrival, Johnson was assigned to the Flight Research Division. She never went back to that segregated office.

Computers wore skirts

Katherine Johnson was one of several hundred female mathematicians at NASA hired to solve complex math problems for research engineers.

In the 1950s, there weren't hand-held calculators or laptop computers to do the math required to map out the path for a space mission. Johnson once remarked, "In those days, computers wore skirts!"—meaning computers weren't machines, they were *women*. The job they performed was crucial to the space race, since getting the calculations right meant the difference between the astronauts arriving home safely, or not at all.

Not just a number-cruncher!

Still, Katherine Johnson wasn't satisfied with being a number-cruncher, doing calculations for engineers. At the time, women weren't permitted to attend *briefings* (meetings where projects—some of them top secret!—were explained). This made it difficult for Johnson to learn what her calculations were for. She said she often read *Aviation Week* magazine to figure out the purpose of her projects.

In an interview with science historian Dr. Wini Warren, Johnson recalled how eager she felt to be included in the meetings that shaped the direction of her work.

"I would ask what had gone on in the briefing—I'd listen and listen, and ask questions. Then, of course, I'd ask why I couldn't go myself, and eventually they just got tired of answering all my questions and just let me in [to the briefings]."

Photo courtesy
of Katherine Johnson

Johnson faced other hurdles even after she began attending briefings. She explained, "In the early years at NASA, women were not allowed to put their names on the reports . . . I was working with Ted Skopinski and he wanted to leave and go to Houston . . . but our supervisor—who was not a fan of women—kept pushing him to finish the report we were working on. Finally, Ted told him, 'Katherine should finish the report, she's done most of the work, anyway.' So Ted left him with no choice; I finished the report and my name went on it, and that was the first time that a woman in our division had her name on something."

Katherine Johnson's report became the guide that NASA used to plan the launch, pathway, and safe return of the first manned space flights!

Before she retired from NASA in 1986, Johnson was also involved in creating an emergency navigation system for astronauts. Using this system, astronauts can determine their position using the stars seen out of spacecraft windows. Johnson is especially proud to have been a part of NASA at both the birth of the space program in the 1950s and the birth of the international space station in the 1980s. Her last project was to figure out how to best position the station's solar reflectors.

Find your mission!

In May 2006, 88-year-old Katherine Johnson received an honorary doctor of science degree from Capitol College in Laurel, Maryland. She told the graduating class, "From the time I entered elementary school, I was the youngest and the shortest in my class—and I talked the most! Sometimes I got in a little trouble for helping other students, but I really wanted everybody to make it."

Katherine's first job after college was teaching math and French. She explained, "When I first began teaching, that was one of my procedures. I had my students find a buddy and help each other. As you move ahead, you try that. It works!"

Katherine left the graduates with these words: "Your assignment is to find your mission and pursue it with passion. Choose something you love. Be busy learning and teaching your whole life."

Katherine Johnson's eighth grade class. She is third from the left.
Photo courtesy of Katherine Johnson

QUESTIONS

1. How did Katherine Johnson help bring the Apollo 13 astronauts home safely?

2. Name two obstacles Katherine Johnson overcame during her career at NASA.

3. Johnson says that you should "find your mission." What kinds of things do you like to do? Describe two careers that involve skills and talents that you enjoy.

Making an Astrolabe

In this activity you will build an astrolabe. Using the astrolabe and the North Star, you will calculate your latitude.

The astrolabe is an ancient scientific tool used by early astronomers and navigators. Early astronomers used the astrolabe to solve problems dealing with time and the location of the Sun, other stars, and planets in the sky. Navigators, on the other hand, used the astrolabe, along with the stars, to help identify their location.

Polaris, the North Star, is currently the star nearest the North Pole. At the North Pole, Polaris would be almost directly overhead. Spotting Polaris tells you the direction of the North Pole. Navigators used their angle from the Polaris to tell them their latitude.

Materials

30-centimeter piece of string, protractor, small metal washer, drinking straw, masking tape, flashlight, a partner

What you will do

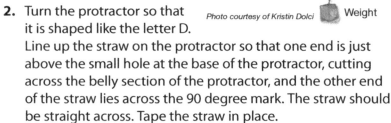
To the stars
Straw
Viewer
Photo courtesy of Kristin Dolci   Weight

1. Tie one end of the string into the small hole at the base of the protractor. Tie or tape the small washer to the other end of the string so that it acts as a weight.

2. Turn the protractor so that it is shaped like the letter D. Line up the straw on the protractor so that one end is just above the small hole at the base of the protractor, cutting across the belly section of the protractor, and the other end of the straw lies across the 90 degree mark. The straw should be straight across. Tape the straw in place.

3. Be sure that the string still swings freely.

4. Stand outside on a dark, clear night. To locate the North Star, find the Big Dipper. Find two stars that form the outermost edge of the cup of the Big Dipper, furthest from the handle. Line the stars up and follow where they point until you see the faint North Star.

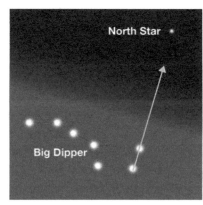
North Star
Big Dipper

5. View the North Star through the straw on your astrolabe.

6. Continue to peer at the North Star with the astrolabe while your partner uses the flashlight to determine at what degree the string on the astrolabe falls. Be sure to use the numbers between 0 and 90. This is your latitude.

Applying your knowledge

a. Explain how the astrolabe works.

b. What value did you get as your latitude from your astrolabe?

c. Use the Web site provided or a map to determine and list your actual latitude. http://www.census.gov/cgi-bin/gazetteer

d. Calculate the percentage of error in your measurements. Use the following formula:

$$\% \text{ Error} = \frac{\text{Actual latitude - Your measurement}}{\text{Actual latitude}} \times 100$$

e. Why might there have been errors or inaccuracies with your measurement?

f. Where would you be located if your astrolabe read 0° latitude? What about 90° latitude?

Chapter 19 Assessment

Vocabulary

Select the correct term to complete the sentences.

spectroscopy	brightness	universe
Big Bang theory	galaxy	scientific notation
light year	telescope	nebula
constellation		

Section 19.1

1. Very large or very small numbers can be written using _____.

2. Astronomers use _____ to measure the vast distances in space.

3. The _____ is everything that exists including all matter and energy.

4. A _____ is a huge collection of gas, dust, and billions of stars.

5. A _____ is used to look at objects that are far away.

Section 19.2

6. Orion is an example of a _____, or a group of stars that form a pattern in the night sky.

7. _____ describes the amount of light per second falling on an object.

8. Astronomers use _____ to analyze the light from a star.

9. Stars are born inside a huge cloud of gas and dust called a _____.

Section 19.3

10. The _____ describes how many scientists think the universe was formed.

Concepts

Section 19.1

1. Why are light years used to measure distances to stars instead of kilometers?

2. What is the difference between a refracting telescope and a reflecting telescope?

3. Why is scientific notation often used in astronomy?

4. What are the advantages to placing a telescope on a satellite?

5. Refracting and reflecting telescopes "see" light. What are some other types of telescopes and what do they "see"?

Section 19.2

6. Describe the conditions necessary to create a star.

7. Explain why spectroscopy is an important tool of astronomy.

8. What information does the color of a star provide?

9. What are the three main characteristics used to classify stars?

10. What is the difference between brightness and luminosity?

11. Describe the life cycle of a Sun-like star. Include in your description the following terms: nebula, protostar, red giant, planetary nebula, white dwarf, and black dwarf.

12. How long a star lives is related to which of the following quantities: (a) size; (b) temperature; (c) mass; or (d) color.

Section 19.3

13. How do astronomers classify galaxies?

14. What is Doppler shift? How does Doppler shift provide evidence for the Big Bang theory?

Math and Writing Skills

Section 19.1

1. Write the following values using scientific notation.
   a. 156,000,000,000 kilometers
   b. 18.5 pounds
   c. 0.0000000000000000000000025 centimeters
   d. 47,000,000,000,000 kilometers
   e. 93,000,000 miles
   f. 17,000 light years

Section 19.2

2. Arrange the stars in the table below in order, from highest temperature, to lowest temperature.

Star	Color
A	white
B	orange
C	blue
D	red
E	blue-white
F	yellow

3. The diagram below shows a group of stars as seen in the night sky. In the diagram, the relative size of each star indicates how bright it appears in the sky (its brightness). Next to each star, its distance from Earth, in light years (ly) is shown. Use the diagram to answer the three questions in the next column.

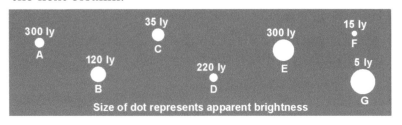

a. If all of the stars in the diagram were moved to the same distance from Earth, which star would appear the brightest?
b. Which star do you think has the lowest luminosity? Explain your answer.

Section 19.3

4. The light from two stars (A and B) is analyzed using a spectrometer. The spectral lines for these stars are shown below. Also shown are the spectral lines for hydrogen from a light source that is not moving.

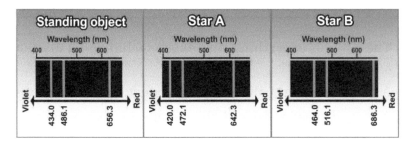

Which star is moving toward Earth? Which star is moving away from Earth? Explain your answer in both cases.

Chapter Project—Astronomy Catalog

Create a printed catalog or computer presentation about the astronomical objects you learned about in this unit (planets, stars, galaxies, etc. Follow these steps.

a. Make a list of all of the astronomical objects you learned about in this unit (planets, stars, etc.).
b. Write a definition and description of each type of object.
c. Using the Internet, find images of each type of object to use for your catalog or presentation.

Glossary

A glossary is an alphabetical list of important words found in a book. Use this glossary just as you would use a dictionary—to learn the meaning of unfamiliar words. This glossary gives the scientific meanings of words as they are used in this book. As with any subject, science has its own vocabulary. Therefore, learning these words and their meanings will enrich your study of science.

A

absolute dating – a method of estimating the age of a rock sample in years.

accurate – a measurement that is factual.

active volcano – a volcano that is erupting or that has erupted recently.

aftershock – a small tremor that follows an earthquake.

air – the mixture of gases that make up Earth's atmosphere.

altitude – a measure of the distance an object is above sea level.

amplitude – the vertical distance between a wave crest or trough and the average level of motion.

aquifer – a underground area of sediment and rocks that is filled with groundwater.

asteroid – an object that orbits the Sun but is too small to be considered a planet.

asthenosphere – the lower part of the upper mantle. Lithospheric plates slide on this layer.

astronomical unit – equal to 150 million km, or the distance from Earth to the Sun.

atmosphere – the layer of gases that surrounds Earth.

atmospheric pressure – a measure of the force per unit area of air molecules in the atmosphere given altitude.

atom – a particle of matter.

aurora – a phenomenon that occurs when Earth's atmosphere is energized by solar winds.

axis – the imaginary line that passes through the center of a planet from pole to pole.

B

barometer – an instrument that measures atmospheric pressure.

basalt – a dark-colored igneous rock with fine crystals

bathymetric map – a map that shows the depths of a body of water such as a lake or an ocean.

beach – a sandy zone above the foreshore in a shallow marine environment.

Big Bang theory – a theory that the universe began as a huge explosion 10 billion to 20 billion years ago.

biomes – major climate regions with particular plant and animal communities. Earth has six important biomes.

body waves – seismic waves that travel through the interior of Earth.

braided stream – a stream that has many channels that criss-cross each other.

brightness – measures the amount of light reaching Earth.

buoyant force – an upward lifting force that acts on an object when it pushes aside a fluid.

C

caldera – the bowl-shaped vent of a volcano after it has erupted.

cementation – the process by which sediment particles are "glued" together to make sedimentary rock.

channel – the path that a river or stream follows.

chemical weathering – weathering of rock that involves chemical reactions.

cinder cone – a volcano that has low-silica magma with high levels of dissolved gas; these volcanoes produce "fire fountain" eruptions.

cleavage plane – a surface along which a mineral cleanly splits.

climate – the long-term record of temperature, precipitation, and wind for a region.

cloud – a group of water droplets or ice crystals that you can see in the atmosphere.

coast – the boundary between land and a body of water like the ocean.

cold front – a front that occurs when a cold air mass moves in and replaces a warm air mass.

comet – an object in space made mostly of ice and dust.

compaction – the process by which sediment is pressed together as more and more layers or beds of sediment form on top of each other.

composite volcano – a tall, explosive, cone-shaped volcano formed by layers of silica-rich lava and ash.

condensation – the process by which a substance in its gaseous phase loses energy and enters the liquid phase.

conduction – transfer of heat by direct contact of atoms and molecules.

constellation – a group of stars that, when seen from Earth, form a pattern.

continental drift – the idea that continents move around on Earth's surface.

continental margin – the region around continents that includes the continental shelf and continental slope.

continental plates – thick, less-dense lithospheric plates that are made of granite and form the continents.

continental shelf – the ocean bottom that extends from a coast; where the continental shelf ends, the ocean become distinctly deeper.

contour lines – curved lines on a map that indicate all the points where the elevation or depth is the same.

contour lines – curved lines on a topographic (or bathymetric) map that indicate all the points where the elevation is the same.

control variable – a variable that is held constant in an experiment.

convection – transfer of heat through the motion of liquids and gases.

convection cells – large wind patterns in Earth's atmosphere caused by convection.

convergent boundary – a lithospheric plate boundary where two plates come together.

core – the center of Earth; it is divided into the inner core and the outer core.

Coriolis effect – the bending of currents of air or water due to Earth's rotation.

craters – large, round pits formed by impacts from large space objects.

crest – the high point of a wave.

cross bedding – when a graded bedding pattern in a sedimentary rock is cut off and covered with another graded bedding pattern running in another direction.

crust – the outermost surface of Earth.

crystallization – the process by which crystals grow in size.

cyclone – a low-pressure center surrounded by rotating winds.

D

data – pieces of information collected to test a hypothesis.

deep ocean currents – density- and temperature-driven currents that move slowly within the ocean, also called thermohaline currents.

density – the mass of an object divided by the object's volume.

dependent variable – a variable that is affected by the change to the independent variable.

deposition – the process of depositing sediment after it has been moved by water, wind, ice, or gravity.

desert – a climate region that averages less than 35 centimeters of rainfall per year.

dew point – the temperature at which more water condenses than evaporates in an air mass at a constant atmospheric pressure.

direction of younging – the order in which sedimentary rock layers are formed–from larger to finer particles.

disturbance – a movement that begins in one location and sets things in motion farther away.

divergent boundary – a lithospheric plate boundary where two plates move apart.

dormant volcano – a volcano that is not erupting now, but that may erupt in the future.

E

earthquake – the movement of Earth's crust as a result of the buildup of friction between two lithospheric plates.

element – a substance composed of only one kind of atom.

elevation – the height of an object measured from a reference level.

emissions – tiny particles and gases released into the air.

epicenter – a point on Earth's surface right above the focus of an earthquake.

equator – an imaginary line around the middle of Earth between the north and south poles.

erosion – the process of moving sediment by wind, water, ice, or gravity.

evaporation – the process by which a substance in its liquid phase gains energy and enters its gaseous phase.

exosphere – the region of the atmosphere that begins at about 500 km above Earth and extends into space.

experiment – an activity performed to prove or disprove a hypothesis.

extinct volcano – a volcano that no longer erupts and is in the process of eroding.

extrusive rock – an igneous rock that forms outside of Earth's crust.

F

fault – a region on Earth's surface that is split into two pieces.

fetch – the amount of open water over which wind blows.

floodplain – flat land near a river that tends to flood and that is usually located some distance form the source of the river.

fluid – matter that can flow, usually a liquid or a gas.

focus – the point below Earth's surface where a rock breaks and causes an earthquake.

foreshock – a small burst of shaking that occurs before a large earthquake.

formed from lava that is not silica-rich.

fossil – a part of a dead anima or plant that has been preserved for a long time.

fossil fuels – substances found in Earth's crust that were formed over millions of years from the remains of dead organisms.

front – the border between two different air masses.

frost wedging – physical weathering that results from freezing water.

G

galaxy – a huge collection of gas, dust, and billions of stars.

gas giants – planets that are made mostly of hydrogen and helium.

geologic time scale – a model of the history of life on Earth.

geology – the study of rocks and rock formations.

giant impact theory – explains how the Moon was formed.

glacier – a huge mass of ice that forms on land when snow and ice accumulate faster than they melt.

globe – a map of Earth that models its shape, and the locations and relative sizes of oceans and continents.

graded bedding – the order of rocks from large to small that settle on a lake or pond bottom when water flow slows down.

gram – the basic unit of mass in the SI Units measuring system; one-thousandth of a liter.

granite – an igneous rock with large, visible crystals, formed from silic-rich magma.

graph – a picture that shows how two variables are related.

grasslands – climate regions with too little rainfall to support a forest. Grasslands have grasses as the main vegetation.

gravitational force – the force of attraction between all objects.

groundwater – water that collects under ground.

gyres – large rotating ocean current systems.

H

half-life – the amount of time it takes for half of the unstable atoms in a sample to decay.

heat – a form of energy caused by the motion of atoms and molecules.

high-pressure center – a high-pressure area created by sinking cold air.

hot spot – the top of an established mantle plume.

humus – the dark, organic material in soil produced by the decay of plant and animal matter.

hurricane – a tropical cyclone with wind speeds of at least 74 miles per hour (119 kilometers per hour).

hydrosphere – an Earth system that includes all the water on the planet.

hypothesis – a possible answer to a scientific question based on observations.

I

energy – a measure of a system's ability to change.

igneous rock – a rock formed from the cooling and crystallizing of magma or lava.

independent variable – a variable that is changed in an experiment.

inference – a statement based on experiences.

international dateline – an imaginary longitude line located 180 degrees from the prime meridian.

intertidal zone – the zone of a marine environment below the beach and between the high and low tide lines; also called the foreshore.

intrusive rock – an igneous rock that forms inside of Earth's crust.

ion – a charged element or molecule.

ionosphere – portions of the atmosphere in the region of the thermosphere where electricity can be transmitted.

isobar – a line on a weather map that connects places that have the same atmospheric pressure.

J

jet streams – high-altitude, fast-moving winds.

K

kinetic energy – motion energy.

L

lahars – a mudflow that results from a volcanic eruption.

landslide – a large mass of soil or rock that slides down a volcano or mountain. Landslides can be caused by volcanic events, earthquakes, or other factors.

latitude – east-west lines that are north or south of the equator.

lava – magma that has reached and cooled on Earth's surface.

lava bombs – blobs of glowing lava thrown from an explosive eruption.

lava lake – a lake that contains lava that has formed in a caldera.

law of universal gravitation – states that the strength of the gravitational force depends on the mass of the objects and the distance between them.

leaching – a process by which water dissolves substances and causes them to be removed from one location to another.

legend – a special area on a map that lists the symbols that are used.

light year – a measurement that is equal to the distance that light travels through space in one year.

lightning – a bright spark of light that occurs inside a storm cloud, between a cloud and Earth's surface, or between two clouds.

liter – the basic unit of volume in the SI Units measuring system.

lithosphere – a layer of Earth that includes the crust and a thin part of he upper mantle.

lithospheric plates – large pieces of Earth's lithosphere that move over the asthenosphere.

longitude – north-south lines that are east or west of the prime meridian.

longshore drift – the flow of sand along a coast.

low-pressure center – a low-pressure area created by rising warm air.

luminosity – the total amount of light given off by a star.

lunar cycle – the gradual change in the appearance of the Moon due to the positions of Earth, the Moon, and the Sun.

lunar eclipse – occurs when Earth's shadow falls on the moon.

M

magma – underground melted rock.

magma chamber – a location where magma collects inside Earth.

mantle – the warm, flowing, solid layer of Earth between the crust and the core.

mantle plume – heated lower mantle rock that rises toward the lithosphere because it is less dense than surrounding mantle rock.

marine – a term that describes things that are part of or from the ocean.

mass – the amount of matter that an object has.

mass wasting – the downhill movement of large amounts of rock and sediment due to the force of gravity.

matter – the substance of all objects; all matter is made of atoms and has mass.

meanders – S-shaped curves in a river.

measurement – a number that includes a unit.

Mercalli Intensity scale – a scale that rates the damage suffered by buildings, the ground, and people during an earthquake.

mesosphere – a layer of atmosphere that occurs from about 50 km to 80 km above Earth's surface.

metamorphic rock – ba rock formed from another rock because of heat and pressure.

meteor – a chunk of burning rock traveling through Earth's atmosphere.

meteorite – a meteor that passes through Earth's atmosphere and strikes the ground.

meteorologist – an individual who uses scientific principles to forecast the weather.

meter – the basic distance unit for the SI Units system of measurement.

mid-ocean ridges – long chains of undersea mountains.

mineral – a solid, naturally-occurring, crystalline object with a defined chemical composition.

Mohs hardness scale – a scale to identify minerals based on their hardness or resistance to being scratched.

Moment Magnitude scale – a scale that rates the total energy released by earthquakes.

N

natural resource – a feature of Earth that benefits people.

nebula – a huge cloud of gas (mostly hydrogen) and dust from which stars are formed.

nonrenewable resource – a natural resource that is not replaced as it is used.

O

oceanic plates – thin, dense lithospheric plates that are made of basalt and form the ocean floor.

orbit – regular, repeating path that an object in space follows around another object.

P

paleontologist – a scientist who studies and identifies fossils.

Pangaea – an ancient, huge landmass composed of earlier forms of today's continents; an ancient supercontinent.

percolation – the process of liquid moving through a porous substance.

period – the time it takes for one wavelength to pass a single point.

permafrost – a permanently frozen soil located from 25 to about 100 centimeters below Earth's surface.

petroleum – another name for the natural resource called oil.

physical weathering – physical forces that break rocks down into smaller pieces.

planet – a massive object orbiting a star like the Sun.

plate tectonics – a theory explaining how the pieces of Earth's surface (the plates) move.

pollution – a change to the environment that is harmful to humans or other living things.

potential energy – stored energy.

power plant – a place where electricity is generated.

precipitation – condensed water vapor in the atmosphere falling back to Earth in the form of rain, hail, sleet, or snow.

precise – a measurement that is consistent although it may or may not be accurate.

prime meridian – an imaginary line through Greenwich, England that is perpendicular to the equator.

P-waves – seismic waves that move with a forward-and-back motion; these waves are faster than S-waves.

pyroclastic flow – a destructive cloud of volcanic material that moves quickly down the side of a volcano after an explosive eruption.

R

radiation – heat transfer that involves energy waves and no direct contact or movement by atoms.

radioactive decay – refers to how unstable atoms lose energy and matter over time.

relative dating – a method of putting events in the order in which they happened.

relief – the distance between a high and low place on a map.

renewable resource – a natural resource that can be replaced.

reservoir – a protected artificial or natural lake that is used to store water.

resource conservation – protecting, preserving, and managing Earth's natural resources.

resurgent dome – a mound in the vent of an erupted volcano.

revolution – the motion of Earth moving around the Sun; one revolution is called a year.

Richter scale – a scale that rates earthquakes according to the size of the seismic waves.

Ring of Fire – a region of Earth's plate boundaries where oceanic crust is subducting under other plates.

river – a large body of water that flows into an ocean or lake.

rock – a naturally-formed solid made of one or more minerals.

rock cycle – the formation and recycling of rocks by geologic processes.

rockfall – an event that results in a large amount of rock splitting off of a landform.

rotation – the motion of Earth spinning on its axis; one rotation is called a day.

S

salinity – a term that describes the saltiness of water.

satellite – an object in orbit around another object.

science – a process for answering questions.

scientific law – a statement that describes an observed phenomenon; it is supported by evidence collected from many observations and experiments.

scientific method – a series of steps including observation, forming a question, stating a hypothesis, collecting data, and reaching a conclusion.

scientific notation – a mathematical abbreviation, using powers of 10, for writing very large or very small numbers.

scientific theory – a statement that explains a complex idea; it is supported by evidence collected from many experiments.

sea level – the average level of the ocean; the halfway point between high tide and low tide.

sea-floor spreading – a hypothesis that new sea floor is created at mid-ocean ridges and that in the process the continents are pushed apart from each other.

sediment – small rock particles, minerals, and bits of once-living things.

sedimentary rock – a rock made of sediments that are cemented together by pressure and chemical changes.

seismic waves – vibrations that travel through Earth and are caused by events like earthquakes or human-made blasts.

seismograph – an instrument that measures and records seismic waves.

seismologist – a scientist who detects and interprets seismic waves.

shield volcano – a flat and wide volcano that has low-silica magma with low or high levels of dissolved gas.

slope – a measure of how steep land is, also called gradient.

slumping – an event that occurs when soil particles become surrounded by water so that the ground sinks or "slumps."

slumping – an event that occurs when soil particles become surrounded by water so that the ground slides or "slumps."

soil – the portion of Earth's surface that consists of organic matter, sediment, air, and water.

soil profile – cross-section that shows the different layers of soil in the ground.

solar eclipse – an eclipse that takes place when the new moon passes between Earth and the sun and the shadow formed reaches Earth; may be classified as total, partial, or annular.

solar energy – energy from the Sun.

solar system – the Sun and all objects that are bound by gravitational force to the Sun.

specific heat – the amount of energy needed to raise the temperature of 1 gram of a substance by 1 degree Celsius.

spectroscopy – a measurement of the electromagnetic radiation (including visible light) produced by a star or other object (called its spectrum).

star – a giant, hot ball of gas held together by gravity.

storm cell – a convection cell within a cloud that is associated with a storm.

stratosphere – a layer of atmosphere that occurs from about 11 km to 50 km above Earth's surface.

stream – a small river.

subduction – a process that involves a lithospheric plate sinking into the mantle.

sunspot – a dark area in the photosphere of the sun caused by a lowered temperature.

surface ocean currents – wind-driven currents that move at the ocean surface, often for long distances.

surface runoff – water that flows over land until it reaches lakes, rivers, and oceans.

surface water – water found on Earth's surface in places like oceans, lakes, rivers, and reservoirs.

surface waves – body waves that reach and travel along Earth's surface.

S-waves – seismic waves that move with a side-to-side motion and are slower than P-waves.

swells – long, fast-moving waves.

system – a group of objects and the factors that affect the objects.

T

taiga – the largest climate region, found in the higher latitudes; also known as a boreal or coniferous forest.

telescope – any device that collects radiation, which may be in the form of electromagnetic or particle radiation, from a limited direction in space.

temperate deciduous forests – climate regions in the mid-latitudes that have seasons.

temperature – measure of the speed of an individual atom or the average speed of a sample containing lost of atoms.

terrestrial planets – planets that are made mostly from rock and metal.

thermal – small heat-driven air current.

thermosphere – a layer of atmosphere that occurs from about 80 km to about 500 km. This layer has a low density of air molecules and a very high temperature.

thunder – a sound that occurs when a lightning spark heats air and the air expands.

tidal flat – a flat, muddy area in the intertidal zone.

tide – the daily rising and falling of an ocean's water levels.

topographic map – maps that use contour lines to show elevation.

tornado – a system of rotating winds around a low-pressure center. A tornado is smaller than a hurricane, but has faster winds.

transform fault boundary – a lithospheric plate boundary where two plates slide by each other.

transpiration – the process by which plants lose water through tiny pores on their leaves.

trench – a valley in the ocean created where one lithospheric plate subducts under another.

tropical rainforests – climate regions found near the equator that have a lot of rainfall and high biodiversity.

troposphere – a layer of atmosphere that occurs from 0 to about 11 kilometers above Earth's surface and where all weather occurs.

trough – the low point of a wave.

tsunami – a huge wave made by a large disturbance like an underwater earthquake, landslide, or volcanic eruption.

tundra – a climate region located in high latitudes; known as the coldest land biome.

U

unit – a specific quantity that is counted to make a measurement.

universe – everything that exists, including all matter and energy.

V

variable – a factor that affects an object; examples include mass, temperature, speed, and time.

volcanic island – a volcano that forms away from a plate boundary on an oceanic plate.

volcanic island chain – a series of volcanoes formed by a hot spot as a lithospheric plate moves over the hot spot.

volcanic neck – solid remains of magma that filled the conduit of an extinct volcano. The neck is exposed as the volcano erodes.

volcano – an erupting vent through which molten rock reaches Earth's surface, or a mountain built from the products of an eruption.

volume – a measurement of how much space is occupied by an object.

W

warm front – a front that occurs when a warm air mass moves in and replaces a cold air mass.

water cycle – a set of processes energized by the Sun that keep water moving from place to place on Earth.

water table – the upper level of water under ground. Below the water table, all spaces are filled with groundwater.

water vapor – water in gas form.

watershed – an area of land that catches all precipitation and surface runoff and collects it in a body of water such as a river.

wave train – many waves traveling together.

wavelength – the distance between two wave crests, or the distance between two wave troughs.

weather – the condition of the atmosphere as it is affected by wind, water, temperature, and atmospheric pressure.

weathering – the process of breaking down rock and minerals.

weathering – the process of breaking down rock.

weight – a measure of mass and the force of gravity on an object.

wind – air that flows, often because of heating and cooling of air or unequal air pressure.

Index

The index gives the page numbers where you can find a word, definition, information about a topic or a large category. You can use the index when you are studying and need to find information quickly. The index is a good place to look up a vocabulary word to get more information about the meaning of a word.

Index

Index

Index

EXPLORE FURTHER

**Earth
Science**
Appendix

Table of Contents

Exploring The Engineering Cycle

EXPLORATION SUMMARY

In this exploration, you will learn how to choose the best design for a tool. Then you will use the engineering design to create a new tool.

Materials List

- Various materials that can be used to build a prototype

- Logbook (notebook or stapled pages)

A common tool that is used by geologists in the field is the geological hammer (Figure 1). This tool fractures and breaks rock. The hammer head of a geological hammer often has two sides. One side is flat for blunt hits to rock and the other side may be a chisel or a pick. The chisel can be used to brush away debris or pry open cracks in a rock. The pick can be used for more precise and harder attacks on rock.

Part 1: **The decision-matrix method**

The chart on the next page is a decision-matrix that is used to select the best design for a product or tool. The late design engineer Stuart Pugh is credited with inventing this method.

This particular chart compares the design of one hammer (the datum) to three other designs.

For this example, the best hammer design should be able to break all kinds of rock and be able to pry and remove debris. The cost of the hammer doesn't matter, so it is okay if it is made of higher-quality, hardened steel rather than wood.

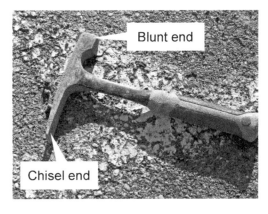

Blunt end

Chisel end

Pick end

Blunt end

Figure 1: *Samples of geologists' hammers.*

Your teacher will show you examples of geological hammers and use these examples to review this chart with you.

Description			Geological hammer	Size of head	Shape of head	Material used in shaft
Sketch			Small, flat head and chisel head, hardened steel shaft	Large, flat head and chisel head, hardened steel shaft	Small, flat head and pick head, hardened steel shaft	Small, flat head and chisel head, wood shaft
Criteria	Weight		Datum (basic design for comparison)	Design 1	Design 2	Design 3
Breaks rocks of low hardness	3		0	+	0	0
Breaks medium hard rocks	3		0	+	0	0
Breaks very hard rocks	2		0	+	0	0
Prying and removing debris	2		0	0	–	0
Durability	3		0	0	0	–
Cost	1		0	0	0	+
Total +			0	8	0	1
Total 0			6	2	5	4
Total –			0	0	2	3
Net Score			0	8	–2	–2

Notes about the chart:

To use this chart, you first describe and sketch a series of designs. One design is selected as the "datum." The other designs will be compared to the datum.

Give a weight to each of the criteria based on its importance in the final design. For example, if cost doesn't matter, give it a weight of "1." However, if it's important to make the cost affordable for most people, give it a rating of "3."

Add zeroes to the datum column. Fill in the columns based on how the other designs compare to the datum. Add a plus sign if the design is better than datum, and a negative sign if it is not as good.

Multiply the weight by the plus or minus sign in each row and write the sum of each sign in the table's bottom rows. Add the positive and negative values to get a net score for each design.

a. Look at the net scores for each design. Which was the best design and why?

b. Design 2 and 3 had the same score. Explain why each of these designs was the least desirable.

c. Let's say you need a geologic hammer that can break very hard rocks and that needs to be able to make breaks with precision. Describe what kind of hammer you would need.

Part 2: **The engineering cycle**

In order to design a new tool or redesign an existing tool, engineers use the engineering cycle.

Engineering Cycle

Your assignment is to design a new tool that can be used on geology field trips. The following steps will guide you in using the engineering cycle. Keep a logbook of your work.

Step 1: *Identify a need*

First you need to define the problem and set the goal of the project. Identify the criteria and constraints. Criteria are features that your tool needs to have. Constraints are features that your tool should not have (i.e., it might need to be lightweight).

a. Talk to a geologist and learn about the types of activities you need to accomplish while on a geology field trip. Identify one task that needs to be accomplished. Now, identify the type of tool you will design for this task. This is your goal.

b. List the criteria and constraints.

Step 2: *Design*

Brainstorm to create a list of ideas. Be creative. It is okay if some ideas seem far-fetched. Do some research to refine your ideas. Then, select the best ideas. Use the ideas to create a design. Choose materials, make drawings, and decide what you will build. Optional: Use the decision-matrix to evaluate your various design ideas.

a. Select your best design and make a final sketch of it. Be sure to add labels to your sketch.

b. Make a list of materials you would need to build your tool.

Step 3: *Prototype*

Follow your design to build a prototype.

a. What difficulties did you have while building your prototype?

b. What did you learn about your design while building your prototype?

Step 4: *Test*

Find out if your prototype works. *Note*: You may only be able to build a nonworking model of your tool. This means that you may not be able to test its strength by hitting a rock, for example! Instead, you may want to show your tool design to an expert and get their feedback about whether they think your design will work.

a. What are the strengths and weaknesses of your prototype?

b. If you are able to show your design to an expert, what did they have to say?

Step 5: *Evaluate*

Once the prototype is tested, evaluate the design and brainstorm new ideas for improving it. The engineering cycle is repeated as many times as needed to create and improve products.

a. Summarize your experience in working with the engineering cycle.

b Give one or two reasons why using the engineering cycle and a decision-matrix are good methods for creating the best design for a product or tool.

c. You probably worked with a team in order to complete this exploration. Explain why it is important to work with a team of people in order to create the best design for a product or tool.

Exploring Earth's Energy

EXPLORATION SUMMARY

In Chapter 3, you learned that energy causes events to happen under and on Earth's surface. Here you will explore how this energy drives plate tectonics and weather.

A review of Earth's heat energy.

Surface and internal heat
Massive nuclear reactions in the Sun produce radiant energy that warms Earth. In fact, most of Earth's surface heat energy comes from this radiant energy, which includes visible light, infrared radiation (heat), and ultraviolet light. Earth's internal heat energy mostly comes from its core (Figure 2). Much of Earth's internal heat energy is left over from when Earth first formed and comes from the breakdown of radioactive atoms.

A cooling planet
Ever since Earth formed, it has been cooling down. The brittle crust of Earth formed when Earth became cool enough. However, because of plate tectonics, much of the crust has been recycled over its 4.6 billion–year lifespan. Scientists think that Earth will continue to cool down for another 4 to 5 million years. At the end of that time, plate tectonics will stop. There will no longer be volcanoes or the formation of mountains and the number of earthquakes will diminish.

How planets and planetary bodies lose heat
Planets and planetary bodies (like the Moon) lose heat when the internal heat radiates to space. Here are three ways that this can happen.

(1) One way is through volcanic activity. A great deal of the Moon's internal heat was lost this way millions of years ago when meteorites slammed into its surface. Meteorite impacts can break through crust material and release magma. The dark patches you see on the Moon called mares (or seas) are impact craters lined with solidified volcanic rock (Figure 3).

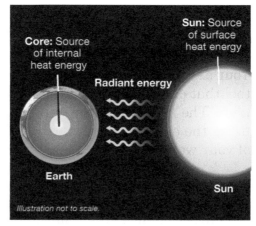

Figure 2: *Earth is warmed from the inside by heat from its core. Earth is warmed on its surface by radiant energy from the Sun.*

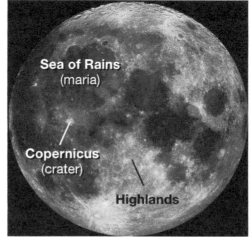

Photo courtesy NASA/JPL-Caltech

Figure 3: *The Moon's surface has impact craters, highlands, and ancient solidified lava flows called maria.*

(2) Another way that heat is lost is by hot spots. Large volcanoes, like the ones on the Hawaiian islands, are deeply connected to Earth's core by hot spots. A hot spot on Mars fed the huge volcano Olympus Mons, currently the highest mountain in the solar system. Loss of heat through this volcano when it was active is one reason why Mars cooled down relatively quickly after it formed. Mars also cooled down quickly because it is a smaller than Earth and lacks heat-producing nuclear reactions in its core.

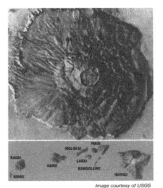

Image courtesy of USGS

Image of scale of Olympus Mons volcano and Hawaiin Islands courtesy USGS

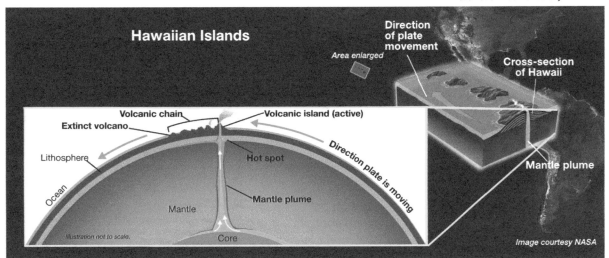

Image courtesy NASA

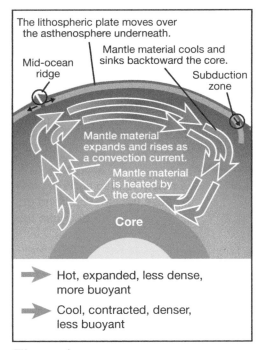

The lithospheric plate moves over the asthenosphere underneath.

Mantle material cools and sinks backtoward the core.

Mid-ocean ridge

Subduction zone

Mantle material expands and rises as a convection current.

Mantle material is heated by the core.

Core

→ Hot, expanded, less dense, more buoyant

→ Cool, contracted, denser, less buoyant

Figure 4: *A simplified model of convection in the mantle. Convection in the mantle is much more complex.*

(3) Various convection cells inside Earth's mantle are another way internal heat is lost. As a convection cell current nears the lithosphere, it turns and runs along underneath. When the convection current does cool down, it sinks back toward the core where it is heated again. A recent hypothesis suggests that it is not the convection current that cools, rather the lithospheric plate cools, subducts, and cools the mantle as it dives. The result is the sinking current of a convection cell (Figure 4). A convection cell cycle may take a billion years to complete.

Energy and plate tectonics

Subduction, the death of a plate Oceanic plates float on the underlying asthenosphere, near where they are made at a mid-ocean ridge. But far from the ridge, the plate is older, cooler, and too dense to float. The plate breaks and the dense end subducts through the asthenosphere and into the lower mantle. The subducting plate cools adjacent mantle material. Cooling makes the nearby material denser and it sinks deeper into the mantle. This sinking drives the down-flowing side of mantle convection.

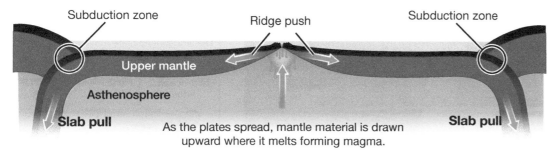

Mid-ocean ridge

Subduction zone

Ridge push

Subduction zone

Upper mantle

Asthenosphere

Slab pull

Slab pull

As the plates spread, mantle material is drawn upward where it melts forming magma.

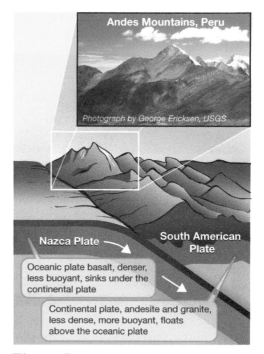

Andes Mountains, Peru

Photograph by George Ericksen, USGS

Nazca Plate

South American Plate

Oceanic plate basalt, denser, less buoyant, sinks under the continental plate

Continental plate, andesite and granite, less dense, more buoyant, floats above the oceanic plate

Figure 5: *The collision of the Nazca and South American Plates has deformed and pushed up the land to form the high peaks of the Andes Mountains.*

The newly-formed ends of plates experience ridge push. The ends experience slab pull because they are cool and denser than the upper mantle so they sink. They are cool because they have lost heat to the ocean above.

Oceanic and continental plate subduction The rock of continental plates is always less dense than the basalt of oceanic plates. This means a continental plate is too buoyant to subduct under an oceanic plate. Therefore, the oceanic plate must subduct under the continental plate. A good example of this is the Nazca Plate off the coast of South America. The Nazca Plate is subducting under the South American Plate (Figure 5).

Subduction and large earthquakes

Where do the world's largest earthquakes occur? You have learned that earthquakes commonly occur at the boundaries of lithospheric plates. The largest earthquakes occur at subduction zones where oceanic plates are sliding under continental plates. These large earthquakes are called "megathrust earthquakes."

Here are a few examples of some of the world's largest and most destructive earthquakes and where they occurred.

Figure 6: *The Tōhuku earthquake of 2011 may be the most expensive natural disaster ever recorded.*

Name	Date	Moment Magnitude	Subduction	Notes
Great Chilean Earthquake	1960	9.5	Nazca Plate under the South American Plate	Largest recorded
Great Alaskan Earthquake	1964	9.2	Pacific Plate under the North American Plate	
Indian Ocean earthquake and tsunami	2004	9.3	Indian Plate (part of the Indo-Australian Plate) slid under the Burma Plate (part of the Eurasian Plate)	
Chile earthquake	2010	8.8	Nazca Plate under the South American Plate	
Tōhoku (Japan) earthquake and tsunami (Figures 6 and 7)	2011	9.0	Pacific Plate under the Ohotsk Plate (a small plate connected to the Eurasian Plate)	May be the most expensive natural disaster ever recorded

Why subduction zones? Subduction zones are sites where brittle and cold oceanic crust slides into the mantle. If the subducting plate gets stuck and then breaks free, huge amount of stored energy is released and an earthquake happens. The nature of a subduction zone means that a large area of the associated brittle lithosphere can break and this is why the earthquakes can be large. If the sea floor is affected by this breaking, a tsunami may result.

Figure 7: *An aerial view of damage in the Tōhoku region with black smoke coming from an oil refinery.*

How ecosystems are affected by catastrophic events

How severe weather affects people   The energy source for weather is the Sun. This means that the Sun is involved in severe weather events which can inflict terrible damage to entire communities of people. For example, in May 2011, an extremely large multi-vortex tornado tore through Joplin, Missouri (Figure 8), and killed over 130 people. The cost to rebuild Joplin might be as high as $3 billion. By June 1, 2011, over 500 people had been killed by tornadoes in the southeastern United States (compared to over 500 deaths in the previous 10 years).

Catastrophic events are disturbances   Within ecosystems, producers and consumers are connected by food webs. When a major disturbance like a hurricane, a tornado, flooding, or a dust storm occurs, some or all of the parts of a food web are lost. Additionally, habitats are damaged or destroyed. Ecosystems can recover from a disturbance by the process of succession (the pattern of changes that occur in a community over time). Wildlife biologists, conservationists, and citizens also play roles in helping an ecosystem recover from a catastrophic event.

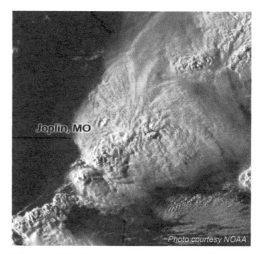

Figure 8: *This photo shows the cloud formations associated with the tornado that tore through Joplin, Missouri, in May 2011.*

Succession

Forest   After a severe storm   Grasslands   Small trees   Forest

Time

Hurricanes   Hurricanes have a significant impact on coastal ecosystems, which include wetlands (areas that are usually covered in water; examples include bogs, marshes, and swamps). These areas can experience severe water erosion, which causes a loss of habitat for plants and animals, and they can become flooded with salt water. The salt water makes it harder for plants to grow and for animals to return. Restoration of the wetlands takes years of deposition of soil and nutrients, rebalancing of the salinity of the water in the region, and flushing out of any pollutants deposited during the hurricane.

Tornadoes The central part of the United States is prone to tornadoes and often called Tornado Alley. Tornadoes can be severe disturbances to an ecosystem since they can tear down trees. It takes a while for the ecosystem to recover if forests are lost. More easily-established plants, like grasses and smaller animals, can recover more quickly.

Flooding During flooding, water, nutrients, sediments, and debris cover the floodplain. In ecosystems near a river, flooding causes the soil to become enriched so it can better support plant growth. Additionally, flooding recharges the groundwater in a region. However, flooding is disruptive for all living things on the floodplain. Animals are displaced and trees are uprooted.

Dust storms Dust storms and sand storms diminish the richness of soil (Figure 9). Organic matter and nutrients are moved out of the ecosystem, making the soil less able to support the basis of all land ecosystems—plants! On the other hand, the particles that are transported elsewhere can potentially enrich the soil of the ecosystems in which they are deposited. Sandhill and beach dune ecosystems, for example, are regions that benefit from transported sand.

Image courtesy of NOAA

Figure 9: *A Dust Bowl storm approaches Stratford, Texas, in 1935.*

QUESTIONS

1. List the main sources of Earth's surface heat energy and internal heat energy.

2. Describe the three ways that a planet or planetary body loses internal heat to space.

3. Explain why subduction zones are sites for Earth's largest earthquakes. Use the term *energy* in your answer.

4. Why is the process of succession important after a severe weather event that affects a forest?

5. Why is the Sun's energy important to the recovery of an ecosystem after a severe weather event?

6. Name one positive and one negative long-term impact of a severe weather event.

Explore activity:

The Sun's energy causes severe weather events and Earth's internal energy is related to severe events like earthquakes. Human beings cannot control the weather or plate tectonics. But, it is possible to plan ahead so that you can be safe during severe weather or other kinds of catastrophic events. Pick a catastrophic event and find out what scientists are doing to help keep people safe during these events. Examples of an event you might choose: earthquake, volcanic eruption, hurricane, tornado, flooding, and dust storm.

Exploring Global Climate Change

EXPLORATION SUMMARY

Today, the average temperature on Earth is warmer that is ever has been over the past 1,000 years. This warming is part of a set of changes called global climate change. If you were to read a newspaper article about climate change, you would find other terms like *greenhouse gases* and *global warming*. In this exploration, you will learn how these terms are related, and you will learn about the role that human activities and natural processes play in causing climate change.

Looking at global climate change

Causes of global climate change Global climate change or "climate change" refers to changes in the factors used to describe a climate (such as temperature, precipitation, or wind) that last for two or more decades. Climate change can be caused by natural processes and human activity. Since the Sun and the oceans affect weather patterns, changes in the Sun's intensity or in ocean circulation can cause climate change. Human activities that affect our climate include burning fossil fuels and altering the land. For example, cutting down or burning forests affects our atmosphere. Through photosynthesis, trees contribute to the oxygen and carbon cycles. Forests are considered to be "carbon sinks" since they absorb and store carbon in their tissues. Therefore, removing large areas of trees affects these cycles.

What are greenhouse gases? Greenhouse gases "blanket" our planet by trapping heat from the Sun so that Earth's average temperature is hospitable for living things. Nitrogen and oxygen gas make up 99% of Earth's atmosphere. Greenhouse gases represent a small portion of the atmosphere, but they are very important. The greenhouse gases are water vapor, carbon dioxide, methane, nitrous oxide, ozone, and carbon compounds produced by industry.

What is global warming? In the past 200 years, the concentrations and types of greenhouse gases in our atmosphere have increased. The most significant cause of this increase is the burning of fossil fuels (Figure 10) and deforestation (the removal of forests). Other sources of greenhouse gases include agriculture and industry (see sidebar on page 505). The increase of greenhouse gases in the atmosphere leads to the greenhouse effect that is causing global warming. Global warming is the increase of Earth's average temperature as a result of increased concentrations of greenhouse gases in the atmosphere. Global warming is contributing to global climate change that is happening now.

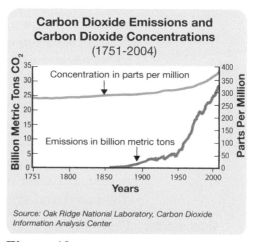

Carbon Dioxide Emissions and Carbon Dioxide Concentrations (1751-2004)

Source: Oak Ridge National Laboratory, Carbon Dioxide Information Analysis Center

Figure 10: *This graph shows that an increase in carbon dioxide (CO_2) produced by human activity (green line) coincides with an increase in atmospheric carbon dioxide concentration (blue line). In the last 100 years, the increase has accelerated.*

How greenhouse gases work

Trapping heat A greenhouse full of plants is a warm place, even on a cold day. Why is that? The glass walls and ceiling of a greenhouse allow sunlight that is needed for photosynthesis. The glass also traps heat from the Sun so the greenhouse stays warm (Figure 11). Like glass, greenhouse gases allow the Sun's radiation to reach Earth's surface. Some of the Sun's radiation is emitted by Earth's surface as infrared radiation (or heat). This form of radiation cannot escape into space easily or quickly. Instead, it gets trapped by greenhouse gases.

Figure 11: *The glass in a greenhouse lets in sunlight and traps heat from the Sun.*

The greenhouse effect and Earth's energy balance The greenhouse effect is the warming of Earth that results when greenhouse gases trap heat emitted from the planet's surface (Figure 12). This effect happens in spite of the fact that for every 100 units of radiation that enter Earth's atmosphere, 100 units exit. Here's why. Radiation that reaches Earth's surface is mostly in the form of visible and ultraviolet light. Radiation reflects from the surface as infrared waves. Infrared waves have lower frequency and longer wavelengths so they take longer to pass back through the atmosphere than the higher frequency waves. The time lag between incoming and outgoing radiation means energy is available in the atmosphere to keep Earth warm.

Global warming and climate change are serious concerns The greenhouse gases mentioned above occur in nature. Why then is global warming a serious concern? The answer to this question is two-fold. First, greenhouse gases are dramatically increasing because of fossil fuel use, deforestation, and activities of agriculture and industry. More greenhouse gases in the atmosphere will trap more heat and cause our planet's average temperature to increase. Second, an increased average temperature or one that continues to rise will mean global climate change with known and unknown consequences for all living things. Regions around the globe will be affected differently by climate change in negative, but possibly in positive ways as well.

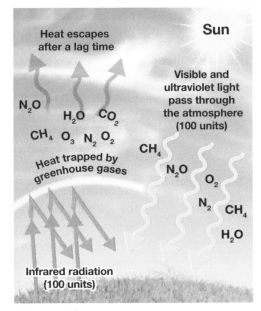

Figure 12: *The greenhouse effect. Without greenhouse gases, Earth's average temperature would be about 16°C less!*

Upsetting the balance in our atmosphere

The Industrial Revolution
The Industrial Revolution, which lasted from the late 1700s to the mid-1800s, was a period in which many manual tasks in agriculture and manufacturing were replaced by machines. Over time, our world has become full of useful machines. Think of the machines that you use each day. Each of these devices requires an energy source. In our modern world, fossil fuels are used the most as energy sources because they are easily available and affordable.

Combustion
Using fossil fuels as an energy source requires the process of combustion, which is very similar to respiration. Respiration is how living organisms use oxygen to convert food to energy. A combustion reaction, also called burning, takes place when a carbon-based substance—such as wood, oil, or natural gas—combines with oxygen and releases a large amount of energy in the form of light and heat. The products of a combustion reaction are carbon dioxide and water. The general equation for a combustion reaction is shown at the right.

The atmospheric balance
Carbon dioxide, produced by many combustion reactions since the Industrial Revolution, is one of the main causes of global warming. Carbon dioxide also enters the atmosphere whenever respiration takes place. With about 1 million species of living organisms on our planet, that's a lot of respiration! Balancing respiration, plants turn carbon dioxide into biomass during photosynthesis. Global warming is happening because of the extra amount of carbon dioxide and other greenhouse gases added to the atmosphere above the natural balance for Earth. Greenhouse gases produced by human activity include carbon dioxide, methane, nitrous oxide, and carbon compounds such as chlorofluorocarbons (CFCs) from industry. Other greenhouse gases include ozone and water vapor, which is the most abundant greenhouse gas. See the sidebar on next page for more information about these gases.

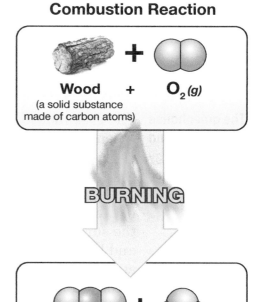

Combustion Reaction

Wood + O_2 (g)
(a solid substance made of carbon atoms)

BURNING

CO_2 (g) + H_2O (l)

Today and the future

The current state The amount of carbon dioxide in our atmosphere is 35 percent more than it was 200 years ago. Below are other indicators that global climate change is happening.

- Warming temperatures: As of 2007, 11 of the previous 12 years have been the warmest since 1850. A number of warm years in a row indicates that the cause is probably global warming rather than random chance.
- Rising sea level: The change in sea level from 1993 to 2003 was approximately 3 millimeters per year for a total rise of about 33 millimeters. The rise is due to (1) oceans absorbing more heat and water expands when it is heated, and (2) more water entering the ocean as glaciers and ice sheets melt.
- Decreasing ice coverage: There have been reductions in Arctic Ocean sea ice since 1978 and reductions in the size of glaciers.
- Increasing water vapor in the atmosphere: As temperatures rise, more evaporation takes place, leading to more water vapor in the atmosphere. Water vapor is actually the most abundant and effective greenhouse gas. With more water vapor in the atmosphere, more precipitation and more severe weather have occurred in certain regions of the world.

The future The Intergovernmental Panel on Climate Change (IPCC) states that even if greenhouse gases were to stabilize at their current levels, climate change would continue for centuries. This is partly due to the fact that our oceans have a high specific-heat capacity, meaning that they hold heat for a long time. Predictions for the 21st century include:

- an increase in global temperatures ranging from 1.8 to 4.0°C;
- a rise in sea level ranging from 30 to 40 centimeters; and
- effects on the oceans, ice cover, and cloud cover that could cause yet-unknown effects on other systems.

Greenhouse Gases

Carbon dioxide (CO_2): 82% of emissions; from burning fossil fuels, respiration, and volcanic activity

Methane (CH_4): 9% of emissions; from landfills, the petroleum industry, and agriculture

Nitrous oxide (N_2O): 5% of emissions; from fertilizer, burning fossil fuels, and industrial and waste management processes

Ozone (O_3): formed when sunlight reacts with air pollutants.

Chlorofluorocarbons (CFCs): used as refrigerants. Because these human-made gases also deplete the ozone layer, their production has been banned in many countries.

This table lists the levels of greenhouse gases for the time before the Industrial Revolution and today.

Greenhouse Gases

Gas	Before the Industrial Revolution	Current Level (2011)
Carbon dioxide	280 ppm	389 ppm
Methane	700 ppb	1,745 ppb
Nitrous oxide	270 ppb	322 ppb

ppm = parts per million
ppb = parts per billion

What can be done? Global climate change is a serious concern for all people. At present, governments and other organizations are looking at ways to reduce greenhouse gas emissions. What can you do to make a difference?

Global climate change and you

What governments can do With growing evidence that global climate change is happening due to human activities, more governments worldwide are taking action. Here's what some governments are doing: enacting laws that force the reduction of greenhouse gas emissions; developing alternative, nonpolluting energy resources; and working with other governments to address climate change.

What you can do Most of the energy used in the United States comes from fossil fuels, and most of the greenhouse gas emissions (such as carbon dioxide) come from the use of fossil fuels. What can you do to help reduce greenhouse gas emissions? To start, you can reduce your carbon footprint. Your carbon footprint is how much greenhouse gas emissions are produced as a result of your activities, both directly and indirectly. Here are suggestions for reducing your carbon footprint:

- Reduce your use of electricity. For example, turn off lights when you leave rooms and use efficient lighting sources (like compact fluorescent lamps).
- Use less hot water when you take showers and wash your clothes. Heating water takes a lot of energy.
- Use less energy to heat or cool your house. Wear a sweater in the winter to stay warm. Close curtains or blinds to keep your house cooler during the summer and warmer in the winter.
- Use your own energy for transportation. Walk more or use your bicycle to get from place to place. Or use public transportation to cut down on using fossil fuels for your transportation needs.

SCIENCE FACT:

How do Scientists Know that Human Activities are Increasing Greenhouse Gases?

1. Some greenhouse gases that are accumulating in our atmosphere only come from human sources (e.g., CFCs).

2. Concentrations of greenhouse gases differ from place to place. The highest greenhouse gas concentrations are over the Northern Hemisphere, which has a higher human population.

3. A study of carbon isotopes reveals that the increased levels of carbon dioxide in our atmosphere come directly from the burning of fossil fuels. Isotopes can be traced back to their carbon source.

Source of information:

Collins, W., R. Colman, J. Haywood, M. R. Manning, and P. Mote. 2007. The Physical Science Behind Climate Change. Scientific American. 297 (2).

[This article was based on Climate Change 2007: The Physical Science Basis. Contribution of Working Group I to the Fourth Assessment Report of the IPCC.]

- Use fewer products made from petrochemicals. For example, reduce your need for plastic bags by taking your own bags to the grocery store.
- Grow plants. Plant a tree or a garden.
- Educate yourself about global climate change.

SOLVE IT!

Emissions Trading

One way to reduce greenhouse gases is by "emissions trading." Emissions trading depends on businesses having credits to match the amount of emissions they produce. A business that produces less greenhouse emissions than allowed by law can sell credits to a business that produces more. Emissions trading is controversial. Find out why.

QUESTIONS

1. What is global climate change? Does an unusually warm winter provide evidence for global climate change? Why or why not?

2. Why are greenhouse gases such an important component of our atmosphere? What might Earth be like without greenhouse gases?

3. What are the two main human activities that scientists believe have caused our current condition of global climate change? Explain why each of these activities has led to global climate change.

4. The Industrial Revolution was a revolution in using machines to do more work, more efficiently. How did this revolution affect our global climate?

5. If greenhouse gases are a natural part of Earth's atmosphere, why are increasing concentrations of these gases a worldwide concern?

6. List two current and two possible future effects of global climate change.

7. What is a carbon footprint?

8. Can an infant have a carbon footprint? Explain your answer.

9. List five ways that you can reduce the size of your carbon footprint. Which of these do you think will have the greatest impact on reducing greenhouse gas emissions?

Exploring Human Impact on Earth

EXPLORATION SUMMARY

Earth's surface changes over time due to weathering, erosion, and plate tectonics. Human activity also changes Earth's surface. These changes can have positive or negative effects for people and the places where they live. The focus of this exploration will be how these human activities—water diversion, mineral extraction, and fossil fuel removal—impact Earth. These activities involve the use or removal of important resources. As you read, think about how you rely on water, minerals, and fossil fuel.

Water diversion

What is water diversion? Water is important for all living things. Fortunately, it is easy to obtain—often you just turn on a faucet! The water that you drink may come from groundwater or surface water (lakes, streams, and rivers). Water diversion is the redirecting of surface water so that it can be collected and provided to people. Dams are built in order to divert and trap surface water so that it can be provided to communities of people. Dams are also built so that the power of water can be converted into electricity (Figure 13). This hydroelectric power is considered to be a renewable energy source.

The positive effects The positive effects of water diversion are the water can be easily collected so that it can be distributed to communities. And by diverting water using dams, the water power can be converted to electricity. Because water and power are necessary for people and society, the need to divert water for human needs is something that is unavoidable.

Figure 13: *The Hoover Dam on the Colorado River provides hydroelectric power in the American Southwest.*

The negative effects The negative effects of water diversion mainly affect the environment. When water from a stream or river is diverted, the wildlife that live in and near the stream or river are affected. Fish are the most obvious wildlife affected. If a river changes course or is blocked by a dam, fish can't migrate and avoid predators. Another, negative effect of water diversion is soil erosion. Altering the natural path of water means that riverbanks are more likely to be eroded and the eroded sediment is often deposited in places where it isn't wanted.

New ideas It is possible to lower the impact of water diversion on the environment and wildlife. Some ways that have a lower impact than dams include:

- pulling water up from the water table below stream beds with pumps at specific locations,

- using screened pipes in a river or stream to remove water,

- using seasonal dams that alternate between trapping and releasing water (Figure 14), and

- replacing multiple dams with one and removing old dams.

For each of these methods to have a low impact, they must be designed to protect wildlife. For example, the pipes must be covered with screens to prevent fish from entering the pipe. Also, the buildup of sediment is a problem that must be addressed for these mechanisms to work.

Figure 14: The Tempe Town Inflatable Dam in Arizona is an example of a seasonal dam.

Mineral extraction

What is mineral extraction? In Chapter 13, you learned that rocks are made of minerals. In Chapter 15, you completed an activity that simulated extracting minerals and learned that minerals are valuable to humans. They are used in cosmetics, in health care products, as supplements in foods, for commercial and industrial uses, and for jewelry. Mineral extraction is the term used to describe the various processes that are used to remove minerals from Earth. Mining is a term used to describe how resources (like minerals) are removed from the ground.

The positive effects Mining is used to obtain resources that can't be produced through agriculture or artificially. These resources include minerals and rocks such as diamonds and other precious gems, metals, rock salt, coal, and uranium. The category of metals includes both "base metals" and precious metals. Examples of base metals are iron, copper, nickel, zinc, aluminum, and many others used in industry included the "rare earths" (which aren't really rare, but are hard to extract because they combine with other elements). Chances are you depend on metals in ways you may not even realize. For example, neodymium is a rare earth element used in magnets found in hybrid cars, computer hard drives, and microphones. Other uses for rare earths include smartphones, TV screens, LEDs, wind turbines, and lasers. Mined resources are important because we all rely on the products made with them.

The negative effects Mining can have serious negative effects on the environment, wildlife, and people. Mining increases erosion and may lead to sinkholes. Chemicals used and left behind during mining can poison the soil and groundwater. For example, one negative effect is called acid mine drainage (Figure 15). When groundwater percolates up through mines, it picks up elements that are not common on the surface. These elements are typically highly acidic and include toxic materials. When these acidic waters escape into streams, they frequently kill off living organisms those waters.

Photo courtesy USGS

Figure 15: *This image shows a yellow, iron precipitate in a stream. The precipitate is harmful to living things and is caused by acidic drainage from a coal mine.*

World mining Unlike our water supply, the minerals that are needed by people and industries in the United States are mostly found in other countries. Regarding rare earths, China mines 130,000 metric tons, or 97 percent of the 133,000 metric tons mined worldwide each year. Currently, the United States has only one mine in Mountain Pass, California. Because of the high demand for rare earths in our technology and concern that China has begun to restrict supplies of rare earths, there is pressure to develop more mines in the United States. Recently, Japan announced that it had located rare earths on the floor of the Pacific Ocean. Researchers speculate that one of the sampling areas could supply 20 percent of the demand for rare earths. However, there is concern that mining from the ocean floor will not be cost-effective and may disrupt fragile ecosystems.

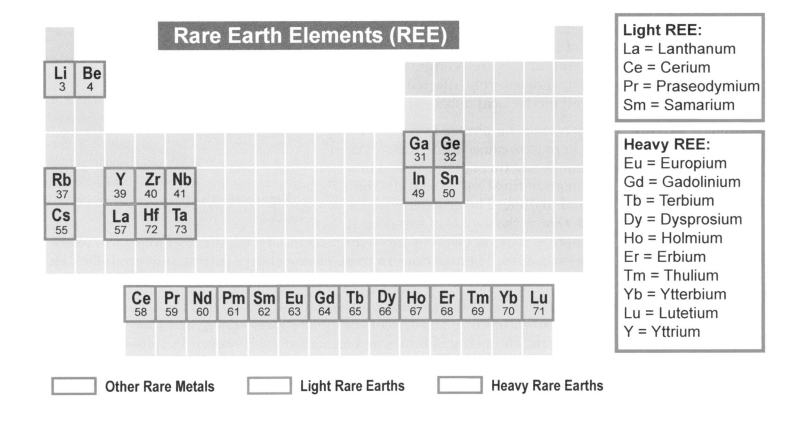

Rare Earth Elements (REE)

Light REE:
La = Lanthanum
Ce = Cerium
Pr = Praseodymium
Sm = Samarium

Heavy REE:
Eu = Europium
Gd = Gadolinium
Tb = Terbium
Dy = Dysprosium
Ho = Holmium
Er = Erbium
Tm = Thulium
Yb = Ytterbium
Lu = Lutetium
Y = Yttrium

☐ **Other Rare Metals**   ☐ **Light Rare Earths**   ☐ **Heavy Rare Earths**

Fossil Fuels

How do we get fossil fuels?
In day-to-day living, obtaining fossil fuels is as easy as going to a gas pump for oil or turning on a stove to get natural gas. But what is involved in getting oil, natural gas, or coal from the ground? It turns out that there are many ways to go about obtaining fossil fuels. However, few of these ways are trouble-free for the environment or people.

Oil and gas drilling
Oil and gas drilling takes place in deserts in the Middle East and in various other land areas. For example, in the United States, oil drilling takes place in Alaska and Texas. Oil drilling also takes place off-shore in the Gulf of Mexico (Figure 16). In 2010, the Deepwater Horizon oil spill occurred and it took months to cap the well so that tens of thousands of barrels of oil did not continue to flow into the Gulf of Mexico. Wildlife and habitats along the coast were severely affected by this huge disaster as well as the local fisheries and tourism.

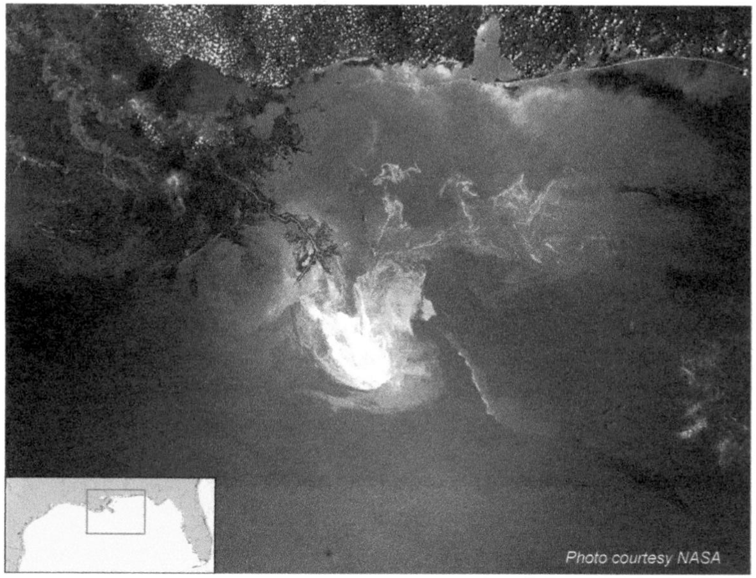

Photo courtesy NASA

Figure 16: The Deepwater Horizon oil spill in 2010.

Hydraulic fracturing
Hydraulic fracturing is a phrase that is currently in the media in part because it is a controversial process. Hydraulic fracturing is a method to extract even more natural gas from wells than with traditional drilling. The process involves breaking rock that is thousands of feet deep so as to release and capture natural gas. The problems associated with this technique are related to the chemicals needed in the procedure. There is concern these chemicals are getting into groundwater.

Coal mining
In coal mining, workers enter deep inside earth to assist in the extraction of coal. For this reason, mining is a dangerous job because miners can get trapped underground and the occupation can result in health problems. Fortunately, the U.S. Department of Labor's Mine Safety and Health Administration (MSHA) focuses on improving the safety of mines and miner safety. However, in spite of efforts, there was a mining tragedy as recently as 2006 when the Sago Mine Disaster killed 12 miners. Coal mining also has an impact on the environment because huge amount of earth are disrupted. The adverse effects include destroying habitats, soil quality, and polluting groundwater and other waterways. In spite of these issues, coal is an abundant and reliable energy resource in the United States, and so it will continue to be mined.

QUESTIONS

1. Is it practical to stop all water diversion that takes place in the United States? Why or why not?

2. One way to make a seasonal dam is to have it be inflatable. When the dam is inflated, water is trapped and may create a lake. When the dam is not inflated, the river water flows and allows fish to migrate. Research an example of an inflatable dam in the world and write down three things you learned about it.

3. Rare earth metals are especially important in the high-tech industry. Are these metals really rare?

4. Why is there increased pressure to develop more mines for mineral extraction in the United States?

5. Because of the issues associated with obtaining and using fossil fuels, there is interest in developing alternative, renewable energy sources. However, even renewable energy sources can have negative effects on the environment. Check out page 383 in Chapter 16. Pick one energy source in the table and find out more about how obtaining and using this resource affects the environment.

6. Write down how you rely on water, minerals, and fossil fuels each day. Then, list some actions you could take to conserve these resources.

Explore activity:

Pick one or more of the following and answer it. You may wish to present your work in the form of a speech to your class, a poster, or a magazine article.

a. In 2010, 60 dams were removed from around the United States. Visit www.americanrivers.org to find out more about dam removal. What are the benefits to wildlife and people when a dam is removed?

b. The Colorado River in the American Southwest and its tributaries have over 20 dams and most of the water diverted from the river is used for irrigation. Because of the high demand for water and evaporation, the river does not consistently reach the Gulf of California. Research the Colorado River and find out at least one thing that is being done to protect this river.

c. Pick one mineral resource and find out about its uses and how it is mined.

d. Stories about energy resources are in the news all the time. Check out a recent newspaper for a week or so and summarize on any stories you read that are about energy resources.